The Interpretation of NMR Spectra

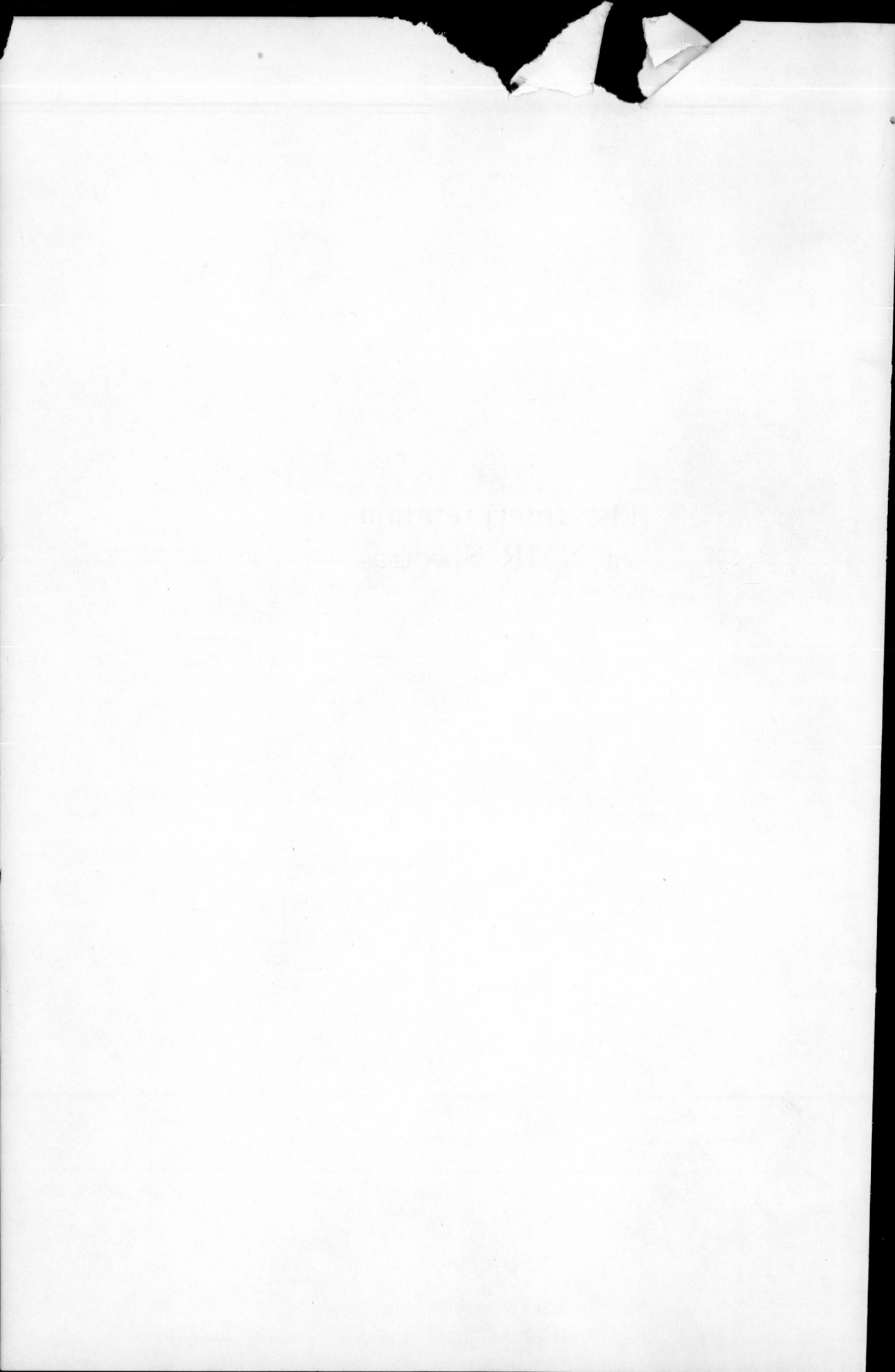

The Interpretation of NMR Spectra

Kenneth B. Wiberg
Yale University

Bernard J. Nist
University of Washington

W. A. Benjamin, Inc. New York 1962

INTERPRETATION OF NMR SPECTRA

Library of Congress Catalog Card Number 62-15647
Manufactured in the United States of America

This manuscript was received
March 9, 1962 and published
August 24, 1962

The dust jacket was designed
by Joan Wall

W. A. Benjamin, Inc.
2465 Broadway, New York 25, New York

Preface

Nuclear magnetic resonance spectroscopy has established a firm place among the major tools of the organic chemist. In some cases, the NMR spectrum is very simple, and first-order considerations permit a straightforward interpretation of the spectrum. In other cases, the spectrum contains so many overlapping bands that it is almost impossible to give a detailed interpretation of the spectrum. However, with a very large number of compounds of reasonable molecular weight, the bands are sufficiently resolved to be useful, but a simple first-order treatment is not adequate to permit an interpretation. This work is directed toward simplifying the interpretation of such spectra.

What is the advantage of having a complete interpretation rather than just a simple empirical correlation of band positions as is usually done with infrared spectroscopy? It is that much structural information is contained in the fine details of the bands, and that this information is often vital in a structural study. A complete interpretation will often indicate which sets of bands correspond to hydrogens on adjacent carbons, and how many hydrogens of each type are involved. In many cases, the magnitude of the coupling constant will give useful information about the geometrical arrangement of the hydrogens. Finally, a complete interpretation will give the correct values of the chemical shifts.

The method for calculating the detailed NMR spectrum that should arise from a given set of parameters (chemical shifts and coupling constants) is well established. Except for the most simple cases, it is a laborious procedure, which is best handled using a large digital computor.

Even with this aid, the matching of an experimental spectrum with a theoretical spectrum is a time-consuming process for it involves a succession of guesses as to the values of the chemical shifts and coupling constants until the theoretical spectrum converges upon the experimental one. The matching itself is rendered difficult by the large number of lines (56 for a four-proton case and 210 for a five-proton case).

In order to expedite this process, we have written a program that would calculate the spectrum arising from a given set of parameters and would then replace each line by a Gaussian curve having a specified width at half-height. This was followed by summing the curves where they overlapped and by printing the result on the off-line printer. Spectra for a large number of sets of parameters were obtained so that the determination of the approximate parameters could be accomplished simply by a comparison of the experimental spectrum with the set of calculated spectra. This procedure also has the advantage of minimizing the chance of finding an incorrect set of parameters that closely fits the observed spectrum, since one may make the comparison with most of the possible combinations.

The spectra were calculated using a chemical shift of 6 sec^{-1} between protons A and B (which gives a convenient ratio of height to width in the computor print-out), and a variety of coupling constants between 1 and 18 sec^{-1}, including some negative values. The line width at half-height was set as 0.3 sec^{-1}. It should be noted that all the parameters may be multiplied by a constant factor without changing the appearance of the spectrum. Thus, when a match is found, the scale factor between the experimental and calculated spectra is easily found, and the parameters used are then multiplied by this factor. In some cases, it is useful to have the positions and intensities of each of the many lines, and this is also included with each of the spectra.

This work is designed to make the spectra available to other chemists who are interested in NMR spectroscopy. It is hoped that they, also, will find this collection useful.

In closing, we wish to express our appreciation to Dr. A. A. Bothner-By of the Mellon Institute for making available the NMR program on which ours is based, and to the Research Computor Laboratory of the University of Washington for making the necessary computing time available.

K. B. Wiberg
B. J. Nist

Seattle, Washington
March 1962

Contents

Presentation of the Spectra

Throughout this work, the spectra have been calculated with the aid of an IBM-709 computor, the plots have been prepared by the computor and have been printed by its associated output equipment. The chemical shift between A and B has been maintained at 6 sec^{-1}, corresponding to 0.1 ppm at 60 mc. The plots were made by replacing the spectral lines with Gaussian curves having a width of 0.3 sec^{-1} at half height, followed by summing the curves where they overlap.

The data supplied with the spectra are the following: the spin-coupling constants; a sorted list of frequencies and intensities (for convenience in computation, 100 sec^{-1} has been added to all frequency values); and the intensity of the highest peak in the plot. The last usually does not correspond to any of the values in the table, for the highest peak generally contains contributions from the Gaussian curves representing two or more lines. The value given corresponds to a height of 25 X's.

All chemical shifts and coupling constants for a given spectrum may be multiplied by a constant. This will result in the relative line positions that shift by the same factor. Thus, the spectrum will be relatively unchanged by such a multiplication. The only factor that will contribute to a change in the appearance of the spectrum is the line width at half height. If all parameters and relative line positions were multiplied by a factor of 10, the spectrum given would correspond to a line width of 3 sec^{-1}, whereas modern spectrometers have a much better resolving power. If the parameters are multiplied by a constant, the observed spectrum may be better resolved than that given here, and, if they are divided by a constant, the reverse will be true.

Note: As a result of mechanical print-out problems, complete accuracy in preparing the base-line scales for these calculated spectra was not possible. It is suggested that, after an approximate match is found between the calculated spectrum and the reader's experimental curve, final calculations be made by interpolation from the table accompanying each calculated spectrum. An error of as much as ± 0.1 unit may occur if the base-line scale, as it appears under each spectrum, is used for fine measurement.

1

The AB *Case*

The spin coupling of two protons leads to the AB case. Here, there is one chemical shift and one coupling constant, giving a spectrum that is a function of the ratio $J/\Delta\nu$. The change in the spectrum as this ratio is increased is shown in Spectra 1-1 through 1-12

The spectra consist of four lines, two for the A part and two for the B part. In this case, the spacing between the two lines for either part is equal to the coupling constant. If we designate the spacing between the first and third lines (or between the second and fourth lines) as Q, the chemical shift between A and B is given by

$$\Delta\nu = (Q^2 - J^2)^{1/2} \tag{1-1}$$

Thus, both the coupling constant and the chemical shift are easily obtained.

As a check on the assignments, one may calculate the ratio of the intensities of the inner and outer lines:

$$\text{Rel. int.} = \frac{(\Delta\nu^2 + J^2)^{1/2} - J}{(\Delta\nu^2 + J^2)^{1/2} + J} = \frac{Q - J}{Q + J} \tag{1-2}$$

This may then be compared with the observed intensity ratio.

1-1

J = 0.0

Maximum summed intensity = 2.000

LINE	FREQ	INTEN
1	97.00	1.000
2	97.00	1.000
3	103.00	1.000
4	103.00	1.000

1-2

J = 0.5

Maximum summed intensity = 1.033

LINE	FREQ	INTEN
1	96.74	0.917
2	97.24	1.083
3	102.76	1.083
4	103.26	0.917

1-3

J = 1.0

Maximum summed intensity = 1.105

LINE	FREQ	INTEN
1	96.46	0.836
2	97.46	1.164
3	102.54	1.164
4	103.54	0.836

1-4

J = 2.0

Maximum summed intensity = 1.260

LINE	FREQ	INTEN
1	95.84	0.684
2	97.84	1.316
3	102.16	1.316
4	104.16	0.684

1-5

J = 3.0

Maximum summed intensity = 1.356

LINE	FREQ	INTEN
1	95.15	0.553
2	98.15	1.447
3	101.85	1.447
4	104.85	0.553

1-6

J = 4.0

Maximum summed intensity = 1.553

LINE	FREQ	INTEN
1	94.39	0.445
2	98.39	1.555
3	101.61	1.555
4	105.61	0.445

1-7

J = 6.0

Maximum summed intensity = 1.614

LINE	FREQ	INTEN
1	92.76	0.293
2	98.76	1.707
3	101.24	1.707
4	107.24	0.293

1-8

J = 8.0

Maximum summed intensity = 1.800

LINE	FREQ	INTEN
1	91.00	0.200
2	99.00	1.800
3	101.00	1.800
4	109.00	0.200

1-9

J = 10.0

Maximum summed intensity = 1.803

LINE	FREQ	INTEN
1	89.17	0.143
2	99.17	1.857
3	100.83	1.857
4	110.83	0.143

1-10

J = 12.0

Maximum summed intensity = 1.891

LINE	FREQ	INTEN
1	87.29	0.106
2	99.29	1.894
3	100.71	1.894
4	112.71	0.106

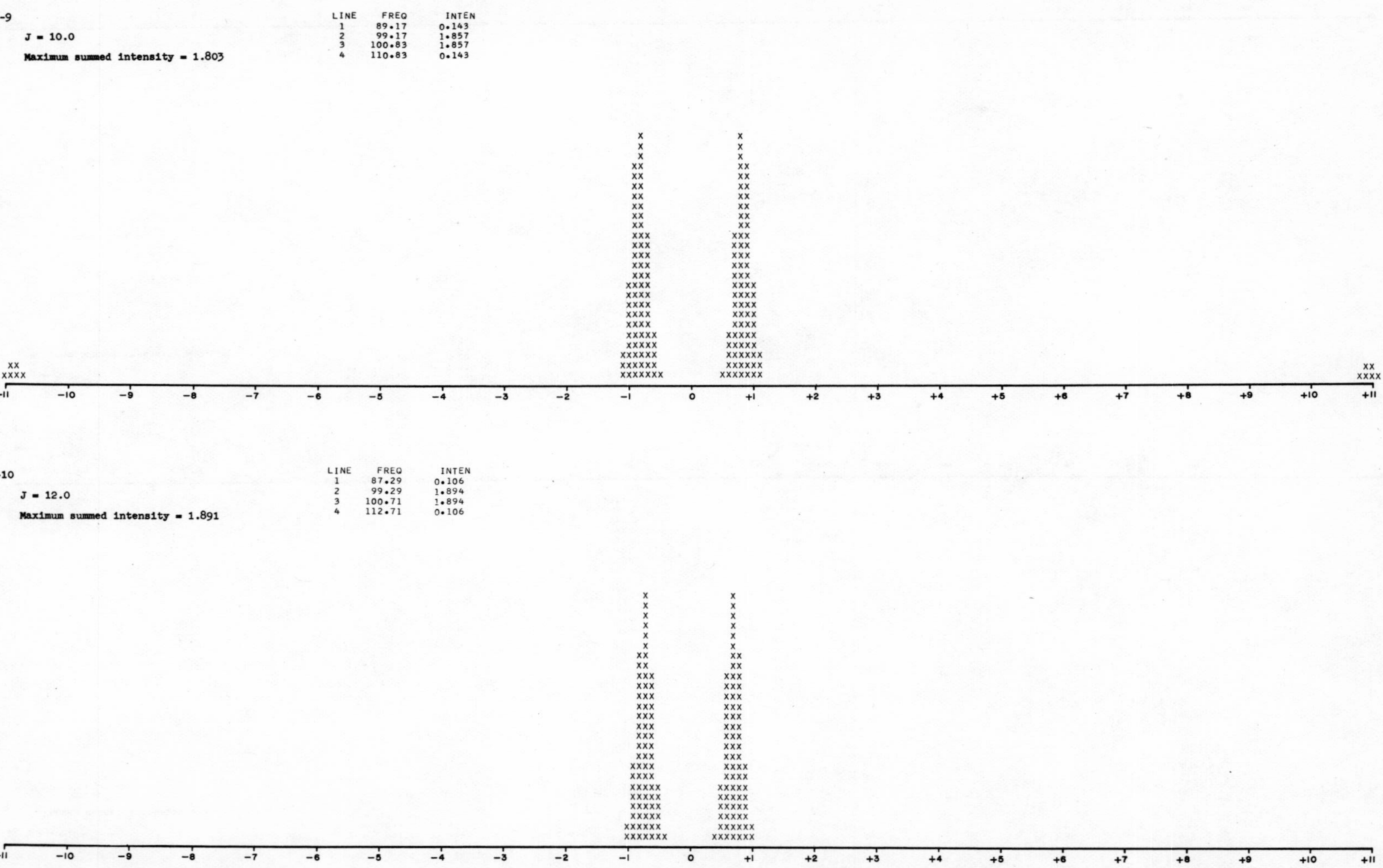

1-11

J = 15.0

Maximum summed intensity = 1.899

LINE	FREQ	INTEN
1	84.42	0.072
2	99.42	1.928
3	100.58	1.928
4	115.58	0.072

−11 −10 −9 −8 −7 −6 −5 −4 −3 −2 −1 0 +1 +2 +3 +4 +5 +6 +7 +8 +9 +10 +11

1-12

J = 18.0

Maximum summed intensity = 1.938

LINE	FREQ	INTEN
1	81.51	0.051
2	99.51	1.949
3	100.49	1.949
4	118.49	0.051

−11 −10 −9 −8 −7 −6 −5 −4 −3 −2 −1 0 +1 +2 +3 +4 +5 +6 +7 +8 +9 +10 +11

2

The AB_2 *Case*

The spectrum arising from the spin-coupling of three protons is considerably simplified if two of the protons are identical, giving the AB_2 case. Here, the coupling between the B protons does not affect the spectrum, and we need only be concerned with the chemical shift and the coupling constant between A and B. The spectrum will simply be a function of the ratio $J/\Delta\nu$. The change in spectrum as this ratio is increased is shown in Spectra 2-1 through 2-12.

The spectrum consists of nine lines, four for the A part, four for the B part, and a weak combination line. Thus, four of the fifteen lines found in an ABC case are forbidden in the AB_2 case. When J is small compared to $\Delta\nu$ (commonly referred to as an AX_2 case), the two central lines of the A part come together giving a triplet, and, similarly, the lines of the B part come together giving a doublet. This can be seen in Spectrum 2-2.

If the line of the A part of the spectrum that is farthest from the B part is designated as 1, it can be seen that the third line is always centered on the frequency for A(ν_A). When $J/\Delta\nu$ is large, lines 1 and 2 may have a very low intensity and may not easily be found. However, a comparison of the observed spectrum with those given here will always allow this line to be picked out.

The chemical shift for the B part may be determined from the average of lines 5 and 7 (the fifth and seventh nonzero intensity lines in the list). Here again, when the coupling constant is large with respect to the chemical shift, it may not be possible to pick out all the lines for the B part.

However, reference to the spectra given here will make it possible to identify the two lines.

The value of J_{AB} may now be determined by a comparison of the observed spectrum with calculated line positions based on values of J_{AB}, which are close to correct as judged from a comparison of the spectrum with those given here. The detailed comparison is best made by plotting the line positions given with the spectra as a function of $J/\Delta\nu$ on a large sheet of coordinate paper, and matching the observed positions after adjusting them to the standard value of $\Delta\nu$ (6 sec^{-1}).

2-1

J=0	Line	Freq.	Inten.	Line	Freq.	Inten.
	1	97.00	1.000	9	103.00	1.000
	2	97.00	1.000	10	103.00	1.000
	3	97.00	0.	11	103.00	1.000
	4	97.00	0.	12	103.00	1.000
	5	97.00	1.000	13	103.00	1.000
	6	97.00	1.000	14	103.00	1.000
	7	103.00	1.000	15	109.00	0.
	8	103.00	1.000			

Maximum summed intensity = 8.000

-11 -10 -9 -8 -7 -6 -5 -4 -3 -2 -1 0 +1 +2 +3 +4 +5 +6 +7 +8 +9 +10 +11

2-2

J=0.5	Line	Freq.	Inten.	Line	Freq.	Inten.
	1	96.48	0.844	9	102.77	2.156
	2	96.96	0.979	10	102.77	0.000
	3*	96.98	0.000	11	103.25	1.844
	4	96.98	0.000	12	103.25	0.000
	5	97.00	1.000	13	103.27	0.000
	6	97.48	1.176	14	103.27	1.824
	7	102.75	0.000	15	109.04	0.000
	8	102.75	2.176			

Maximum summed intensity = 4.128

-11 -10 -9 -8 -7 -6 -5 -4 -3 -2 -1 0 +1 +2 +3 +4 +5 +6 +7 +8 +9 +10 +11

2-3

J=1.0

Line	Freq.	Inten.	Line	Freq.	Inten.
1	95.92	0.711	9	102.58	2.289
2	96.83	0.921	10	102.59	0.000
3	96.91	0.000	11	103.49	1.711
4	96.92	0.000	12	103.50	0.000
5	97.00	1.000	13	103.58	0.000
6	97.91	1.368	14	103.59	1.632
7	102.50	0.000	15	109.17	0.000
8	102.51	2.368			

Maximum summed intensity = 4.270

-11 -10 -9 -8 -7 -6 -5 -4 -3 -2 -1 0 +1 +2 +3 +4 +5 +6 +7 +8 +9 +10 +11

2-4

J=2

Line	Freq.	Inten.	Line	Freq.	Inten.
1	94.73	0.507	9	102.27	2.493
2	96.35	0.734	10	102.37	0.000
3	96.63	0.000	11	103.90	1.505
4	96.73	0.000	12	104.00	0.000
5	97.00	1.000	13	104.27	0.000
6	98.63	1.761	14	104.37	1.239
7	102.00	0.000	15	109.65	0.002
8	102.10	2.759			

Maximum summed intensity = 4.092

-11 -10 -9 -8 -7 -6 -5 -4 -3 -2 -1 0 +1 +2 +3 +4 +5 +6 +7 +8 +9 +10 +11

2-5

J=3.0

Line	Freq.	Inten.	Line	Freq.	Inten.
1	93.44	0.368	9	102.06	2.632
2	95.60	0.531	10	102.34	0.000
3	96.16	0.000	11	104.22	1.363
4	96.44	0.000	12	104.50	0.000
5	97.00	1.000	13	105.06	0.000
6	99.16	2.106	14	105.34	0.894
7	101.50	0.000	15	110.40	0.006
8	101.78	3.101			

Maximum summed intensity is 3.412

−11 −10 −9 −8 −7 −6 −5 −4 −3 −2 −1 0 +1 +2 +3 +4 +5 +6 +7 +8 +9 +10 +11

2-6

J=4.0

Line	Freq.	Inten	Line	Freq.	Inten.
1	92.10	0.275	9	101.90	2.725
2	94.64	0.369	10	102.46	0.000
3	95.54	0.000	11	104.43	1.265
4	96.10	0.000	12	105.00	0.000
5	97.00	1.000	13	105.90	0.000
6	99.54	2.366	14	106.46	0.634
7	101.00	0.000	15	111.36	0.010
8	101.57	3.356			

Maximum summed intensity is 3.406

−11 −10 −9 −8 −7 −6 −5 −4 −3 −2 −1 0 +1 +2 +3 +4 +5 +6 +7 +8 +9 +10 +11

2-7

J=6.0

Line	Freq.	Inten.	Line	Freq.	Inten.
1	89.32	0.166	9	101.68	2.834
2	92.32	0.182	10	103.00	0.000
3	94.00	0.000	11	104.68	1.152
4	95.32	0.000	12	106.00	0.000
5	97.00	1.000	13	107.68	0.000
6	100.00	0.000	14	109.00	0.333
7	100.00	2.667	15	113.68	0.014
8	101.32	3.652			

Maximum summed intensity is 3.656

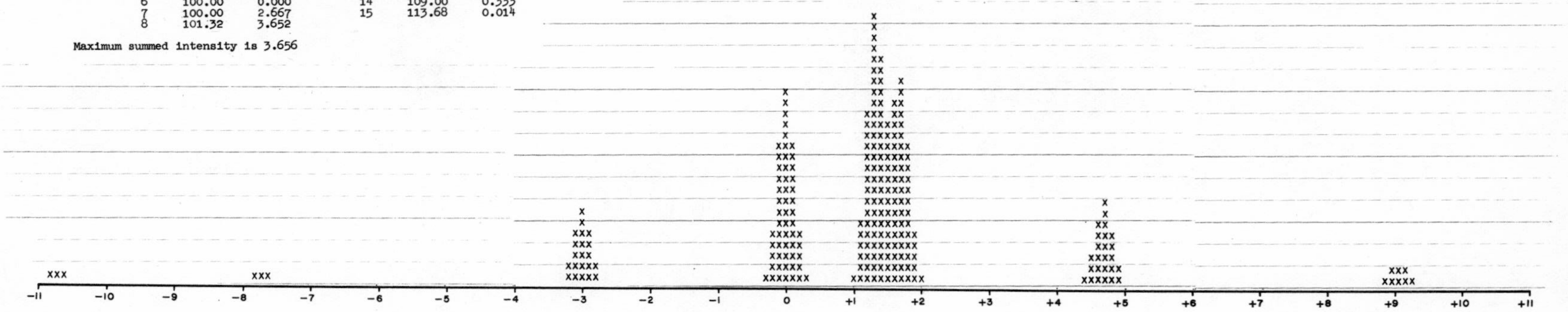

2-8

J=8.0

Line	Freq.	Inten.	Line	Freq.	Inten.
1	86.45	0.109	9	101.55	2.891
2	89.71	0.099	10	103.74	0.000
3	92.26	0.000	11	104.81	1.095
4	94.45	0.000	12	107.00	0.000
5	97.00	1.000	13	109.55	0.000
6	99.00	0.000	14	111.74	0.194
7	100.26	2.806	15	116.29	0.014
8	101.19	3.791			

Maximum summed intensity is 3.855

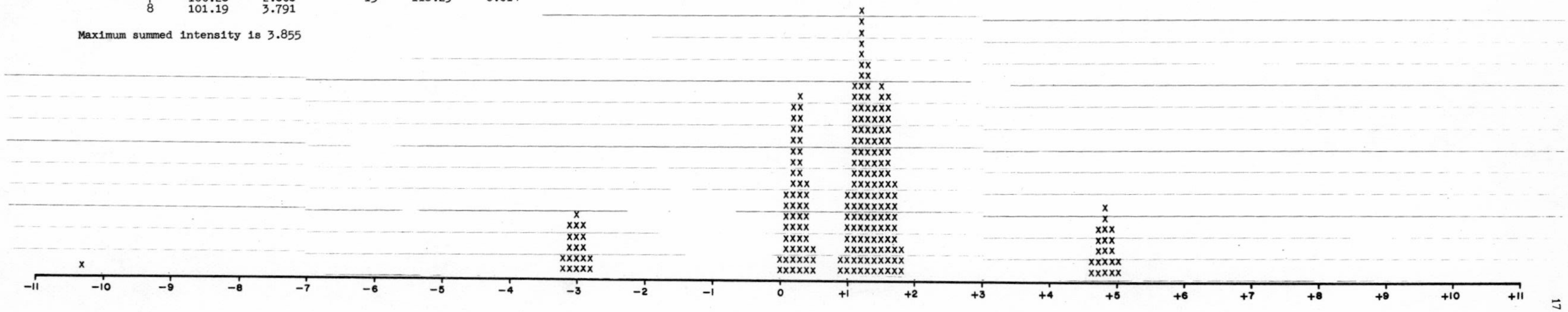

2-9

J=10.0	Line	Freq.	Inten.	Line	Freq.	Inten.
	1	83.54	0.077	9	101.46	2.923
	2	86.95	0.060	10	104.59	0.000
	3	90.41	0.000	11	104.87	1.064
	4	93.54	0.000	12	108.00	0.000
	5	97.00	1.000	13	111.46	0.000
	6	98.00	0.000	14	114.59	0.125
	7	100.41	2.875	15	119.05	0.013
	8	101.13	3.863			

Maximum summed intensity = 3.810

−11 −10 −9 −8 −7 −6 −5 −4 −3 −2 −1 0 +1 +2 +3 +4 +5 +6 +7 +8 +9 +10 +11

2-10

J=12.0	Line	Freq.	Inten.	Line	Freq.	Inten.
	1	80.61	0.057	9	101.39	2.943
	2	84.12	0.040	10	104.91	1.046
	3	88.51	0.000	11	105.49	0.000
	4	92.61	0.000	12	109.00	0.000
	5	97.00	1.000	13	113.39	0.000
	6	97.00	0.000	14	117.49	0.086
	7	100.51	2.914	15	121.88	0.011
	8	101.09	3.904			

Maximum summed intensity is 4.109

−11 −10 −9 −8 −7 −6 −5 −4 −3 −2 −1 0 +1 +2 +3 +4 +5 +6 +7 +8 +9 +10 +11

2-11

J=15.0

Line	Freq.	Inten.	Line	Freq.	Inten.
1	76.18	0.038	9	101.32	2.962
2	79.79	0.024	10	104.94	1.030
3	85.62	0.000	11	106.88	0.000
4	91.18	0.000	12	110.50	0.000
5	95.50	0.000	13	116.32	0.000
6	97.00	1.000	14	121.88	0.054
7	100.62	2.946	15	126.21	0.008
8	101.06	3.938			

Maximum summed intensity = 4.404

−11 −10 −9 −8 −7 −6 −5 −4 −3 −2 −1 0 +1 +2 +3 +4 +5 +6 +7 +8 +9 +10 +11

2-12

J=18.0

Line	Freq.	Inten.	Line	Freq.	Inten.
1	71.73	0.028	9	101.27	2.972
2	75.41	0.016	10	104.96	1.021
3	82.68	0.000	11	108.32	0.000
4	89.73	0.000	12	112.00	0.000
5	94.00	0.000	13	119.27	0.000
6	97.00	1.000	14	126.32	0.037
7	100.68	2.963	15	130.59	0.007
8	101.04	3.957			

Maximum summed intensity is 4.769

−11 −10 −9 −8 −7 −6 −5 −4 −3 −2 −1 0 +1 +2 +3 +4 +5 +6 +7 +8 +9 +10 +11

3

The ABX *and* ABC *Cases*

The coupling between three nonequivalent protons leads to the ABC case. When the chemical shift toward one of the protons is much greater than that toward the others, it is commonly referred to as an ABX case, where X is the remote proton. The spectrum consists of two quartets (usually overlapping) for the A and B parts, and six lines for the X part. Two of these last lines are combination lines and often have a low intensity. Thus, they may not be observed.

The effect of changes in coupling constants on ABX spectra are shown in Fig. 3-1. Here, one of the quartets is shown by light lines and the other by dark lines. Each of the two quartets is a typical AB spectrum, and the spacing of the outer lines for either set will give J_{AB}. This parameter is therefore relatively easily determined. The spacing between lines 9 and 12 in the X spectrum (dark lines) is equal to $|J_{AX} + J_{BX}|$, and the center of the sextet 9-14 gives ν_X.

When $J_{AB} \gg (\nu_A - \nu_B) + (J_{AX} - J_{BX})/2$, lines 10 and 11 coincide, and the X part becomes a triplet. Thus, even when the X part has the simple appearance of being a triplet, suggesting that $J_{AX} = J_{BX}$, the actual case may be that one of these coupling constants is small (perhaps zero) and that the spacing between lines 9 and 12 is approximately equal to the other constant.

In order to determine the coupling constants, we must obtain two more parameters, D_+ and D_-. These are the separations between the centers of the doublets forming the quartets and are conveniently measured as

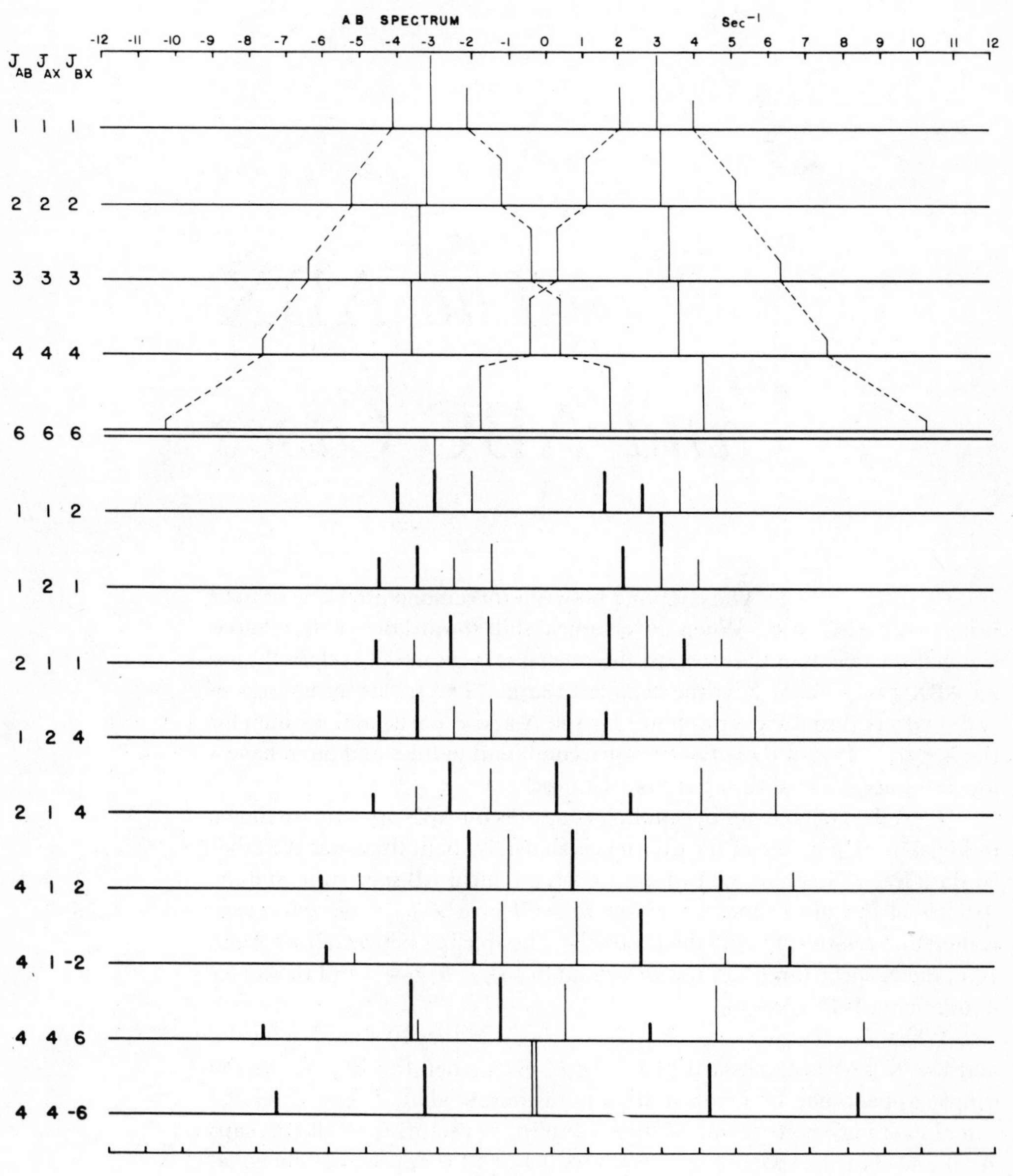
AB SPECTRUM
Sec⁻¹
-12 -11 -10 -9 -8 -7 -6 -5 -4 -3 -2 -1 0 1 2 3 4 5 6 7 8 9 10 11 12
J AB J AX J BX
1 1 1
2 2 2
3 3 3
4 4 4
6 6 6
1 1 2
1 2 1
2 1 1
1 2 4
2 1 4
4 1 2
4 1 -2
4 4 6
4 4 -6

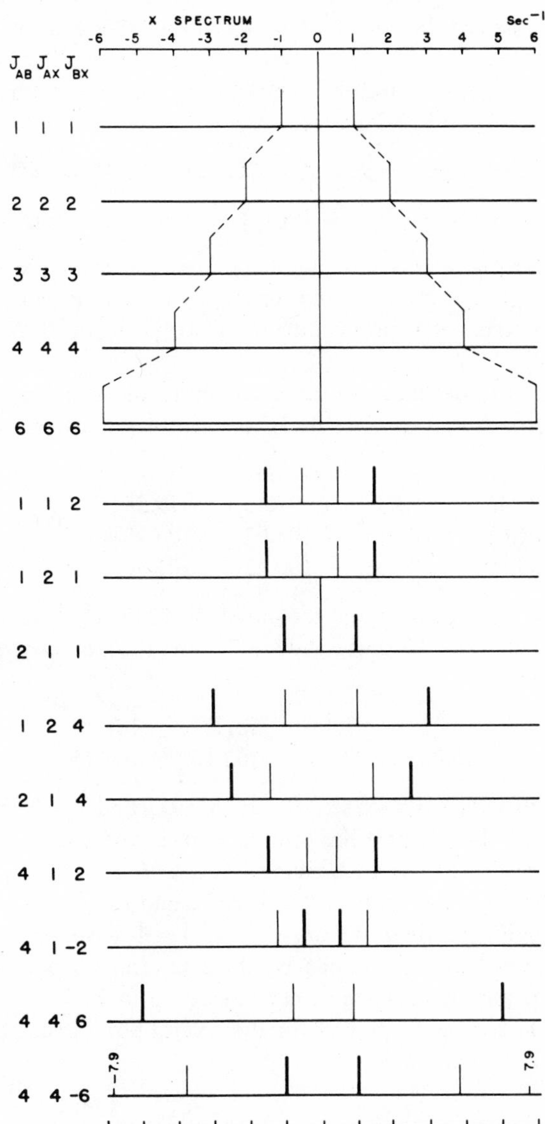

Fig. 3-1. Effect of spin-coupling constants on ABX spectra ($\Delta\nu_{AB} = 6\ \sec^{-1}$). The left-hand part is the AB spectrum; the right-hand part is the X spectrum.

the spacing between lines 1 and 5 (or 3 and 7) for one and between lines 2 and 6 (or 4 and 8) for the other. It is, however, not possible to know which should be assigned as D_+ and which as D_-.

The values thus obtained may be checked as follows. The spacing between lines 10 and 11 is $2|D_+ - D_-|$ and that between 14 and 15 is $2|D_+ + D_-|$. Also, the spacing between the centers of the two quartets will be $\frac{1}{2}|J_{AX} + J_{BX}|$. There may be several ways in which the lines of the AB part may be paired, but only one set should give agreement with the above criteria.

Having $|J_{AX} + J_{BX}|$, D_+ and D_-, the rest of the parameters may be obtained from Eqs. (3-1) and (3-2).

$$(\nu_A - \nu_B) + (J_{AX} - J_{BX})/2 = \pm(4D_+^2 - J_{AB}^2)^{1/2} \tag{3-1}$$

$$(\nu_A - \nu_B) - (J_{AX} - J_{BX})/2 = \pm(4D_-^2 - J_{AB}^2)^{1/2} \tag{3-2}$$

More than one set of assignments may usually be made, since one does not know if J_{AX} and J_{BX} have the same sign or if they have different signs. This may often be determined from the intensity distribution in the X part of the spectrum.

As an example, let us obtain the chemical shifts and coupling constants for one of the spectra given in Table 3-3 (see p. 30). The frequencies are as follows:

93.43	95.35	97.43	99.35	AB part
101.07	102.15	105.07	106.15	
98.50	99.58	100.42	101.50	X part

with the AB and X parts presumably separated by 1000 sec^{-1} or more. The repeating interval in the AB part is 4.00 sec^{-1}, and thus the two quartets may be as below:

93.43	97.43	101.07	105.07
95.35	99.35	102.15	106.15

from which we see that $J_{AB} = 4.00\ sec^{-1}$, and that D_+ and D_- have the values 3.82 and 3.40. The X part has only four lines, and consequently the outside two are probably 9 and 12, giving $|J_{AX} + J_{BX}| = 3.00\ sec^{-1}$. The center of the first AB quartet is at 99.25 sec^{-1}, and the center of the second is at 100.75 sec^{-1}, leading to $\frac{1}{2}|J_{AX} + J_{BX}| = 1.50$ in agreement with the value obtained above. Similarly, the separation between the inner lines of the X part is 0.84 sec^{-1}, corresponding to $2|D_+ - D_-|$.

Using Eqs. (3-1) and (3-2), and taking the several possible combinations of signs, one finds that either

$$|\Delta\nu| = 6.00\ sec^{-1} \qquad |J_{AX} - J_{BX}| = 1.00\ sec^{-1}$$

or

$$|\Delta\nu| = 0.50\ sec^{-1} \qquad |J_{AX} - J_{BX}| = 12.00\ sec^{-1}$$

Using the previously determined value of $|J_{AX} + J_{BX}|$, we find, in the first case, that $J_{AX} = 2.00\ sec^{-1}$ and $J_{BX} = 1.00\ sec^{-1}$ and, in the second, that $J_{AX} = 7.5\ \text{sec}^{-1}$ and $J_{BX} = -4.5\ \text{sec}^{-1}$. If we examine the data given in Table 3-3, it may be seen that, for the case in which J_{AX} and J_{BX} have the same sign, the outer lines for the X part have zero intensity giving a four-line spectrum, as observed. For the set of constants in which these coupling constants have opposite signs, the ratio $J/\Delta\nu_{AB}$ is large, and this will lead to a six-line X spectrum (*cf.* the end of Table 3-3). Thus, the observed spectrum indicates that the two coupling constants have the same sign.

The remaining ambiguity with respect to the sign of $\nu_A - \nu_B$ may be removed by a consideration of the data in Table 3-1; it is found that, using the values given above, $\nu_A - \nu_B = -6.00$. The relative intensities may also be calculated using the data given in this table.

Table 3-1 Line Positions and Intensities for the ABX Case[a]

Line	Energy	Rel. intensity
1	$\nu_{AB} + \frac{1}{4}(-2J_{AB} - J_{AX} - J_{BX}) - D_-$	$1 - \sin 2\phi_-$
2	$\nu_{AB} + \frac{1}{4}(-2J_{AB} + J_{AX} + J_{BX}) - D_+$	$1 - \sin 2\phi_+$
3	$\nu_{AB} + \frac{1}{4}(2J_{AB} - J_{AX} - J_{BX}) - D_-$	$1 + \sin 2\phi_-$
4	$\nu_{AB} + \frac{1}{4}(2J_{AB} + J_{AX} + J_{BX}) - D_+$	$1 + \sin 2\phi_+$
5	$\nu_{AB} + \frac{1}{4}(-2J_{AB} - J_{AX} - J_{BX}) + D_-$	$1 + \sin 2\phi_-$
6	$\nu_{AB} + \frac{1}{4}(-2J_{AB} + J_{AX} + J_{BX}) + D_+$	$1 + \sin 2\phi_+$
7	$\nu_{AB} + \frac{1}{4}(2J_{AB} - J_{AX} - J_{BX}) + D_-$	$1 - \sin 2\phi_-$
8	$\nu_{AB} + \frac{1}{4}(2J_{AB} + J_{AX} + J_{BX}) + D_+$	$1 - \sin 2\phi_+$
9	$\nu_X - \frac{1}{2}(J_{AX} + J_{BX})$	1
10	$\nu_X + D_+ - D_-$	$\cos^2(\phi_+ - \phi_-)$
11	$\nu_X - D_+ + D_-$	$\cos^2(\phi_+ - \phi_-)$
12	$\nu_X + \frac{1}{2}(J_{AX} + J_{BX})$	1
13	$\nu_X - D_+ - D_-$	$\sin^2(\phi_+ - \phi_-)$
14	$\nu_X + D_+ + D_-$	$\sin^2(\phi_+ - \phi_-)$

$$D_\pm = \tfrac{1}{2}\{[\nu_A - \nu_B \pm \tfrac{1}{2}(J_{AX} - J_{BX})]^2 + J_{AB}{}^2\}^{1/2}$$
$$\sin 2\phi_+ = J_{AB}/2D_+ \qquad \sin 2\phi_- = J_{AB}/2D_-$$
$$\cos 2\phi_+ = [2\nu_A - 2\nu_B + J_{AX} - J_{BX}]/4D_+$$
$$\cos 2\phi_- = [2\nu_A - 2\nu_B - J_{AX} + J_{BX}]/4D_-$$
$$\nu_{AB} = \tfrac{1}{2}(\nu_A + \nu_B)$$

[a] J. A. Pople, W. G. Schneider, and H. J. Bernstein, *High-Resolution Nuclear Magnetic Resonance*, McGraw-Hill, New York, 1959, p. 134.

In the above calculation, the parameters were quite different when the sign of J_{BX} was changed. Suppose the coupling constants were $J_{AB} = 4.0$, $J_{AX} = 2.0$, and $J_{BX} = -1.0\ \text{sec}^{-1}$; how would this affect the spectrum? The calculated line positions would now be as follows:

93.49	95.24	97.49	99.24	AB part		
101.26	102.01	105.26	106.01			
92.73	98.75	99.50	100.50	101.25	107.27	X part

These values differ by only 0.1 to 0.2 sec^{-1} from those obtained when all the coupling constants have the same sign. This is often within the experimental error of measurement. A comparison of the relative intensities for the two cases indicates there is a small difference. However, it is probably within the experimental error of measurement. In this case, one cannot readily choose between the two assignments for J_{BX}.

The use of relative intensities to determine the relative signs of J_{AX} and J_{BX} is limited to those cases in which the coupling constant is reasonably large compared to the chemical shift between A and B. For example, the spectra for which $J/\Delta\nu = 0.17$ (see Table 3-3) are not affected by changing the sign of one of the coupling constants. Only when $J/\Delta\nu \geq 0.5$ can this criterion be used.

The change in spectrum as the chemical shift between A and X is decreased may be seen by comparing the data in Table 3-3 with the spectra in group 3E where the chemical shifts between A and B and between B and C are both 6 sec^{-1}. In Spectrum 3E-13, for example, two overlapping quartets may readily be picked out for the AB part, whereas the C part is a triplet. The constant J_{AB} may be obtained as before, and the analysis may be performed as above, giving constants that are quite close to the correct ones. The spectra in this section are a useful guide for estimating the error caused by using the ABX approximation for cases in which the AX chemical shift is not large.

If one can estimate the coupling constants and chemical shifts using the ABX approximation, or can estimate these values from other data or previous experience, one may then use the spectra in this catalog to help improve the estimated values. Alternately, one may compare the observed spectrum with each of the calculated spectra (and their mirror images) until a reasonable match is found, and then work from there. For the spectra presented in the following pages, the chemical shifts are given in Table 3-2. In each case, 100 sec^{-1} have been added to the values given in the lists of frequencies shown with each spectrum.

Table 3-2 Chemical Shifts

Group	ν_A	ν_B	ν_C	$\Delta\nu_{AB}$	$\Delta\nu_{BC}$
A	−3.0	3.0	3.0	6.0	0.0
B	−3.0	3.0	4.0	6.0	1.0
C	−3.0	3.0	5.0	6.0	2.0
D	−3.0	3.0	7.0	6.0	4.0
E	−6.0	0.0	6.0	6.0	6.0

It may be noted that the C part of the spectrum is a triplet if $J_{AB} \gg (\nu_A - \nu_B) + \frac{1}{2}(J_{AC} + J_{BC})$, just as with the ABX spectra. The C part will be close to a triplet even when J_{AB} is only somewhat larger than the other quantity. This is well illustrated by Spectrum 3A-18, in which we consider the left-hand portion as the C part, and the right-hand, as the AB part.

In the next group, it is interesting to compare Spectra 3B-1, 3B-11, and 3B-23. It can be seen that, when J_{BC} becomes large with respect to $\Delta\nu_{BC}$, the spectrum suggests that $\Delta\nu_{BC} = 0$, whereas this is incorrect. This may also be seen in a comparison of Spectra 3B-12, 3B-14, and 3B-71. Even when the chemical shift between B and C is larger the same trend may be noted. Compare, for example, Spectra 3D-11, 3D-17, 3D-23, 3D-29, 3D-31, and 3D-33. The first of these resembles an ABX spectrum, which then becomes two triplets in the third and fourth spectra, and finally approaches a triplet and a doublet in the last spectrum.

This is a general phenomenon. When the chemical shift is much smaller than the coupling constant between two nuclei, the resonance lines tend to merge giving a single peak. This may, in turn, be split by another nucleus giving the spectra discussed above.

Once the approximate values of the parameters have been found, they may be improved by preparing plots of how the spectrum changes with the changes in parameters near the correct values, and comparing these with the observed spectrum. As a check on the final values, it is advisable to calculate the spectrum that should result from this set of parameters and to compare the calculated and observed spectra.

The possible energy levels for a system of three spin-coupled protons are obtained as follows:

$$E_1 = \tfrac{1}{2}(\nu_A + \nu_B + \nu_C) + \tfrac{1}{4}(J_{AB} + J_{BC} + J_{AC}) \qquad (3\text{-}3)$$

E_2, E_3, and E_4 are the three roots of the determinant [Eq. (3-4)].

E_5, E_6, and E_7 are the three roots of the determinant [Eq. (3-5)], and $E_8 = \frac{1}{2}(-\nu_A - \nu_B - \nu_C) + \frac{1}{4}(J_{AB} + J_{BC} + J_{AC})$.

Having a set of coupling constants and chemical shifts, the eight energy levels are easily obtained. The possible transitions are as follows:

$E_2 \to E_1$	$E_7 \to E_2$	$E_6 \to E_4$
$E_3 \to E_1$	$E_5 \to E_3$	$E_7 \to E_4$
$E_4 \to E_1$	$E_6 \to E_3$	$E_8 \to E_5$
$E_5 \to E_2$	$E_7 \to E_3$	$E_8 \to E_6$
$E_6 \to E_2$	$E_5 \to E_4$	$E_8 \to E_7$

Thus, the transition energies (in sec^{-1}) are given by subtracting the energy of the first state from that of the second for each of the fifteen cases. The intensities may also be calculated, and the details are available elsewhere.*

* J. D. Roberts, *An Introduction to the Analysis of Spin-Spin Splitting in High-Resolution Nuclear Magnetic Resonance Spectra*, W. A. Benjamin, New York, 1961, pp. 85–86; J. A. Pople, W. G. Schneider, and H. J. Bernstein, *High-Resolution Nuclear Magnetic Resonance*, McGraw-Hill, New York, 1959, p. 132.

$$\begin{vmatrix} \frac{1}{2}(\nu_A + \nu_B - \nu_C) + \frac{1}{4}(J_{AB} - J_{BC} - J_{AC}) - E & \frac{1}{2}J_{BC} & \frac{1}{2}J_{AC} \\ \frac{1}{2}J_{BC} & \frac{1}{2}(\nu_A - \nu_B + \nu_C) + \frac{1}{4}(-J_{AB} - J_{BC} + J_{AC}) - E & \frac{1}{2}J_{AB} \\ \frac{1}{2}J_{AC} & \frac{1}{2}J_{AB} & \frac{1}{2}(-\nu_A + \nu_B + \nu_C) + \frac{1}{4}(-J_{AB} + J_{BC} - J_{AC}) - E \end{vmatrix} = 0 \quad (3\text{-}4)$$

$$\begin{vmatrix} \frac{1}{2}(\nu_A - \nu_B - \nu_C) + \frac{1}{4}(-J_{AB} + J_{BC} - J_{AC}) - E & \frac{1}{2}J_{AB} & \frac{1}{2}J_{AC} \\ \frac{1}{2}J_{AB} & \frac{1}{2}(-\nu_A + \nu_B - \nu_C) + \frac{1}{4}(-J_{AB} - J_{BC} + J_{AC}) - E & \frac{1}{2}J_{BC} \\ \frac{1}{2}J_{AC} & \frac{1}{2}J_{BC} & \frac{1}{2}(-\nu_A - \nu_B + \nu_C) + \frac{1}{4}(J_{AB} - J_{BC} - J_{AC}) - E \end{vmatrix} = 0 \qquad (3\text{-}5)$$

Table 3-3 Theoretical Spectra for ABX Cases

J_{AB}	J_{AX}	J_{BX}	AB part, line number[a] 1	3	2	4	5	7	6	8	X part, line number 13	9	11	10	12	14
1	1	1	95.96	96.96	96.96	97.96	102.04	103.04	103.04	104.04	93.92	99.00	100.00	100.00	101.00	106.08
			0.84	1.16	0.84	1.16	1.16	0.84	1.16	0.84	0.00	1.00	1.00	1.00	1.00	0.00
2	2	2	94.84	96.84	96.84	98.84	101.16	103.16	103.16	105.16	93.68	98.00	100.00	100.00	102.00	106.33
			0.68	1.32	0.68	1.32	1.32	0.68	1.32	0.68	0.00	1.00	1.00	1.00	1.00	0.00
3	3	3	93.65	96.65	96.65	99.65	100.35	103.35	103.35	106.35	93.30	97.00	100.00	100.00	103.00	106.70
			0.55	1.45	0.55	1.45	1.45	0.55	1.45	0.55	0.00	1.00	1.00	1.00	1.00	0.00
4	4	4	92.39	96.39	96.39	100.39	99.61	103.61	103.61	107.61	92.79	96.00	100.00	100.00	104.00	107.21
			0.45	1.55	0.45	1.55	1.55	0.45	1.55	0.45	0.00	1.00	1.00	1.00	1.00	0.00
6	6	6	89.76	95.76	95.76	101.76	98.24	104.24	104.24	110.24	91.51	94.00	100.00	100.00	106.00	108.49
			0.29	1.71	0.29	1.71	1.71	0.29	1.71	0.29	0.00	1.00	1.00	1.00	1.00	0.00
8	8	8	87.00	95.00	95.00	103.00	97.00	105.00	105.00	113.00	90.00	92.00	100.00	100.00	108.00	110.00
			0.20	1.80	0.20	1.80	1.80	0.20	1.80	0.20	0.00	1.00	1.00	1.00	1.00	0.00
10	10	10	84.17	94.17	94.17	104.17	95.83	105.83	105.83	115.83	88.31	90.00	100.00	100.00	110.00	111.69
			0.14	1.86	0.14	1.86	1.86	0.14	1.86	0.14	0.00	1.00	1.00	1.00	1.00	0.00
12	12	12	81.29	93.29	93.29	105.29	94.71	106.71	106.71	118.71	86.58	88.00	100.00	100.00	112.00	113.42
			0.11	1.89	0.11	1.89	1.89	0.11	1.89	0.11	0.00	1.00	1.00	1.00	1.00	0.00
1	1	2	95.95	96.95	96.95	97.95	101.54	102.54	103.54	104.54	93.92	98.50	99.51	100.49	101.50	106.08
			0.82	1.18	0.85	1.15	1.18	0.82	1.15	0.85	0.00	1.00	1.00	1.00	1.00	0.00
1	2	1	95.46	96.46	97.45	98.45	102.04	103.04	103.04	104.04	93.92	98.50	99.51	100.49	101.50	106.08
			0.85	1.15	0.82	1.18	1.15	0.85	1.18	0.82	0.00	1.00	1.00	1.00	1.00	0.00
2	1	1	95.34	97.34	96.34	98.34	101.66	103.66	102.66	104.66	93.67	99.00	100.00	100.00	101.00	106.33
			0.68	1.32	0.68	1.32	1.32	0.68	1.32	0.68	0.00	1.00	1.00	1.00	1.00	0.00
1	2	2	95.46	96.46	97.46	98.46	101.54	102.54	103.54	104.54	93.67	98.50	100.00	100.00	101.50	106.33
			0.83	1.16	0.84	1.17	1.16	0.83	1.17	0.84	0.00	1.00	1.00	1.00	1.00	0.00
2	2	1	94.85	96.85	96.82	98.82	101.65	103.65	102.68	104.68	93.67	98.50	99.52	100.48	101.50	106.33
			0.71	1.29	0.66	1.34	1.29	0.71	1.34	0.66	0.00	1.00	1.00	1.00	1.00	0.00
2	1	2	95.32	97.32	96.35	98.35	101.18	103.18	103.15	105.15	93.67	98.50	99.52	100.48	101.50	106.33
			0.66	1.34	0.71	1.29	1.34	0.66	1.29	0.71	0.00	1.00	1.00	1.00	1.00	0.00
1	1	4	95.95	96.95	96.97	97.97	100.55	101.55	104.53	105.53	93.92	97.50	98.52	101.48	102.50	106.09
			0.78	1.22	0.87	1.13	1.22	0.78	1.13	0.87	0.00	1.00	1.00	1.00	1.00	0.00

1	4	1	94.46	95.46	98.44	99.44	102.03	103.03	103.05	104.05	93.91	97.50	98.52	101.48	102.50	106.09
			0.87	1.13	0.79	1.22	1.13	0.87	1.22	0.79	0.00	1.00	1.00	1.00	1.00	0.00
4	1	1	93.89	97.89	94.89	98.89	101.11	105.11	102.11	106.11	92.79	99.00	100.00	100.00	101.00	107.21
			0.45	1.55	0.45	1.55	1.55	0.45	1.55	0.45	0.00	1.00	1.00	1.00	1.00	0.00
1	4	4	94.45	95.45	98.45	99.45	100.55	101.55	104.55	105.55	93.92	96.00	100.00	100.00	104.00	106.09
			0.83	1.16	0.84	1.17	1.16	0.83	1.17	0.84	0.00	1.00	1.00	1.00	1.00	0.00
4	4	1	92.50	96.50	96.24	100.24	101.00	105.00	102.26	107.50	92.74	97.50	98.76	101.24	102.50	107.27
			0.53	1.47	0.34	1.67	1.47	0.53	1.67	0.34	0.01	1.00	0.99	0.99	1.00	0.01
4	1	4	93.74	97.74	95.00	99.00	99.76	103.76	103.50	107.50	92.75	97.50	98.76	101.24	102.50	107.25
			0.34	1.66	0.53	1.47	1.66	0.33	1.47	0.53	0.01	1.00	1.00	1.00	1.00	0.00
1	1	6	95.93	96.93	96.97	97.97	99.57	100.57	105.53	106.53	93.92	96.50	97.54	102.46	103.50	106.09
			0.73	1.27	0.89	1.11	1.27	0.73	1.11	0.89	0.01	1.00	0.99	0.99	1.00	0.01
1	6	1	93.47	94.47	99.43	100.43	102.03	103.03	103.07	104.07	93.90	96.50	97.54	102.46	103.50	106.10
			0.89	1.11	0.73	1.27	1.11	0.89	1.27	0.73	0.01	1.00	0.99	0.99	1.00	0.01
6	1	1	92.26	98.26	93.26	99.26	100.74	106.74	101.74	107.74	91.51	99.00	100.00	100.00	101.00	108.49
			0.29	1.71	0.29	1.71	1.71	0.29	1.71	0.29	0.00	1.00	1.00	1.00	1.00	0.00
1	6	6	93.46	94.46	99.46	100.46	99.54	100.54	105.54	106.54	93.92	94.00	100.00	100.00	106.00	106.08
			0.83	1.16	0.84	1.17	1.16	0.83	1.17	0.83	0.00	1.00	1.00	1.00	1.00	0.00
6	6	1	90.05	96.05	95.28	100.28	100.45	106.45	102.22	101.22	91.32	96.50	98.27	101.74	103.50	108.68
			0.42	1.58	0.14	1.86	1.58	0.42	1.86	1.14	0.05	1.00	0.95	0.95	1.00	0.05
6	1	6	91.78	97.78	93.55	99.55	98.72	104.72	103.95	109.95	91.32	96.50	98.27	101.74	103.50	108.68
			0.14	1.86	0.42	1.58	1.86	0.14	1.58	0.42	0.05	1.00	0.95	0.95	1.00	0.05
2	2	4	94.81	96.81	96.86	98.86	100.20	102.20	104.14	106.14	93.67	97.00	99.05	100.95	103.00	106.33
			0.63	1.37	0.73	1.28	1.37	0.63	1.28	0.73	0.00	1.00	1.00	1.00	1.00	0.00
2	4	2	93.86	95.86	97.80	99.80	100.14	103.14	103.19	105.19	93.67	97.00	99.05	100.95	103.00	106.33
			0.73	1.27	0.63	1.38	1.27	0.73	1.38	0.63	0.00	1.00	1.00	1.00	1.00	0.00
4	2	2	93.39	97.39	95.39	99.39	100.61	104.61	102.61	106.61	92.79	98.00	100.00	100.00	102.00	107.21
			0.45	1.55	0.45	1.55	1.55	0.45	1.55	0.45	0.00	1.00	1.00	1.00	1.00	0.00
2	4	4	93.84	95.84	97.84	99.84	100.16	102.16	104.16	106.16	93.67	96.00	100.00	100.00	104.00	106.33
			0.68	1.31	0.69	1.32	1.31	0.68	1.32	0.69	0.00	1.00	1.00	1.00	1.00	0.00
4	2	4	93.30	97.30	95.47	99.47	99.70	103.70	103.53	107.53	92.78	97.00	99.17	100.84	103.00	107.23
			0.38	1.62	0.50	1.50	1.62	0.38	1.50	0.50	0.01	1.00	0.99	0.99	1.00	0.01
4	4	2	92.47	96.47	96.30	100.30	100.53	104.53	102.70	106.70	92.77	97.00	99.18	100.83	103.00	107.23
			0.50	1.50	0.38	1.63	1.50	0.50	1.63	0.38	0.01	1.00	0.99	0.99	1.00	0.01
2	2	6	94.76	96.76	96.88	98.88	99.24	101.24	105.12	107.12	93.66	96.00	98.11	101.90	104.00	106.36
			0.55	1.45	0.76	1.24	1.45	0.55	1.24	0.76	0.01	1.00	0.99	0.99	1.00	0.01

Table 3-3 (*continued*) Theoretical Spectra for ABX Cases

			AB part, line number[a]								X part, line number					
J_{AB}	J_{AX}	J_{BX}	1	3	2	4	5	7	6	8	13	9	11	10	12	14
2	6	2	92.88	94.88	98.76	100.76	101.12	103.12	103.24	105.24	93.64	96.00	98.11	101.90	104.00	106.37
			0.75	1.24	0.55	1.45	1.24	0.76	1.45	0.55	0.01	1.00	0.99	0.99	1.00	0.01
6	2	2	91.76	97.76	93.76	99.76	100.24	106.24	102.24	108.24	91.50	98.00	100.00	100.00	102.00	108.50
			0.29	1.70	0.29	1.71	1.70	0.29	1.71	0.29	0.00	1.00	1.00	1.00	1.00	0.00
2	6	6	92.84	94.84	98.84	100.84	99.16	101.16	105.16	107.16	93.67	94.00	100.00	100.00	106.00	106.33
			0.68	1.31	0.69	1.32	1.31	0.68	1.32	0.69	0.00	1.00	1.00	1.00	1.00	0.00
6	2	6	91.39	97.39	94.00	100.00	98.61	104.61	104.00	110.00	91.40	96.00	98.60	101.40	104.00	108.60
			0.17	1.83	0.40	1.60	1.82	0.17	1.61	0.40	0.03	1.00	0.97	0.97	1.00	0.03
6	6	2	90.00	96.00	95.39	101.38	100.00	106.00	102.61	108.61	91.40	96.00	98.60	101.40	104.00	108.60
			0.40	1.59	0.17	1.84	1.59	0.40	1.84	0.17	0.03	1.00	0.97	0.97	1.00	0.03
4	4	6	92.30	96.30	96.46	100.46	98.70	102.70	104.53	108.53	92.77	95.00	99.18	100.82	105.00	107.23
			0.38	1.62	0.50	1.50	1.62	0.38	1.50	0.50	0.01	1.00	0.99	0.99	1.00	0.01
4	6	4	91.46	95.46	97.30	101.30	99.53	103.53	103.70	107.70	92.77	95.00	99.18	100.82	105.00	107.23
			0.50	1.50	0.38	1.62	1.50	0.50	1.62	0.38	0.01	1.00	0.99	0.99	1.00	0.01
1	2	4	95.45	96.45	97.46	98.46	100.55	101.55	104.53	105.53	93.92	97.00	99.00	101.00	103.00	106.09
			0.80	1.19	0.86	1.14	1.19	0.80	1.14	0.86	0.00	1.00	1.00	1.00	1.00	0.00
1	4	2	94.46	95.46	98.45	99.45	101.53	102.53	103.55	104.55	93.92	97.00	99.00	101.00	103.00	106.09
			0.86	1.14	0.81	1.20	1.14	0.86	1.20	0.80	0.00	1.00	1.00	1.00	1.00	0.00
2	1	4	95.29	97.29	96.37	98.37	100.21	102.21	104.13	106.13	93.66	97.50	98.58	101.42	102.50	106.34
			0.60	1.40	0.74	1.26	1.40	0.60	1.26	0.74	0.01	1.00	0.99	0.99	1.00	0.01
2	4	1	93.87	95.87	97.78	99.78	101.63	103.63	102.71	104.71	93.66	97.50	98.58	101.42	102.50	106.34
			0.74	1.26	0.60	1.41	1.26	0.74	1.40	0.60	0.01	1.00	0.99	0.99	1.00	0.01
4	1	2	93.85	97.85	94.93	98.93	100.65	104.65	102.57	106.57	92.78	98.50	99.58	100.42	101.50	107.22
			0.41	1.59	0.48	1.52	1.59	0.41	1.52	0.48	0.00	1.00	1.00	1.00	1.00	0.00
4	2	1	93.43	97.43	95.35	99.35	101.07	105.07	102.15	106.15	92.78	98.50	99.58	100.42	101.50	107.22
			0.48	1.52	0.41	1.59	1.52	0.48	1.59	0.41	0.00	1.00	1.00	1.00	1.00	0.00

2	4	6	93.81	95.81	97.86	99.86	99.19	101.19	105.14	107.14	93.67	95.00	99.05	100.95	105.00	106.33
			0.63	1.36	0.73	1.28	1.36	0.63	1.28	0.73	0.00	1.00	1.00	1.00	1.00	0.00
2	6	4	92.86	94.86	98.81	100.81	100.14	102.14	104.19	106.19	93.67	95.00	99.05	100.95	105.00	106.33
			0.72	1.27	0.63	1.38	1.27	0.73	1.38	0.93	0.00	1.00	1.00	1.00	1.00	0.00
4	2	6	93.17	97.17	95.53	99.53	98.83	102.83	104.47	108.47	92.70	96.00	98.35	101.65	104.00	107.30
			0.29	1.70	0.55	1.45	1.70	0.29	1.45	0.55	0.03	1.00	0.97	0.97	1.00	0.03
4	6	2	91.53	95.53	97.17	101.17	100.47	104.47	102.83	106.83	92.70	96.00	98.35	101.65	104.00	107.30
			0.55	1.45	0.30	1.71	1.45	0.55	1.71	0.29	0.03	1.00	0.97	0.97	1.00	0.03
1	1	−1	95.96	96.96	96.95	97.95	103.04	104.04	102.05	103.05	93.92	99.00	100.00	100.00	101.00	106.09
			0.86	1.14	0.81	1.19	1.14	0.86	1.19	0.81	0.00	1.00	1.00	1.00	1.00	0.00
1	−1	1	96.95	97.95	95.96	96.96	102.05	103.05	103.04	104.04	93.92	99.00	100.00	100.00	101.00	106.09
			0.81	1.19	0.86	1.14	1.19	0.81	1.14	0.86	0.00	1.00	1.00	1.00	1.00	0.00
1	1	−2	95.97	96.97	96.94	97.94	103.53	104.53	101.55	102.55	93.91	98.50	99.50	100.50	101.50	106.09
			0.87	1.13	0.78	1.22	1.13	0.87	1.22	0.78	0.00	1.00	1.00	1.00	1.00	0.00
1	−2	1	97.44	98.44	95.47	96.47	102.05	103.05	103.03	104.03	93.91	98.50	99.50	100.50	101.50	106.09
			0.78	1.22	0.87	1.13	1.22	0.78	1.13	0.87	0.00	1.00	1.00	1.00	1.00	0.00
1	1	−4	95.97	96.97	96.93	97.93	104.53	105.53	100.57	101.57	93.91	97.55	98.50	101.50	102.45	106.09
			0.88	1.12	0.73	1.27	1.12	0.88	1.27	0.73	0.01	0.99	1.00	1.00	0.99	0.01
1	−4	1	98.43	99.43	94.47	95.47	102.07	103.07	103.03	104.03	93.90	97.55	98.50	101.50	102.45	106.10
			0.73	1.28	0.88	1.11	1.27	0.73	1.12	0.88	0.01	0.99	1.00	1.00	0.99	0.01
2	2	−6	94.90	96.90	96.59	98.59	105.10	107.10	99.41	101.41	93.50	96.31	98.00	102.00	103.70	106.50
			0.80	1.20	0.30	1.71	1.20	0.81	1.70	0.29	0.09	0.91	1,00	1.00	0.91	0.09
2	−6	2	98.59	100.59	92.90	94.90	101.41	103.41	103.10	105.10	93.50	96.31	98.00	102.00	103.70	106.50
			0.30	1.71	0.80	1.19	1.71	0.29	1.20	0.81	0.09	0.91	1.00	1.00	0.91	0.09
4	4	−4	92.59	96.59	95.76	99.76	103.41	107.41	100.24	104.24	92.39	96.85	100.00	100.00	103.16	107.63
			0.62	1.37	0.11	1.89	1.38	0.63	1.89	0.11	0.12	0.88	1.00	1.00	0.88	0.12
4	4	−6	92.65	96.65	95.44	99.44	104.35	108.35	99.56	103.56	92.09	96.23	99.00	101.00	103.80	107.93
			0.65	1.34	0.03	1.97	1.35	0.66	1.97	0.03	0.22	0.78	1.00	1.00	0.78	0.22
4	−6	4	96.44	100.44	91.65	95.65	100.56	104.56	103.35	107.35	92.09	96.23	99.00	101.00	103.80	107.93
			0.03	1.97	0.65	1.34	1.97	0.03	1.34	0.66	0.22	0.78	1.00	1.00	0.78	0.22

[a] The lines are numbered in accordance with Table 3-1 when all coupling constants are positive. In each case, the upper line gives the frequencies and the lower gives the relative intensities.

3A-1

J_{AB}	J_{AC}	J_{BC}
1	1	X

X = -6 → +18

Maximum summed intensity = 4.270

LINE	FREQ	INTEN
1	94.92	0.000
2	95.92	0.711
3	96.83	0.921
4	97.00	1.000
5	97.91	1.368
6	98.91	0.
7	100.50	0.
8	101.58	0.000
9	102.51	2.368
10	102.58	2.289
11	103.49	1.711
12	103.59	1.632
13	104.59	0.
14	105.50	0.
15	109.17	0.000

3A-2

J_{AB}	J_{AC}	J_{BC}
1	2	1
2	1	1

Maximum summed intensity = 3.734

LINE	FREQ	INTEN
1	95.31	0.592
2	95.68	0.140
3	96.71	0.669
4	96.89	0.752
5	97.91	0.292
6	98.28	1.555
7	101.24	0.091
8	102.28	2.508
9	102.44	2.316
10	102.82	0.219
11	103.48	0.047
12	103.84	1.373
13	103.85	1.334
14	104.87	0.111
15	109.41	0.001

3A-3

J_{AB}	J_{AC}	J_{BC}
1	2	2
2	1	2

Maximum summed intensity = 4.036

LINE	FREQ	INTEN
1	94.76	0.031
2	95.31	0.590
3	96.67	0.794
4	96.92	0.910
5	98.28	1.557
6	98.83	0.118
7	100.26	0.040
8	101.88	0.081
9	102.29	2.545
10	102.43	2.370
11	103.79	1.509
12	103.90	1.421
13	104.46	0.011
14	105.81	0.022
15	109.41	0.001

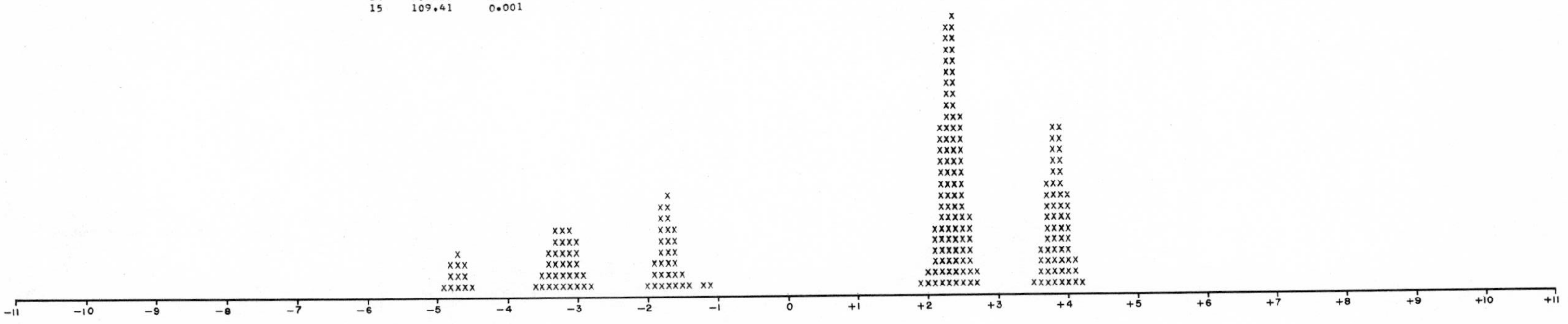

3A-4

J_{AB}	J_{AC}	J_{BC}
2	2	X

$X = -6 \rightarrow +18$

Maximum summed intensity = 4.092

LINE	FREQ	INTEN
1	94.73	0.507
2	95.73	0.000
3	96.35	0.734
4	97.00	1.000
5	97.63	0.000
6	98.63	1.761
7	101.00	0.000
8	102.10	2.759
9	102.27	2.493
10	103.27	0.000
11	103.37	0.000
12	103.90	1.505
13	104.37	1.239
14	105.00	0.000
15	109.65	0.002

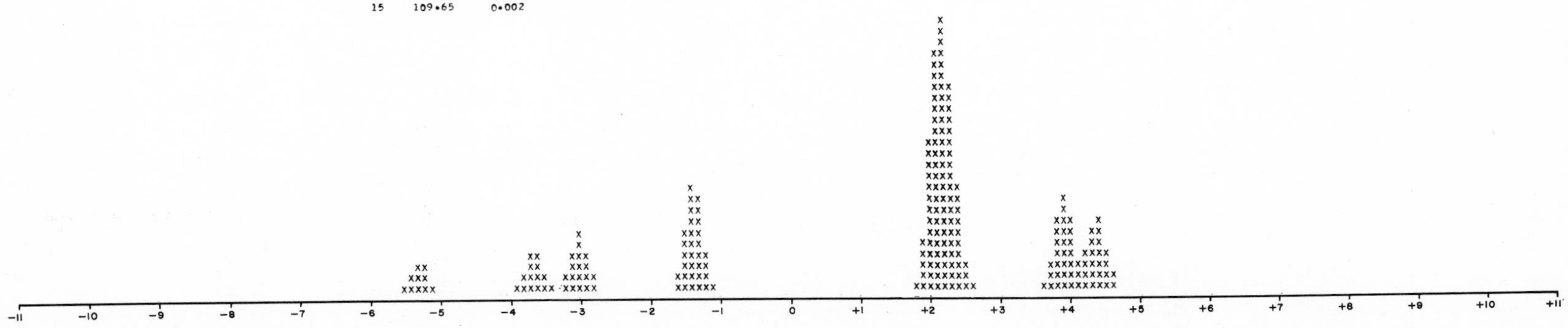

3A-5

J_{AB}	J_{AC}	J_{BC}
1	4	1
4	1	1

Maximum summed intensity = 2.459

LINE	FREQ	INTEN
1	93.88	0.397
2	94.51	0.303
3	96.05	0.237
4	96.65	0.240
5	98.19	0.971
6	98.82	1.853
7	100.79	0.415
8	101.85	2.646
9	102.33	2.189
10	102.96	0.729
11	103.39	0.206
12	104.02	0.877
13	105.10	0.666
14	106.16	0.270
15	110.30	0.001

−11 −10 −9 −8 −7 −6 −5 −4 −3 −2 −1 0 +1 +2 +3 +4 +5 +6 +7 +8 +9 +10 +11

3A-6

J_{AB}	J_{AC}	J_{BC}
1	4	4
4	1	4

Maximum summed intensity = 3.131

LINE	FREQ	INTEN
1	92.18	0.034
2	93.73	0.362
3	96.24	0.595
4	96.34	0.662
5	98.06	0.138
6	98.85	1.888
7	100.40	0.460
8	100.67	0.332
9	101.94	2.871
10	102.21	2.500
11	104.55	1.084
12	104.72	1.028
13	106.09	0.016
14	108.60	0.028
15	110.42	0.001

−11 −10 −9 −8 −7 −6 −5 −4 −3 −2 −1 0 +1 +2 +3 +4 +5 +6 +7 +8 +9 +10 +11

3A-7

J_{AB}	J_{AC}	J_{BC}
4	4	X

X = -6 → +18

Maximum summed intensity = 3.406

LINE	FREQ	INTEN
1	92.10	0.275
2	94.64	0.369
3	95.10	0.000
4	96.54	0.000
5	97.00	1.000
6	99.54	2.366
7	100.00	0.000
8	101.57	3.356
9	101.90	2.725
10	103.46	0.000
11	104.43	1.265
12	104.90	0.000
13	106.00	0.000
14	106.46	0.634
15	111.36	0.010

−11 −10 −9 −8 −7 −6 −5 −4 −3 −2 −1 0 +1 +2 +3 +4 +5 +6 +7 +8 +9 +10 +11

3A-8

J_{AB}	J_{AC}	J_{BC}
1	6	1
6	1	1

Maximum summed intensity = 2.546

LINE	FREQ	INTEN
1	92.25	0.266
2	92.95	0.243
3	94.77	0.095
4	96.65	0.117
5	98.47	1.233
6	99.17	2.048
7	100.47	0.650
8	101.55	2.725
9	102.28	2.084
10	102.99	0.888
11	103.37	0.322
12	104.07	0.727
13	106.68	0.377
14	107.76	0.225
15	111.58	0.002

−11 −10 −9 −8 −7 −6 −5 −4 −3 −2 −1 0 +1 +2 +3 +4 +5 +6 +7 +8 +9 +10 +11

3A-9

J_{AB}	J_{AC}	J_{BC}
1	6	6
6	1	6

Maximum summed intensity = 3.230

LINE	FREQ	INTEN
1	89.47	0.024
2	91.61	0.188
3	95.19	0.400
4	95.68	0.448
5	96.34	0.208
6	99.26	2.152
7	99.91	0.599
8	101.39	0.790
9	101.69	3.133
10	102.05	2.604
11	105.27	0.826
12	106.12	0.588
13	107.41	0.018
14	111.48	0.022
15	112.13	0.001

−11 −10 −9 −8 −7 −6 −5 −4 −3 −2 −1 0 +1 +2 +3 +4 +5 +6 +7 +8 +9 +10 +11

3A-10

J_{AB}	J_{AC}	J_{BC}
6	6	X

X = −6 → +18

Maximum summed intensity = 3.656

LINE	FREQ	INTEN
1	89.32	0.166
2	92.32	0.182
3	94.32	0.000
4	95.00	0.000
5	97.00	1.000
6	99.00	0.000
7	100.00	2.667
8	101.32	3.652
9	101.68	2.834
10	104.00	0.000
11	104.68	1.152
12	106.68	0.000
13	107.00	0.000
14	109.00	0.333
15	113.68	0.014

−11 −10 −9 −8 −7 −6 −5 −4 −3 −2 −1 0 +1 +2 +3 +4 +5 +6 +7 +8 +9 +10 +11

3A-11

J_{AB}	J_{AC}	J_{BC}
9	9	X

X = -6 → +18

Maximum summed intensity = 3.812

LINE	FREQ	INTEN
1	85.00	0.091
2	88.34	0.077
3	92.34	0.000
4	93.00	0.000
5	97.00	1.000
6	97.50	0.000
7	100.34	2.846
8	101.16	3.833
9	101.50	2.909
10	104.84	1.077
11	105.16	0.000
12	108.50	0.000
13	109.50	0.000
14	113.16	0.154
15	117.66	0.013

-11 -10 -9 -8 -7 -6 -5 -4 -3 -2 -1 0 +1 +2 +3 +4 +5 +6 +7 +8 +9 +10 +11

3A-12

J_{AB}	J_{AC}	J_{BC}
12	12	X

X = -6 → +18

Maximum summed intensity = 4.109

LINE	FREQ	INTEN
1	80.61	0.057
2	84.12	0.040
3	89.51	0.000
4	91.61	0.000
5	96.00	0.000
6	97.00	1.000
7	100.51	2.914
8	101.09	3.904
9	101.39	2.943
10	104.91	1.046
11	106.49	0.000
12	110.00	0.000
13	112.39	0.000
14	117.49	0.086
15	121.88	0.011

-11 -10 -9 -8 -7 -6 -5 -4 -3 -2 -1 0 +1 +2 +3 +4 +5 +6 +7 +8 +9 +10 +11

3A-13

J_{AB}	J_{AC}	J_{BC}
18	18	X

X = -6 → +18

Maximum summed intensity = 4.769

LINE	FREQ	INTEN
1	71.73	0.028
2	75.41	0.016
3	83.68	0.000
4	88.73	0.000
5	93.00	0.000
6	97.00	1.000
7	100.68	2.963
8	101.04	3.957
9	101.27	2.972
10	104.96	1.021
11	109.32	0.000
12	113.00	0.000
13	118.27	0.000
14	126.32	0.037
15	130.59	0.007

-11 -10 -9 -8 -7 -6 -5 -4 -3 -2 -1 0 +1 +2 +3 +4 +5 +6 +7 +8 +9 +10 +11

3A-14

J_{AB}	J_{AC}	J_{BC}
2	4	2
4	2	2

Maximum summed intensity = 3.179

LINE	FREQ	INTEN
1	93.33	0.353
2	94.03	0.099
3	95.91	0.424
4	96.56	0.636
5	98.43	0.414
6	99.13	2.077
7	99.57	0.075
8	101.78	3.048
9	102.09	2.572
10	102.79	0.369
11	104.30	0.024
12	104.67	0.980
13	105.00	0.818
14	106.87	0.105
15	110.54	0.005

-11 -10 -9 -8 -7 -6 -5 -4 -3 -2 -1 0 +1 +2 +3 +4 +5 +6 +7 +8 +9 +10 +11

3A-15

J_{AB}	J_{AC}	J_{BC}
2	4	4
4	2	4

Maximum summed intensity = 3.296

LINE	FREQ	INTEN
1	92.24	0.018
2	93.29	0.343
3	95.74	0.516
4	96.68	0.819
5	97.64	0.050
6	99.13	2.085
7	100.18	0.224
8	101.03	0.180
9	101.79	3.074
10	102.08	2.607
11	104.53	1.159
12	105.19	0.898
13	106.23	0.007
14	108.68	0.017
15	110.58	0.004

3A-16

J_{AB}	J_{AC}	J_{BC}
6	2	2
2	6	2

Maximum summed intensity = 3.005

LINE	FREQ	INTEN
1	91.73	0.243
2	92.66	0.141
3	95.39	0.284
4	95.78	0.224
5	98.51	0.836
6	99.27	0.186
7	99.45	2.278
8	101.55	3.207
9	102.00	2.571
10	102.94	0.733
11	104.28	0.066
12	105.22	0.564
13	106.06	0.504
14	108.34	0.158
15	111.83	0.005

3A-17

J_{AB}	J_{AC}	J_{BC}
2	6	6
6	2	6

Maximum summed intensity = 3.366

LINE	FREQ	INTEN
1	89.54	0.017
2	91.35	0.197
3	95.06	0.369
4	95.71	0.119
5	95.77	0.530
6	99.48	2.315
7	100.13	0.470
8	101.29	0.576
9	101.58	3.299
10	101.94	2.685
11	105.65	0.722
12	106.00	0.667
13	107.81	0.012
14	111.52	0.018
15	112.17	0.004

3A-18

J_{AB}	J_{AC}	J_{BC}
1	2	4
2	1	4

Maximum summed intensity = 4.163

LINE	FREQ	INTEN
1	92.79	0.005
2	95.29	0.581
3	96.65	0.828
4	96.92	0.945
5	98.28	1.559
6	98.29	0.030
7	99.93	0.053
8	100.78	0.082
9	102.29	2.557
10	102.42	2.390
11	103.78	1.527
12	103.93	1.437
13	106.42	0.002
14	107.79	0.003
15	109.43	0.001

3A-19

J_{AB}	J_{AC}	J_{BC}
1	4	2
4	1	2

Maximum summed intensity = 2.845

LINE	FREQ	INTEN
1	93.85	0.389
2	93.87	0.142
3	96.24	0.485
4	96.43	0.453
5	98.80	0.664
6	98.83	1.869
7	99.89	0.215
8	101.91	2.801
9	102.26	2.396
10	102.29	0.496
11	104.28	0.066
12	104.30	1.009
13	104.85	0.892
14	106.86	0.122
15	110.32	0.001

−11 −10 −9 −8 −7 −6 −5 −4 −3 −2 −1 0 +1 +2 +3 +4 +5 +6 +7 +8 +9 +10 +11

3A-20

J_{AB}	J_{AC}	J_{BC}
2	4	1
4	2	1

Maximum summed intensity = 2.956

LINE	FREQ	INTEN
1	93.35	0.356
2	94.71	0.265
3	96.17	0.242
4	96.30	0.325
5	97.76	0.746
6	99.12	2.071
7	100.53	0.146
8	101.76	2.991
9	102.12	2.498
10	103.35	0.075
11	103.48	0.712
12	104.71	0.628
13	104.94	0.640
14	106.17	0.302
15	110.53	0.004

−11 −10 −9 −8 −7 −6 −5 −4 −3 −2 −1 0 +1 +2 +3 +4 +5 +6 +7 +8 +9 +10 +11

3A-21

J_{AB}	J_{AC}	J_{BC}
2	4	6
4	2	6

Maximum summed intensity = 3.434

LINE	FREQ	INTEN
1	90.31	0.005
2	93.16	0.308
3	95.68	0.530
4	95.77	0.075
5	96.61	0.777
6	99.14	2.089
7	99.22	0.223
8	101.79	3.081
9	101.99	0.294
10	102.07	2.617
11	104.60	1.082
12	105.24	0.906
13	108.09	0.004
14	110.62	0.005
15	110.70	0.004

3A-22

J_{AB}	J_{AC}	J_{BC}
2	6	4
6	2	4

Maximum summed intensity = 3.755

LINE	FREQ	INTEN
1	91.27	0.047
2	91.59	0.227
3	95.29	0.335
4	95.78	0.502
5	97.45	0.115
6	99.47	2.302
7	99.80	0.592
8	101.58	3.275
9	101.63	0.502
10	101.96	2.658
11	105.65	0.720
12	105.76	0.647
13	106.09	0.021
14	109.78	0.051
15	111.94	0.005

3A-23

J_{AB}	J_{AC}	J_{BC}
4	6	2
6	4	2

Maximum summed intensity = 3.507

LINE	FREQ	INTEN
1	90.63	0.206
2	92.80	0.137
3	94.40	0.120
4	96.02	0.304
5	97.62	0.714
6	98.57	0.028
7	99.79	2.531
8	101.42	3.509
9	101.79	2.767
10	103.96	0.772
11	104.64	0.010
12	105.56	0.422
13	106.80	0.256
14	108.41	0.213
15	112.58	0.012

−11 −10 −9 −8 −7 −6 −5 −4 −3 −2 −1 0 +1 +2 +3 +4 +5 +6 +7 +8 +9 +10 +11

3A-24

J_{AB}	J_{AC}	J_{BC}
1	-1	1
-1	1	1

Maximum summed intensity = 3.463

LINE	FREQ	INTEN
1	95.51	0.321
2	96.85	0.455
3	96.90	0.949
4	96.93	0.967
5	96.98	0.494
6	98.32	0.815
7	101.83	0.407
8	101.88	0.493
9	102.80	1.851
10	102.85	1.743
11	103.22	1.557
12	103.29	1.542
13	104.19	0.224
14	104.27	0.182
15	109.17	0.000

−11 −10 −9 −8 −7 −6 −5 −4 −3 −2 −1 0 +1 +2 +3 +4 +5 +6 +7 +8 +9 +10 +11

3A-25

J_{AB}	J_{AC}	J_{BC}
1	-2	1
-2	1	1

Maximum summed intensity = 1.841

LINE	FREQ	INTEN
1	95.01	0.384
2	96.32	0.784
3	96.78	0.280
4	96.80	0.252
5	97.27	1.049
6	98.58	1.252
7	101.50	0.618
8	101.97	0.822
9	102.45	1.962
10	102.92	1.465
11	103.28	1.431
12	103.76	1.129
13	104.23	0.254
14	104.71	0.318
15	109.42	0.001

−11 −10 −9 −8 −7 −6 −5 −4 −3 −2 −1 0 +1 +2 +3 +4 +5 +6 +7 +8 +9 +10 +11

3A-26

J_{AB}	J_{AC}	J_{BC}
1	-4	1
-4	1	1

Maximum summed intensity = 2.863

LINE	FREQ	INTEN
1	93.66	0.324
2	94.88	0.501
3	95.94	0.099
4	96.75	0.092
5	97.80	1.189
6	99.02	1.797
7	101.00	0.919
8	101.92	2.164
9	102.06	1.199
10	102.98	1.189
11	103.28	1.268
12	104.20	0.335
13	105.14	0.612
14	106.06	0.310
15	110.32	0.002

−11 −10 −9 −8 −7 −6 −5 −4 −3 −2 −1 0 +1 +2 +3 +4 +5 +6 +7 +8 +9 +10 +11

3A-27

J_{AB}	J_{AC}	J_{BC}
1	-6	1
-6	1	1

Maximum summed intensity = 2.227

LINE	FREQ	INTEN
1	92.06	0.232
2	93.25	0.324
3	94.67	0.044
4	96.72	0.042
5	98.15	1.262
6	99.34	2.098
7	100.67	1.103
8	101.57	2.298
9	102.10	1.374
10	102.99	1.088
11	103.29	1.156
12	104.18	0.378
13	106.76	0.364
14	107.65	0.233
15	111.60	0.003

3A-28

J_{AB}	J_{AC}	J_{BC}
2	-2	2
-2	2	2

Maximum summed intensity =3.110

LINE	FREQ	INTEN
1	93.92	0.218
2	96.39	0.334
3	96.54	0.776
4	96.75	0.894
5	96.90	0.476
6	99.37	1.305
7	100.85	0.570
8	101.00	0.818
9	102.63	1.985
10	102.78	1.713
11	103.46	1.406
12	103.83	1.204
13	105.25	0.179
14	105.61	0.121
15	109.71	0.002

3A-29

J_{AB}	J_{AC}	J_{BC}
2	-4	2
-4	2	2

Maximum summed intensity = 2.261

LINE	FREQ	INTEN
1	92.70	0.221
2	95.35	0.564
3	96.16	0.132
4	96.18	0.219
5	97.00	0.818
6	99.65	2.051
7	100.43	0.804
8	101.27	1.406
9	102.08	2.278
10	102.92	1.335
11	103.92	1.007
12	104.73	0.776
13	105.57	0.158
14	106.38	0.222
15	110.65	0.007

3A-30

J_{AB}	J_{AC}	J_{BC}
2	-6	2
-6	2	2

Maximum summed intensity = 2.530

LINE	FREQ	INTEN
1	91.16	0.175
2	93.73	0.359
3	94.97	0.104
4	96.05	0.056
5	97.29	0.822
6	99.87	2.494
7	100.16	0.950
8	101.41	1.736
9	101.73	2.460
10	102.97	1.163
11	103.98	0.863
12	105.54	0.181
13	106.30	0.442
14	107.86	0.186
15	111.98	0.009

3A-31

J_{AB}	J_{AC}	J_{BC}
4	-4	4
-4	4	4

Maximum summed intensity = 2.361

LINE	FREQ	INTEN
1	90.54	0.115
2	94.42	0.098
3	94.83	0.332
4	96.22	0.722
5	96.62	0.414
6	99.74	0.849
7	100.14	1.553
8	100.51	2.333
9	102.35	2.216
10	102.76	1.586
11	104.03	1.115
12	105.82	0.469
13	106.64	0.122
14	108.44	0.062
15	111.96	0.013

−11 −10 −9 −8 −7 −6 −5 −4 −3 −2 −1 0 +1 +2 +3 +4 +5 +6 +7 +8 +9 +10 +11

3A-32

J_{AB}	J_{AC}	J_{BC}
4	-6	4
-6	4	4

Maximum summed intensity = 4.794

LINE	FREQ	INTEN
1	89.14	0.106
2	94.04	0.035
3	94.66	0.448
4	95.00	0.310
5	95.61	0.217
6	99.59	0.928
7	100.51	2.902
8	100.55	2.063
9	101.94	2.483
10	102.89	1.304
11	105.45	0.627
12	106.06	0.364
13	107.79	0.126
14	108.41	0.069
15	113.34	0.018

−11 −10 −9 −8 −7 −6 −5 −4 −3 −2 −1 0 +1 +2 +3 +4 +5 +6 +7 +8 +9 +10 +11

3A-33

J_{AB}	J_{AC}	J_{BC}
1	2	-1
2	1	-1

Maximum summed intensity = 4.517

LINE	FREQ	INTEN
1	95.32	0.594
2	95.66	0.128
3	96.60	0.659
4	97.00	0.795
5	97.94	0.275
6	98.27	1.548
7	101.42	0.160
8	102.36	2.388
9	102.37	2.322
10	102.69	0.137
11	103.31	0.084
12	103.65	1.528
13	104.03	1.315
14	104.99	0.066
15	109.41	0.001

3A-34

J_{AB}	J_{AC}	J_{BC}
1	4	-1
4	1	-1

Maximum summed intensity = 2.187

LINE	FREQ	INTEN
1	93.93	0.406
2	94.47	0.303
3	95.71	0.177
4	97.00	0.305
5	98.23	1.014
6	98.78	1.796
7	101.07	0.786
8	101.92	2.199
9	102.30	2.009
10	102.85	0.504
11	103.15	0.395
12	103.70	1.220
13	105.37	0.700
14	106.22	0.185
15	110.30	0.001

3A-35

J_{AB}	J_{AC}	J_{BC}
1	4	-2
4	1	-2

Maximum summed intensity = 3.899

LINE	FREQ	INTEN
1	93.76	0.136
2	93.94	0.409
3	95.75	0.370
4	96.93	0.576
5	98.74	1.736
6	98.92	0.774
7	100.24	0.396
8	102.03	2.482
9	102.05	0.442
10	102.23	2.339
11	103.84	1.317
12	104.03	0.109
13	105.22	0.822
14	107.01	0.092
15	110.32	0.001

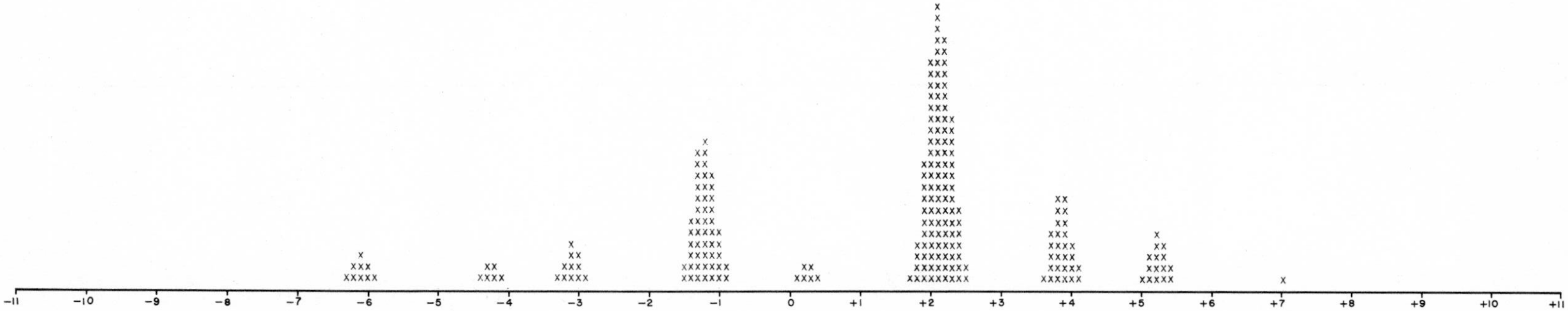

−11 −10 −9 −8 −7 −6 −5 −4 −3 −2 −1 0 +1 +2 +3 +4 +5 +6 +7 +8 +9 +10 +11

3A-36

J_{AB}	J_{AC}	J_{BC}
2	4	-1
4	2	-1

Maximum summed intensity = 4.197

LINE	FREQ	INTEN
1	93.37	0.360
2	94.69	0.234
3	95.48	0.240
4	96.99	0.487
5	97.78	0.637
6	99.11	2.047
7	101.18	0.680
8	101.92	2.240
9	101.98	2.362
10	102.71	0.401
11	103.30	0.220
12	104.03	1.259
13	105.60	0.733
14	106.33	0.096
15	110.52	0.004

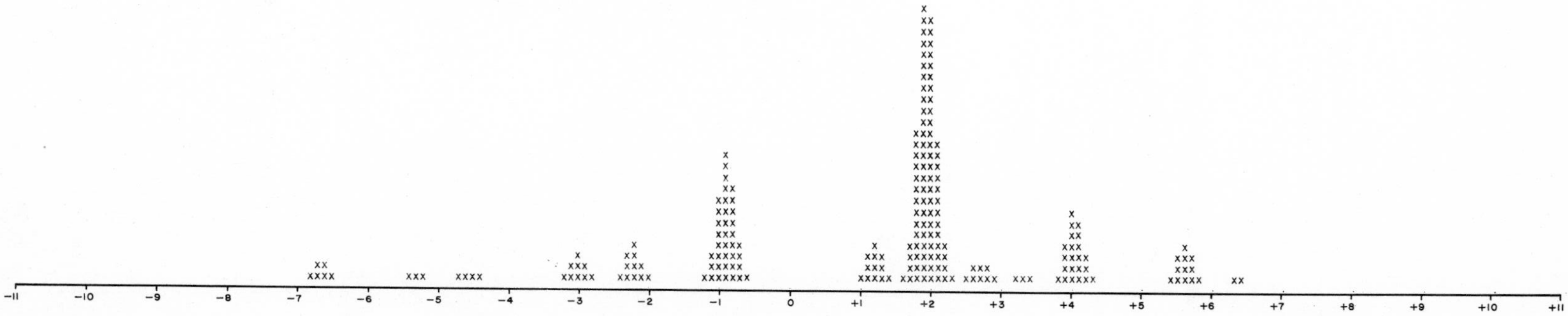

−11 −10 −9 −8 −7 −6 −5 −4 −3 −2 −1 0 +1 +2 +3 +4 +5 +6 +7 +8 +9 +10 +11

3A-37

J_{AB}	J_{AC}	J_{BC}
2	4	-2
4	2	-2

Maximum summed intensity = 4.751

LINE	FREQ	INTEN
1	93.38	0.361
2	93.86	0.074
3	95.48	0.410
4	96.99	0.781
5	98.61	0.359
6	99.09	2.020
7	100.29	0.213
8	101.91	2.803
9	102.00	2.571
10	102.39	0.183
11	103.62	0.068
12	104.10	1.314
13	105.52	0.797
14	107.23	0.043
15	110.53	0.004

-11 -10 -9 -8 -7 -6 -5 -4 -3 -2 -1 0 +1 +2 +3 +4 +5 +6 +7 +8 +9 +10 +11

3B-1

J_{AB}	J_{AC}	J_{BC}
1	1	1

Maximum summed intensity = 2.267

LINE	FREQ	INTEN
1	95.52	0.001
2	95.93	0.728
3	96.87	0.924
4	96.98	1.005
5	97.92	1.340
6	98.33	0.002
7	101.80	0.311
8	102.82	2.035
9	102.85	0.270
10	103.27	1.960
11	103.86	1.385
12	104.21	1.459
13	104.28	0.305
14	105.22	0.276
15	110.15	0.000

−11 −10 −9 −8 −7 −6 −5 −4 −3 −2 −1 0 +1 +2 +3 +4 +5 +6 +7 +8 +9 +10 +11

3B-2

J_{AB}	J_{AC}	J_{BC}
2	2	2

Maximum summed intensity = 2.681

LINE	FREQ	INTEN
1	94.51	0.002
2	94.74	0.531
3	96.43	0.756
4	96.97	1.002
5	98.66	1.705
6	98.89	0.004
7	100.40	0.110
8	102.48	2.600
9	102.63	0.096
10	102.86	2.359
11	104.55	1.434
12	104.71	1.194
13	104.95	0.103
14	106.63	0.100
15	110.60	0.002

−11 −10 −9 −8 −7 −6 −5 −4 −3 −2 −1 0 +1 +2 +3 +4 +5 +6 +7 +8 +9 +10 +11

3B-3

J_{AB}	J_{AC}	J_{BC}
3	3	3

Maximum summed intensity = 3.005

LINE	FREQ	INTEN
1	93.31	0.003
2	93.47	0.393
3	95.72	0.566
4	96.96	1.001
5	98.94	0.053
6	99.22	2.037
7	99.38	0.005
8	102.19	2.986
9	102.43	0.046
10	102.59	2.554
11	104.85	1.343
12	105.68	0.914
13	105.85	0.046
14	108.10	0.049
15	111.31	0.005

3B-4

J_{AB}	J_{AC}	J_{BC}
4	4	4

Maximum summed intensity = 3.178

LINE	FREQ	INTEN
1	92.02	0.002
2	92.14	0.298
3	94.81	0.405
4	96.96	1.001
5	97.46	0.030
6	99.63	2.298
7	99.75	0.005
8	101.97	3.264
9	102.28	0.026
10	102.40	2.672
11	105.07	1.263
12	106.79	0.673
13	106.91	0.025
14	109.58	0.029
15	112.23	0.009

3B-5

J_{AB}	J_{AC}	J_{BC}
6	6	6

Maximum summed intensity = 3.600

LINE	FREQ	INTEN
1	89.29	0.002
2	89.37	0.183
3	92.57	0.207
4	94.48	0.014
5	96.96	1.000
6	100.15	2.617
7	100.24	0.004
8	101.70	3.594
9	102.07	0.011
10	102.15	2.803
11	105.34	1.158
12	109.29	0.369
13	109.37	0.009
14	112.56	0.013
15	114.47	0.014

−11 −10 −9 −8 −7 −6 −5 −4 −3 −2 −1 0 +1 +2 +3 +4 +5 +6 +7 +8 +9 +10 +11

3B-6

J_{AB}	J_{AC}	J_{BC}
8	8	8

Maximum summed intensity = 3.620

LINE	FREQ	INTEN
1	86.46	0.001
2	86.52	0.122
3	90.01	0.115
4	91.49	0.008
5	96.96	1.000
6	100.45	2.773
7	100.51	0.003
8	101.56	3.754
9	101.93	0.006
10	101.99	2.871
11	105.48	1.101
12	112.00	0.220
13	112.06	0.005
14	115.55	0.008
15	117.03	0.014

−11 −10 −9 −8 −7 −6 −5 −4 −3 −2 −1 0 +1 +2 +3 +4 +5 +6 +7 +8 +9 +10 +11

3B-7

J_{AB}	J_{AC}	J_{BC}
10	10	10

Maximum summed intensity = 3.855

LINE	FREQ	INTEN
1	83.58	0.001
2	83.63	0.086
3	87.30	0.071
4	88.49	0.005
5	96.96	1.000
6	100.63	2.853
7	100.68	0.002
8	101.49	3.837
9	101.83	0.004
10	101.88	2.909
11	105.55	1.069
12	114.82	0.142
13	114.87	0.003
14	118.54	0.005
15	119.74	0.013

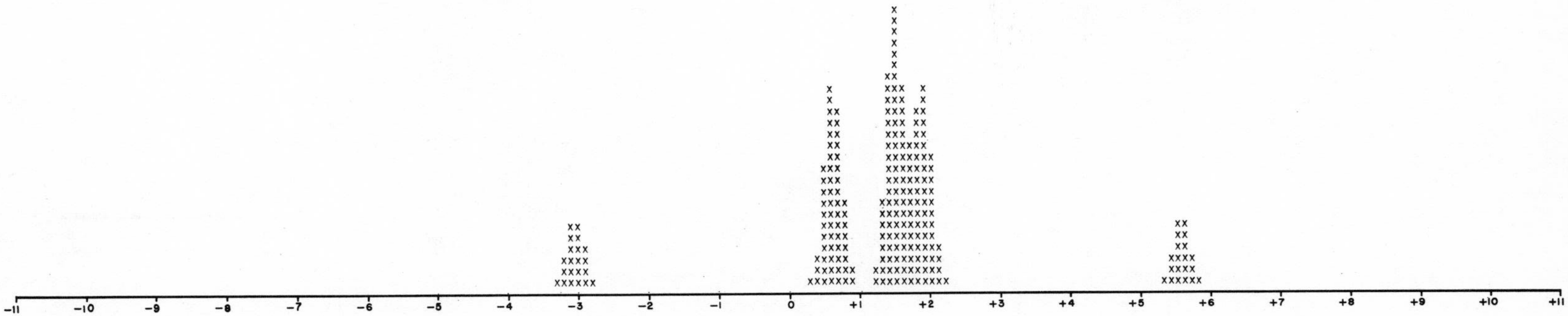

-11
-10
-9
-8
-7
-6
-5
-4
-3
-2
-1
0
+1
+2
+3
+4
+5
+6
+7
+8
+9
+10
+11

3B-8

J_{AB}	J_{AC}	J_{BC}
12	12	12

Maximum summed intensity = 3.708

LINE	FREQ	INTEN
1	80.66	0.001
2	80.70	0.064
3	84.49	0.047
4	85.50	0.003
5	96.96	1.000
6	100.76	2.898
7	100.80	0.002
8	101.44	3.885
9	101.76	0.003
10	101.80	2.933
11	105.59	1.050
12	117.71	0.098
13	117.75	0.002
14	121.54	0.003
15	122.54	0.011

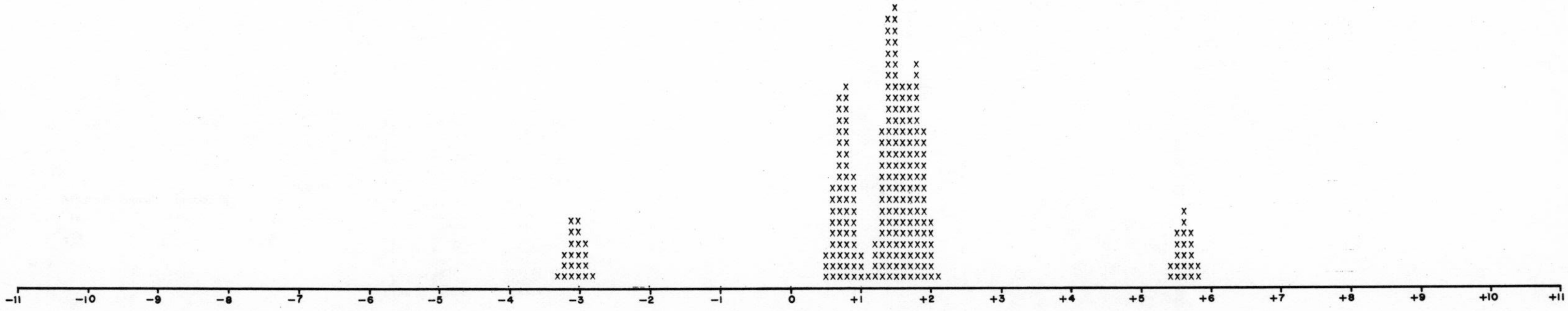

-11
-10
-9
-8
-7
-6
-5
-4
-3
-2
-1
0
+1
+2
+3
+4
+5
+6
+7
+8
+9
+10
+11

3B-9

J_{AB}	J_{AC}	J_{BC}
15	15	15

Maximum summed intensity = 4.054

LINE	FREQ	INTEN
1	76.25	0.000
2	76.28	0.044
3	80.19	0.028
4	81.00	0.002
5	96.96	1.000
6	100.88	2.936
7	100.91	0.001
8	101.41	3.926
9	101.68	0.002
10	101.72	2.954
11	105.63	1.033
12	122.09	0.062
13	122.12	0.001
14	126.04	0.002
15	126.84	0.009

−11 −10 −9 −8 −7 −6 −5 −4 −3 −2 −1 0 +1 +2 +3 +4 +5 +6 +7 +8 +9 +10 +11

3B-10

J_{AB}	J_{AC}	J_{BC}
18	18	18

Maximum summed intensity = 4.300

LINE	FREQ	INTEN
1	71.81	0.000
2	71.84	0.031
3	75.83	0.018
4	76.51	0.002
5	96.96	1.000
6	100.96	2.956
7	100.98	0.001
8	101.38	3.948
9	101.63	0.001
10	101.66	2.967
11	105.65	1.023
12	126.51	0.043
13	126.54	0.001
14	130.53	0.002
15	131.21	0.007

−11 −10 −9 −8 −7 −6 −5 −4 −3 −2 −1 0 +1 +2 +3 +4 +5 +6 +7 +8 +9 +10 +11

3B-11

J_{AB}	J_{AC}	J_{BC}
1	1	2

Maximum summed intensity = 2.260

LINE	FREQ	INTEN
1	94.69	0.000
2	95.93	0.728
3	96.85	0.926
4	96.99	1.007
5	97.92	1.339
6	99.15	0.000
7	100.89	0.118
8	101.95	0.091
9	102.90	2.229
10	103.18	2.154
11	103.96	1.563
12	104.11	1.637
13	105.20	0.111
14	106.12	0.098
15	110.15	0.000

3B-12

J_{AB}	J_{AC}	J_{BC}
1	2	1

Maximum summed intensity = 3.270

LINE	FREQ	INTEN
1	95.28	0.055
2	95.33	0.626
3	96.56	0.812
4	97.08	0.870
5	98.30	1.507
6	98.36	0.131
7	101.69	0.109
8	102.72	2.340
9	102.92	0.499
10	102.98	2.265
11	103.95	1.128
12	104.00	0.166
13	104.72	1.127
14	105.75	0.365
15	110.36	0.001

3B-13

J_{AB}	J_{AC}	J_{BC}
2	1	1

Maximum summed intensity = 2.943

LINE	FREQ	INTEN
1	95.32	0.604
2	95.46	0.031
3	96.37	0.733
4	97.24	1.034
5	98.15	0.078
6	98.29	1.521
7	101.45	0.513
8	102.48	2.119
9	103.23	1.883
10	103.37	0.037
11	104.26	0.401
12	104.28	1.567
13	104.40	1.378
14	105.31	0.101
15	110.40	0.000

−11 −10 −9 −8 −7 −6 −5 −4 −3 −2 −1 0 +1 +2 +3 +4 +5 +6 +7 +8 +9 +10 +11

3B-14

J_{AB}	J_{AC}	J_{BC}
1	2	2

Maximum summed intensity = 3.541

LINE	FREQ	INTEN
1	94.50	0.026
2	95.33	0.626
3	96.71	0.880
4	96.92	0.871
5	98.30	1.508
6	99.14	0.089
7	100.73	0.027
8	102.11	0.254
9	102.75	2.450
10	102.94	2.347
11	104.14	1.332
12	104.53	1.372
13	104.97	0.058
14	106.56	0.160
15	110.37	0.001

−11 −10 −9 −8 −7 −6 −5 −4 −3 −2 −1 0 +1 +2 +3 +4 +5 +6 +7 +8 +9 +10 +11

3B-15

J_{AB}	J_{AC}	J_{BC}
2	2	1

Maximum summed intensity = 2.412

LINE	FREQ	INTEN
1	94.74	0.531
2	95.31	0.014
3	96.49	0.749
4	96.91	0.968
5	98.08	0.033
6	98.66	1.706
7	101.33	0.272
8	102.42	2.433
9	102.93	2.197
10	103.50	0.322
11	104.01	0.271
12	104.58	0.989
13	104.67	1.207
14	105.76	0.305
15	110.60	0.002

−11 −10 −9 −8 −7 −6 −5 −4 −3 −2 −1 0 +1 +2 +3 +4 +5 +6 +7 +8 +9 +10 +11

3B-16

J_{AB}	J_{AC}	J_{BC}
2	1	2

Maximum summed intensity = 2.473

LINE	FREQ	INTEN
1	94.60	0.015
2	95.31	0.600
3	96.47	0.775
4	97.13	1.016
5	98.29	1.521
6	99.00	0.073
7	100.58	0.255
8	102.40	0.002
9	102.60	2.355
10	103.11	2.145
11	104.27	1.598
12	104.42	1.446
13	105.13	0.166
14	106.29	0.033
15	110.40	0.000

−11 −10 −9 −8 −7 −6 −5 −4 −3 −2 −1 0 +1 +2 +3 +4 +5 +6 +7 +8 +9 +10 +11

3B-17

J_{AB}	J_{AC}	J_{BC}
1	1	4

Maximum summed intensity = 3.470

LINE	FREQ	INTEN
1	92.81	0.000
2	95.93	0.727
3	96.85	0.928
4	97.00	1.006
5	97.92	1.339
6	98.94	0.038
7	100.01	0.021
8	101.04	0.000
9	102.95	2.308
10	103.13	2.236
11	104.02	1.633
12	104.05	1.705
13	107.14	0.031
14	108.06	0.028
15	110.15	0.000

-11 -10 -9 -8 -7 -6 -5 -4 -3 -2 -1 0 +1 +2 +3 +4 +5 +6 +7 +8 +9 +10 +11

3B-18

J_{AB}	J_{AC}	J_{BC}
1	4	1

Maximum summed intensity = 4.161

LINE	FREQ	INTEN
1	93.95	0.447
2	94.29	0.188
3	95.51	0.401
4	97.33	0.567
5	98.56	0.609
6	98.90	1.789
7	101.41	0.016
8	102.47	2.782
9	102.63	2.537
10	102.97	0.770
11	103.69	0.005
12	104.03	0.852
13	106.01	0.676
14	107.07	0.359
15	111.15	0.002

-11 -10 -9 -8 -7 -6 -5 -4 -3 -2 -1 0 +1 +2 +3 +4 +5 +6 +7 +8 +9 +10 +11

3B-19

J_{AB}	J_{AC}	J_{BC}
4	1	1

Maximum summed intensity = 2.232

LINE	FREQ	INTEN
1	93.88	0.402
2	94.60	0.332
3	95.84	0.164
4	96.88	0.262
5	98.11	1.033
6	98.83	1.807
7	100.92	0.812
8	101.97	2.290
9	103.20	1.786
10	103.92	0.559
11	104.25	0.516
12	104.97	1.039
13	105.15	0.842
14	106.20	0.153
15	111.29	0.001

3B-20

J_{AB}	J_{AC}	J_{BC}
1	4	4

Maximum summed intensity = 4.063

LINE	FREQ	INTEN
1	92.02	0.036
2	93.85	0.431
3	96.13	0.653
4	96.63	0.690
5	98.52	0.029
6	98.92	1.820
7	100.75	0.373
8	100.80	0.394
9	102.45	2.815
10	102.63	2.541
11	104.74	1.098
12	105.42	1.034
13	106.56	0.003
14	109.35	0.083
15	111.24	0.002

3B-21

J_{AB}	J_{AC}	J_{BC}
4	1	1

Maximum summed intensity = 3.130

LINE	FREQ	INTEN
1	92.14	0.299
2	94.36	0.168
3	95.33	0.246
4	96.44	0.482
5	97.41	0.517
6	99.63	2.298
7	100.39	0.158
8	101.90	3.130
9	102.47	2.543
10	103.98	0.159
11	104.69	0.867
12	105.66	0.422
13	106.20	0.185
14	107.17	0.517
15	112.23	0.009

3B-22

J_{AB}	J_{AC}	J_{BC}
4	1	4

Maximum summed intensity = 2.678

LINE	FREQ	INTEN
1	92.22	0.031
2	93.73	0.358
3	95.93	0.569
4	96.67	0.770
5	98.41	0.294
6	98.87	1.835
7	100.38	0.438
8	101.35	0.200
9	102.27	2.748
10	102.86	2.348
11	105.06	1.158
12	105.21	1.164
13	106.72	0.086
14	108.92	0.001
15	111.40	0.000

3B-23

J_{AB}	J_{AC}	J_{BC}
1	1	6

Maximum summed intensity = 3.809

LINE	FREQ	INTEN
1	90.85	0.000
2	95.93	0.720
3	96.85	0.929
4	96.96	0.027
5	97.00	1.009
6	97.92	1.339
7	98.03	0.004
8	102.97	2.325
9	103.00	0.003
10	103.11	2.254
11	104.03	1.716
12	104.04	1.648
13	109.12	0.014
14	110.04	0.013
15	110.16	0.000

−11 −10 −9 −8 −7 −6 −5 −4 −3 −2 −1 0 +1 +2 +3 +4 +5 +6 +7 +8 +9 +10 +11

3B-24

J_{AB}	J_{AC}	J_{BC}
1	6	1

Maximum summed intensity = 3.280

LINE	FREQ	INTEN
1	92.38	0.316
2	92.89	0.208
3	94.23	0.189
4	97.45	0.334
5	98.79	0.963
6	99.30	1.992
7	101.14	0.185
8	102.22	2.957
9	102.48	2.498
10	102.99	0.885
11	103.56	0.033
12	104.07	0.726
13	107.55	0.429
14	108.63	0.282
15	112.32	0.002

−11 −10 −9 −8 −7 −6 −5 −4 −3 −2 −1 0 +1 +2 +3 +4 +5 +6 +7 +8 +9 +10 +11

3B-25

J_{AB}	J_{AC}	J_{BC}
6	1	1

Maximum summed intensity = 2.322

LINE	FREQ	INTEN
1	92.25	0.269
2	93.05	0.271
3	95.66	0.071
4	95.77	0.054
5	98.39	1.342
6	99.18	1.994
7	100.57	0.998
8	101.63	2.409
9	103.18	1.733
10	103.98	0.859
11	104.25	0.584
12	105.05	0.804
13	106.70	0.408
14	107.77	0.202
15	112.57	0.001

3B-26

J_{AB}	J_{AC}	J_{BC}
1	6	6

Maximum summed intensity =3.526

LINE	FREQ	INTEN
1	89.34	0.027
2	91.88	0.259
3	95.11	0.417
4	96.14	0.531
5	96.68	0.104
6	99.37	2.083
7	99.91	0.608
8	101.90	0.687
9	102.19	3.079
10	102.45	2.637
11	105.42	0.865
12	106.70	0.647
13	107.96	0.000
14	112.22	0.052
15	112.76	0.004

3B-27

J_{AB}	J_{AC}	J_{BC}
6	6	1

Maximum summed intensity = 3.261

LINE	FREQ	INTEN
1	89.38	0.184
2	92.37	0.174
3	94.38	0.037
4	95.15	0.093
5	97.16	0.910
6	99.42	0.086
7	100.15	2.616
8	101.65	3.519
9	102.20	2.730
10	104.43	0.083
11	105.19	1.112
12	107.20	0.058
13	107.42	0.005
14	109.43	0.379
15	114.47	0.014

3B-28

J_{AB}	J_{AC}	J_{BC}
6	1	6

Maximum summed intensity = 2.861

LINE	FREQ	INTEN
1	89.59	0.023
2	91.63	0.182
3	95.37	0.437
4	95.55	0.488
5	96.70	0.334
6	99.29	2.086
7	100.62	0.493
8	101.33	0.784
9	102.04	3.024
10	102.66	2.485
11	105.96	0.909
12	106.41	0.689
13	108.00	0.062
14	111.75	0.005
15	113.08	0.000

3B-29

J_{AB}	J_{AC}	J_{BC}
1	1	9

Maximum summed intensity = 3.999

LINE	FREQ	INTEN
1	87.87	0.000
2	93.97	0.004
3	95.04	0.010
4	95.93	0.734
5	96.85	0.930
6	97.00	0.996
7	97.92	1.339
8	102.98	2.332
9	103.10	2.262
10	104.01	1.724
11	104.05	1.656
12	105.97	0.001
13	110.15	0.000
14	112.11	0.006
15	113.03	0.006

−11 −10 −9 −8 −7 −6 −5 −4 −3 −2 −1 0 +1 +2 +3 +4 +5 +6 +7 +8 +9 +10 +11

3B-30

J_{AB}	J_{AC}	J_{BC}
9	9	1

Maximum summed intensity = 3.763

LINE	FREQ	INTEN
1	85.09	0.103
2	88.56	0.085
3	92.57	0.018
4	93.06	0.004
5	97.07	0.987
6	97.95	0.040
7	100.55	2.817
8	101.49	3.768
9	101.96	2.858
10	105.44	1.078
11	105.50	0.035
12	108.98	0.001
13	109.93	0.010
14	113.47	0.182
15	118.37	0.014

XX

−11 −10 −9 −8 −7 −6 −5 −4 −3 −2 −1 0 +1 +2 +3 +4 +5 +6 +7 +8 +9 +10 +11

3B-31

J_{AB}	J_{AC}	J_{BC}
1	1	12

Maximum summed intensity = 4.083

LINE	FREQ	INTEN
1	84.89	0.000
2	90.98	0.003
3	92.05	0.004
4	95.93	0.732
5	96.85	0.931
6	97.00	0.999
7	97.92	1.339
8	102.99	2.335
9	103.09	2.266
10	104.01	1.727
11	104.06	1.658
12	108.96	0.000
13	110.15	0.000
14	115.10	0.004
15	116.02	0.003

3B-32

J_{AB}	J_{AC}	J_{BC}
12	12	1

Maximum summed intensity = 3.802

LINE	FREQ	INTEN
1	80.71	0.065
2	84.42	0.046
3	89.78	0.007
4	91.68	0.001
5	96.47	0.022
6	97.04	0.998
7	100.75	2.896
8	101.43	3.867
9	101.83	2.914
10	105.54	1.049
11	106.79	0.017
12	110.49	0.002
13	112.80	0.004
14	117.76	0.102
15	122.54	0.012

3B-33

J_{AB}	J_{AC}	J_{BC}
1	1	18

Maximum summed intensity = 4.157

LINE	FREQ	INTEN
1	78.90	0.000
2	84.99	0.001
3	86.06	0.002
4	95.93	0.731
5	96.85	0.931
6	97.00	1.000
7	97.92	1.338
8	103.00	2.337
9	103.08	2.268
10	104.00	1.729
11	104.07	1.660
12	110.15	0.000
13	114.95	0.000
14	121.10	0.002
15	122.01	0.001

3B-34

J_{AB}	J_{AC}	J_{BC}
18	18	1

Maximum summed intensity = 4.160

LINE	FREQ	INTEN
1	71.85	0.032
2	75.78	0.019
3	83.97	0.002
4	88.82	0.000
5	93.48	0.009
6	97.02	1.001
7	100.95	2.954
8	101.38	3.941
9	101.68	2.959
10	105.61	1.023
11	109.57	0.006
12	113.50	0.002
13	118.65	0.001
14	126.55	0.044
15	131.20	0.007

3B-35

J_{AB}	J_{AC}	J_{BC}
2	2	4

Maximum summed intensity = 2.890

LINE	FREQ	INTEN
1	92.62	0.000
2	94.74	0.529
3	96.41	0.759
4	96.99	1.007
5	98.45	0.038
6	98.66	1.705
7	100.70	0.019
8	100.78	0.000
9	102.53	2.673
10	102.81	2.432
11	104.48	1.509
12	104.78	1.269
13	106.90	0.031
14	108.56	0.027
15	110.60	0.001

−11 −10 −9 −8 −7 −6 −5 −4 −3 −2 −1 0 +1 +2 +3 +4 +5 +6 +7 +8 +9 +10 +11

3B-36

J_{AB}	J_{AC}	J_{BC}
2	4	2

Maximum summed intensity = 3.227

LINE	FREQ	INTEN
1	93.40	0.395
2	93.73	0.079
3	96.21	0.653
4	96.40	0.543
5	98.88	0.325
6	99.21	2.009
7	100.06	0.002
8	102.25	2.980
9	102.54	2.603
10	102.87	0.483
11	104.73	0.024
12	105.06	0.776
13	105.54	0.908
14	107.73	0.215
15	111.39	0.005

−11 −10 −9 −8 −7 −6 −5 −4 −3 −2 −1 0 +1 +2 +3 +4 +5 +6 +7 +8 +9 +10 +11

3B-37

J_{AB}	J_{AC}	J_{BC}
4	2	2

Maximum summed intensity = 2.738

LINE	FREQ	INTEN
1	93.34	0.364
2	94.13	0.072
3	95.50	0.436
4	97.01	0.815
5	98.37	0.306
6	99.16	2.011
7	99.89	0.303
8	102.07	2.825
9	102.77	2.333
10	103.56	0.117
11	104.92	1.244
12	104.94	0.182
13	105.73	0.986
14	107.10	0.004
15	111.49	0.003

−11 −10 −9 −8 −7 −6 −5 −4 −3 −2 −1 0 +1 +2 +3 +4 +5 +6 +7 +8 +9 +10 +11

3B-38

J_{AB}	J_{AC}	J_{BC}
2	4	4

Maximum summed intensity = 3.302

LINE	FREQ	INTEN
1	92.07	0.022
2	93.37	0.393
3	96.07	0.583
4	96.51	0.797
5	98.10	0.001
6	99.21	2.015
7	100.51	0.196
8	101.23	0.250
9	102.26	3.002
10	102.53	2.606
11	105.24	1.138
12	105.39	0.916
13	106.69	0.008
14	109.40	0.069
15	111.42	0.005

−11 −10 −9 −8 −7 −6 −5 −4 −3 −2 −1 0 +1 +2 +3 +4 +5 +6 +7 +8 +9 +10 +11

3B-39

J_{AB}	J_{AC}	J_{BC}
4	2	4

Maximum summed intensity = 2.787

LINE	FREQ	INTEN
1	92.27	0.012
2	93.29	0.347
3	95.57	0.525
4	96.89	0.912
5	98.05	0.161
6	99.18	2.018
7	100.19	0.188
8	101.65	0.077
9	102.16	2.954
10	102.67	2.492
11	104.95	1.268
12	105.76	0.982
13	106.78	0.061
14	109.06	0.001
15	111.54	0.002

−11 −10 −9 −8 −7 −6 −5 −4 −3 −2 −1 0 +1 +2 +3 +4 +5 +6 +7 +8 +9 +10 +11

3B-40

J_{AB}	J_{AC}	J_{BC}
4	4	2

Maximum summed intensity =3.086

LINE	FREQ	INTEN
1	92.14	0.298
2	93.83	0.036
3	94.93	0.372
4	96.84	0.886
5	97.94	0.118
6	99.42	0.076
7	99.63	2.298
8	101.94	3.218
9	102.43	2.626
10	104.12	0.255
11	104.95	0.071
12	105.23	1.035
13	106.63	0.525
14	107.74	0.177
15	112.23	0.009

−11 −10 −9 −8 −7 −6 −5 −4 −3 −2 −1 0 +1 +2 +3 +4 +5 +6 +7 +8 +9 +10 +11

3B-41

J_{AB}	J_{AC}	J_{BC}
2	2	6

Maximum summed intensity = 3.217

LINE	FREQ	INTEN
1	90.66	0.000
2	94.74	0.524
3	96.40	0.761
4	96.47	0.026
5	96.99	1.009
6	98.66	1.704
7	98.72	0.003
8	102.55	2.689
9	102.73	0.002
10	102.80	2.450
11	104.46	1.520
12	104.80	1.284
13	108.88	0.014
14	110.54	0.012
15	110.61	0.001

−11 −10 −9 −8 −7 −6 −5 −4 −3 −2 −1 0 +1 +2 +3 +4 +5 +6 +7 +8 +9 +10 +11

3B-42

J_{AB}	J_{AC}	J_{BC}
2	6	2

Maximum summed intensity = 3.409

LINE	FREQ	INTEN
1	91.85	0.287
2	92.45	0.116
3	95.01	0.361
4	96.42	0.361
5	98.99	0.661
6	99.58	2.221
7	99.79	0.022
8	102.06	3.214
9	102.36	2.691
10	102.95	0.739
11	104.62	0.000
12	105.22	0.563
13	106.93	0.542
14	109.20	0.216
15	112.57	0.006

−11 −10 −9 −8 −7 −6 −5 −4 −3 −2 −1 0 +1 +2 +3 +4 +5 +6 +7 +8 +9 +10 +11

3B-43

J_{AB}	J_{AC}	J_{BC}
6	2	2

Maximum summed intensity = 2.950

LINE	FREQ	INTEN
1	91.73	0.248
2	92.91	0.170
3	95.15	0.170
4	96.07	0.291
5	98.32	0.919
6	99.49	2.206
7	99.56	0.452
8	101.79	2.959
9	102.72	2.300
10	103.89	0.648
11	104.95	0.243
12	106.13	0.684
13	106.14	0.595
14	108.38	0.110
15	112.78	0.004

3B-44

J_{AB}	J_{AC}	J_{BC}
2	6	6

Maximum summed intensity = 3.307

LINE	FREQ	INTEN
1	89.40	0.021
2	91.57	0.258
3	95.49	0.432
4	95.68	0.545
5	96.07	0.045
6	99.60	2.251
7	100.18	0.481
8	101.78	0.500
9	102.04	3.243
10	102.36	2.697
11	106.15	0.702
12	106.28	0.769
13	108.33	0.000
14	112.25	0.047
15	112.83	0.008

3B-45

J_{AB}	J_{AC}	J_{BC}
6	2	6

Maximum summed intensity = 2.989

LINE	FREQ	INTEN
1	89.67	0.015
2	91.36	0.193
3	94.85	0.380
4	96.05	0.622
5	96.13	0.217
6	99.54	2.244
7	100.82	0.365
8	101.23	0.547
9	101.95	3.195
10	102.51	2.590
11	106.01	0.826
12	106.64	0.754
13	108.33	0.048
14	111.82	0.002
15	113.10	0.002

-11 -10 -9 -8 -7 -6 -5 -4 -3 -2 -1 0 +1 +2 +3 +4 +5 +6 +7 +8 +9 +10 +11

3B-46

J_{AB}	J_{AC}	J_{BC}
6	6	2

Maximum summed intensity = 3.467

LINE	FREQ	INTEN
1	89.38	0.184
2	92.31	0.155
3	93.48	0.054
4	96.04	0.207
5	97.22	0.797
6	98.44	0.048
7	100.15	2.617
8	101.67	3.559
9	102.18	2.768
10	105.11	0.986
11	105.40	0.043
12	106.29	0.184
13	108.34	0.035
14	109.51	0.349
15	114.47	0.014

-11 -10 -9 -8 -7 -6 -5 -4 -3 -2 -1 0 +1 +2 +3 +4 +5 +6 +7 +8 +9 +10 +11

3B-47

J_{AB}	J_{AC}	J_{BC}
2	2	9

Maximum summed intensity = 3.446

LINE	FREQ	INTEN
1	87.69	0.000
2	93.47	0.001
3	94.75	0.540
4	95.72	0.019
5	96.40	0.763
6	97.00	0.986
7	98.66	1.704
8	102.56	2.696
9	102.78	2.459
10	104.44	1.519
11	104.82	1.291
12	105.72	0.009
13	110.59	0.002
14	111.88	0.006
15	113.53	0.005

−11 −10 −9 −8 −7 −6 −5 −4 −3 −2 −1 0 +1 +2 +3 +4 +5 +6 +7 +8 +9 +10 +11

3B-48

J_{AB}	J_{AC}	J_{BC}
9	9	2

Maximum summed intensity =3.787

LINE	FREQ	INTEN
1	85.09	0.103
2	88.56	0.086
3	92.08	0.003
4	93.55	0.024
5	96.96	0.026
6	97.07	0.981
7	100.55	2.818
8	101.50	3.782
9	101.95	2.871
10	105.43	1.072
11	106.49	0.021
12	108.95	0.016
13	109.97	0.000
14	113.48	0.182
15	118.37	0.014

−11 −10 −9 −8 −7 −6 −5 −4 −3 −2 −1 0 +1 +2 +3 +4 +5 +6 +7 +8 +9 +10 +11

3B-49

J_{AB}	J_{AC}	J_{BC}
2	2	12

Maximum summed intensity = 3.592

LINE	FREQ	INTEN
1	84.70	0.000
2	90.48	0.002
3	92.73	0.005
4	94.74	0.536
5	96.40	0.763
6	97.00	0.998
7	98.66	1.704
8	102.57	2.698
9	102.78	2.462
10	104.43	1.529
11	104.82	1.293
12	108.70	0.001
13	110.60	0.002
14	114.86	0.003
15	116.52	0.003

3B-50

J_{AB}	J_{AC}	J_{BC}
12	12	2

Maximum summed intensity = 3.779

LINE	FREQ	INTEN
1	80.71	0.065
2	84.42	0.046
3	90.69	0.000
4	90.77	0.008
5	95.47	0.016
6	97.04	0.996
7	100.75	2.897
8	101.43	3.873
9	101.82	2.920
10	105.53	1.048
11	107.78	0.012
12	111.49	0.001
13	111.80	0.005
14	117.76	0.102
15	122.54	0.012

3B-51

J_{AB}	J_{AC}	J_{BC}
2	2	18

Maximum summed intensity = 3.737

LINE	FREQ	INTEN
1	78.72	0.000
2	84.49	0.001
3	86.74	0.002
4	94.74	0.534
5	96.40	0.764
6	97.00	1.000
7	98.66	1.703
8	102.57	2.700
9	102.77	2.464
10	104.43	1.531
11	104.83	1.295
12	110.60	0.002
13	114.69	0.000
14	120.86	0.002
15	122.51	0.001

−11 −10 −9 −8 −7 −6 −5 −4 −3 −2 −1 0 +1 +2 +3 +4 +5 +6 +7 +8 +9 +10 +11

3B-52

J_{AB}	J_{AC}	J_{BC}
18	18	2

Maximum summed intensity = 4.184

LINE	FREQ	INTEN
1	71.85	0.032
2	75.78	0.019
3	84.97	0.002
4	87.83	0.000
5	92.48	0.007
6	97.02	1.000
7	100.95	2.954
8	101.38	3.942
9	101.67	2.961
10	105.61	1.023
11	110.57	0.005
12	114.50	0.002
13	117.65	0.001
14	126.55	0.044
15	131.20	0.007

−11 −10 −9 −8 −7 −6 −5 −4 −3 −2 −1 0 +1 +2 +3 +4 +5 +6 +7 +8 +9 +10 +11

3B-53

J_{AB}	J_{AC}	J_{BC}
4	4	9

Maximum summed intensity = 3.303

LINE	FREQ	INTEN
1	87.09	0.000
2	92.09	0.237
3	92.53	0.071
4	94.78	0.409
5	96.94	0.923
6	97.38	0.082
7	99.63	2.297
8	101.99	3.283
9	102.38	2.692
10	104.63	0.138
11	105.07	1.150
12	106.84	0.698
13	111.84	0.010
14	112.28	0.004
15	114.53	0.005

−11 −10 −9 −8 −7 −6 −5 −4 −3 −2 −1 0 +1 +2 +3 +4 +5 +6 +7 +8 +9 +10 +11

3B-54

J_{AB}	J_{AC}	J_{BC}
9	9	4

Maximum summed intensity = 3.789

LINE	FREQ	INTEN
1	85.08	0.102
2	88.52	0.083
3	90.14	0.007
4	94.97	0.014
5	95.49	0.079
6	97.11	0.924
7	100.55	2.818
8	101.51	3.794
9	101.94	2.884
10	105.38	1.016
11	107.00	0.072
12	108.48	0.010
13	111.91	0.003
14	113.54	0.178
15	118.37	0.014

−11 −10 −9 −8 −7 −6 −5 −4 −3 −2 −1 0 +1 +2 +3 +4 +5 +6 +7 +8 +9 +10 +11

3B-55

J_{AB}	J_{AC}	J_{BC}
4	4	12

Maximum summed intensity = 3 318

LINE	FREQ	INTEN
1	84.11	0.000
2	89.47	0.001
3	92.15	0.304
4	94.33	0.011
5	94.78	0.410
6	97.00	0.992
7	99.63	2.297
8	101.99	3.285
9	102.37	2.695
10	105.00	1.284
11	106.85	0.700
12	107.68	0.006
13	112.21	0.010
14	114.89	0.002
15	117.52	0.003

3B-56

J_{AB}	J_{AC}	J_{BC}
12	12	4

Maximum summed intensity = 3.744

LINE	FREQ	INTEN
1	80.71	0.064
2	84.42	0.047
3	88.71	0.000
4	92.75	0.013
5	93.48	0.009
6	97.04	0.990
7	100.75	2.897
8	101.44	3.879
9	101.81	2.926
10	105.52	1.043
11	109.77	0.006
12	109.81	0.010
13	113.48	0.000
14	117.77	0.102
15	122.54	0.012

3B-57

J_{AB}	J_{AC}	J_{BC}
4	4	18

Maximum summed intensity = 3.328

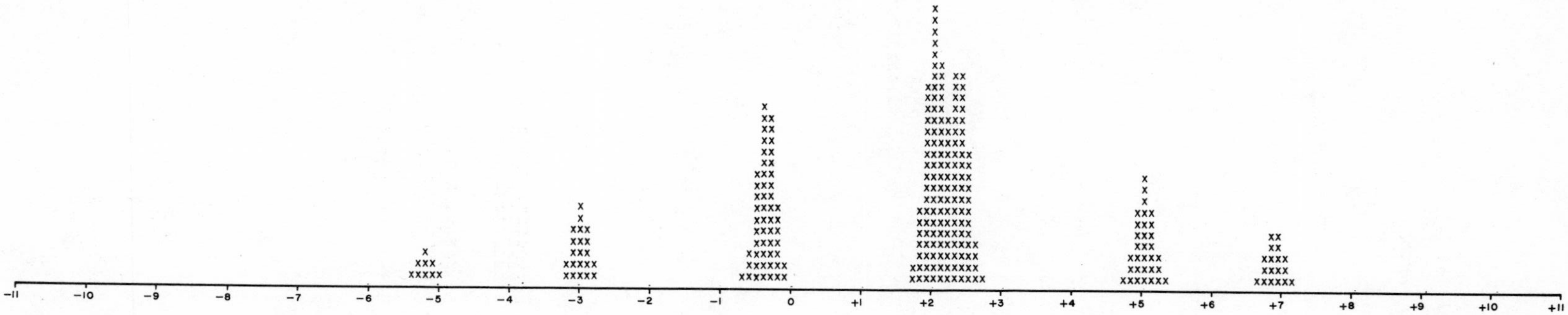

−11 −10 −9 −8 −7 −6 −5 −4 −3 −2 −1 0 +1 +2 +3 +4 +5 +6 +7 +8 +9 +10 +11

3B-58

J_{AB}	J_{AC}	J_{BC}
18	18	4

Maximum summed intensity = 4.218

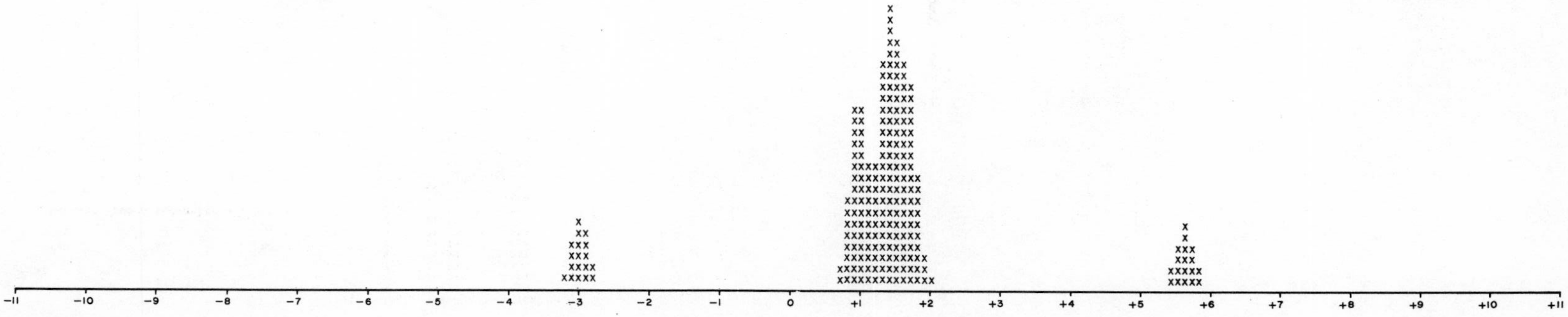

−11 −10 −9 −8 −7 −6 −5 −4 −3 −2 −1 0 +1 +2 +3 +4 +5 +6 +7 +8 +9 +10 +11

3B-59

J_{AB}	J_{AC}	J_{BC}
6	6	9

Maximum summed intensity = 3.603

−11 −10 −9 −8 −7 −6 −5 −4 −3 −2 −1 0 +1 +2 +3 +4 +5 +6 +7 +8 +9 +10 +11

3B-60

J_{AB}	J_{AC}	J_{BC}
9	9	6

Maximum summed intensity = 3.780

−11 −10 −9 −8 −7 −6 −5 −4 −3 −2 −1 0 +1 +2 +3 +4 +5 +6 +7 +8 +9 +10 +11

3B-61

J_{AB}	J_{AC}	J_{BC}
6	6	12

Maximum summed intensity = 3.601

LINE	FREQ	INTEN
1	83.34	0.000
2	88.45	0.001
3	89.42	0.188
4	92.54	0.210
5	96.06	0.056
6	97.03	0.946
7	100.16	2.617
8	101.71	3.601
9	102.13	2.811
10	105.26	1.116
11	106.23	0.054
12	109.32	0.380
13	114.43	0.016
14	115.39	0.001
15	118.52	0.003

−11 −10 −9 −8 −7 −6 −5 −4 −3 −2 −1 0 +1 +2 +3 +4 +5 +6 +7 +8 +9 +10 +11

3B-62

J_{AB}	J_{AC}	J_{BC}
12	12	6

Maximum summed intensity = 3.720

LINE	FREQ	INTEN
1	80.71	0.064
2	84.40	0.046
3	86.74	0.001
4	91.49	0.006
5	94.72	0.034
6	97.06	0.968
7	100.75	2.898
8	101.44	3.882
9	101.81	2.929
10	105.50	1.021
11	107.84	0.031
12	111.76	0.004
13	115.45	0.000
14	117.80	0.102
15	122.54	0.012

−11 −10 −9 −8 −7 −6 −5 −4 −3 −2 −1 0 +1 +2 +3 +4 +5 +6 +7 +8 +9 +10 +11

3B-63

J_{AB}	J_{AC}	J_{BC}
6	6	18

Maximum summed intensity = 3.594

LINE	FREQ	INTEN
1	77.36	0.000
2	82.48	0.001
3	89.39	0.186
4	90.10	0.003
5	92.54	0.211
6	97.00	0.998
7	100.16	2.617
8	101.71	3.602
9	102.13	2.813
10	105.29	1.169
11	109.33	0.381
12	112.19	0.002
13	114.46	0.014
14	121.36	0.001
15	124.51	0.001

3B-64

J_{AB}	J_{AC}	J_{BC}
18	18	6

Maximum summed intensity = 4.241

LINE	FREQ	INTEN
1	71.84	0.032
2	75.78	0.019
3	83.84	0.000
4	88.49	0.004
5	88.96	0.004
6	97.02	0.998
7	100.95	2.955
8	101.38	3.946
9	101.67	2.965
10	105.60	1.022
11	113.66	0.003
12	114.56	0.002
13	118.49	0.001
14	126.55	0.044
15	131.20	0.007

3B-65

J_{AB}	J_{AC}	J_{BC}
9	9	12

Maximum summed intensity = 3.756

LINE	FREQ	INTEN
1	82.05	0.000
2	85.07	0.099
3	87.01	0.007
4	88.65	0.090
5	96.96	1.000
6	98.91	0.002
7	100.55	2.819
8	101.52	3.803
9	101.93	2.894
10	103.57	0.004
11	105.51	1.084
12	113.42	0.178
13	116.44	0.003
14	118.38	0.013
15	120.03	0.003

−11 −10 −9 −8 −7 −6 −5 −4 −3 −2 −1 0 +1 +2 +3 +4 +5 +6 +7 +8 +9 +10 +11

3B-66

J_{AB}	J_{AC}	J_{BC}
12	12	9

Maximum summed intensity = 3.696

LINE	FREQ	INTEN
1	80.70	0.064
2	83.55	0.007
3	84.60	0.040
4	88.49	0.004
5	96.86	0.891
6	97.91	0.111
7	100.75	2.898
8	101.44	3.884
9	101.80	2.932
10	104.65	0.123
11	105.70	0.929
12	114.75	0.002
13	117.60	0.080
14	118.65	0.022
15	122.54	0.011

−11 −10 −9 −8 −7 −6 −5 −4 −3 −2 −1 0 +1 +2 +3 +4 +5 +6 +7 +8 +9 +10 +11

3B-67

J_{AB}	J_{AC}	J_{BC}
9	9	18

Maximum summed intensity = 3.744

LINE	FREQ	INTEN
1	76.06	0.000
2	80.98	0.000
3	85.10	0.104
4	88.65	0.091
5	92.89	0.007
6	97.00	0.994
7	100.55	2.820
8	101.53	3.804
9	101.92	2.895
10	105.47	1.083
11	109.59	0.006
12	113.43	0.179
13	118.35	0.015
14	122.47	0.001
15	126.02	0.001

−11 −10 −9 −8 −7 −6 −5 −4 −3 −2 −1 0 +1 +2 +3 +4 +5 +6 +7 +8 +9 +10 +11

3B-68

J_{AB}	J_{AC}	J_{BC}
18	18	9

Maximum summed intensity = 4.265

LINE	FREQ	INTEN
1	71.84	0.032
2	75.78	0.019
3	80.85	0.000
4	85.49	0.002
5	91.95	0.008
6	97.02	0.993
7	100.95	2.956
8	101.38	3.947
9	101.66	2.966
10	105.59	1.018
11	110.67	0.007
12	117.55	0.001
13	121.48	0.000
14	126.56	0.044
15	131.20	0.007

−11 −10 −9 −8 −7 −6 −5 −4 −3 −2 −1 0 +1 +2 +3 +4 +5 +6 +7 +8 +9 +10 +11

3B-69

J_{AB}	J_{AC}	J_{BC}
12	12	18

Maximum summed intensity = 3.743

LINE	FREQ	INTEN
1	74.68	0.000
2	79.45	0.000
3	80.75	0.066
4	84.48	0.047
5	95.73	0.046
6	97.03	0.955
7	100.76	2.899
8	101.45	3.886
9	101.80	2.934
10	105.52	1.008
11	106.82	0.045
12	117.73	0.100
13	122.49	0.012
14	123.79	0.000
15	127.52	0.001

3B-70

J_{AB}	J_{AC}	J_{BC}
18	18	12

Maximum summed intensity = 4.280

LINE	FREQ	INTEN
1	71.84	0.032
2	75.75	0.019
3	77.89	0.000
4	82.50	0.002
5	94.91	0.034
6	97.05	0.967
7	100.96	2.956
8	101.38	3.948
9	101.66	2.966
10	105.56	0.991
11	107.71	0.033
12	120.55	0.001
13	124.45	0.000
14	126.59	0.044
15	131.20	0.007

3B-71

J_{AB}	J_{AC}	J_{BC}
1	2	4

Maximum summed intensity =3.914

LINE	FREQ	INTEN
1	92.66	0.006
2	95.32	0.626
3	96.80	0.873
4	96.83	0.924
5	98.31	1.511
6	98.76	0.001
7	100.27	0.116
8	100.96	0.060
9	102.77	2.493
10	102.92	2.372
11	104.28	1.443
12	104.40	1.510
13	106.94	0.018
14	108.42	0.046
15	110.38	0.001

3B-72

J_{AB}	J_{AC}	J_{BC}
1	4	2

Maximum summed intensity = 4.405

LINE	FREQ	INTEN
1	93.64	0.108
2	93.93	0.444
3	95.83	0.529
4	97.00	0.635
5	98.90	1.802
6	99.19	0.483
7	100.44	0.017
8	102.34	0.584
9	102.46	2.796
10	102.63	2.539
11	104.37	0.977
12	104.66	0.004
13	105.70	0.858
14	107.73	0.221
15	111.17	0.002

3B-73

J_{AB}	J_{AC}	J_{BC}
2	1	4

Maximum summed intensity = 2.573

LINE	FREQ	INTEN
1	92.71	0.003
2	95.29	0.583
3	96.55	0.816
4	97.03	1.003
5	98.30	1.522
6	98.70	0.125
7	100.44	0.005
8	100.87	0.073
9	102.69	2.473
10	103.02	2.292
11	104.28	1.578
12	104.43	1.467
13	107.01	0.049
14	108.27	0.011
15	110.42	0.000

-11 -10 -9 -8 -7 -6 -5 -4 -3 -2 -1 0 +1 +2 +3 +4 +5 +6 +7 +8 +9 +10 +11

3B-74

J_{AB}	J_{AC}	J_{BC}
2	4	1

Maximum summed intensity = 3.093

LINE	FREQ	INTEN
1	93.41	0.396
2	94.37	0.142
3	95.87	0.510
4	96.74	0.503
5	98.25	0.449
6	99.21	2.004
7	101.04	0.016
8	102.25	2.943
9	102.55	2.588
10	103.51	0.729
11	103.75	0.057
12	104.71	0.615
13	105.88	0.663
14	107.08	0.380
15	111.38	0.004

-11 -10 -9 -8 -7 -6 -5 -4 -3 -2 -1 0 +1 +2 +3 +4 +5 +6 +7 +8 +9 +10 +11

3B-75

J_{AB}	J_{AC}	J_{BC}
4	1	2

Maximum summed intensity = 2.474

LINE	FREQ	INTEN
1	93.85	0.392
2	93.95	0.141
3	95.86	0.399
4	96.83	0.597
5	98.75	0.652
6	98.85	1.819
7	100.13	0.507
8	102.13	2.561
9	103.02	2.101
10	103.12	0.289
11	105.02	0.258
12	105.03	1.102
13	105.12	1.153
14	107.03	0.027
15	111.31	0.001

-11 -10 -9 -8 -7 -6 -5 -4 -3 -2 -1 0 +1 +2 +3 +4 +5 +6 +7 +8 +9 +10 +11

3B-76

J_{AB}	J_{AC}	J_{BC}
4	2	1

Maximum summed intensity = 2.475

LINE	FREQ	INTEN
1	93.36	0.369
2	94.91	0.293
3	95.48	0.193
4	97.04	0.385
5	97.60	0.759
6	99.16	2.005
7	100.76	0.536
8	101.96	2.608
9	102.88	2.095
10	104.09	0.393
11	104.44	0.460
12	105.00	0.906
13	105.64	0.858
14	106.20	0.137
15	111.48	0.003

-11 -10 -9 -8 -7 -6 -5 -4 -3 -2 -1 0 +1 +2 +3 +4 +5 +6 +7 +8 +9 +10 +11

3B-77

J_{AB}	J_{AC}	J_{BC}
2	4	6

Maximum summed intensity = 3.544

LINE	FREQ	INTEN
1	90.20	0.008
2	93.30	0.381
3	95.94	0.589
4	96.17	0.013
5	96.57	0.790
6	99.21	2.018
7	99.44	0.231
8	102.26	3.009
9	102.31	0.219
10	102.53	2.607
11	105.18	1.144
12	105.52	0.953
13	108.62	0.003
14	111.26	0.029
15	111.49	0.006

-11 -10 -9 -8 -7 -6 -5 -4 -3 -2 -1 0 +1 +2 +3 +4 +5 +6 +7 +8 +9 +10 +11

3B-78

J_{AB}	J_{AC}	J_{BC}
2	6	4

Maximum summed intensity = 3.345

LINE	FREQ	INTEN
1	91.07	0.049
2	91.75	0.278
3	95.53	0.516
4	95.81	0.414
5	97.89	0.027
6	99.59	2.239
7	100.28	0.511
8	101.67	0.535
9	102.05	3.232
10	102.36	2.695
11	105.83	0.661
12	106.42	0.736
13	106.52	0.000
14	110.58	0.100
15	112.65	0.007

-11 -10 -9 -8 -7 -6 -5 -4 -3 -2 -1 0 +1 +2 +3 +4 +5 +6 +7 +8 +9 +10 +11

3B-79

J_{AB}	J_{AC}	J_{BC}
4	2	6

Maximum summed intensity = 3.086

LINE	FREQ	INTEN
1	90.33	0.003
2	93.16	0.305
3	95.61	0.548
4	96.21	0.154
5	96.74	0.864
6	99.18	2.022
7	99.79	0.134
8	102.02	0.260
9	102.19	2.990
10	102.63	2.541
11	105.07	1.170
12	105.77	0.977
13	108.60	0.031
14	111.05	0.001
15	111.65	0.001

3B-80

J_{AB}	J_{AC}	J_{BC}
4	6	2

Maximum summed intensity = 3.394

LINE	FREQ	INTEN
1	90.72	0.234
2	92.51	0.106
3	94.95	0.205
4	95.71	0.432
5	98.15	0.555
6	99.04	0.007
7	99.94	2.480
8	101.82	3.448
9	102.24	2.759
10	104.02	0.713
11	105.03	0.019
12	106.47	0.509
13	106.81	0.269
14	109.25	0.251
15	113.34	0.012

3B-81

J_{AB}	J_{AC}	J_{BC}
6	2	4

Maximum summed intensity =3.136

LINE	FREQ	INTEN
1	91.45	0.047
2	91.59	0.228
3	94.92	0.331
4	96.20	0.587
5	97.83	0.258
6	99.52	2.230
7	99.67	0.580
8	101.90	3.136
9	102.43	0.381
10	102.58	2.514
11	105.90	0.844
12	106.51	0.755
13	106.65	0.091
14	109.97	0.016
15	112.88	0.003

3B-82

J_{AB}	J_{AC}	J_{BC}
6	4	2

Maximum summed intensity = 3.247

LINE	FREQ	INTEN
1	90.66	0.218
2	93.21	0.177
3	93.92	0.094
4	96.63	0.272
5	97.34	0.785
6	98.96	0.168
7	99.89	2.463
8	101.73	3.342
9	102.38	2.613
10	104.93	0.740
11	105.14	0.112
12	105.64	0.469
13	107.70	0.348
14	108.41	0.188
15	113.45	0.010

3B-83

J_{AB}	J_{AC}	J_{BC}
1	1	-1

Maximum summed intensity = 2.029

LINE	FREQ	INTEN
1	95.51	0.000
2	95.93	0.729
3	96.87	0.957
4	96.98	0.970
5	97.92	1.340
6	98.34	0.004
7	101.87	0.384
8	102.81	0.207
9	102.85	1.917
10	103.23	1.956
11	103.80	1.495
12	104.22	0.355
13	104.28	1.452
14	105.26	0.233
15	110.15	0.000

-11 -10 -9 -8 -7 -6 -5 -4 -3 -2 -1 0 +1 +2 +3 +4 +5 +6 +7 +8 +9 +10 +11

3B-84

J_{AB}	J_{AC}	J_{BC}
1	-1	1

Maximum summed intensity = 3.474

LINE	FREQ	INTEN
1	95.30	0.180
2	96.36	0.588
3	96.91	0.929
4	96.93	0.991
5	97.48	0.812
6	98.55	0.501
7	101.95	0.777
8	102.53	0.017
9	102.93	1.526
10	103.50	2.000
11	103.59	1.912
12	104.14	1.294
13	104.57	0.009
14	105.11	0.465
15	110.16	0.000

-11 -10 -9 -8 -7 -6 -5 -4 -3 -2 -1 0 +1 +2 +3 +4 +5 +6 +7 +8 +9 +10 +11

3B-85

J_{AB}	J_{AC}	J_{BC}
-1	1	1

Maximum summed intensity = 3.687

LINE	FREQ	INTEN
1	95.34	0.168
2	96.25	0.572
3	96.91	0.984
4	96.93	0.951
5	97.60	0.891
6	98.51	0.434
7	101.93	0.686
8	102.59	0.016
9	102.90	1.623
10	103.50	2.000
11	103.57	1.941
12	104.18	1.298
13	104.48	0.009
14	105.16	0.426
15	110.16	0.000

-11 -10 -9 -8 -7 -6 -5 -4 -3 -2 -1 0 +1 +2 +3 +4 +5 +6 +7 +8 +9 +10 +11

3B-86

J_{AB}	J_{AC}	J_{BC}
1	1	-2

Maximum summed intensity = 3.264

LINE	FREQ	INTEN
1	94.68	0.000
2	95.93	0.729
3	96.86	0.946
4	96.99	0.983
5	97.92	1.341
6	99.16	0.002
7	100.96	0.140
8	101.89	0.072
9	102.95	2.148
10	103.13	2.200
11	103.88	1.641
12	104.19	1.587
13	105.12	0.123
14	106.18	0.087
15	110.15	0.000

-11 -10 -9 -8 -7 -6 -5 -4 -3 -2 -1 0 +1 +2 +3 +4 +5 +6 +7 +8 +9 +10 +11

3B-87

J_{AB}	J_{AC}	J_{BC}
1	-2	1

Maximum summed intensity = 2.682

LINE	FREQ	INTEN
1	94.86	0.286
2	96.06	0.373
3	96.34	0.830
4	97.29	1.014
5	97.57	0.552
6	98.76	0.945
7	102.00	0.961
8	102.28	0.176
9	102.96	1.365
10	103.24	2.156
11	103.47	1.837
12	104.43	0.014
13	104.71	1.025
14	105.66	0.464
15	110.37	0.001

-11 -10 -9 -8 -7 -6 -5 -4 -3 -2 -1 0 +1 +2 +3 +4 +5 +6 +7 +8 +9 +10 +11

3B-88

J_{AB}	J_{AC}	J_{BC}
-2	1	1

Maximum summed intensity = 3.005

LINE	FREQ	INTEN
1	94.98	0.336
2	96.00	0.273
3	96.32	0.772
4	97.28	1.095
5	97.60	0.487
6	98.62	1.037
7	101.57	0.851
8	102.53	1.768
9	102.85	0.385
10	103.81	1.697
11	103.87	1.520
12	104.19	1.244
13	104.83	0.075
14	105.15	0.460
15	110.40	0.000

-11 -10 -9 -8 -7 -6 -5 -4 -3 -2 -1 0 +1 +2 +3 +4 +5 +6 +7 +8 +9 +10 +11

3B-89

J_{AB}	J_{AC}	J_{BC}
1	1	-4

Maximum summed intensity = 4.162

LINE	FREQ	INTEN
1	92.80	0.000
2	95.93	0.729
3	96.85	0.939
4	97.00	0.986
5	97.92	1.343
6	99.02	0.047
7	99.94	0.015
8	101.05	0.003
9	103.01	2.238
10	103.08	2.296
11	103.93	1.703
12	104.14	1.642
13	107.06	0.033
14	108.13	0.026
15	110.15	0.000

-11 -10 -9 -8 -7 -6 -5 -4 -3 -2 -1 0 +1 +2 +3 +4 +5 +6 +7 +8 +9 +10 +11

3B-90

J_{AB}	J_{AC}	J_{BC}
1	-4	1

Maximum summed intensity = 2.480

LINE	FREQ	INTEN
1	93.63	0.312
2	94.95	0.566
3	95.20	0.153
4	97.63	0.249
5	97.88	1.139
6	99.20	1.583
7	101.82	0.560
8	102.06	1.216
9	102.74	2.313
10	102.98	1.180
11	103.38	1.577
12	104.31	0.121
13	106.06	0.645
14	106.99	0.384
15	111.17	0.002

-11 -10 -9 -8 -7 -6 -5 -4 -3 -2 -1 0 +1 +2 +3 +4 +5 +6 +7 +8 +9 +10 +11

3B-91

J_{AB}	J_{AC}	J_{BC}
-4	1	1

Maximum summed intensity = 1.975

LINE	FREQ	INTEN
1	93.70	0.342
2	94.88	0.495
3	95.84	0.059
4	96.86	0.109
5	97.82	1.258
6	99.00	1.738
7	101.04	1.099
8	101.98	2.005
9	103.02	1.049
10	103.96	1.242
11	104.20	1.159
12	105.14	0.500
13	105.16	0.693
14	106.09	0.252
15	111.30	0.001

−11 −10 −9 −8 −7 −6 −5 −4 −3 −2 −1 0 +1 +2 +3 +4 +5 +6 +7 +8 +9 +10 +11

3B-92

J_{AB}	J_{AC}	J_{BC}
1	1	-6

Maximum summed intensity = 4.132

LINE	FREQ	INTEN
1	90.84	0.000
2	95.93	0.729
3	96.85	0.937
4	96.96	0.556
5	97.08	0.458
6	97.88	1.013
7	98.00	0.333
8	102.97	0.770
9	103.03	2.256
10	103.09	1.550
11	103.95	1.717
12	104.12	1.654
13	109.04	0.015
14	110.07	0.007
15	110.19	0.005

−11 −10 −9 −8 −7 −6 −5 −4 −3 −2 −1 0 +1 +2 +3 +4 +5 +6 +7 +8 +9 +10 +11

3B-93

J_{AB}	J_{AC}	J_{BC}
1	-6	1

Maximum summed intensity = 2.540

LINE	FREQ	INTEN
1	92.12	0.252
2	93.38	0.386
3	94.01	0.073
4	97.65	0.129
5	98.28	1.207
6	99.54	1.957
7	101.46	0.822
8	102.10	1.373
9	102.36	2.412
10	102.99	1.095
11	103.36	1.382
12	104.26	0.203
13	107.63	0.420
14	108.52	0.288
15	112.34	0.003

3B-94

J_{AB}	J_{AC}	J_{BC}
-6	1	1

Maximum summed intensity = 2.139

LINE	FREQ	INTEN
1	92.11	0.245
2	93.25	0.321
3	95.62	0.038
4	95.80	0.021
5	98.17	1.352
6	99.31	2.024
7	100.70	1.255
8	101.62	2.157
9	103.07	1.264
10	103.99	1.101
11	104.21	1.095
12	105.13	0.522
13	106.76	0.384
14	107.68	0.219
15	112.58	0.001

JB-95

J_{AB}	J_{AC}	J_{BC}
2	2	-2

Maximum summed intensity = 4.463

LINE	FREQ	INTEN
1	94.43	0.000
2	94.74	0.532
3	96.43	0.791
4	96.96	0.954
5	98.65	1.708
6	98.96	0.017
7	100.72	0.200
8	102.41	0.033
9	102.63	2.314
10	102.72	2.506
11	104.32	1.468
12	104.63	0.154
13	104.94	1.259
14	106.85	0.062
15	110.60	0.002

−11 −10 −9 −8 −7 −6 −5 −4 −3 −2 −1 0 +1 +2 +3 +4 +5 +6 +7 +8 +9 +10 +11

JB-96

J_{AB}	J_{AC}	J_{BC}
2	-2	2

Maximum summed intensity = 2.039

LINE	FREQ	INTEN
1	93.80	0.196
2	96.24	0.442
3	96.57	0.747
4	96.77	0.941
5	97.10	0.506
6	99.54	1.171
7	101.07	0.991
8	101.60	0.317
9	102.86	1.624
10	103.40	2.040
11	104.04	1.427
12	104.37	1.262
13	105.83	0.019
14	106.16	0.314
15	110.66	0.003

−11 −10 −9 −8 −7 −6 −5 −4 −3 −2 −1 0 +1 +2 +3 +4 +5 +6 +7 +8 +9 +10 +11

3B-97

J_{AB}	J_{AC}	J_{BC}
-2	2	2

Maximum summed intensity = 3.470

LINE	FREQ	INTEN
1	93.89	0.200
2	95.76	0.330
3	96.59	0.868
4	96.76	0.871
5	97.59	0.675
6	99.46	1.057
7	100.94	0.719
8	101.77	0.425
9	102.77	1.879
10	103.60	1.832
11	103.64	1.707
12	104.64	1.148
13	105.46	0.038
14	106.47	0.250
15	110.65	0.001

−11 −10 −9 −8 −7 −6 −5 −4 −3 −2 −1 0 +1 +2 +3 +4 +5 +6 +7 +8 +9 +10 +11

3B-98

J_{AB}	J_{AC}	J_{BC}
2	2	-4

Maximum summed intensity = 4.905

LINE	FREQ	INTEN
1	92.54	0.000
2	94.74	0.532
3	96.41	0.778
4	96.98	0.963
5	98.65	1.710
6	98.79	0.075
7	100.45	0.002
8	100.85	0.019
9	102.66	2.633
10	102.69	2.430
11	104.36	1.510
12	104.90	1.288
13	106.56	0.038
14	108.80	0.020
15	110.61	0.002

−11 −10 −9 −8 −7 −6 −5 −4 −3 −2 −1 0 +1 +2 +3 +4 +5 +6 +7 +8 +9 +10 +11

3B-99

J_{AB}	J_{AC}	J_{BC}
2	-4	2

Maximum summed intensity = 3.434

LINE	FREQ	INTEN
1	92.63	0.217
2	95.42	0.635
3	95.50	0.240
4	97.00	0.260
5	97.08	0.777
6	99.87	1.879
7	101.19	0.579
8	101.27	1.437
9	102.86	2.309
10	102.94	1.329
11	104.06	1.190
12	105.64	0.786
13	105.73	0.056
14	107.31	0.297
15	111.50	0.009

−11 −10 −9 −8 −7 −6 −5 −4 −3 −2 −1 0 +1 +2 +3 +4 +5 +6 +7 +8 +9 +10 +11

3B-100

J_{AB}	J_{AC}	J_{BC}
-4	2	2

Maximum summed intensity = 3.221

LINE	FREQ	INTEN
1	92.78	0.238
2	95.35	0.553
3	95.41	0.107
4	97.02	0.269
5	97.07	0.949
6	99.65	1.888
7	100.48	0.932
8	102.15	1.150
9	102.20	2.170
10	103.87	1.394
11	104.72	1.013
12	104.78	0.901
13	106.45	0.278
14	106.50	0.155
15	111.57	0.003

−11 −10 −9 −8 −7 −6 −5 −4 −3 −2 −1 0 +1 +2 +3 +4 +5 +6 +7 +8 +9 +10 +11

3B-101

J_{AB}	J_{AC}	J_{BC}
2	2	-6

Maximum summed intensity = 3.940

LINE	FREQ	INTEN
1	90.58	0.000
2	94.74	0.532
3	96.40	0.774
4	96.74	0.089
5	97.05	0.927
6	98.41	0.400
7	98.71	1.306
8	102.57	2.216
9	102.72	2.451
10	102.88	0.461
11	104.38	1.521
12	104.88	1.295
13	108.54	0.016
14	110.55	0.000
15	110.85	0.011

−11 −10 −9 −8 −7 −6 −5 −4 −3 −2 −1 0 +1 +2 +3 +4 +5 +6 +7 +8 +9 +10 +11

3B-102

J_{AB}	J_{AC}	J_{BC}
2	-6	2

Maximum summed intensity = 2.412

LINE	FREQ	INTEN
1	91.16	0.186
2	93.86	0.427
3	94.36	0.132
4	96.92	0.137
5	97.42	0.772
6	100.12	2.359
7	100.90	0.762
8	101.41	1.733
9	102.47	2.488
10	102.97	1.178
11	104.11	0.998
12	105.67	0.085
13	107.17	0.495
14	108.73	0.237
15	112.72	0.012

−11 −10 −9 −8 −7 −6 −5 −4 −3 −2 −1 0 +1 +2 +3 +4 +5 +6 +7 +8 +9 +10 +11

3B-103

J_{AB}	J_{AC}	J_{BC}
-6	2	2

Maximum summed intensity = 2.323

LINE	FREQ	INTEN
1	91.26	0.191
2	93.73	0.353
3	95.27	0.038
4	95.85	0.107
5	97.38	0.982
6	99.86	2.334
7	100.18	1.067
8	101.84	2.352
9	102.30	1.537
10	103.95	1.182
11	104.78	0.911
12	106.31	0.480
13	106.43	0.295
14	107.97	0.166
15	112.88	0.005

3B-104

J_{AB}	J_{AC}	J_{BC}
4	4	-4

Maximum summed intensity = 4.506

LINE	FREQ	INTEN
1	91.53	0.000
2	92.14	0.299
3	94.81	0.426
4	96.94	0.912
5	98.82	0.144
6	99.61	2.283
7	100.23	0.091
8	101.49	0.011
9	102.11	3.129
10	102.28	2.645
11	104.95	1.280
12	105.57	0.056
13	106.90	0.706
14	110.37	0.009
15	112.25	0.010

3B-105

J_{AB}	J_{AC}	J_{BC}
4	-4	4

Maximum summed intensity = 2.304

LINE	FREQ	INTEN
1	90.46	0.120
2	94.92	0.307
3	95.21	0.165
4	95.98	0.367
5	96.27	0.798
6	100.16	1.616
7	100.45	0.741
8	100.73	2.262
9	102.81	1.590
10	103.11	2.177
11	104.92	1.077
12	105.97	0.547
13	107.57	0.189
14	108.63	0.025
15	112.81	0.018

3B-106

J_{AB}	J_{AC}	J_{BC}
-4	4	4

Maximum summed intensity = 3.086

LINE	FREQ	INTEN
1	90.62	0.123
2	93.97	0.099
3	95.08	0.465
4	96.23	0.696
5	97.33	0.533
6	99.68	0.896
7	100.69	2.090
8	100.78	1.254
9	102.53	2.185
10	103.63	1.625
11	104.14	1.281
12	106.40	0.561
13	106.98	0.064
14	109.24	0.119
15	112.69	0.007

3B-107

J_{AB}	J_{AC}	J_{BC}
4	4	-6

Maximum summed intensity = 3.531

LINE	FREQ	INTEN
1	89.56	0.000
2	92.14	0.299
3	94.80	0.421
4	96.67	0.186
5	97.13	0.835
6	99.32	0.816
7	99.79	1.477
8	101.90	2.291
9	102.31	2.679
10	102.37	0.967
11	104.96	1.285
12	106.89	0.707
13	107.55	0.021
14	112.07	0.001
15	112.53	0.014

3B-108

J_{AB}	J_{AC}	J_{BC}
4	-6	4

Maximum summed intensity = 3.155

LINE	FREQ	INTEN
1	89.10	0.115
2	94.77	0.527
3	94.87	0.077
4	95.03	0.223
5	95.13	0.280
6	100.29	0.841
7	100.55	2.051
8	100.80	2.804
9	102.65	2.440
10	102.91	1.332
11	106.22	0.414
12	106.32	0.669
13	108.58	0.033
14	108.68	0.170
15	114.10	0.025

3B-109

J_{AB}	J_{AC}	J_{BC}
-6	4	4

Maximum summed intensity = 2.544

LINE	FREQ	INTEN
1	89.29	0.118
2	93.54	0.031
3	94.66	0.435
4	95.28	0.450
5	96.40	0.258
6	99.50	0.977
7	100.65	2.719
8	101.23	1.849
9	102.11	2.439
10	103.84	1.325
11	105.49	0.701
12	106.61	0.462
13	108.10	0.098
14	109.22	0.126
15	114.06	0.011

-11 -10 -9 -8 -7 -6 -5 -4 -3 -2 -1 0 +1 +2 +3 +4 +5 +6 +7 +8 +9 +10 +11

3B-110

J_{AB}	J_{AC}	J_{BC}
1	2	-1

Maximum summed intensity = 4.305

LINE	FREQ	INTEN
1	95.30	0.023
2	95.34	0.626
3	96.35	0.785
4	97.29	1.031
5	98.30	1.500
6	98.34	0.036
7	101.84	0.184
8	102.81	2.137
9	102.86	0.361
10	102.89	2.315
11	103.82	1.331
12	103.85	0.237
13	104.84	1.139
14	105.81	0.294
15	110.36	0.000

-11 -10 -9 -8 -7 -6 -5 -4 -3 -2 -1 0 +1 +2 +3 +4 +5 +6 +7 +8 +9 +10 +11

3B-111

J_{AB}	J_{AC}	J_{BC}
2	1	-1

Maximum summed intensity = 2.179

LINE	FREQ	INTEN
1	95.32	0.609
2	95.38	0.067
3	96.59	0.742
4	97.01	0.859
5	98.23	0.206
6	98.28	1.518
7	101.56	0.693
8	102.52	1.889
9	103.20	1.824
10	103.25	0.008
11	104.16	0.502
12	104.21	1.548
13	104.47	1.474
14	105.42	0.060
15	110.40	0.001

3B-112

J_{AB}	J_{AC}	J_{BC}
2	2	-1

Maximum summed intensity = 2.225

LINE	FREQ	INTEN
1	94.74	0.532
2	95.25	0.008
3	96.49	0.805
4	96.91	0.904
5	98.14	0.046
6	98.65	1.707
7	101.60	0.569
8	102.51	1.987
9	102.83	2.136
10	103.35	0.103
11	103.75	0.481
12	104.26	1.377
13	105.00	1.190
14	105.91	0.153
15	110.60	0.002

3B-113

J_{AB}	J_{AC}	J_{BC}
1	4	-1

Maximum summed intensity = 4.470

LINE	FREQ	INTEN
1	93.99	0.451
2	94.39	0.177
3	95.14	0.365
4	97.72	0.792
5	98.46	0.475
6	98.87	1.741
7	101.75	0.033
8	102.50	2.707
9	102.63	2.547
10	102.91	0.562
11	103.38	0.001
12	103.79	1.156
13	106.23	0.697
14	107.11	0.295
15	111.15	0.001

-11 -10 -9 -8 -7 -6 -5 -4 -3 -2 -1 0 +1 +2 +3 +4 +5 +6 +7 +8 +9 +10 +11

3B-114

J_{AB}	J_{AC}	J_{BC}
4	1	-1

Maximum summed intensity = 1.862

LINE	FREQ	INTEN
1	93.93	0.415
2	94.42	0.284
3	96.16	0.232
4	96.55	0.249
5	98.29	1.056
6	98.78	1.764
7	101.12	1.155
8	101.97	1.913
9	103.25	1.608
10	103.74	0.358
11	104.10	0.671
12	104.59	1.345
13	105.48	0.878
14	106.33	0.069
15	111.29	0.001

-11 -10 -9 -8 -7 -6 -5 -4 -3 -2 -1 0 +1 +2 +3 +4 +5 +6 +7 +8 +9 +10 +11

3B-115

J_{AB}	J_{AC}	J_{BC}
4	4	-1

Maximum summed intensity = 2.250

LINE	FREQ	INTEN
1	92.14	0.299
2	94.14	0.072
3	95.11	0.379
4	96.66	0.588
5	97.63	0.373
6	99.63	2.298
7	101.46	1.473
8	101.94	1.568
9	102.43	1.816
10	102.91	1.133
11	104.43	0.007
12	104.91	1.243
13	106.95	0.695
14	107.43	0.047
15	112.23	0.009

3B-116

J_{AB}	J_{AC}	J_{BC}
1	4	-2

Maximum summed intensity =4.683

LINE	FREQ	INTEN
1	93.63	0.100
2	94.00	0.453
3	95.37	0.448
4	97.48	0.864
5	98.84	1.694
6	99.21	0.441
7	100.79	0.038
8	102.16	0.488
9	102.52	2.655
10	102.63	2.545
11	104.00	1.270
12	104.37	0.003
13	106.00	0.818
14	107.84	0.182
15	111.16	0.000

3B-117

J_{AB}	J_{AC}	J_{BC}
4	1	-2

Maximum summed intensity = 2.249

LINE	FREQ	INTEN
1	93.74	0.135
2	93.95	0.420
3	96.29	0.437
4	96.40	0.452
5	98.74	1.720
6	98.95	0.836
7	100.41	0.758
8	102.20	2.250
9	102.85	0.293
10	103.07	1.962
11	104.64	1.399
12	104.85	0.330
13	105.41	0.987
14	107.20	0.020
15	111.31	0.001

3B-118

J_{AB}	J_{AC}	J_{BC}
4	4	-2

Maximum summed intensity = 5.207

LINE	FREQ	INTEN
1	92.14	0.299
2	93.40	0.007
3	94.89	0.430
4	96.87	0.851
5	98.37	0.125
6	99.62	2.297
7	100.70	0.448
8	102.18	2.395
9	102.19	2.839
10	103.45	0.001
11	103.68	0.306
12	104.93	1.265
13	106.92	0.702
14	108.40	0.024
15	112.23	0.009

3B-119

J_{AB}	J_{AC}	J_{BC}
2	4	-1

Maximum summed intensity = 4.300

LINE	FREQ	INTEN
1	93.42	0.396
2	94.53	0.030
3	95.15	0.520
4	97.47	1.038
5	98.09	0.030
6	99.20	1.989
7	101.70	0.185
8	102.32	2.800
9	102.48	2.350
10	103.10	0.253
11	103.43	0.289
12	104.21	1.172
13	106.37	0.722
14	107.15	0.220
15	111.38	0.004

−11 −10 −9 −8 −7 −6 −5 −4 −3 −2 −1 0 +1 +2 +3 +4 +5 +6 +7 +8 +9 +10 +11

3B-120

J_{AB}	J_{AC}	J_{BC}
4	2	-1

Maximum summed intensity = 1.926

LINE	FREQ	INTEN
1	93.38	0.375
2	94.53	0.199
3	96.22	0.345
4	96.29	0.377
5	97.98	0.725
6	99.13	1.983
7	101.22	1.209
8	101.96	1.840
9	102.90	1.770
10	103.65	0.785
11	104.06	0.108
12	104.81	1.366
13	105.81	0.909
14	106.56	0.006
15	111.49	0.004

−11 −10 −9 −8 −7 −6 −5 −4 −3 −2 −1 0 +1 +2 +3 +4 +5 +6 +7 +8 +9 +10 +11

3B-121

J_{AB}	J_{AC}	J_{BC}
2	4	-2

Maximum summed intensity = 3.996

LINE	FREQ	INTEN
1	93.43	0.396
2	93.72	0.039
3	95.28	0.502
4	97.35	0.998
5	98.90	0.095
6	99.19	1.973
7	100.74	0.011
8	102.30	2.959
9	102.51	2.556
10	102.59	0.218
11	104.06	0.048
12	104.36	1.268
13	106.22	0.809
14	107.98	0.125
15	111.38	0.003

−11 −10 −9 −8 −7 −6 −5 −4 −3 −2 −1 0 +1 +2 +3 +4 +5 +6 +7 +8 +9 +10 +11

3B-122

J_{AB}	J_{AC}	J_{BC}
4	2	-2

Maximum summed intensity = 2.293

LINE	FREQ	INTEN
1	93.39	0.377
2	93.78	0.077
3	96.01	0.484
4	96.49	0.593
5	98.72	0.513
6	99.11	1.959
7	100.48	0.664
8	102.19	2.288
9	102.70	2.291
10	103.09	0.107
11	104.42	0.334
12	104.81	1.373
13	105.80	0.934
14	107.52	0.001
15	111.50	0.004

−11 −10 −9 −8 −7 −6 −5 −4 −3 −2 −1 0 +1 +2 +3 +4 +5 +6 +7 +8 +9 +10 +11

3C-1

J_{AB}	J_{AC}	J_{BC}
1	1	1

Maximum summed intensity = 2.184

LINE	FREQ	INTEN
1	94.70	0.001
2	95.93	0.742
3	96.90	0.920
4	96.96	1.019
5	97.92	1.318
6	99.15	0.001
7	101.90	0.613
8	102.91	1.725
9	102.93	0.486
10	103.94	1.176
11	104.16	1.645
12	105.13	1.255
13	105.17	0.593
14	106.14	0.506
15	111.15	0.000

−11 −10 −9 −8 −7 −6 −5 −4 −3 −2 −1 0 +1 +2 +3 +4 +5 +6 +7 +8 +9 +10 +11

3C-2

J_{AB}	J_{AC}	J_{BC}
2	2	2

Maximum summed intensity = 2.534

LINE	FREQ	INTEN
1	93.93	0.003
2	94.75	0.549
3	96.51	0.765
4	96.92	1.016
5	98.68	1.661
6	99.50	0.006
7	100.63	0.327
8	102.71	2.355
9	102.80	0.243
10	103.61	2.123
11	104.87	1.077
12	105.38	1.305
13	105.69	0.305
14	107.45	0.262
15	111.57	0.001

−11 −10 −9 −8 −7 −6 −5 −4 −3 −2 −1 0 +1 +2 +3 +4 +5 +6 +7 +8 +9 +10 +11

3C-3

J_{AB}	J_{AC}	J_{BC}
3	3	3

Maximum summed intensity = 2.848

LINE	FREQ	INTEN
1	92.90	0.005
2	93.49	0.412
3	95.86	0.585
4	96.89	1.011
5	99.26	0.184
6	99.27	1.979
7	99.86	0.011
8	102.48	2.814
9	102.66	0.135
10	103.25	2.404
11	105.63	1.273
12	105.88	0.870
13	106.48	0.182
14	108.85	0.151
15	112.24	0.004

3C-4

J_{AB}	J_{AC}	J_{BC}
4	4	4

Maximum summed intensity = 3.145

LINE	FREQ	INTEN
1	91.71	0.006
2	92.17	0.315
3	95.00	0.429
4	96.88	1.008
5	97.83	0.113
6	99.71	2.238
7	100.17	0.013
8	102.29	3.137
9	102.54	0.083
10	103.00	2.571
11	105.83	1.225
12	107.00	0.667
13	107.46	0.093
14	110.29	0.096
15	113.12	0.006

3c-5

J_{AB}	J_{AC}	J_{BC}
6	6	6

Maximum summed intensity = 3.345

−11 −10 −9 −8 −7 −6 −5 −4 −3 −2 −1 0 +1 +2 +3 +4 +5 +6 +7 +8 +9 +10 +11

3c-6

J_{AB}	J_{AC}	J_{BC}
8	8	8

Maximum summed intensity = 3.703

−11 −10 −9 −8 −7 −6 −5 −4 −3 −2 −1 0 +1 +2 +3 +4 +5 +6 +7 +8 +9 +10 +11

3C-7

J_{AB}	J_{AC}	J_{BC}
10	10	10

Maximum summed intensity = 3.703

−11 −10 −9 −8 −7 −6 −5 −4 −3 −2 −1 0 +1 +2 +3 +4 +5 +6 +7 +8 +9 +10 +11

3C-8

J_{AB}	J_{AC}	J_{BC}
12	12	12

Maximum summed intensity = 3.841

−11 −10 −9 −8 −7 −6 −5 −4 −3 −2 −1 0 +1 +2 +3 +4 +5 +6 +7 +8 +9 +10 +11

3c-9

J_{AB}	J_{AC}	J_{BC}
15	15	15

Maximum summed intensity = 3.692

LINE	FREQ	INTEN
1	76.23	0.002
2	76.36	0.048
3	80.62	0.031
4	81.50	0.009
5	96.86	1.001
6	101.12	2.924
7	101.25	0.004
8	101.74	3.911
9	102.01	0.006
10	102.14	2.944
11	106.39	1.032
12	122.25	0.068
13	122.38	0.004
14	126.63	0.008
15	127.52	0.009

3c-10

J_{AB}	J_{AC}	J_{BC}
18	18	18

Maximum summed intensity = 3.935

LINE	FREQ	INTEN
1	71.81	0.001
2	71.92	0.034
3	76.27	0.021
4	77.02	0.006
5	96.86	1.000
6	101.21	2.948
7	101.32	0.003
8	101.72	3.937
9	101.96	0.004
10	102.06	2.959
11	106.42	1.023
12	126.66	0.046
13	126.77	0.003
14	131.12	0.006
15	131.86	0.007

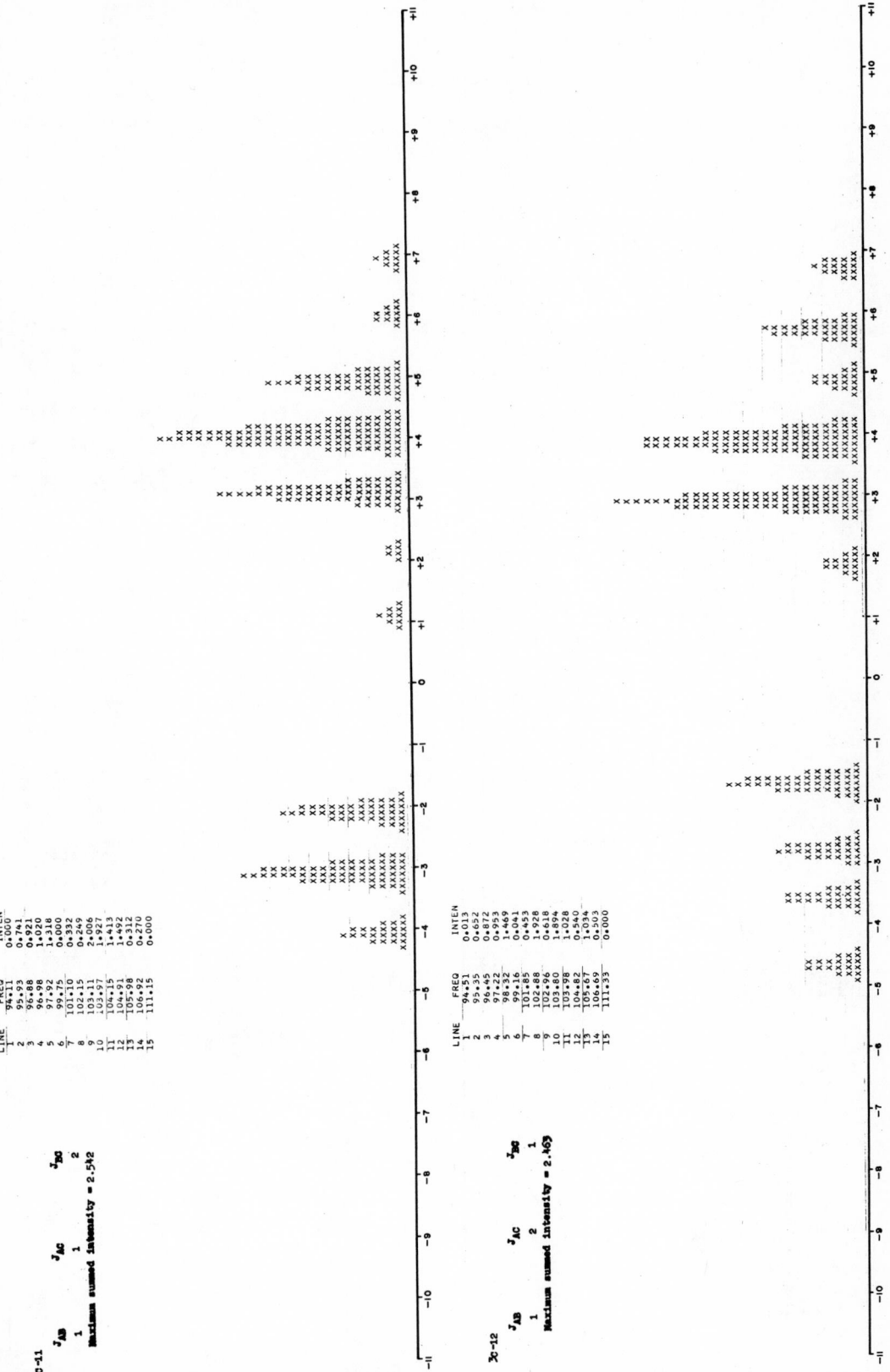

3c-11

J_{AB}	J_{AC}	J_{BC}
1	1	2

Maximum summed intensity = 2.542

LINE	FREQ	INTEN
1	94.11	0.000
2	95.93	0.741
3	96.88	0.921
4	96.98	1.020
5	97.92	1.318
6	99.75	0.000
7	101.10	0.332
8	102.15	0.249
9	103.11	2.006
10	103.97	1.927
11	104.15	1.413
12	104.91	1.492
13	105.98	0.312
14	106.92	0.270
15	111.15	0.000

3c-12

J_{AB}	J_{AC}	J_{BC}
1	2	1

Maximum summed intensity = 2.463

LINE	FREQ	INTEN
1	94.51	0.013
2	95.35	0.652
3	96.45	0.872
4	97.22	0.953
5	98.32	1.469
6	99.16	0.041
7	101.85	0.453
8	102.88	1.928
9	102.96	0.618
10	103.80	1.894
11	103.98	1.028
12	104.82	0.540
13	105.67	1.034
14	106.69	0.503
15	111.33	0.000

3C-13

J_{AB}	J_{AC}	J_{BC}
2	1	1

Maximum summed intensity = 1.804

LINE	FREQ	INTEN
1	94.69	0.001
2	95.32	0.613
3	96.30	0.749
4	97.31	1.135
5	98.29	1.495
6	98.92	0.007
7	101.53	0.778
8	102.55	1.859
9	103.53	0.299
10	104.15	1.609
11	104.55	1.069
12	105.13	1.313
13	105.17	0.635
14	106.16	0.436
15	111.39	0.000

−11 −10 −9 −8 −7 −6 −5 −4 −3 −2 −1 0 +1 +2 +3 +4 +5 +6 +7 +8 +9 +10 +11

3C-14

J_{AB}	J_{AC}	J_{BC}
1	2	2

Maximum summed intensity = 2.171

LINE	FREQ	INTEN
1	93.93	0.013
2	95.35	0.654
3	96.58	0.894
4	97.09	0.922
5	98.32	1.470
6	99.74	0.047
7	101.00	0.200
8	102.23	0.395
9	103.02	2.211
10	103.65	2.146
11	104.26	1.228
12	105.40	1.258
13	105.68	0.259
14	107.42	0.301
15	111.33	0.001

−11 −10 −9 −8 −7 −6 −5 −4 −3 −2 −1 0 +1 +2 +3 +4 +5 +6 +7 +8 +9 +10 +11

3c-15

J_{AB}	J_{AC}	J_{BC}
2	2	1

Maximum summed intensity = 1.997

LINE	FREQ	INTEN
1	94.52	0.006
2	94.75	0.550
3	96.59	0.767
4	96.84	0.993
5	98.68	1.663
6	98.91	0.022
7	101.46	0.597
8	102.54	2.079
9	103.55	0.490
10	103.79	1.853
11	104.63	0.849
12	104.86	0.582
13	105.62	1.059
14	106.70	0.489
15	111.57	0.001

−11 −10 −9 −8 −7 −6 −5 −4 −3 −2 −1 0 +1 +2 +3 +4 +5 +6 +7 +8 +9 +10 +11

3c-16

J_{AB}	J_{AC}	J_{BC}
2	1	2

Maximum summed intensity = 2.151

LINE	FREQ	INTEN
1	94.07	0.004
2	95.31	0.607
3	96.37	0.765
4	97.24	1.101
5	98.30	1.494
6	99.54	0.030
7	100.76	0.490
8	102.69	0.096
9	102.77	2.134
10	103.93	1.902
11	104.70	1.306
12	104.99	1.511
13	105.94	0.360
14	107.00	0.200
15	111.39	0.000

−11 −10 −9 −8 −7 −6 −5 −4 −3 −2 −1 0 +1 +2 +3 +4 +5 +6 +7 +8 +9 +10 +11

3c-17

J_{AB}	J_{AC}	J_{BC}
1	1	4

Maximum summed intensity = 2.180

LINE	FREQ	INTEN
1	92.46	0.000
2	95.93	0.737
3	96.86	0.927
4	96.99	1.019
5	97.92	1.317
6	99.27	0.131
7	100.33	0.078
8	101.39	0.000
9	103.28	2.205
10	103.80	2.132
11	104.34	1.586
12	104.73	1.659
13	107.81	0.112
14	108.74	0.098
15	111.15	0.000

-11 -10 -9 -8 -7 -6 -5 -4 -3 -2 -1 0 +1 +2 +3 +4 +5 +6 +7 +8 +9 +10 +11

3c-18

J_{AB}	J_{AC}	J_{BC}
1	4	1

Maximum summed intensity = 2.650

LINE	FREQ	INTEN
1	93.73	0.060
2	94.01	0.490
3	95.27	0.576
4	97.70	0.896
5	98.96	1.734
6	99.24	0.245
7	101.73	0.167
8	102.78	2.387
9	102.98	0.792
10	103.26	2.343
11	104.04	0.838
12	104.32	0.346
13	106.95	0.696
14	108.01	0.428
15	112.03	0.002

-11 -10 -9 -8 -7 -6 -5 -4 -3 -2 -1 0 +1 +2 +3 +4 +5 +6 +7 +8 +9 +10 +11

3C-19

J_{AB}	J_{AC}	J_{BC}
4	1	1

Maximum summed intensity = 2.054

LINE	FREQ	INTEN
1	93.88	0.406
2	94.45	0.159
3	95.11	0.325
4	97.61	0.787
5	98.28	0.551
6	98.84	1.774
7	100.98	1.028
8	102.02	2.062
9	104.14	1.565
10	104.70	0.068
11	105.18	0.691
12	105.37	1.337
13	105.75	1.213
14	106.41	0.014
15	112.28	0.001

−11 −10 −9 −8 −7 −6 −5 −4 −3 −2 −1 0 +1 +2 +3 +4 +5 +6 +7 +8 +9 +10 +11

3C-20

J_{AB}	J_{AC}	J_{BC}
1	4	4

Maximum summed intensity = 2.933

LINE	FREQ	INTEN
1	91.68	0.031
2	93.93	0.486
3	95.94	0.667
4	96.97	0.775
5	98.91	0.001
6	98.97	1.761
7	100.91	0.450
8	101.22	0.284
9	102.87	2.708
10	103.16	2.514
11	104.87	1.091
12	106.20	1.032
13	107.13	0.051
14	110.16	0.148
15	112.10	0.003

−11 −10 −9 −8 −7 −6 −5 −4 −3 −2 −1 0 +1 +2 +3 +4 +5 +6 +7 +8 +9 +10 +11

3C-21

J_{AB}	J_{AC}	J_{BC}
4	4	1

Maximum summed intensity = 2.704

LINE	FREQ	INTEN
1	92.18	0.318
2	93.70	0.063
3	95.54	0.384
4	96.34	0.727
5	98.18	0.276
6	99.70	2.239
7	100.59	0.444
8	102.07	2.791
9	103.23	2.238
10	104.70	0.440
11	104.76	0.714
12	106.23	0.256
13	106.59	0.596
14	108.07	0.505
15	113.12	0.008

3C-22

J_{AB}	J_{AC}	J_{BC}
4	1	4

Maximum summed intensity = 2.586

LINE	FREQ	INTEN
1	92.04	0.022
2	93.73	0.355
3	95.65	0.551
4	96.97	0.906
5	98.67	0.465
6	98.89	1.793
7	100.58	0.373
8	101.90	0.087
9	102.52	2.607
10	103.60	2.180
11	105.52	1.268
12	105.75	1.191
13	107.44	0.185
14	109.36	0.016
15	112.38	0.000

3C-23

J_{AB}	J_{AC}	J_{BC}
1	1	6

Maximum summed intensity = 2.203

LINE	FREQ	INTEN
1	90.61	0.000
2	95.93	0.722
3	96.86	0.930
4	96.99	1.026
5	97.35	0.086
6	97.92	1.316
7	98.41	0.022
8	103.24	0.006
9	103.35	2.262
10	103.73	2.192
11	104.41	1.636
12	104.66	1.700
13	109.73	0.054
14	110.66	0.048
15	111.15	0.000

−11 −10 −9 −8 −7 −6 −5 −4 −3 −2 −1 0 +1 +2 +3 +4 +5 +6 +7 +8 +9 +10 +11

3C-24

J_{AB}	J_{AC}	J_{BC}
1	6	1

Maximum summed intensity = 3.649

LINE	FREQ	INTEN
1	92.49	0.362
2	92.55	0.102
3	93.90	0.349
4	98.00	0.728
5	99.35	0.522
6	99.41	1.939
7	101.58	0.016
8	102.65	2.792
9	102.93	2.622
10	102.99	0.884
11	104.01	0.145
12	104.07	0.726
13	108.44	0.475
14	109.52	0.335
15	113.10	0.003

−11 −10 −9 −8 −7 −6 −5 −4 −3 −2 −1 0 +1 +2 +3 +4 +5 +6 +7 +8 +9 +10 +11

3C-25

J_{AB}	J_{AC}	J_{BC}
6	1	1

Maximum summed intensity = 2.177

LINE	FREQ	INTEN
1	92.25	0.271
2	93.08	0.275
3	94.85	0.040
4	96.60	0.087
5	98.36	1.373
6	99.19	1.954
7	100.62	1.189
8	101.67	2.225
9	104.13	1.540
10	104.96	0.794
11	105.19	0.729
12	106.02	0.889
13	106.73	0.476
14	107.78	0.157
15	113.55	0.001

−11 −10 −9 −8 −7 −6 −5 −4 −3 −2 −1 0 +1 +2 +3 +4 +5 +6 +7 +8 +9 +10 +11

3C-26

J_{AB}	J_{AC}	J_{BC}
1	6	6

Maximum summed intensity = 3.405

LINE	FREQ	INTEN
1	89.09	0.028
2	92.09	0.326
3	95.00	0.442
4	96.55	0.610
5	97.00	0.034
6	99.46	2.020
7	99.91	0.619
8	102.46	0.581
9	102.63	3.002
10	102.91	2.640
11	105.54	0.891
12	107.37	0.700
13	108.54	0.011
14	113.00	0.089
15	113.45	0.007

−11 −10 −9 −8 −7 −6 −5 −4 −3 −2 −1 0 +1 +2 +3 +4 +5 +6 +7 +8 +9 +10 +11

3C-27

J_{AB}	J_{AC}	J_{BC}
6	6	1

Maximum summed intensity = 3.134

LINE	FREQ	INTEN
1	89.43	0.200
2	92.09	0.117
3	94.45	0.119
4	95.25	0.307
5	97.61	0.705
6	99.70	0.288
7	100.27	2.567
8	101.86	3.276
9	102.87	2.512
10	105.03	0.276
11	105.52	0.986
12	107.68	0.022
13	107.89	0.197
14	110.04	0.412
15	115.30	0.014

3C-28

J_{AB}	J_{AC}	J_{BC}
6	1	6

Maximum summed intensity = 2.851

LINE	FREQ	INTEN
1	89.56	0.021
2	91.65	0.177
3	95.06	0.423
4	95.91	0.595
5	97.00	0.471
6	99.32	2.033
7	101.26	0.385
8	101.41	0.752
9	102.33	2.908
10	103.35	2.353
11	106.59	0.967
12	106.76	0.792
13	108.68	0.124
14	112.09	0.001
15	114.03	0.000

3C-29

J_{AB}	J_{AC}	J_{BC}
1	1	9

Maximum summed intensity = 2.918

LINE	FREQ	INTEN
1	87.72	0.000
2	94.39	0.012
3	95.45	0.042
4	95.94	0.764
5	96.86	0.934
6	97.00	0.981
7	97.92	1.315
8	103.40	2.290
9	103.67	2.224
10	104.47	1.662
11	104.59	1.722
12	106.15	0.007
13	111.14	0.001
14	112.69	0.024
15	113.61	0.022

−11 −10 −9 −8 −7 −6 −5 −4 −3 −2 −1 0 +1 +2 +3 +4 +5 +6 +7 +8 +9 +10 +11

3C-30

J_{AB}	J_{AC}	J_{BC}
9	9	1

Maximum summed intensity = 3.393

LINE	FREQ	INTEN
1	85.16	0.113
2	88.59	0.082
3	92.82	0.077
4	93.06	0.018
5	97.29	0.941
6	98.30	0.149
7	100.72	2.783
8	101.75	3.636
9	102.53	2.737
10	105.97	1.056
11	105.98	0.132
12	109.41	0.002
13	110.43	0.042
14	113.87	0.215
15	119.12	0.015

−11 −10 −9 −8 −7 −6 −5 −4 −3 −2 −1 0 +1 +2 +3 +4 +5 +6 +7 +8 +9 +10 +11

3C-31

J_{AB}	J_{AC}	J_{BC}
1	1	12

Maximum summed intensity = 3.160

LINE	FREQ	INTEN
1	84.77	0.000
2	91.42	0.011
3	92.48	0.017
4	95.94	0.753
5	96.86	0.935
6	97.00	0.996
7	97.92	1.315
8	103.43	2.300
9	103.65	2.236
10	104.49	1.672
11	104.57	1.736
12	109.09	0.001
13	111.14	0.000
14	115.66	0.014
15	116.58	0.013

−11 −10 −9 −8 −7 −6 −5 −4 −3 −2 −1 0 +1 +2 +3 +4 +5 +6 +7 +8 +9 +10 +11

3C-32

J_{AB}	J_{AC}	J_{BC}
12	12	1

Maximum summed intensity = 3.785

LINE	FREQ	INTEN
1	80.80	0.072
2	84.59	0.049
3	90.06	0.029
4	91.69	0.003
5	96.86	0.085
6	97.17	0.988
7	100.95	2.872
8	101.71	3.791
9	102.34	2.843
10	106.13	1.044
11	107.19	0.068
12	110.97	0.007
13	113.23	0.016
14	118.08	0.121
15	123.25	0.013

−11 −10 −9 −8 −7 −6 −5 −4 −3 −2 −1 0 +1 +2 +3 +4 +5 +6 +7 +8 +9 +10 +11

3C-33

J_{AB}	J_{AC}	J_{BC}
1	1	18

Maximum summed intensity = 3.604

LINE	FREQ	INTEN
1	78.82	0.000
2	85.44	0.006
3	86.51	0.007
4	95.93	0.750
5	96.86	0.937
6	97.00	0.999
7	97.92	1.314
8	103.46	2.308
9	103.62	2.245
10	104.52	1.680
11	104.54	1.743
12	111.14	0.000
13	115.03	0.000
14	121.63	0.006
15	122.56	0.006

3C-34

J_{AB}	J_{AC}	J_{BC}
18	18	1

Maximum summed intensity = 3.879

LINE	FREQ	INTEN
1	71.96	0.036
2	76.07	0.021
3	84.28	0.008
4	88.87	0.000
5	93.92	0.036
6	97.08	1.002
7	101.19	2.941
8	101.68	3.907
9	102.13	2.928
10	106.24	1.023
11	109.89	0.025
12	114.01	0.007
13	119.04	0.005
14	126.80	0.052
15	131.85	0.008

3C-35

J_{AB}	J_{AC}	J_{BC}
2	2	4

Maximum summed intensity = 2.464

LINE	FREQ	INTEN
1	92.29	0.001
2	94.75	0.545
3	96.46	0.771
4	96.96	1.025
5	98.68	1.659
6	98.79	0.135
7	101.00	0.068
8	101.14	0.000
9	102.86	2.548
10	103.46	2.319
11	105.07	1.247
12	105.18	1.477
13	107.53	0.111
14	109.25	0.093
15	111.57	0.001

−11 −10 −9 −8 −7 −6 −5 −4 −3 −2 −1 0 +1 +2 +3 +4 +5 +6 +7 +8 +9 +10 +11

3C-36

J_{AB}	J_{AC}	J_{BC}
2	4	2

Maximum summed intensity = 2.696

LINE	FREQ	INTEN
1	93.21	0.046
2	93.45	0.430
3	95.98	0.712
4	96.74	0.652
5	99.27	1.951
6	99.52	0.214
7	100.39	0.111
8	102.57	2.761
9	102.92	0.545
10	103.16	2.459
11	105.10	0.746
12	105.34	0.185
13	106.45	0.880
14	108.63	0.303
15	112.27	0.005

−11 −10 −9 −8 −7 −6 −5 −4 −3 −2 −1 0 +1 +2 +3 +4 +5 +6 +7 +8 +9 +10 +11

3C-37

J_{AB}	J_{AC}	J_{BC}
4	2	2

Maximum summed intensity = 2.473

LINE	FREQ	INTEN
1	93.35	0.372
2	93.81	0.016
3	95.25	0.483
4	97.29	1.078
5	98.73	0.096
6	99.19	1.958
7	100.08	0.545
8	102.24	2.584
9	103.57	2.082
10	104.03	0.003
11	105.47	1.367
12	105.72	0.372
13	106.18	0.945
14	107.63	0.097
15	112.46	0.002

−11 −10 −9 −8 −7 −6 −5 −4 −3 −2 −1 0 +1 +2 +3 +4 +5 +6 +7 +8 +9 +10 +11

3C-38

J_{AB}	J_{AC}	J_{BC}
2	4	4

Maximum summed intensity = 2.784

LINE	FREQ	INTEN
1	91.72	0.021
2	93.43	0.432
3	96.34	0.801
4	96.37	0.639
5	98.47	0.023
6	99.27	1.954
7	100.99	0.158
8	101.38	0.313
9	102.63	2.885
10	103.09	2.545
11	105.54	0.910
12	106.03	1.113
13	107.25	0.065
14	110.19	0.135
15	112.29	0.005

−11 −10 −9 −8 −7 −6 −5 −4 −3 −2 −1 0 +1 +2 +3 +4 +5 +6 +7 +8 +9 +10 +11

3C-39

J_{AB}	J_{AC}	J_{BC}
4	2	4

Maximum summed intensity = 2.704

LINE	FREQ	INTEN
1	92.06	0.006
2	93.29	0.351
3	95.44	0.527
4	97.06	1.015
5	98.36	0.307
6	99.21	1.963
7	100.44	0.139
8	102.13	0.013
9	102.44	2.809
10	103.35	2.343
11	105.51	1.336
12	106.21	1.002
13	107.43	0.152
14	109.58	0.035
15	112.50	0.001

−11 −10 −9 −8 −7 −6 −5 −4 −3 −2 −1 0 +1 +2 +3 +4 +5 +6 +7 +8 +9 +10 +11

3C-40

J_{AB}	J_{AC}	J_{BC}
4	4	2

Maximum summed intensity =2.968

LINE	FREQ	INTEN
1	92.18	0.318
2	93.26	0.031
3	95.22	0.404
4	96.66	0.895
5	98.62	0.122
6	99.70	2.239
7	99.71	0.254
8	102.18	2.994
9	103.11	2.429
10	104.19	0.374
11	105.58	0.237
12	106.16	0.936
13	106.66	0.462
14	108.63	0.299
15	113.12	0.008

−11 −10 −9 −8 −7 −6 −5 −4 −3 −2 −1 0 +1 +2 +3 +4 +5 +6 +7 +8 +9 +10 +11

3C-41

J_{AB}	J_{AC}	J_{BC}
2	2	6

Maximum summed intensity = 2.701

LINE	FREQ	INTEN
1	90.44	0.000
2	94.74	0.533
3	96.45	0.776
4	96.86	0.088
5	96.97	1.029
6	98.68	1.658
7	99.09	0.016
8	102.93	2.603
9	102.98	0.005
10	103.39	2.379
11	105.10	1.516
12	105.15	1.296
13	109.46	0.054
14	111.17	0.045
15	111.58	0.001

3C-42

J_{AB}	J_{AC}	J_{BC}
2	6	2

Maximum summed intensity = 3.248

LINE	FREQ	INTEN
1	91.95	0.326
2	92.05	0.077
3	94.75	0.451
4	96.91	0.510
5	99.60	0.475
6	99.70	2.168
7	100.17	0.020
8	102.43	3.067
9	102.87	2.654
10	102.96	0.742
11	105.13	0.094
12	105.22	0.562
13	107.82	0.577
14	110.08	0.270
15	113.35	0.007

3C-43

J_{AB}	J_{AC}	J_{BC}
6	2	2

Maximum summed intensity = 2.650

LINE	FREQ	INTEN
1	91.73	0.251
2	92.99	0.158
3	94.46	0.170
4	96.80	0.419
5	98.27	0.856
6	99.53	2.148
7	99.73	0.696
8	101.93	2.724
9	103.54	2.052
10	104.80	0.457
11	105.75	0.421
12	106.27	0.792
13	107.00	0.818
14	108.47	0.034
15	113.74	0.003

−11 −10 −9 −8 −7 −6 −5 −4 −3 −2 −1 0 +1 +2 +3 +4 +5 +6 +7 +8 +9 +10 +11

3C-44

J_{AB}	J_{AC}	J_{BC}
2	6	6

Maximum summed intensity = 3.224

LINE	FREQ	INTEN
1	89.14	0.023
2	91.75	0.313
3	95.56	0.568
4	95.89	0.491
5	96.41	0.006
6	99.71	2.191
7	100.23	0.493
8	102.32	0.424
9	102.46	3.166
10	102.84	2.680
11	106.27	0.725
12	106.98	0.810
13	108.88	0.014
14	113.02	0.084
15	113.54	0.010

−11 −10 −9 −8 −7 −6 −5 −4 −3 −2 −1 0 +1 +2 +3 +4 +5 +6 +7 +8 +9 +10 +11

3c-45

J_{AB}	J_{AC}	J_{BC}
6	2	6

Maximum summed intensity = 2.862

LINE	FREQ	INTEN
1	89.64	0.012
2	91.36	0.190
3	94.63	0.384
4	96.32	0.730
5	96.48	0.335
6	99.59	2.184
7	101.31	0.501
8	101.44	0.261
9	102.25	3.080
10	103.16	2.475
11	106.43	0.929
12	107.21	0.814
13	108.93	0.104
14	112.20	0.003
15	114.05	0.000

-11 -10 -9 -8 -7 -6 -5 -4 -3 -2 -1 0 +1 +2 +3 +4 +5 +6 +7 +8 +9 +10 +11

3c-46

J_{AB}	J_{AC}	J_{BC}
6	6	2

Maximum summed intensity = 3.282

LINE	FREQ	INTEN
1	89.43	0.200
2	91.94	0.096
3	93.75	0.134
4	95.95	0.477
5	97.76	0.540
6	98.78	0.176
7	100.28	2.568
8	101.93	3.395
9	102.79	2.625
10	105.30	0.778
11	105.94	0.159
12	107.11	0.407
13	108.46	0.081
14	110.27	0.351
15	115.29	0.014

-11 -10 -9 -8 -7 -6 -5 -4 -3 -2 -1 0 +1 +2 +3 +4 +5 +6 +7 +8 +9 +10 +11

3C-47

J_{AB}	J_{AC}	J_{BC}
2	2	9

Maximum summed intensity = 2.632

LINE	FREQ	INTEN
1	87.54	0.000
2	93.86	0.001
3	94.79	0.588
4	96.10	0.103
5	96.44	0.780
6	97.02	0.918
7	98.68	1.657
8	102.97	2.631
9	103.35	2.411
10	105.00	1.481
11	105.21	1.322
12	105.93	0.061
13	111.53	0.005
14	112.46	0.021
15	114.11	0.021

3C-48

J_{AB}	J_{AC}	J_{BC}
9	9	2

Maximum summed intensity =3.652

LINE	FREQ	INTEN
1	85.16	0.113
2	88.59	0.084
3	92.14	0.015
4	93.74	0.099
5	97.29	0.918
6	97.35	0.101
7	100.72	2.785
8	101.78	3.686
9	102.49	2.786
10	105.93	1.032
11	106.93	0.084
12	109.48	0.067
13	110.37	0.000
14	113.91	0.215
15	119.12	0.015

3C-49

J_{AB}	J_{AC}	J_{BC}
2	2	12

Maximum summed intensity = 2.740

LINE	FREQ	INTEN
1	84.59	0.000
2	90.91	0.008
3	93.15	0.022
4	94.76	0.568
5	96.44	0.783
6	97.00	0.991
7	98.68	1.656
8	103.00	2.640
9	103.32	2.424
10	105.00	1.544
11	105.24	1.332
12	108.85	0.004
13	111.55	0.002
14	115.41	0.013
15	117.08	0.012

−11 −10 −9 −8 −7 −6 −5 −4 −3 −2 −1 0 +1 +2 +3 +4 +5 +6 +7 +8 +9 +10 +11

3C-50

J_{AB}	J_{AC}	J_{BC}
12	12	2

Maximum summed intensity = 3.733

LINE	FREQ	INTEN
1	80.80	0.072
2	84.60	0.050
3	90.73	0.002
4	91.03	0.033
5	95.89	0.062
6	97.16	0.981
7	100.96	2.874
8	101.73	3.814
9	102.32	2.866
10	106.11	1.038
11	108.16	0.048
12	111.96	0.004
13	112.25	0.021
14	118.09	0.122
15	123.24	0.013

−11 −10 −9 −8 −7 −6 −5 −4 −3 −2 −1 0 +1 +2 +3 +4 +5 +6 +7 +8 +9 +10 +11

3C-51

J_{AB}	J_{AC}	J_{BC}
2	2	18

Maximum summed intensity = 2.951

LINE	FREQ	INTEN
1	78.65	0.000
2	84.94	0.005
3	87.18	0.007
4	94.76	0.562
5	96.44	0.786
6	97.00	0.998
7	98.68	1.655
8	103.02	2.647
9	103.30	2.433
10	104.98	1.553
11	105.26	1.340
12	111.56	0.002
13	114.79	0.001
14	121.37	0.006
15	123.06	0.006

−11 −10 −9 −8 −7 −6 −5 −4 −3 −2 −1 0 +1 +2 +3 +4 +5 +6 +7 +8 +9 +10 +11

3C-52

J_{AB}	J_{AC}	J_{BC}
18	18	2

Maximum summed intensity = 3.914

LINE	FREQ	INTEN
1	71.96	0.036
2	76.08	0.021
3	85.27	0.009
4	87.88	0.000
5	92.93	0.029
6	97.07	1.000
7	101.19	2.942
8	101.69	3.914
9	102.12	2.935
10	106.24	1.022
11	110.88	0.019
12	115.00	0.006
13	118.04	0.006
14	126.81	0.052
15	131.85	0.008

−11 −10 −9 −8 −7 −6 −5 −4 −3 −2 −1 0 +1 +2 +3 +4 +5 +6 +7 +8 +9 +10 +11

3C-53

J_{AB}	J_{AC}	J_{BC}
4	4	9

Maximum summed intensity = 3.157

LINE	FREQ	INTEN
1	86.97	0.001
2	92.09	0.243
3	93.00	0.111
4	94.92	0.441
5	96.88	0.982
6	97.79	0.037
7	99.71	2.235
8	102.38	3.205
9	102.91	2.646
10	104.83	0.100
11	105.74	1.204
12	107.17	0.745
13	112.29	0.029
14	113.19	0.002
15	115.12	0.020

3C-54

J_{AB}	J_{AC}	J_{BC}
9	9	4

Maximum summed intensity = 3.672

LINE	FREQ	INTEN
1	85.16	0.113
2	88.44	0.074
3	90.40	0.026
4	95.40	0.055
5	95.49	0.266
6	97.45	0.748
7	100.73	2.788
8	101.82	3.731
9	102.45	2.832
10	105.73	0.859
11	107.69	0.240
12	108.87	0.042
13	112.16	0.014
14	114.11	0.198
15	119.11	0.015

3C-55

J_{AB}	J_{AC}	J_{BC}
4	4	12

Maximum summed intensity = 3.214

LINE	FREQ	INTEN
1	84.03	0.000
2	89.90	0.003
3	92.22	0.340
4	94.70	0.047
5	94.92	0.444
6	97.02	0.964
7	99.72	2.234
8	102.40	3.213
9	102.89	2.658
10	105.58	1.281
11	107.20	0.754
12	107.91	0.029
13	113.07	0.011
14	115.39	0.010
15	118.09	0.011

−11 −10 −9 −8 −7 −6 −5 −4 −3 −2 −1 0 +1 +2 +3 +4 +5 +6 +7 +8 +9 +10 +11

3C-56

J_{AB}	J_{AC}	J_{BC}
12	12	4

Maximum summed intensity = 3.558

LINE	FREQ	INTEN
1	80.80	0.072
2	84.58	0.051
3	88.81	0.002
4	92.95	0.055
5	93.92	0.037
6	97.18	0.956
7	100.96	2.877
8	101.75	3.838
9	102.29	2.891
10	106.07	1.016
11	110.12	0.027
12	110.30	0.043
13	113.91	0.001
14	118.13	0.122
15	123.24	0.013

−11 −10 −9 −8 −7 −6 −5 −4 −3 −2 −1 0 +1 +2 +3 +4 +5 +6 +7 +8 +9 +10 +11

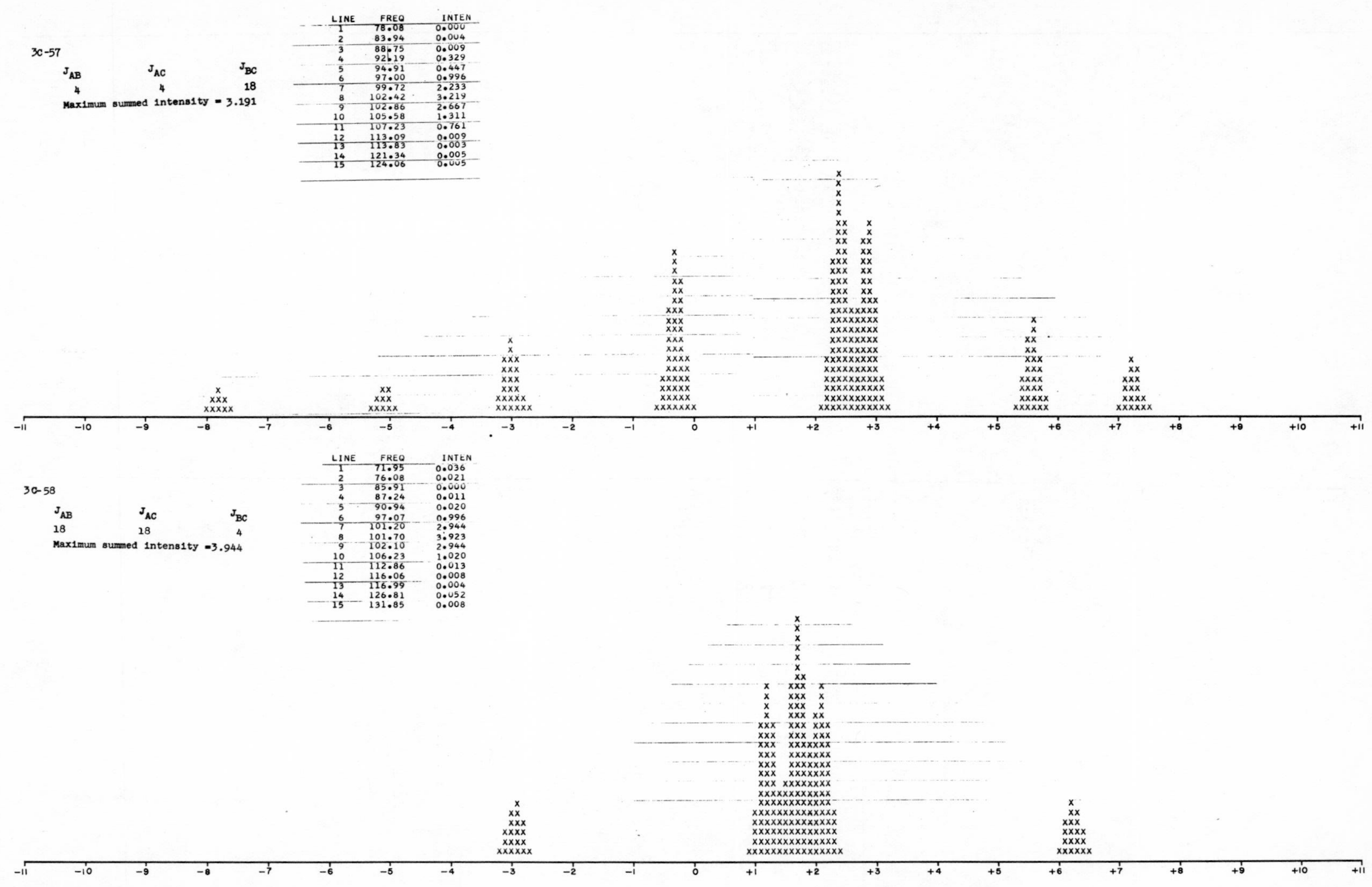

3c-57

LINE	FREQ	INTEN
1	78.08	0.000
2	83.94	0.004
3	88.75	0.009
4	92.19	0.329
5	94.91	0.447
6	97.00	0.996
7	99.72	2.233
8	102.42	3.219
9	102.86	2.667
10	105.58	1.311
11	107.23	0.761
12	113.09	0.009
13	113.83	0.003
14	121.34	0.005
15	124.06	0.005

3c-58

LINE	FREQ	INTEN
1	71.95	0.036
2	76.08	0.021
3	85.91	0.000
4	87.24	0.011
5	90.94	0.020
6	97.07	0.996
7	101.20	2.944
8	101.70	3.923
9	102.10	2.944
10	106.23	1.020
11	112.86	0.013
12	116.06	0.008
13	116.99	0.004
14	126.81	0.052
15	131.85	0.008

3C-59

J_{AB}	J_{AC}	J_{BC}
6	6	9

Maximum summed intensity = 3.430

LINE	FREQ	INTEN
1	86.23	0.002
2	89.40	0.186
3	91.96	0.043
4	92.78	0.232
5	96.91	1.018
6	99.48	0.000
7	100.29	2.569
8	102.07	3.537
9	102.64	2.771
10	103.46	0.004
11	106.02	1.175
12	109.58	0.411
13	112.74	0.022
14	115.31	0.011
15	116.13	0.019

3C-60

J_{AB}	J_{AC}	J_{BC}
9	9	6

Maximum summed intensity = 3.529

LINE	FREQ	INTEN
1	85.15	0.112
2	87.58	0.024
3	89.31	0.077
4	93.43	0.036
5	96.57	0.809
6	98.31	0.202
7	100.74	2.790
8	101.84	3.750
9	102.42	2.852
10	104.85	0.258
11	106.58	0.840
12	110.84	0.025
13	113.26	0.120
14	115.00	0.091
15	119.11	0.014

3c-61

J_{AB}	J_{AC}	J_{BC}
6	6	12

Maximum summed intensity = 3.516

LINE	FREQ	INTEN
1	83.29	0.001
2	88.76	0.010
3	89.62	0.209
4	92.76	0.235
5	96.29	0.292
6	97.15	0.718
7	100.29	2.569
8	102.08	3.544
9	102.62	2.780
10	105.77	0.893
11	106.62	0.292
12	109.61	0.420
13	115.09	0.024
14	115.94	0.001
15	119.09	0.011

−11 −10 −9 −8 −7 −6 −5 −4 −3 −2 −1 0 +1 +2 +3 +4 +5 +6 +7 +8 +9 +10 +11

3c-62

J_{AB}	J_{AC}	J_{BC}
12	12	6

Maximum summed intensity = 3.704

LINE	FREQ	INTEN
1	80.79	0.072
2	84.49	0.049
3	86.94	0.005
4	91.94	0.026
5	94.82	0.138
6	97.27	0.870
7	100.97	2.879
8	101.76	3.849
9	102.27	2.903
10	105.97	0.934
11	108.41	0.126
12	112.09	0.017
13	115.79	0.001
14	118.24	0.120
15	123.24	0.012

−11 −10 −9 −8 −7 −6 −5 −4 −3 −2 −1 0 +1 +2 +3 +4 +5 +6 +7 +8 +9 +10 +11

3C-63

J_{AB}	J_{AC}	J_{BC}
6	6	18

Maximum summed intensity = 3.551

LINE	FREQ	INTEN
1	77.34	0.000
2	82.94	0.003
3	89.46	0.209
4	90.48	0.013
5	92.75	0.238
6	97.01	0.991
7	100.30	2.569
8	102.10	3.550
9	102.60	2.788
10	105.90	1.181
11	109.64	0.426
12	112.42	0.008
13	115.24	0.015
14	121.77	0.004
15	125.06	0.005

−11 −10 −9 −8 −7 −6 −5 −4 −3 −2 −1 0 +1 +2 +3 +4 +5 +6 +7 +8 +9 +10 +11

3C-64

J_{AB}	J_{AC}	J_{BC}
18	18	6

Maximum summed intensity = 3.591

LINE	FREQ	INTEN
1	71.95	0.036
2	76.08	0.022
3	83.94	0.000
4	88.96	0.014
5	89.22	0.016
6	97.07	0.990
7	101.20	2.945
8	101.71	3.928
9	102.09	2.950
10	106.22	1.015
11	114.08	0.013
12	114.84	0.009
13	118.97	0.003
14	126.83	0.053
15	131.84	0.008

−11 −10 −9 −8 −7 −6 −5 −4 −3 −2 −1 0 +1 +2 +3 +4 +5 +6 +7 +8 +9 +10 +11

3C-65

J_{AB}	J_{AC}	J_{BC}
9	9	12

Maximum summed intensity = 3.687

LINE	FREQ	INTEN
1	82.01	0.001
2	85.10	0.102
3	87.51	0.026
4	88.97	0.102
5	96.88	1.007
6	99.29	0.003
7	100.74	2.791
8	101.87	3.768
9	102.38	2.872
10	103.84	0.008
11	106.25	1.088
12	113.65	0.198
13	116.74	0.011
14	119.15	0.012
15	120.61	0.011

3C-66

J_{AB}	J_{AC}	J_{BC}
12	12	9

Maximum summed intensity = 3.799

LINE	FREQ	INTEN
1	80.79	0.071
2	83.35	0.013
3	85.13	0.041
4	88.96	0.017
5	96.63	0.849
6	98.41	0.158
7	100.97	2.880
8	101.78	3.858
9	102.25	2.912
10	104.81	0.184
11	106.59	0.875
12	115.06	0.010
13	117.62	0.074
14	119.40	0.046
15	123.24	0.012

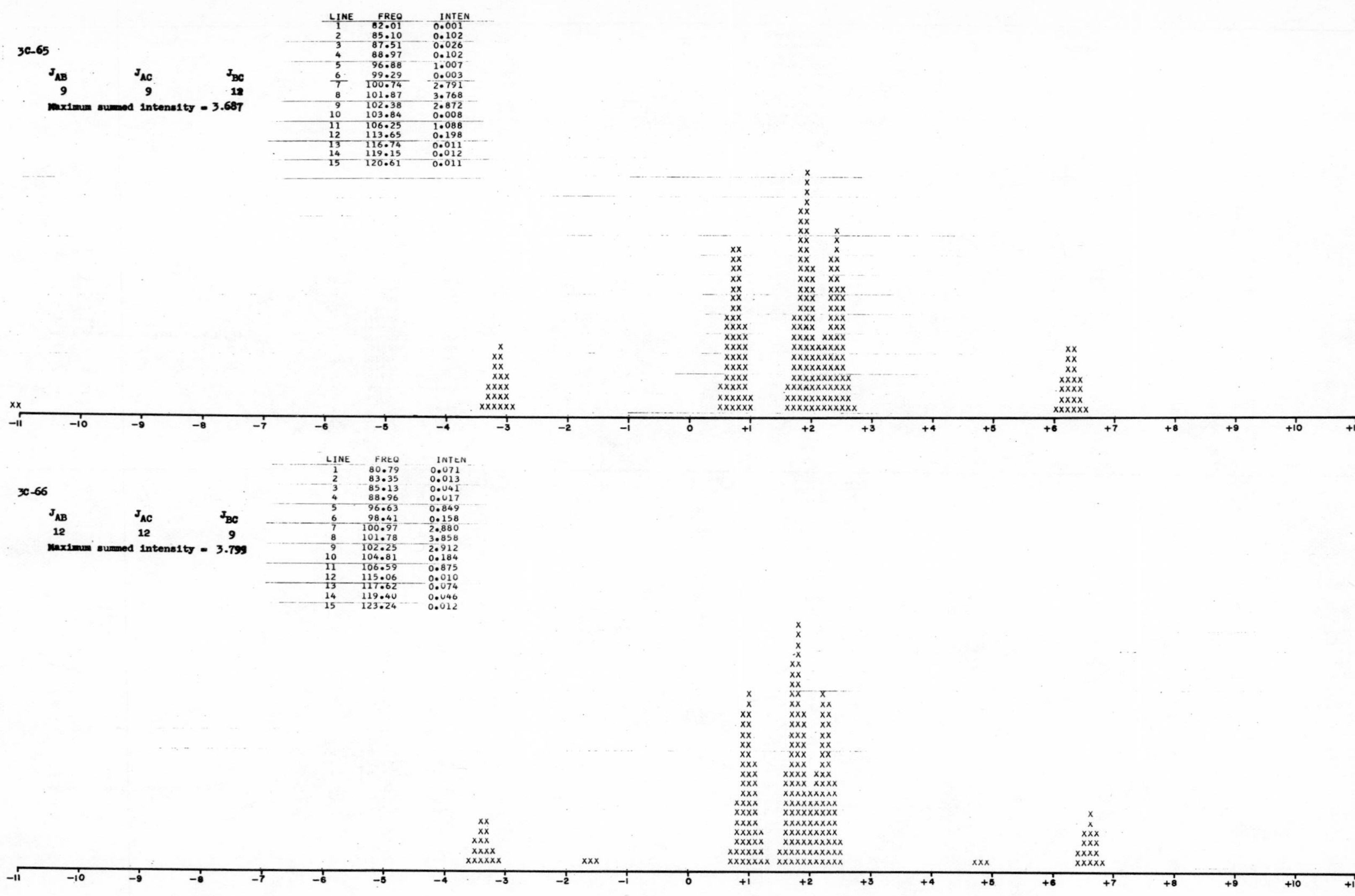

3C-67

J_{AB}	J_{AC}	J_{BC}
9	9	18

Maximum summed intensity = 3.748

LINE	FREQ	INTEN
1	76.07	0.001
2	81.42	0.001
3	85.22	0.121
4	88.94	0.104
5	93.22	0.030
6	97.02	0.974
7	100.75	2.792
8	101.88	3.773
9	102.37	2.878
10	106.09	1.074
11	109.89	0.025
12	113.69	0.203
13	119.03	0.017
14	122.84	0.002
15	126.56	0.005

3C-68

J_{AB}	J_{AC}	J_{BC}
18	18	9

Maximum summed intensity = 3.950

LINE	FREQ	INTEN
1	71.95	0.036
2	76.06	0.022
3	80.99	0.000
4	85.97	0.010
5	92.17	0.033
6	97.10	0.971
7	101.21	2.946
8	101.71	3.932
9	102.08	2.954
10	106.19	0.998
11	111.12	0.030
12	117.82	0.006
13	121.93	0.001
14	126.86	0.053
15	131.84	0.008

3C-69

J_{AB}	J_{AC}	J_{BC}
12	12	18

Maximum summed intensity = 3.870

LINE	FREQ	INTEN
1	74.71	0.001
2	79.78	0.002
3	81.00	0.077
4	84.83	0.055
5	95.93	0.214
6	97.16	0.789
7	100.98	2.882
8	101.79	3.866
9	102.22	2.921
10	106.05	0.847
11	107.28	0.212
12	117.95	0.114
13	123.02	0.016
14	124.24	0.000
15	128.07	0.005

-11 -10 -9 -8 -7 -6 -5 -4 -3 -2 -1 0 +1 +2 +3 +4 +5 +6 +7 +8 +9 +10 +11

3C-70

J_{AB}	J_{AC}	J_{BC}
18	18	12

Maximum summed intensity = 3.945

LINE	FREQ	INTEN
1	71.95	0.036
2	75.93	0.021
3	78.14	0.001
4	82.98	0.008
5	95.02	0.139
6	97.23	0.864
7	101.21	2.947
8	101.72	3.935
9	102.07	2.957
10	106.05	0.893
11	108.26	0.135
12	120.81	0.004
13	124.79	0.001
14	127.00	0.053
15	131.84	0.008

-11 -10 -9 -8 -7 -6 -5 -4 -3 -2 -1 0 +1 +2 +3 +4 +5 +6 +7 +8 +9 +10 +11

3C-71

J_{AB}	J_{AC}	J_{BC}
1	2	4

Maximum summed intensity = 2.281

LINE	FREQ	INTEN
1	92.31	0.006
2	95.34	0.657
3	96.73	0.921
4	96.93	0.903
5	98.32	1.472
6	99.12	0.051
7	100.51	0.192
8	101.35	0.041
9	103.14	2.383
10	103.54	2.291
11	104.53	1.409
12	105.13	1.465
13	107.56	0.089
14	109.15	0.119
15	111.34	0.001

−11 −10 −9 −8 −7 −6 −5 −4 −3 −2 −1 0 +1 +2 +3 +4 +5 +6 +7 +8 +9 +10 +11

3C-72

J_{AB}	J_{AC}	J_{BC}
1	4	2

Maximum summed intensity = 2.514

LINE	FREQ	INTEN
1	93.17	0.060
2	93.99	0.489
3	95.56	0.605
4	97.39	0.813
5	98.96	1.746
6	99.79	0.290
7	100.81	0.042
8	102.38	0.640
9	102.84	2.596
10	103.20	2.468
11	104.41	0.950
12	105.23	0.147
13	106.60	0.847
14	108.63	0.304
15	112.05	0.002

−11 −10 −9 −8 −7 −6 −5 −4 −3 −2 −1 0 +1 +2 +3 +4 +5 +6 +7 +8 +9 +10 +11

3C-73

J_{AB}	J_{AC}	J_{BC}
2	1	4

Maximum summed intensity = 2.686

LINE	FREQ	INTEN
1	92.40	0.002
2	95.29	0.585
3	96.48	0.801
4	97.11	1.061
5	98.30	1.492
6	99.00	0.257
7	100.82	0.006
8	101.19	0.059
9	102.98	2.355
10	103.71	2.158
11	104.81	1.439
12	104.91	1.579
13	107.70	0.137
14	108.89	0.069
15	111.41	0.000

−11 −10 −9 −8 −7 −6 −5 −4 −3 −2 −1 0 +1 +2 +3 +4 +5 +6 +7 +8 +9 +10 +11

3C-74

J_{AB}	J_{AC}	J_{BC}
2	4	1

Maximum summed intensity = 2.522

LINE	FREQ	INTEN
1	93.46	0.429
2	93.74	0.051
3	95.69	0.656
4	97.04	0.697
5	98.99	0.222
6	99.27	1.948
7	101.30	0.276
8	102.48	2.546
9	103.25	2.295
10	103.52	0.735
11	104.43	0.397
12	104.71	0.609
13	106.83	0.690
14	108.02	0.443
15	112.27	0.004

−11 −10 −9 −8 −7 −6 −5 −4 −3 −2 −1 0 +1 +2 +3 +4 +5 +6 +7 +8 +9 +10 +11

3C-75

J_{AB}	J_{AC}	J_{BC}
4	1	2

Maximum summed intensity = 2.235

LINE	FREQ	INTEN
1	93.73	0.078
2	93.85	0.394
3	95.37	0.436
4	97.34	0.886
5	98.86	1.782
6	98.98	0.425
7	100.27	0.745
8	102.26	2.347
9	103.76	0.056
10	103.88	1.861
11	105.40	1.337
12	105.75	1.198
13	105.87	0.435
14	107.39	0.020
15	112.29	0.000

−11 −10 −9 −8 −7 −6 −5 −4 −3 −2 −1 0 +1 +2 +3 +4 +5 +6 +7 +8 +9 +10 +11

3C-76

J_{AB}	J_{AC}	J_{BC}
4	2	1

Maximum summed intensity = 2.198

LINE	FREQ	INTEN
1	93.37	0.379
2	94.51	0.001
3	95.12	0.482
4	97.43	1.182
5	98.04	0.004
6	99.18	1.954
7	100.86	0.817
8	102.04	2.321
9	103.78	1.804
10	104.92	0.165
11	104.96	0.630
12	105.53	1.211
13	106.10	0.697
14	106.71	0.349
15	112.45	0.003

−11 −10 −9 −8 −7 −6 −5 −4 −3 −2 −1 0 +1 +2 +3 +4 +5 +6 +7 +8 +9 +10 +11

3C-77

J_{AB}	J_{AC}	J_{BC}
2	4	6

Maximum summed intensity = 2.996

LINE	FREQ	INTEN
1	89.96	0.010
2	93.39	0.433
3	96.18	0.636
4	96.48	0.807
5	96.54	0.001
6	99.27	1.957
7	99.63	0.251
8	102.66	2.920
9	102.71	0.164
10	103.06	2.566
11	105.75	0.976
12	105.86	1.175
13	109.18	0.030
14	111.97	0.068
15	112.33	0.007

−11 −10 −9 −8 −7 −6 −5 −4 −3 −2 −1 0 +1 +2 +3 +4 +5 +6 +7 +8 +9 +10 +11

3C-78

J_{AB}	J_{AC}	J_{BC}
2	6	4

Maximum summed intensity = 2.972

LINE	FREQ	INTEN
1	90.74	0.044
2	91.88	0.323
3	95.32	0.546
4	96.27	0.492
5	98.27	0.000
6	99.70	2.182
7	100.85	0.421
8	101.70	0.561
9	102.45	3.140
10	102.85	2.677
11	105.88	0.666
12	107.03	0.033
13	107.23	0.753
14	111.42	0.152
15	113.42	0.009

−11 −10 −9 −8 −7 −6 −5 −4 −3 −2 −1 0 +1 +2 +3 +4 +5 +6 +7 +8 +9 +10 +11

3C-79

J_{AB}	J_{AC}	J_{BC}
4	2	6

Maximum summed intensity = 2.843

LINE	FREQ	INTEN
1	90.18	0.002
2	93.16	0.303
3	95.53	0.554
4	96.58	0.255
5	96.85	0.951
6	99.22	1.966
7	100.27	0.067
8	102.20	0.225
9	102.53	2.886
10	103.25	2.442
11	105.62	1.236
12	106.21	1.015
13	109.20	0.079
14	111.57	0.020
15	112.62	0.000

3C-80

J_{AB}	J_{AC}	J_{BC}
4	6	2

Maximum summed intensity =3.230

LINE	FREQ	INTEN
1	90.80	0.259
2	92.05	0.071
3	95.37	0.286
4	95.49	0.543
5	98.80	0.422
6	99.38	0.098
7	100.06	2.430
8	102.12	3.285
9	102.82	2.642
10	104.08	0.680
11	105.56	0.133
12	106.82	0.275
13	107.39	0.567
14	110.13	0.295
15	114.14	0.013

3C-81

J_{AB}	J_{AC}	J_{BC}
6	2	4

Maximum summed intensity = 2.779

LINE	FREQ	INTEN
1	91.44	0.038
2	91.59	0.228
3	94.55	0.331
4	96.61	0.724
5	98.12	0.424
6	99.57	2.170
7	99.72	0.510
8	102.15	2.979
9	103.14	0.238
10	103.29	2.348
11	106.24	0.989
12	107.16	0.829
13	107.32	0.190
14	110.27	0.000
15	113.84	0.001

3C-82

J_{AB}	J_{AC}	J_{BC}
6	4	2

Maximum summed intensity = 2.962

LINE	FREQ	INTEN
1	90.68	0.229
2	93.28	0.009
3	93.52	0.272
4	97.13	1.074
5	97.37	0.022
6	99.24	0.368
7	99.97	2.403
8	101.94	3.122
9	103.09	2.403
10	105.69	0.146
11	105.79	0.272
12	105.93	1.074
13	108.39	0.368
14	108.64	0.229
15	114.35	0.009

3C-83

J_{AB}	J_{AC}	J_{BC}
1	1	-1

Maximum summed intensity = 1.980

LINE	FREQ	INTEN
1	94.70	0.000
2	95.93	0.743
3	96.90	0.992
4	96.96	0.942
5	97.92	1.320
6	99.16	0.004
7	101.94	0.694
8	102.91	0.415
9	102.93	1.621
10	103.90	1.273
11	104.14	1.626
12	105.13	0.636
13	105.17	1.264
14	106.16	0.470
15	111.15	0.000

−11 −10 −9 −8 −7 −6 −5 −4 −3 −2 −1 0 +1 +2 +3 +4 +5 +6 +7 +8 +9 +10 +11

3C-84

J_{AB}	J_{AC}	J_{BC}
1	-1	1

Maximum summed intensity = 1.875

LINE	FREQ	INTEN
1	94.64	0.036
2	96.09	0.729
3	96.91	0.914
4	96.94	1.010
5	97.76	1.171
6	99.21	0.142
7	101.98	0.906
8	102.83	0.153
9	102.96	1.416
10	103.80	1.631
11	104.28	1.760
12	105.10	1.180
13	105.26	0.360
14	106.08	0.593
15	111.15	0.000

−11 −10 −9 −8 −7 −6 −5 −4 −3 −2 −1 0 +1 +2 +3 +4 +5 +6 +7 +8 +9 +10 +11

3C-85

J_{AB}	J_{AC}	J_{BC}
-1	1	1

Maximum summed intensity = 1.902

LINE	FREQ	INTEN
1	94.66	0.024
2	96.02	0.717
3	96.92	1.010
4	96.94	0.938
5	97.84	1.233
6	99.19	0.080
7	101.97	0.826
8	102.86	0.209
9	102.95	1.496
10	103.85	1.525
11	104.22	1.782
12	105.14	1.184
13	105.20	0.412
14	106.12	0.567
15	111.15	0.000

3C-86

J_{AB}	J_{AC}	J_{BC}
1	1	-2

Maximum summed intensity = 2.848

LINE	FREQ	INTEN
1	94.10	0.000
2	95.93	0.743
3	96.88	0.977
4	96.98	0.954
5	97.92	1.322
6	99.75	0.003
7	101.16	0.379
8	102.10	0.209
9	103.15	1.924
10	103.93	1.943
11	104.09	1.492
12	104.98	1.469
13	105.92	0.333
14	106.96	0.251
15	111.15	0.000

3C-87

J_{AB}	J_{AC}	J_{BC}
1	-2	1

Maximum summed intensity = 2.062

LINE	FREQ	INTEN
1	94.37	0.089
2	95.63	0.584
3	96.35	0.865
4	97.31	0.987
5	98.03	1.101
6	99.29	0.374
7	102.01	1.029
8	102.73	0.028
9	102.97	1.311
10	103.69	1.916
11	104.00	1.959
12	104.96	0.218
13	105.68	0.984
14	106.63	0.554
15	111.34	0.001

-11 -10 -9 -8 -7 -6 -5 -4 -3 -2 -1 0 +1 +2 +3 +4 +5 +6 +7 +8 +9 +10 +11

3C-88

J_{AB}	J_{AC}	J_{BC}
-2	1	1

Maximum summed intensity = 3.217

LINE	FREQ	INTEN
1	94.58	0.087
2	95.49	0.522
3	96.32	0.763
4	97.29	1.128
5	98.12	1.193
6	99.03	0.307
7	101.60	0.973
8	102.57	1.655
9	103.40	0.011
10	104.31	1.861
11	104.37	1.581
12	105.14	1.154
13	105.28	0.182
14	106.11	0.582
15	111.39	0.000

-11 -10 -9 -8 -7 -6 -5 -4 -3 -2 -1 0 +1 +2 +3 +4 +5 +6 +7 +8 +9 +10 +11

3C-89

J_{AB}	J_{AC}	J_{BC}
1	1	-4

Maximum summed intensity = 2.090

LINE	FREQ	INTEN
1	92.46	0.000
2	95.93	0.744
3	96.87	0.962
4	96.99	0.959
5	97.92	1.329
6	99.34	0.157
7	100.28	0.058
8	101.40	0.006
9	103.33	2.139
10	103.75	2.171
11	104.26	1.651
12	104.81	1.613
13	107.74	0.117
14	108.79	0.093
15	111.15	0.000

3C-90

J_{AB}	J_{AC}	J_{BC}
1	-4	1

Maximum summed intensity = 2.578

LINE	FREQ	INTEN
1	93.40	0.196
2	94.61	0.307
3	95.01	0.620
4	97.94	1.097
5	98.34	0.734
6	99.55	1.048
7	102.06	1.227
8	102.47	0.089
9	102.99	1.173
10	103.39	2.361
11	103.67	2.006
12	104.60	0.019
13	107.00	0.676
14	107.93	0.445
15	112.05	0.003

3C-91

J_{AB}	J_{AC}	J_{BC}
-4	1	1

Maximum summed intensity = 2.104

LINE	FREQ	INTEN
1	93.69	0.326
2	94.88	0.491
3	94.93	0.074
4	97.79	0.213
5	97.83	1.306
6	99.03	1.590
7	101.06	1.202
8	102.01	1.907
9	103.97	0.793
10	104.91	1.361
11	105.16	1.104
12	105.20	0.901
13	106.11	0.602
14	106.15	0.129
15	112.28	0.001

-11 -10 -9 -8 -7 -6 -5 -4 -3 -2 -1 0 +1 +2 +3 +4 +5 +6 +7 +8 +9 +10 +11

3C-92

J_{AB}	J_{AC}	J_{BC}
1	1	-6

Maximum summed intensity = 2.389

LINE	FREQ	INTEN
1	90.60	0.000
2	95.93	0.744
3	96.86	0.955
4	96.97	0.835
5	97.44	0.221
6	97.90	1.342
7	98.37	0.004
8	103.23	0.126
9	103.40	2.200
10	103.70	2.119
11	104.33	1.698
12	104.73	1.653
13	109.66	0.056
14	110.70	0.043
15	111.17	0.003

-11 -10 -9 -8 -7 -6 -5 -4 -3 -2 -1 0 +1 +2 +3 +4 +5 +6 +7 +8 +9 +10 +11

3C-93

J_{AB}	J_{AC}	J_{BC}
1	-6	1

Maximum summed intensity = 3.274

LINE	FREQ	INTEN
1	92.05	0.217
2	93.41	0.152
3	93.49	0.442
4	98.39	1.158
5	98.47	0.424
6	99.83	1.611
7	102.10	1.373
8	102.17	0.371
9	102.99	1.099
10	103.07	2.547
11	103.54	1.784
12	104.44	0.011
13	108.52	0.468
14	109.41	0.338
15	113.12	0.004

3C-94

J_{AB}	J_{AC}	J_{BC}
-6	1	1

Maximum summed intensity = 1.954

LINE	FREQ	INTEN
1	92.13	0.250
2	93.25	0.319
3	94.85	0.016
4	96.59	0.045
5	98.18	1.413
6	99.31	1.959
7	100.71	1.349
8	101.64	2.067
9	104.05	1.168
10	104.98	1.124
11	105.17	1.063
12	106.10	0.615
13	106.77	0.419
14	107.70	0.194
15	113.56	0.001

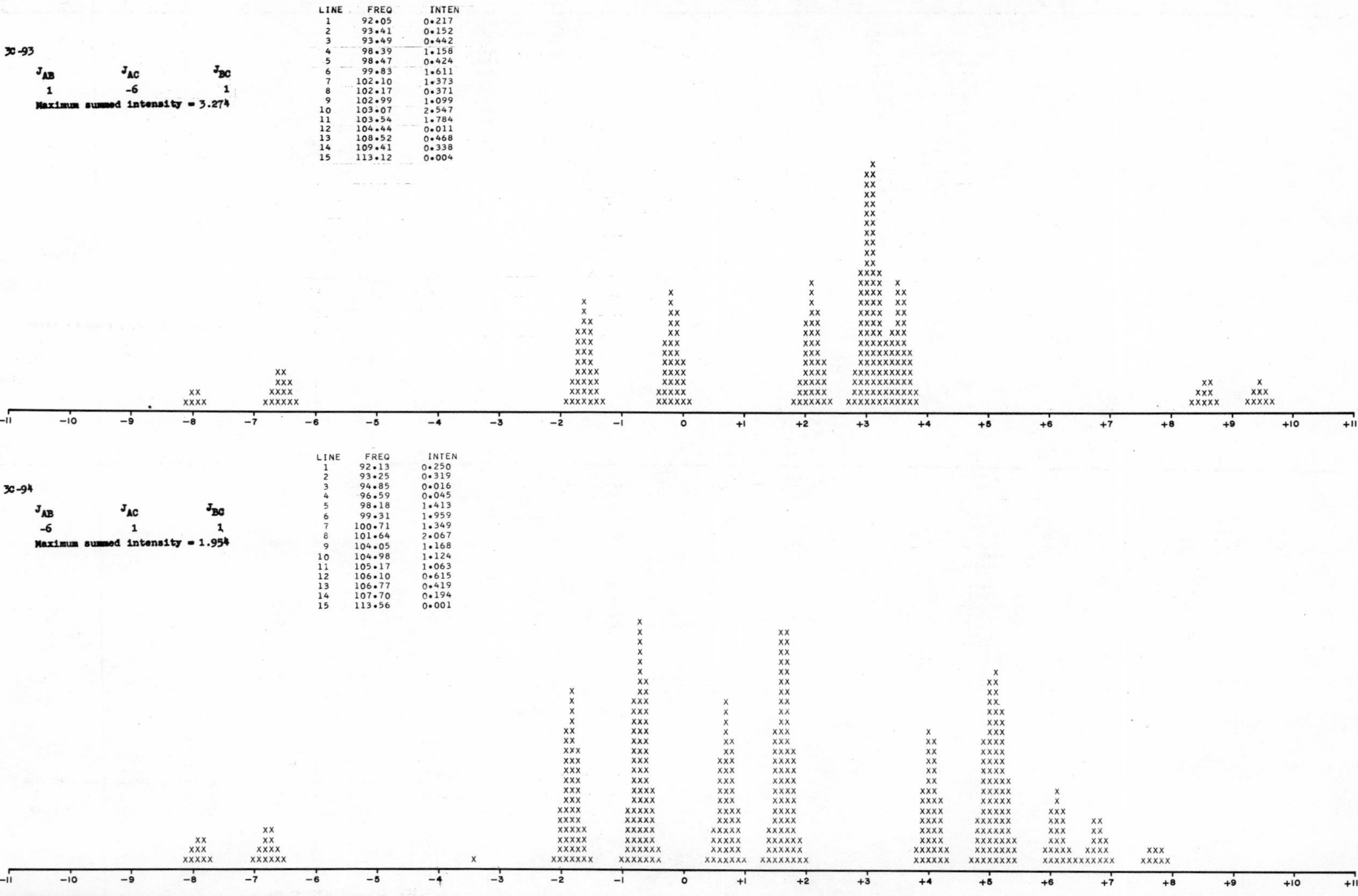

3C-95

J_{AB}	J_{AC}	J_{BC}
2	2	-2

Maximum summed intensity = 2.111

LINE	FREQ	INTEN
1	93.88	0.000
2	94.75	0.553
3	96.52	0.864
4	96.90	0.884
5	98.67	1.669
6	99.54	0.031
7	100.88	0.510
8	102.65	0.111
9	102.80	2.053
10	103.53	2.158
11	104.57	1.355
12	105.44	0.394
13	105.67	1.220
14	107.59	0.195
15	111.57	0.002

−11 −10 −9 −8 −7 −6 −5 −4 −3 −2 −1 0 +1 +2 +3 +4 +5 +6 +7 +8 +9 +10 +11

3C-96

J_{AB}	J_{AC}	J_{BC}
2	-2	2

Maximum summed intensity = 2.009

LINE	FREQ	INTEN
1	93.48	0.129
2	95.69	0.494
3	96.59	0.725
4	96.78	0.977
5	97.68	0.809
6	99.89	0.870
7	101.11	1.094
8	102.19	0.085
9	102.91	1.558
10	104.00	2.000
11	104.41	1.637
12	105.31	1.181
13	106.22	0.023
14	107.11	0.415
15	111.63	0.004

−11 −10 −9 −8 −7 −6 −5 −4 −3 −2 −1 0 +1 +2 +3 +4 +5 +6 +7 +8 +9 +10 +11

3C-97

J_{AB}	J_{AC}	J_{BC}
-2	2	2

Maximum summed intensity = 2.548

LINE	FREQ	INTEN
1	93.62	0.117
2	95.25	0.415
3	96.63	0.935
4	96.77	0.852
5	98.15	1.061
6	99.77	0.620
7	101.00	0.828
8	102.37	0.065
9	102.85	1.789
10	104.00	2.000
11	104.23	1.822
12	105.52	1.107
13	105.86	0.029
14	107.38	0.359
15	111.60	0.000

3C-98

J_{AB}	J_{AC}	J_{BC}
2	2	-4

Maximum summed intensity = 2.476

LINE	FREQ	INTEN
1	92.23	0.000
2	94.76	0.553
3	96.47	0.832
4	96.94	0.896
5	98.66	1.678
6	99.09	0.236
7	100.81	0.014
8	101.19	0.043
9	103.00	2.314
10	103.34	2.439
11	104.72	1.476
12	105.53	1.309
13	107.24	0.132
14	109.43	0.074
15	111.58	0.003

3c-99

J_{AB}	J_{AC}	J_{BC}
2	-4	2

Maximum summed intensity = 2.239

LINE	FREQ	INTEN
1	92.43	0.178
2	94.89	0.299
3	95.47	0.694
4	97.15	0.743
5	97.72	0.508
6	100.19	1.588
7	101.28	1.457
8	101.85	0.314
9	102.96	1.323
10	103.53	2.306
11	104.32	1.419
12	106.00	0.000
13	106.57	0.800
14	108.25	0.361
15	112.38	0.010

−11 −10 −9 −8 −7 −6 −5 −4 −3 −2 −1 0 +1 +2 +3 +4 +5 +6 +7 +8 +9 +10 +11

3c-100

J_{AB}	J_{AC}	J_{BC}
-4	2	2

Maximum summed intensity = 2.412

LINE	FREQ	INTEN
1	92.76	0.226
2	94.64	0.122
3	95.36	0.543
4	97.13	1.044
5	97.85	0.428
6	99.72	1.639
7	100.51	1.030
8	102.28	2.079
9	103.00	0.818
10	104.77	1.483
11	104.87	1.138
12	105.59	1.013
13	106.64	0.058
14	107.36	0.377
15	112.52	0.002

−11 −10 −9 −8 −7 −6 −5 −4 −3 −2 −1 0 +1 +2 +3 +4 +5 +6 +7 +8 +9 +10 +11

3c-101

J_{AB}	J_{AC}	J_{BC}
2	2	-6

Maximum summed intensity = 2.812

LINE	FREQ	INTEN
1	90.37	0.000
2	94.76	0.554
3	96.46	0.819
4	96.83	0.451
5	97.30	0.610
6	98.54	1.333
7	99.00	0.333
8	102.92	0.860
9	103.08	2.385
10	103.39	1.706
11	104.78	1.514
12	105.46	1.333
13	109.17	0.061
14	111.24	0.022
15	111.71	0.018

-11 -10 -9 -8 -7 -6 -5 -4 -3 -2 -1 0 +1 +2 +3 +4 +5 +6 +7 +8 +9 +10 +11

3c-102

J_{AB}	J_{AC}	J_{BC}
2	-6	2

Maximum summed intensity = 3.047

LINE	FREQ	INTEN
1	91.06	0.174
2	93.79	0.179
3	93.96	0.488
4	97.53	0.729
5	97.71	0.310
6	100.44	2.136
7	101.41	1.730
8	101.58	0.526
9	102.98	1.188
10	103.15	2.502
11	104.31	1.188
12	105.88	0.009
13	108.06	0.541
14	109.63	0.285
15	113.50	0.015

-11 -10 -9 -8 -7 -6 -5 -4 -3 -2 -1 0 +1 +2 +3 +4 +5 +6 +7 +8 +9 +10 +11

3C-103

J_{AB}	J_{AC}	J_{BC}
-6	2	2

Maximum summed intensity = 2.256

LINE	FREQ	INTEN
1	91.31	0.199
2	93.73	0.349
3	94.43	0.032
4	96.75	0.131
5	97.45	1.100
6	99.87	2.192
7	100.20	1.158
8	101.91	2.262
9	103.22	1.357
10	104.93	1.213
11	105.64	0.938
12	106.34	0.543
13	107.36	0.389
14	108.05	0.133
15	113.82	0.003

-11 -10 -9 -8 -7 -6 -5 -4 -3 -2 -1 0 +1 +2 +3 +4 +5 +6 +7 +8 +9 +10 +11

3C-104

J_{AB}	J_{AC}	J_{BC}
4	4	-4

Maximum summed intensity = 3.243

LINE	FREQ	INTEN
1	91.30	0.000
2	92.18	0.321
3	95.02	0.502
4	96.81	0.763
5	99.08	0.420
6	99.65	2.211
7	100.53	0.216
8	101.92	0.016
9	102.55	2.497
10	102.80	2.779
11	105.39	1.271
12	106.27	0.182
13	107.43	0.773
14	110.90	0.037
15	113.17	0.012

-11 -10 -9 -8 -7 -6 -5 -4 -3 -2 -1 0 +1 +2 +3 +4 +5 +6 +7 +8 +9 +10 +11

3c-105

J_{AB}	J_{AC}	J_{BC}
4	-4	4

Maximum summed intensity = 2.519

LINE	FREQ	INTEN
1	90.29	0.115
2	95.00	0.286
3	95.36	0.353
4	95.95	0.270
5	96.31	0.860
6	100.17	1.660
7	101.01	2.141
8	101.12	0.618
9	102.86	1.587
10	103.81	2.138
11	105.83	1.054
12	106.19	0.644
13	108.52	0.249
14	108.88	0.002
15	113.69	0.024

3c-106

J_{AB}	J_{AC}	J_{BC}
-4	4	4

Maximum summed intensity = 2.470

LINE	FREQ	INTEN
1	90.60	0.120
2	93.49	0.115
3	95.27	0.588
4	96.24	0.674
5	98.02	0.730
6	99.64	0.944
7	100.91	1.777
8	101.42	0.905
9	102.67	2.147
10	104.31	1.507
11	104.44	1.657
12	107.07	0.640
13	107.33	0.013
14	110.09	0.179
15	113.49	0.004

3C-107

J_{AB}	J_{AC}	J_{BC}
4	4	-6

Maximum summed intensity = 2.543

LINE	FREQ	INTEN
1	89.44	0.000
2	92.18	0.321
3	94.97	0.487
4	96.60	0.319
5	97.43	0.758
6	99.39	1.484
7	100.22	0.739
8	102.14	1.415
9	102.64	2.601
10	102.97	1.700
11	105.43	1.290
12	107.39	0.777
13	108.18	0.078
14	112.60	0.005
15	113.43	0.026

-11 -10 -9 -8 -7 -6 -5 -4 -3 -2 -1 0 +1 +2 +3 +4 +5 +6 +7 +8 +9 +10 +11

3C-108

J_{AB}	J_{AC}	J_{BC}
4	-6	4

Maximum summed intensity = 3.095

LINE	FREQ	INTEN
1	88.99	0.115
2	94.45	0.236
3	94.86	0.596
4	95.24	0.254
5	95.65	0.150
6	100.55	2.042
7	100.96	0.742
8	101.11	2.681
9	102.93	1.353
10	103.34	2.397
11	106.43	0.480
12	107.21	0.704
13	108.80	0.007
14	109.59	0.212
15	114.90	0.032

-11 -10 -9 -8 -7 -6 -5 -4 -3 -2 -1 0 +1 +2 +3 +4 +5 +6 +7 +8 +9 +10 +11

3C-109

J_{AB}	J_{AC}	J_{BC}
-6	4	4

Maximum summed intensity = 2.501

LINE	FREQ	INTEN
1	89.37	0.124
2	92.97	0.033
3	94.67	0.423
4	95.49	0.585
5	97.19	0.332
6	99.43	1.028
7	100.79	2.509
8	101.96	1.606
9	102.25	2.391
10	104.78	1.353
11	105.55	0.809
12	107.26	0.550
13	108.37	0.063
14	110.08	0.185
15	114.84	0.007

3C-110

J_{AB}	J_{AC}	J_{BC}
1	2	-1

Maximum summed intensity = 2.666

LINE	FREQ	INTEN
1	94.52	0.002
2	95.35	0.651
3	96.32	0.846
4	97.35	1.037
5	98.32	1.463
6	99.15	0.001
7	101.95	0.603
8	102.92	0.490
9	102.92	1.707
10	103.75	1.860
11	103.89	1.198
12	104.73	0.642
13	105.76	1.047
14	106.73	0.452
15	111.33	0.000

3C-111

J_{AB}	J_{AC}	J_{BC}
2	1	-1

Maximum summed intensity = 1.789

LINE	FREQ	INTEN
1	94.65	0.012
2	95.33	0.621
3	96.42	0.754
4	97.19	1.043
5	98.28	1.497
6	98.96	0.074
7	101.61	0.940
8	102.57	1.673
9	103.47	0.178
10	104.15	1.556
11	104.43	1.270
12	105.11	0.707
13	105.24	1.326
14	106.20	0.350
15	111.39	0.001

−11 −10 −9 −8 −7 −6 −5 −4 −3 −2 −1 0 +1 +2 +3 +4 +5 +6 +7 +8 +9 +10 +11

3C-112

J_{AB}	J_{AC}	J_{BC}
2	2	-1

Maximum summed intensity =1.673

LINE	FREQ	INTEN
1	94.48	0.003
2	94.75	0.552
3	96.60	0.896
4	96.83	0.844
5	98.67	1.666
6	98.94	0.040
7	101.65	0.916
8	102.57	1.685
9	103.49	0.245
10	103.76	1.748
11	104.41	1.189
12	104.68	0.763
13	105.84	1.089
14	106.76	0.361
15	111.57	0.002

−11 −10 −9 −8 −7 −6 −5 −4 −3 −2 −1 0 +1 +2 +3 +4 +5 +6 +7 +8 +9 +10 +11

3C-113

J_{AB}	J_{AC}	J_{BC}
1	4	-1

Maximum summed intensity = 2.919

LINE	FREQ	INTEN
1	93.81	0.024
2	94.04	0.490
3	94.98	0.577
4	97.99	1.167
5	98.94	1.694
6	99.16	0.049
7	101.99	0.364
8	102.90	1.955
9	102.94	0.597
10	103.17	2.329
11	103.84	1.108
12	104.07	0.556
13	107.12	0.708
14	108.02	0.381
15	112.03	0.001

−11 −10 −9 −8 −7 −6 −5 −4 −3 −2 −1 0 +1 +2 +3 +4 +5 +6 +7 +8 +9 +10 +11

3C-114

J_{AB}	J_{AC}	J_{BC}
4	1	-1

Maximum summed intensity = 1.830

LINE	FREQ	INTEN
1	93.94	0.423
2	94.17	0.166
3	95.46	0.317
4	97.26	0.588
5	98.55	0.765
6	98.78	1.742
7	101.14	1.307
8	101.99	1.786
9	104.23	1.433
10	104.47	0.092
11	105.08	0.791
12	105.31	1.413
13	105.75	1.167
14	106.60	0.009
15	112.28	0.001

−11 −10 −9 −8 −7 −6 −5 −4 −3 −2 −1 0 +1 +2 +3 +4 +5 +6 +7 +8 +9 +10 +11

3C-115

J_{AB}	J_{AC}	J_{BC}
4	4	-1

Maximum summed intensity = 2.236

LINE	FREQ	INTEN
1	92.18	0.320
2	93.53	0.033
3	95.46	0.546
4	96.41	0.559
5	98.34	0.313
6	99.69	2.239
7	101.43	1.591
8	101.95	1.497
9	103.36	1.639
10	103.88	1.183
11	104.71	0.032
12	105.22	1.150
13	107.60	0.729
14	108.11	0.160
15	113.13	0.009

3C-116

J_{AB}	J_{AC}	J_{BC}
1	4	-2

Maximum summed intensity = 4.455

LINE	FREQ	INTEN
1	93.20	0.045
2	94.05	0.490
3	95.16	0.555
4	97.81	1.088
5	98.92	1.657
6	99.77	0.167
7	101.12	0.063
8	102.23	0.522
9	103.00	2.314
10	103.08	2.593
11	104.11	1.222
12	104.95	0.196
13	106.84	0.821
14	108.72	0.268
15	112.03	0.000

3C-117

J_{AB}	J_{AC}	J_{BC}
4	1	-2

Maximum summed intensity = 2.050

LINE	FREQ	INTEN
1	93.48	0.090
2	93.95	0.429
3	95.72	0.415
4	96.97	0.667
5	98.74	1.710
6	99.21	0.690
7	100.50	0.992
8	102.28	2.074
9	103.51	0.115
10	103.98	1.716
11	105.30	1.418
12	105.75	1.175
13	105.77	0.497
14	107.53	0.010
15	112.31	0.002

3C-118

J_{AB}	J_{AC}	J_{BC}
4	4	-2

Maximum summed intensity = 2.231

LINE	FREQ	INTEN
1	92.18	0.320
2	92.95	0.007
3	95.21	0.531
4	96.66	0.695
5	98.92	0.218
6	99.68	2.238
7	100.77	0.913
8	102.28	2.065
9	103.03	2.315
10	103.80	0.006
11	104.54	0.615
12	105.31	1.218
13	107.51	0.756
14	109.02	0.092
15	113.14	0.010

3C-119

J_{AB}	J_{AC}	J_{BC}
2	4	-1

Maximum summed intensity = 2.018

LINE	FREQ	INTEN
1	93.47	0.428
2	93.81	0.000
3	95.21	0.627
4	97.53	0.998
5	98.93	0.011
6	99.27	1.939
7	101.76	0.854
8	102.57	1.719
9	103.16	2.081
10	103.51	0.336
11	103.97	0.853
12	104.31	1.098
13	107.22	0.725
14	108.02	0.327
15	112.26	0.004

−11 −10 −9 −8 −7 −6 −5 −4 −3 −2 −1 0 +1 +2 +3 +4 +5 +6 +7 +8 +9 +10 +11

3C-120

J_{AB}	J_{AC}	J_{BC}
4	2	-1

Maximum summed intensity = 1.805

LINE	FREQ	INTEN
1	93.39	0.388
2	94.11	0.091
3	95.78	0.434
4	96.76	0.656
5	98.43	0.499
6	99.15	1.936
7	101.22	1.379
8	101.98	1.708
9	103.87	1.553
10	104.59	0.004
11	104.63	0.904
12	105.35	1.313
13	106.26	1.059
14	107.01	0.072
15	112.46	0.004

−11 −10 −9 −8 −7 −6 −5 −4 −3 −2 −1 0 +1 +2 +3 +4 +5 +6 +7 +8 +9 +10 +11

3C-121

J_{AB}	J_{AC}	J_{BC}
2	4	-2

Maximum summed intensity = 3.617

LINE	FREQ	INTEN
1	93.23	0.012
2	93.47	0.427
3	95.24	0.598
4	97.50	1.031
5	99.27	1.931
6	99.51	0.005
7	100.96	0.298
8	102.73	0.251
9	102.76	2.232
10	102.97	2.629
11	104.53	1.208
12	104.77	0.341
13	107.00	0.818
14	108.80	0.216
15	112.26	0.003

-11 -10 -9 -8 -7 -6 -5 -4 -3 -2 -1 0 +1 +2 +3 +4 +5 +6 +7 +8 +9 +10 +11

3C-122

J_{AB}	J_{AC}	J_{BC}
4	2	-2

Maximum summed intensity = 2.361

LINE	FREQ	INTEN
1	93.40	0.391
2	93.44	0.048
3	96.05	0.522
4	96.47	0.657
5	99.08	0.469
6	99.12	1.917
7	100.56	0.968
8	102.28	2.071
9	103.60	1.946
10	103.64	0.028
11	105.32	0.538
12	105.35	1.350
13	106.25	1.055
14	107.96	0.037
15	112.48	0.004

-11 -10 -9 -8 -7 -6 -5 -4 -3 -2 -1 0 +1 +2 +3 +4 +5 +6 +7 +8 +9 +10 +11

3D-1

J_{AB}	J_{AC}	J_{BC}
1	1	1

Maximum summed intensity = 2.090

LINE	FREQ	INTEN
1	92.83	0.000
2	95.94	0.760
3	96.92	0.907
4	96.95	1.044
5	97.93	1.288
6	101.04	0.000
7	101.97	0.863
8	102.98	1.470
9	102.98	0.649
10	103.99	1.019
11	106.09	1.377
12	107.07	1.112
13	107.10	0.818
14	108.08	0.693
15	113.13	0.000

−11 −10 −9 −8 −7 −6 −5 −4 −3 −2 −1 0 +1 +2 +3 +4 +5 +6 +7 +8 +9 +10 +11

3D-2

J_{AB}	J_{AC}	J_{BC}
2	2	2

Maximum summed intensity = 2.375

LINE	FREQ	INTEN
1	92.33	0.001
2	94.77	0.576
3	96.62	0.766
4	96.86	1.057
5	98.71	1.597
6	100.85	0.669
7	101.15	0.004
8	102.91	1.988
9	102.94	0.419
10	105.00	0.926
11	105.38	1.756
12	107.23	1.156
13	107.44	0.608
14	109.29	0.477
15	113.52	0.001

−11 −10 −9 −8 −7 −6 −5 −4 −3 −2 −1 0 +1 +2 +3 +4 +5 +6 +7 +8 +9 +10 +11

3D-3

J_{AB}	J_{AC}	J_{BC}
3	3	3

Maximum summed intensity = 2.627

LINE	FREQ	INTEN
1	91.57	0.004
2	93.52	0.440
3	96.09	0.605
4	96.77	1.054
5	99.34	1.890
6	99.64	0.488
7	101.29	0.011
8	102.83	2.463
9	102.89	0.277
10	104.84	2.072
11	106.07	0.775
12	107.40	1.160
13	108.02	0.424
14	110.59	0.335
15	114.14	0.003

−11 −10 −9 −8 −7 −6 −5 −4 −3 −2 −1 0 +1 +2 +3 +4 +5 +6 +7 +8 +9 +10 +11

3D-4

J_{AB}	J_{AC}	J_{BC}
4	4	4

Maximum summed intensity = 2.285

LINE	FREQ	INTEN
1	90.62	0.007
2	92.22	0.341
3	95.34	0.457
4	96.70	1.046
5	98.35	0.352
6	99.83	2.138
7	101.43	0.017
8	102.74	2.843
9	102.84	0.190
10	104.44	2.307
11	107.23	0.620
12	107.56	1.145
13	108.82	0.289
14	111.95	0.242
15	114.96	0.006

−11 −10 −9 −8 −7 −6 −5 −4 −3 −2 −1 0 +1 +2 +3 +4 +5 +6 +7 +8 +9 +10 +11

3D-5

J_{AB}	J_{AC}	J_{BC}
6	6	6

Maximum summed intensity = 3.379

LINE	FREQ	INTEN
1	88.33	0.009
2	89.49	0.216
3	93.36	0.253
4	95.61	0.192
5	96.62	1.030
6	100.50	2.480
7	101.65	0.022
8	102.60	3.329
9	102.75	0.100
10	103.90	2.592
11	107.78	1.105
12	109.73	0.380
13	110.89	0.140
14	114.76	0.139
15	117.01	0.011

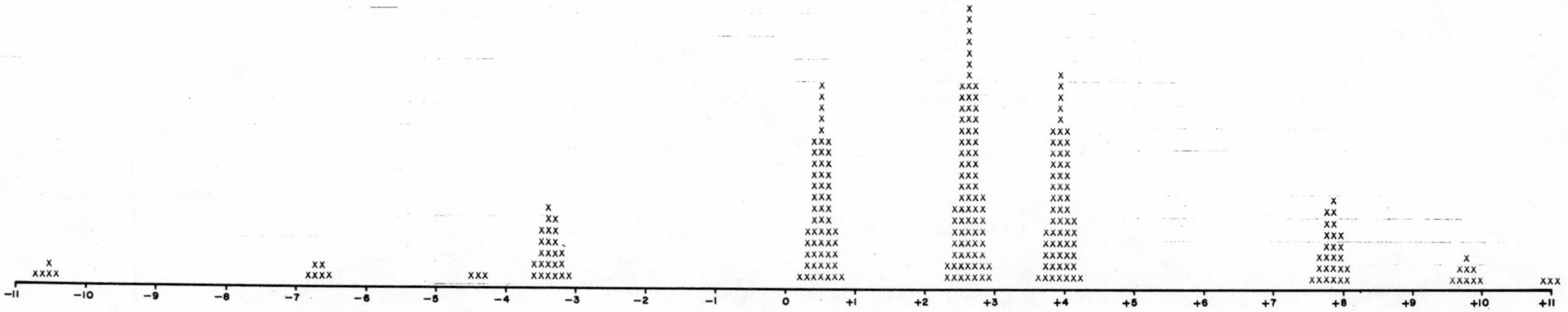

−11 −10 −9 −8 −7 −6 −5 −4 −3 −2 −1 0 +1 +2 +3 +4 +5 +6 +7 +8 +9 +10 +11

3D-6

J_{AB}	J_{AC}	J_{BC}
8	8	8

Maximum summed intensity = 3.593

LINE	FREQ	INTEN
1	85.77	0.009
2	86.66	0.146
3	91.00	0.147
4	92.76	0.116
5	96.59	1.020
6	100.92	2.671
7	101.81	0.020
8	102.51	3.582
9	102.68	0.059
10	103.57	2.738
11	107.90	1.074
12	112.43	0.241
13	113.32	0.076
14	117.65	0.088
15	119.42	0.013

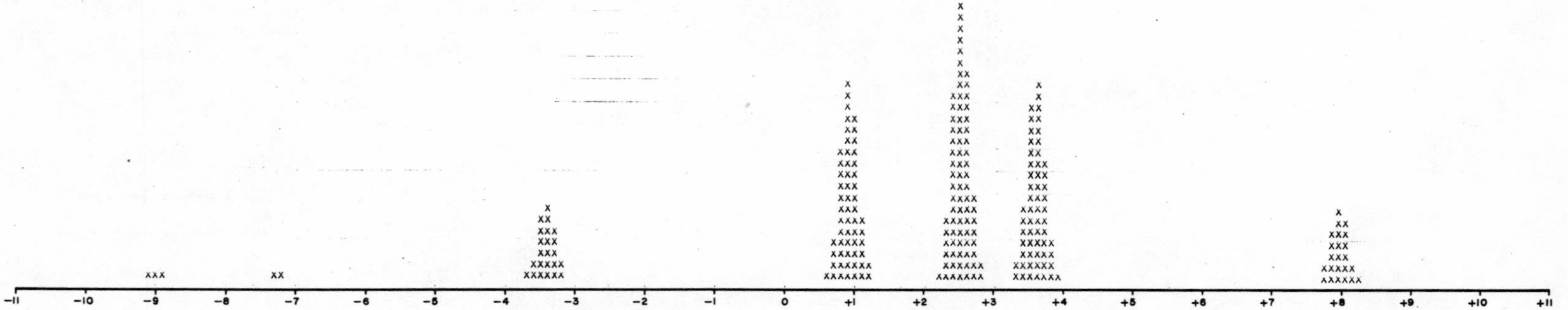

−11 −10 −9 −8 −7 −6 −5 −4 −3 −2 −1 0 +1 +2 +3 +4 +5 +6 +7 +8 +9 +10 +11

3D-7

J_{AB}	J_{AC}	J_{BC}
10	10	10

Maximum summed intensity = 3.537

LINE	FREQ	INTEN
1	83.06	0.008
2	83.79	0.104
3	88.41	0.091
4	89.86	0.076
5	96.56	1.014
6	101.19	2.778
7	101.91	0.017
8	102.46	3.720
9	102.63	0.039
10	103.36	2.819
11	107.98	1.053
12	115.23	0.161
13	115.96	0.046
14	120.58	0.061
15	122.03	0.012

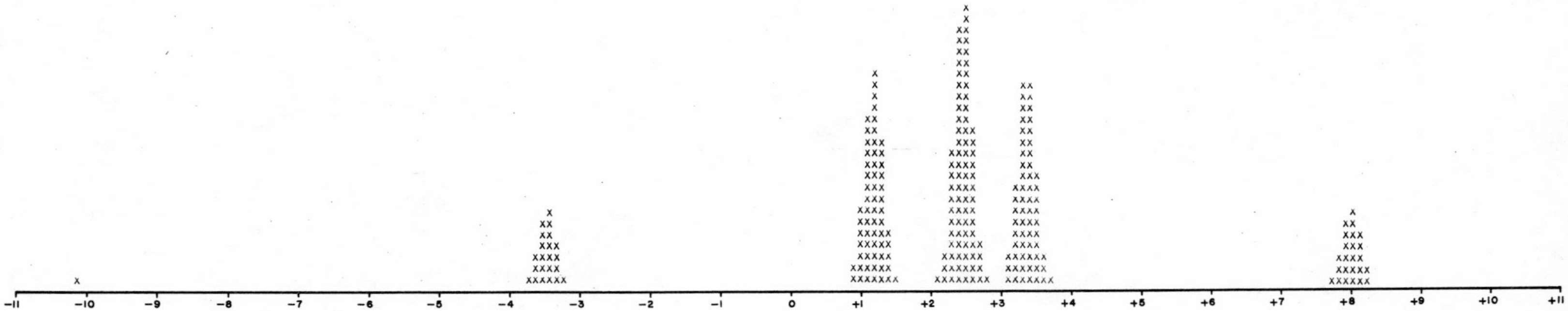

3D-8

J_{AB}	J_{AC}	J_{BC}
12	12	12

Maximum summed intensity = 3.744

LINE	FREQ	INTEN
1	80.27	0.007
2	80.88	0.078
3	85.70	0.061
4	86.92	0.054
5	96.55	1.010
6	101.37	2.842
7	101.98	0.014
8	102.42	3.801
9	102.59	0.027
10	103.20	2.869
11	108.02	1.040
12	118.10	0.114
13	118.71	0.030
14	123.53	0.044
15	124.75	0.011

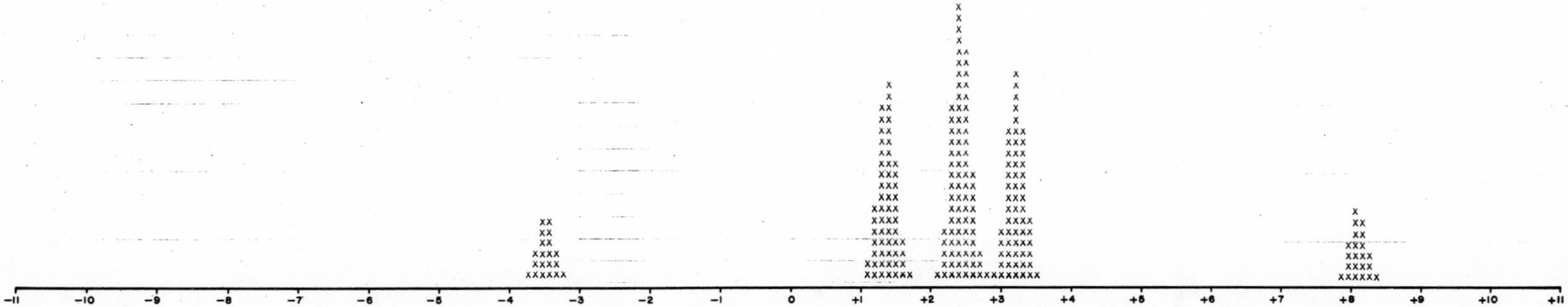

3D-9

J_{AB}	J_{AC}	J_{BC}
15	15	15

Maximum summed intensity = 3.874

LINE	FREQ	INTEN
1	75.98	0.005
2	76.47	0.053
3	81.50	0.037
4	82.48	0.034
5	96.54	1.007
6	101.56	2.897
7	102.06	0.010
8	102.39	3.870
9	102.55	0.017
10	103.04	2.912
11	108.06	1.027
12	122.46	0.073
13	122.95	0.018
14	127.97	0.029
15	128.96	0.009

3D-10

J_{AB}	J_{AC}	J_{BC}
18	18	18

Maximum summed intensity = 3.851

LINE	FREQ	INTEN
1	71.63	0.004
2	72.04	0.039
3	77.20	0.024
4	78.03	0.024
5	96.54	1.005
6	101.69	2.928
7	102.10	0.008
8	102.38	3.909
9	102.52	0.012
10	102.93	2.937
11	108.09	1.019
12	126.87	0.051
13	127.28	0.012
14	132.44	0.021
15	133.26	0.008

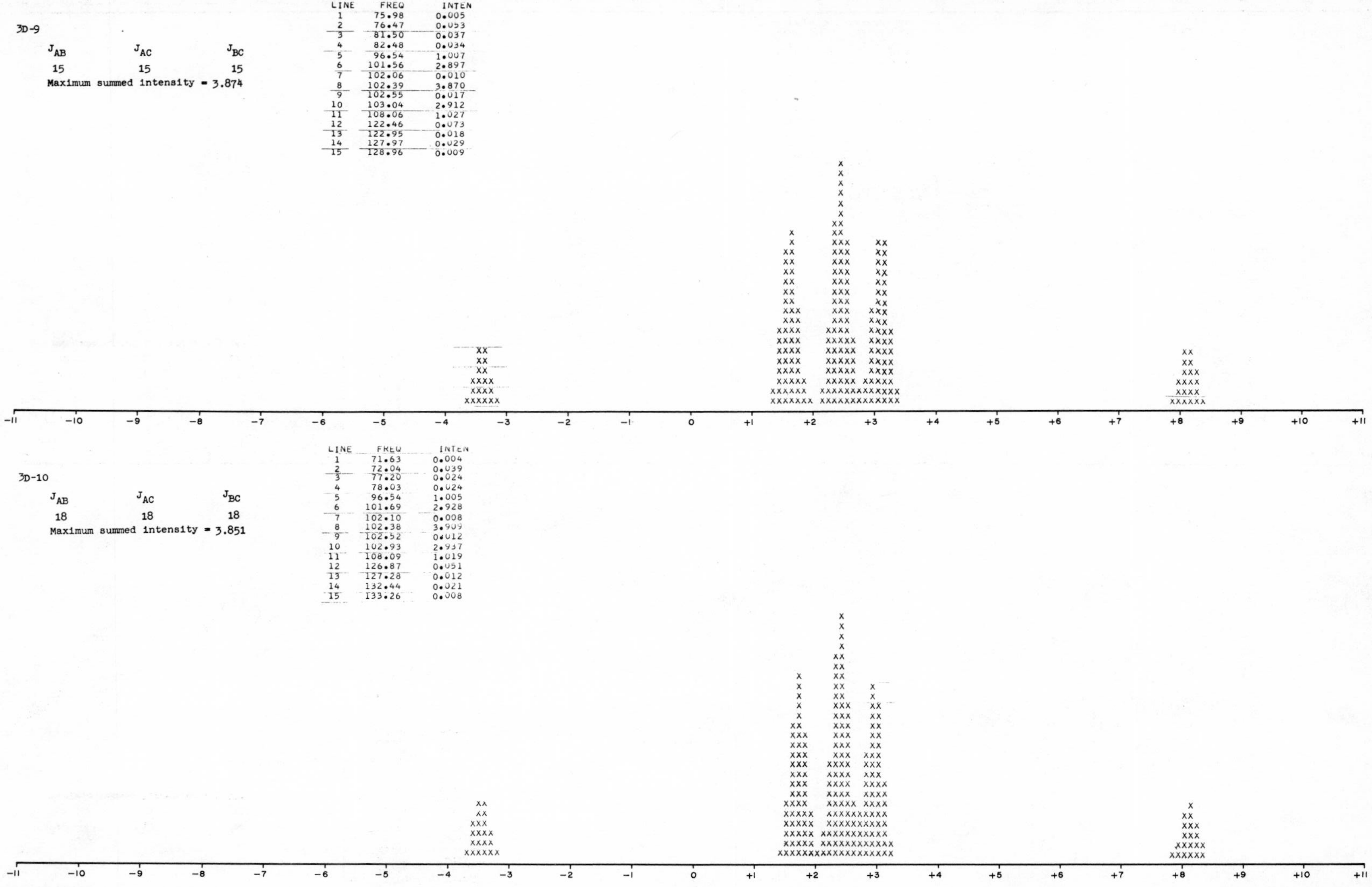

3D-11

J_{AB}	J_{AC}	J_{BC}
1	1	2

Maximum summed intensity = 1.840

LINE	FREQ	INTEN
1	92.48	0.000
2	95.94	0.758
3	96.91	0.909
4	96.96	1.047
5	97.93	1.286
6	101.29	0.639
7	101.39	0.000
8	102.31	0.462
9	103.30	1.694
10	104.32	1.204
11	105.77	1.603
12	106.74	1.295
13	107.78	0.592
14	108.75	0.510
15	113.13	0.000

3D-12

J_{AB}	J_{AC}	J_{BC}
1	2	1

Maximum summed intensity = 2.236

LINE	FREQ	INTEN
1	92.68	0.002
2	95.37	0.690
3	96.41	0.926
4	97.31	0.959
5	98.35	1.414
6	101.04	0.010
7	101.95	0.784
8	102.97	1.565
9	102.99	0.714
10	104.01	0.944
11	105.68	1.526
12	106.70	0.849
13	107.62	0.975
14	108.64	0.642
15	113.28	0.000

3D-13

J_{AB}	J_{AC}	J_{BC}
2	1	1

Maximum summed intensity = 1.909

LINE	FREQ	INTEN
1	92.83	0.000
2	95.32	0.626
3	96.30	0.738
4	97.33	1.177
5	98.30	1.458
6	100.80	0.000
7	101.59	1.005
8	102.61	1.631
9	103.59	0.503
10	104.61	0.861
11	106.09	1.368
12	107.07	1.123
13	107.11	0.828
14	108.08	0.681
15	113.37	0.000

−11 −10 −9 −8 −7 −6 −5 −4 −3 −2 −1 0 +1 +2 +3 +4 +5 +6 +7 +8 +9 +10 +11

3D-14

J_{AB}	J_{AC}	J_{BC}
1	2	2

Maximum summed intensity = 1.760

LINE	FREQ	INTEN
1	92.33	0.003
2	95.37	0.691
3	96.47	0.933
4	97.24	0.945
5	98.35	1.414
6	101.24	0.539
7	101.39	0.014
8	102.35	0.554
9	103.27	1.821
10	104.37	1.096
11	105.39	1.769
12	107.26	1.137
13	107.41	0.593
14	109.28	0.490
15	113.28	0.000

−11 −10 −9 −8 −7 −6 −5 −4 −3 −2 −1 0 +1 +2 +3 +4 +5 +6 +7 +8 +9 +10 +11

3D-15

J_{AB}	J_{AC}	J_{BC}
2	2	1

Maximum summed intensity = 1.741

LINE	FREQ	INTEN
1	92.68	0.001
2	94.77	0.579
3	96.67	0.766
4	96.81	1.045
5	98.71	1.600
6	100.80	0.009
7	101.55	0.902
8	102.61	1.751
9	103.59	0.596
10	104.65	0.758
11	105.68	1.519
12	106.74	0.848
13	107.58	0.982
14	108.64	0.642
15	113.52	0.001

3D-16

J_{AB}	J_{AC}	J_{BC}
2	1	2

Maximum summed intensity = 2.094

LINE	FREQ	INTEN
1	92.47	0.000
2	95.31	0.617
3	96.32	0.749
4	97.30	1.172
5	98.31	1.455
6	100.93	0.792
7	101.15	0.007
8	102.92	0.310
9	102.93	1.841
10	104.92	1.063
11	105.76	1.590
12	106.77	1.307
13	107.77	0.614
14	108.77	0.482
15	113.38	0.000

3D-17

J_{AB}	J_{AC}	J_{BC}
1	1	4

Maximum summed intensity = 1.972

LINE	FREQ	INTEN
1	91.29	0.000
2	95.93	0.749
3	96.89	0.917
4	96.97	1.050
5	97.93	1.283
6	99.69	0.361
7	100.73	0.223
8	102.57	0.001
9	103.70	1.973
10	104.73	1.444
11	105.37	1.890
12	106.33	1.526
13	109.38	0.310
14	110.33	0.273
15	113.13	0.000

3D-18

J_{AB}	J_{AC}	J_{BC}
1	4	1

Maximum summed intensity = 2.486

LINE	FREQ	INTEN
1	92.09	0.007
2	94.09	0.555
3	95.18	0.707
4	97.96	1.026
5	99.05	1.649
6	101.05	0.058
7	101.91	0.631
8	102.95	1.782
9	102.99	0.815
10	104.04	0.821
11	105.00	1.815
12	106.05	0.865
13	108.86	0.737
14	109.91	0.530
15	113.86	0.002

3D-19

J_{AB}	J_{AC}	J_{BC}
4	1	1

Maximum summed intensity = 1.953

LINE	FREQ	INTEN
1	92.81	0.001
2	93.89	0.413
3	94.86	0.474
4	97.87	1.375
5	98.85	1.727
6	99.92	0.011
7	101.03	1.231
8	102.06	1.881
9	105.02	0.250
10	106.05	0.647
11	106.09	1.357
12	107.06	1.163
13	107.12	0.845
14	108.10	0.626
15	114.26	0.000

−11 −10 −9 −8 −7 −6 −5 −4 −3 −2 −1 0 +1 +2 +3 +4 +5 +6 +7 +8 +9 +10 +11

3D-20

J_{AB}	J_{AC}	J_{BC}
1	4	4

Maximum summed intensity = 2.310

LINE	FREQ	INTEN
1	90.59	0.017
2	94.05	0.565
3	95.66	0.719
4	97.44	0.887
5	99.05	1.669
6	99.44	0.122
7	101.05	0.536
8	102.51	0.148
9	103.44	2.410
10	104.51	2.313
11	105.05	1.059
12	107.90	1.024
13	108.51	0.255
14	111.90	0.272
15	113.90	0.004

−11 −10 −9 −8 −7 −6 −5 −4 −3 −2 −1 0 +1 +2 +3 +4 +5 +6 +7 +8 +9 +10 +11

3D-21

J_{AB}	J_{AC}	J_{BC}
4	4	1

Maximum summed intensity = 2.343

LINE	FREQ	INTEN
1	92.05	0.013
2	92.23	0.350
3	95.75	0.456
4	96.28	0.921
5	99.81	2.145
6	99.98	0.124
7	100.77	0.835
8	102.19	2.346
9	104.82	0.626
10	105.00	1.815
11	106.25	0.296
12	106.42	0.790
13	108.53	0.715
14	109.95	0.560
15	114.97	0.008

−11 −10 −9 −8 −7 −6 −5 −4 −3 −2 −1 0 +1 +2 +3 +4 +5 +6 +7 +8 +9 +10 +11

3D-22

J_{AB}	J_{AC}	J_{BC}
4	1	4

Maximum summed intensity = 2.303

LINE	FREQ	INTEN
1	91.10	0.007
2	93.73	0.351
3	95.28	0.533
4	97.36	1.163
5	98.91	1.732
6	99.00	0.758
7	101.54	0.214
8	102.63	0.000
9	102.83	2.351
10	105.27	1.891
11	106.46	1.098
12	106.81	1.351
13	109.09	0.381
14	110.64	0.169
15	114.36	0.001

−11 −10 −9 −8 −7 −6 −5 −4 −3 −2 −1 0 +1 +2 +3 +4 +5 +6 +7 +8 +9 +10 +11

3D-23

J_{AB}	J_{AC}	J_{BC}
1	1	6

Maximum summed intensity = 2.699

LINE	FREQ	INTEN
1	89.74	0.000
2	95.93	0.723
3	96.88	0.924
4	96.98	1.063
5	97.92	0.247
6	97.93	1.281
7	98.96	0.094
8	103.91	2.105
9	104.12	0.008
10	104.96	1.561
11	105.16	2.029
12	106.11	1.629
13	111.15	0.176
14	112.11	0.158
15	113.14	0.000

3D-24

J_{AB}	J_{AC}	J_{BC}
1	6	1

Maximum summed intensity = 2.640

LINE	FREQ	INTEN
1	91.17	0.015
2	92.66	0.437
3	93.79	0.528
4	98.45	1.039
5	99.58	1.850
6	101.07	0.134
7	101.86	0.487
8	102.93	2.022
9	103.00	0.881
10	104.07	0.726
11	104.48	2.075
12	105.56	0.825
13	110.27	0.553
14	111.35	0.424
15	114.76	0.003

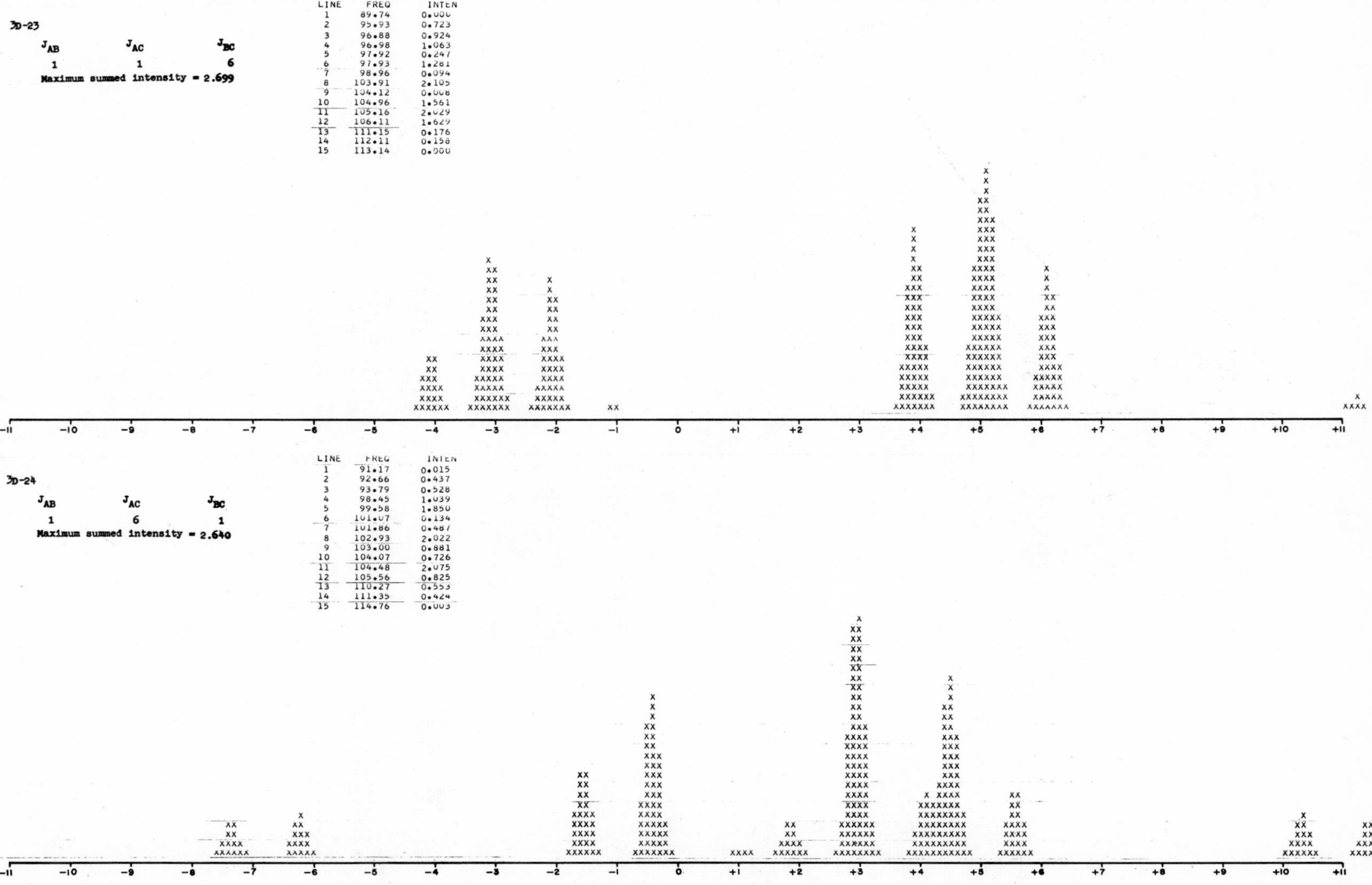

3D-25

J_{AB}	J_{AC}	J_{BC}
6	1	1

Maximum summed intensity = 2.037

LINE	FREQ	INTEN
1	92.25	0.274
2	92.71	0.050
3	93.33	0.260
4	98.13	1.206
5	98.75	0.310
6	99.21	1.900
7	100.66	1.377
8	101.71	2.039
9	106.09	1.349
10	106.54	0.001
11	107.13	0.861
12	107.16	1.273
13	107.59	0.843
14	108.21	0.257
15	115.54	0.000

−11 −10 −9 −8 −7 −6 −5 −4 −3 −2 −1 0 +1 +2 +3 +4 +5 +6 +7 +8 +9 +10 +11

3D-26

J_{AB}	J_{AC}	J_{BC}
1	6	6

Maximum summed intensity = 2.627

LINE	FREQ	INTEN
1	88.30	0.023
2	92.40	0.437
3	94.78	0.506
4	97.23	0.740
5	97.56	0.005
6	99.61	1.912
7	99.93	0.641
8	103.35	2.795
9	103.71	0.392
10	104.04	2.558
11	105.73	0.917
12	108.87	0.786
13	109.84	0.107
14	114.66	0.170
15	114.99	0.011

−11 −10 −9 −8 −7 −6 −5 −4 −3 −2 −1 0 +1 +2 +3 +4 +5 +6 +7 +8 +9 +10 +11

3D-27

J_{AB}	J_{AC}	J_{BC}
6	6	1

Maximum summed intensity = 2.697

LINE	FREQ	INTEN
1	89.52	0.227
2	90.90	0.037
3	94.59	0.226
4	95.38	0.655
5	99.07	0.395
6	100.00	0.681
7	100.46	2.476
8	102.06	2.829
9	104.48	2.092
10	105.87	0.774
11	106.54	0.632
12	107.93	0.059
13	109.56	0.438
14	111.62	0.465
15	117.03	0.015

−11 −10 −9 −8 −7 −6 −5 −4 −3 −2 −1 0 +1 +2 +3 +4 +5 +6 +7 +8 +9 +10 +11

3D-28

J_{AB}	J_{AC}	J_{BC}
6	1	6

Maximum summed intensity = 2.588

LINE	FREQ	INTEN
1	89.07	0.013
2	91.67	0.169
3	94.49	0.403
4	96.55	0.849
5	97.43	0.731
6	99.36	1.952
7	101.96	0.616
8	102.30	0.188
9	102.73	2.684
10	104.90	2.100
11	107.61	0.998
12	107.72	0.979
13	110.21	0.266
14	113.03	0.050
15	115.96	0.002

−11 −10 −9 −8 −7 −6 −5 −4 −3 −2 −1 0 +1 +2 +3 +4 +5 +6 +7 +8 +9 +10 +11

3D-29

J_{AB}	J_{AC}	J_{BC}
1	1	9

Maximum summed intensity = 2.966

LINE	FREQ	INTEN
1	87.10	0.000
2	95.05	0.021
3	95.97	0.858
4	96.10	0.204
5	96.88	0.932
6	97.02	0.878
7	97.93	1.280
8	104.09	2.190
9	104.98	2.121
10	105.14	1.639
11	105.89	1.649
12	106.81	0.058
13	113.10	0.005
14	114.02	0.085
15	114.93	0.082

3D-30

J_{AB}	J_{AC}	J_{BC}
9	9	1

Maximum summed intensity = 3.187

LINE	FREQ	INTEN
1	85.29	0.133
2	88.12	0.054
3	92.99	0.062
4	93.29	0.281
5	98.16	0.776
6	98.77	0.453
7	100.99	2.711
8	102.07	3.298
9	103.94	2.414
10	106.78	0.953
11	107.24	0.395
12	110.07	0.001
13	111.64	0.162
14	114.93	0.288
15	120.72	0.017

3D-31

J_{AB}	J_{AC}	J_{BC}
1	1	12

Maximum summed intensity = 2.216

LINE	FREQ	INTEN
1	84.30	0.000
2	92.17	0.040
3	93.23	0.066
4	95.95	0.799
5	96.88	0.936
6	97.00	0.983
7	97.93	1.278
8	104.19	2.225
9	104.88	2.161
10	105.24	1.673
11	105.81	1.732
12	109.59	0.004
13	113.12	0.001
14	116.90	0.053
15	117.83	0.049

−11 −10 −9 −8 −7 −6 −5 −4 −3 −2 −1 0 +1 +2 +3 +4 +5 +6 +7 +8 +9 +10 +11

3D-32

J_{AB}	J_{AC}	J_{BC}
12	12	1

Maximum summed intensity = 3.507

LINE	FREQ	INTEN
1	80.96	0.086
2	84.54	0.044
3	90.67	0.121
4	91.57	0.015
5	97.45	0.295
6	97.71	0.933
7	101.29	2.816
8	102.12	3.560
9	103.59	2.619
10	107.17	1.004
11	108.26	0.241
12	111.84	0.015
13	114.21	0.067
14	118.87	0.169
15	124.75	0.015

−11 −10 −9 −8 −7 −6 −5 −4 −3 −2 −1 0 +1 +2 +3 +4 +5 +6 +7 +8 +9 +10 +11

3D-33

J_{AB}	J_{AC}	J_{BC}
1	1	18

Maximum summed intensity = 2.249

LINE	FREQ	INTEN
1	78.50	0.000
2	86.28	0.022
3	87.34	0.026
4	95.94	0.785
5	96.88	0.942
6	97.00	0.997
7	97.93	1.276
8	104.29	2.252
9	104.78	2.194
10	105.35	1.701
11	105.71	1.758
12	113.12	0.000
13	115.37	0.001
14	122.79	0.024
15	123.72	0.023

-11 -10 -9 -8 -7 -6 -5 -4 -3 -2 -1 0 +1 +2 +3 +4 +5 +6 +7 +8 +9 +10 +11

3D-34

J_{AB}	J_{AC}	J_{BC}
18	18	1

Maximum summed intensity = 3.788

LINE	FREQ	INTEN
1	72.16	0.044
2	76.42	0.023
3	84.95	0.036
4	88.81	0.000
5	94.66	0.138
6	97.34	1.003
7	101.61	2.904
8	102.21	3.794
9	103.19	2.817
10	107.45	1.013
11	110.74	0.100
12	115.00	0.024
13	119.84	0.021
14	127.39	0.072
15	133.24	0.010

-11 -10 -9 -8 -7 -6 -5 -4 -3 -2 -1 0 +1 +2 +3 +4 +5 +6 +7 +8 +9 +10 +11

3D-35

J_{AB}	J_{AC}	J_{BC}
2	2	4

Maximum summed intensity = 2.266

LINE	FREQ	INTEN
1	91.15	0.001
2	94.76	0.566
3	96.57	0.774
4	96.91	1.068
5	98.71	1.592
6	99.24	0.384
7	101.38	0.189
8	102.33	0.000
9	103.29	2.276
10	105.00	2.051
11	105.43	1.150
12	106.80	1.376
13	109.05	0.316
14	110.85	0.258
15	113.52	0.000

−11 −10 −9 −8 −7 −6 −5 −4 −3 −2 −1 0 +1 +2 +3 +4 +5 +6 +7 +8 +9 +10 +11

3D-36

J_{AB}	J_{AC}	J_{BC}
2	4	2

Maximum summed intensity = 2.780

LINE	FREQ	INTEN
1	91.74	0.013
2	93.53	0.482
3	95.78	0.809
4	97.12	0.750
5	99.37	1.858
6	100.71	0.459
7	101.16	0.091
8	102.88	2.296
9	102.97	0.609
10	104.76	2.059
11	105.13	0.710
12	106.92	0.558
13	108.34	0.869
14	110.50	0.431
15	114.10	0.004

−11 −10 −9 −8 −7 −6 −5 −4 −3 −2 −1 0 +1 +2 +3 +4 +5 +6 +7 +8 +9 +10 +11

3D-37

J_{AB}	J_{AC}	J_{BC}
4	2	2

Maximum summed intensity = 2.245

LINE	FREQ	INTEN
1	92.32	0.000
2	93.36	0.385
3	95.19	0.491
4	97.40	1.240
5	99.23	1.882
6	100.27	0.004
7	100.28	0.879
8	102.40	2.245
9	104.32	0.189
10	105.36	1.736
11	106.45	0.689
12	107.20	1.195
13	107.49	0.635
14	109.32	0.429
15	114.41	0.001

3D-38

J_{AB}	J_{AC}	J_{BC}
2	4	4

Maximum summed intensity = 2.423

LINE	FREQ	INTEN
1	90.61	0.013
2	93.52	0.487
3	96.09	0.844
4	96.80	0.713
5	99.00	0.200
6	99.37	1.858
7	101.57	0.408
8	102.28	0.090
9	103.15	2.587
10	104.48	2.313
11	105.72	0.878
12	107.76	1.074
13	108.63	0.266
14	111.91	0.265
15	114.11	0.005

3D-39

J_{AB}	J_{AC}	J_{BC}
4	2	4

Maximum summed intensity = 2.541

LINE	FREQ	INTEN
1	91.05	0.001
2	93.29	0.356
3	95.31	0.522
4	97.24	1.178
5	98.76	0.597
6	99.26	1.881
7	101.49	0.064
8	102.71	0.022
9	102.80	2.525
10	104.95	2.047
11	106.74	0.919
12	106.97	1.334
13	108.98	0.356
14	111.00	0.200
15	114.45	0.000

−11 −10 −9 −8 −7 −6 −5 −4 −3 −2 −1 0 +1 +2 +3 +4 +5 +6 +7 +8 +9 +10 +11

3D-40

J_{AB}	J_{AC}	J_{BC}
4	4	2

Maximum summed intensity = 2.472

LINE	FREQ	INTEN
1	91.75	0.011
2	92.22	0.348
3	95.57	0.450
4	96.47	0.979
5	99.81	2.142
6	100.03	0.613
7	100.29	0.077
8	102.44	2.579
9	104.27	0.446
10	104.75	2.040
11	106.68	0.422
12	107.16	0.557
13	108.09	0.895
14	110.50	0.436
15	114.96	0.007

−11 −10 −9 −8 −7 −6 −5 −4 −3 −2 −1 0 +1 +2 +3 +4 +5 +6 +7 +8 +9 +10 +11

3D-41

J_{AB}	J_{AC}	J_{BC}
2	2	6

Maximum summed intensity = 2.405

LINE	FREQ	INTEN
1	89.59	0.001
2	94.75	0.540
3	96.54	0.784
4	96.93	1.079
5	97.46	0.266
6	98.71	1.588
7	99.63	0.070
8	103.49	2.408
9	103.88	0.007
10	104.79	2.193
11	105.67	1.262
12	106.58	1.471
13	110.83	0.180
14	112.62	0.150
15	113.54	0.000

3D-42

J_{AB}	J_{AC}	J_{BC}
2	6	2

Maximum summed intensity = 2.851

LINE	FREQ	INTEN
1	90.80	0.026
2	92.11	0.391
3	94.51	0.593
4	97.48	0.691
5	99.87	2.075
6	100.59	0.303
7	101.18	0.232
8	102.83	2.590
9	102.98	0.746
10	104.30	2.306
11	105.23	0.560
12	106.54	0.477
13	109.66	0.637
14	111.90	0.365
15	115.02	0.008

3D-43

J_{AB}	J_{AC}	J_{BC}
6	2	2

Maximum summed intensity = 2.333

LINE	FREQ	INTEN
1	91.73	0.258
2	92.22	0.011
3	93.64	0.308
4	97.67	1.249
5	99.09	0.112
6	99.58	2.064
7	99.91	1.020
8	102.07	2.403
9	105.36	1.722
10	105.84	0.010
11	107.27	1.247
12	107.51	0.659
13	108.00	0.667
14	109.42	0.270
15	115.69	0.001

-11 -10 -9 -8 -7 -6 -5 -4 -3 -2 -1 0 +1 +2 +3 +4 +5 +6 +7 +8 +9 +10 +11

3D-44

J_{AB}	J_{AC}	J_{BC}
2	6	6

Maximum summed intensity =2.899

LINE	FREQ	INTEN
1	88.32	0.020
2	92.00	0.400
3	95.32	0.629
4	96.55	0.588
5	97.00	0.029
6	99.87	2.086
7	100.32	0.517
8	103.13	2.963
9	103.55	0.289
10	104.00	2.571
11	106.45	0.747
12	108.55	0.870
13	110.13	0.110
14	114.68	0.167
15	115.13	0.013

-11 -10 -9 -8 -7 -6 -5 -4 -3 -2 -1 0 +1 +2 +3 +4 +5 +6 +7 +8 +9 +10 +11

3D-45

J_{AB}	J_{AC}	J_{BC}
6	2	6

Maximum summed intensity = 2.851

LINE	FREQ	INTEN
1	89.12	0.005
2	91.37	0.186
3	94.28	0.382
4	96.76	0.965
5	97.00	0.581
6	99.66	2.090
7	101.91	0.373
8	102.39	0.095
9	102.70	2.846
10	104.63	2.233
11	107.54	1.091
12	108.09	0.845
13	110.34	0.243
14	113.24	0.065
15	115.97	0.000

3D-46

J_{AB}	J_{AC}	J_{BC}
6	6	2

Maximum summed intensity = 2.850

LINE	FREQ	INTEN
1	89.51	0.226
2	90.71	0.035
3	94.18	0.221
4	95.80	0.761
5	99.20	0.497
6	99.27	0.294
7	100.47	2.478
8	102.24	3.022
9	104.29	2.277
10	105.49	0.604
11	107.33	0.443
12	108.53	0.122
13	108.96	0.607
14	112.00	0.400
15	117.02	0.014

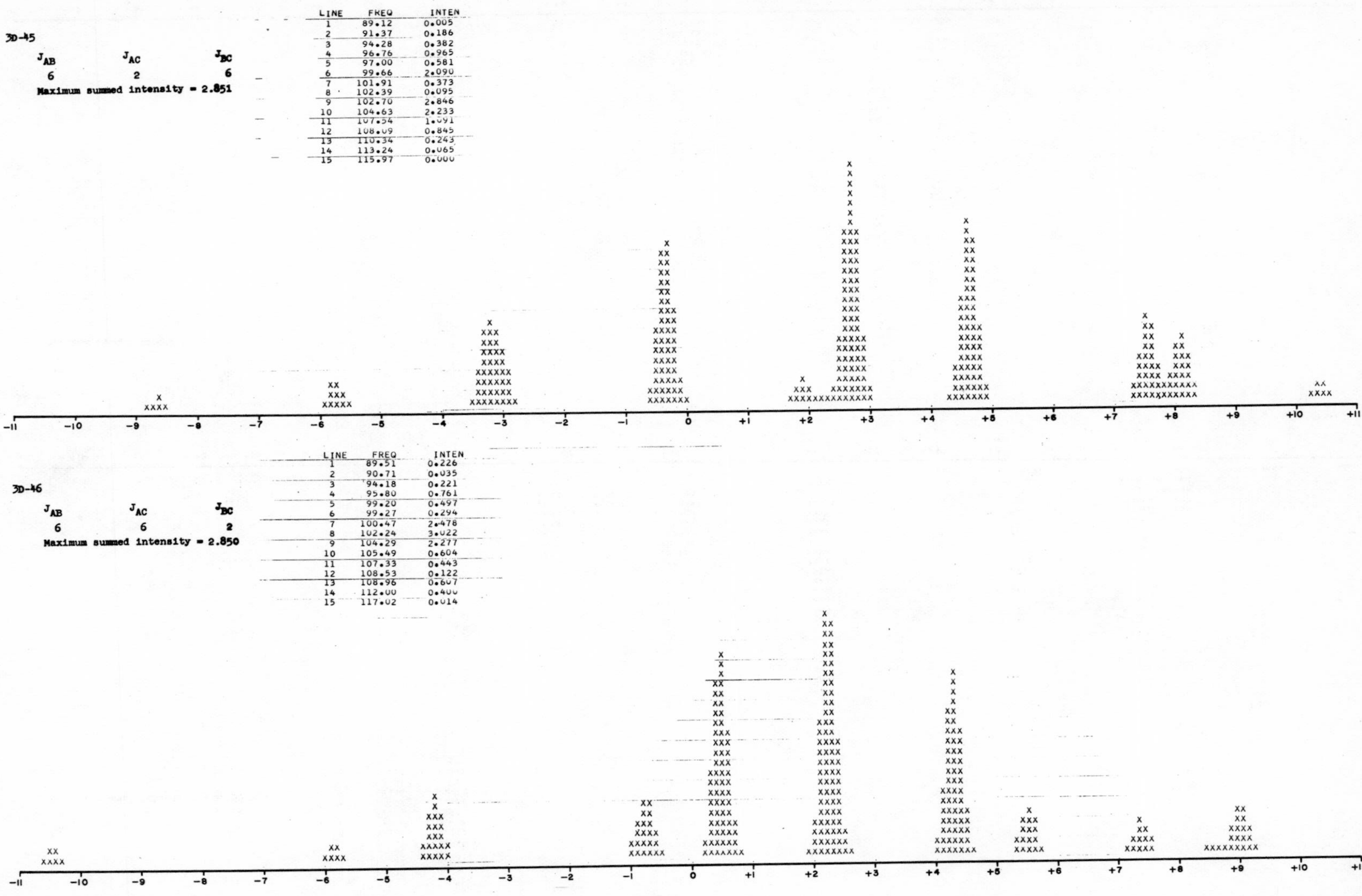

3D- 47

J_{AB}	J_{AC}	J_{BC}
2	2	9

Maximum summed intensity =2.376

LINE	FREQ	INTEN
1	86.95	0.001
2	94.38	0.044
3	95.00	0.667
4	96.52	0.796
5	96.57	0.651
6	97.19	0.426
7	98.72	1.584
8	103.66	2.492
9	104.62	2.289
10	105.85	1.338
11	106.15	0.970
12	106.77	0.572
13	113.28	0.046
14	113.91	0.046
15	115.43	0.078

3D- 48

J_{AB}	J_{AC}	J_{BC}
9	9	2

Maximum summed intensity =3.372

LINE	FREQ	INTEN
1	85.28	0.133
2	88.11	0.057
3	92.27	0.056
4	94.02	0.342
5	97.90	0.336
6	98.18	0.712
7	101.01	2.717
8	102.18	3.418
9	103.81	2.532
10	106.64	0.883
11	108.09	0.282
12	110.80	0.233
13	110.91	0.001
14	115.08	0.282
15	120.71	0.017

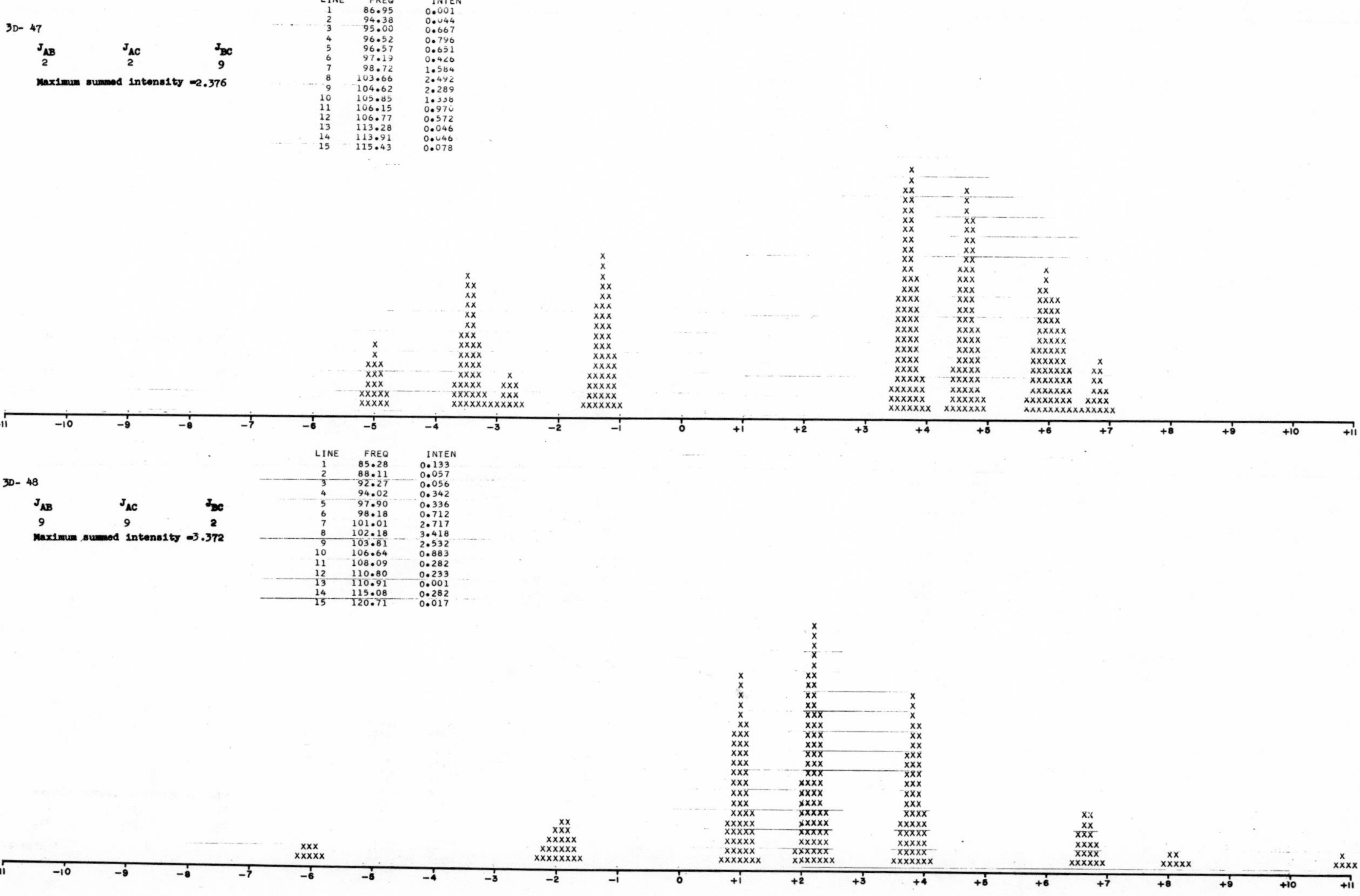

3D-49

J_{AB}	J_{AC}	J_{BC}
2	2	12

Maximum summed intensity = 2.364

LINE	FREQ	INTEN
1	84.14	0.000
2	91.66	0.028
3	93.86	0.089
4	94.81	0.641
5	96.52	0.804
6	97.01	0.957
7	98.72	1.581
8	103.75	2.527
9	104.53	2.331
10	105.96	1.372
11	106.23	1.548
12	109.39	0.019
13	113.47	0.004
14	116.62	0.051
15	118.33	0.047

3D-50

J_{AB}	J_{AC}	J_{BC}
12	12	2

Maximum summed intensity =3.620

LINE	FREQ	INTEN
1	80.95	0.086
2	84.57	0.047
3	90.73	0.012
4	91.53	0.140
5	96.54	0.226
6	97.69	0.908
7	101.30	2.822
8	102.19	3.629
9	103.51	2.688
10	107.12	0.983
11	109.16	0.178
12	112.77	0.009
13	113.28	0.088
14	118.93	0.170
15	124.74	0.015

3D-51

J_{AB}	J_{AC}	J_{BC}
2	2	18

Maximum summed intensity = 2.815

LINE	FREQ	INTEN
1	78.35	0.000
2	85.78	0.019
3	87.99	0.029
4	94.79	0.615
5	96.51	0.813
6	97.00	0.993
7	98.72	1.578
8	103.85	2.552
9	104.43	2.366
10	106.06	1.400
11	106.15	1.584
12	113.49	0.002
13	115.16	0.003
14	122.50	0.024
15	124.22	0.022

−11 −10 −9 −8 −7 −6 −5 −4 −3 −2 −1 0 +1 +2 +3 +4 +5 +6 +7 +8 +9 +10 +11

3D-52

J_{AB}	J_{AC}	J_{BC}
18	18	2

Maximum summed intensity = 3.665

LINE	FREQ	INTEN
1	72.15	0.044
2	76.45	0.024
3	85.89	0.039
4	87.88	0.000
5	93.70	0.113
6	97.32	0.995
7	101.62	2.908
8	102.24	3.819
9	103.15	2.843
10	107.44	1.009
11	111.68	0.079
12	115.98	0.020
13	118.87	0.025
14	127.41	0.072
15	133.23	0.010

−11 −10 −9 −8 −7 −6 −5 −4 −3 −2 −1 0 +1 +2 +3 +4 +5 +6 +7 +8 +9 +10 +11

3D-53

J_{AB}	J_{AC}	J_{BC}
4	4	9

Maximum summed intensity = 2.873

LINE	FREQ	INTEN
1	86.44	0.002
2	92.09	0.245
3	93.79	0.232
4	95.18	0.483
5	96.76	1.066
6	98.46	0.004
7	99.84	2.130
8	103.04	3.038
9	104.12	2.523
10	105.50	0.074
11	107.20	1.241
12	107.71	0.797
13	113.36	0.092
14	115.07	0.000
15	116.45	0.072

−11 −10 −9 −8 −7 −6 −5 −4 −3 −2 −1 0 +1 +2 +3 +4 +5 +6 +7 +8 +9 +10 +11

3D-54

J_{AB}	J_{AC}	J_{BC}
9	9	4

Maximum summed intensity = 3.498

LINE	FREQ	INTEN
1	85.28	0.131
2	87.74	0.048
3	90.99	0.067
4	95.31	0.572
5	96.08	0.203
6	98.56	0.473
7	101.03	2.724
8	102.32	3.551
9	103.65	2.666
10	106.11	0.622
11	109.36	0.493
12	109.89	0.158
13	112.36	0.034
14	115.61	0.242
15	120.69	0.016

−11 −10 −9 −8 −7 −6 −5 −4 −3 −2 −1 0 +1 +2 +3 +4 +5 +6 +7 +8 +9 +10 +11

3D-55

J_{AB}	J_{AC}	J_{BC}
4	4	12

Maximum summed intensity = 3.031

LINE	FREQ	INTEN
1	83.63	0.001
2	90.56	0.003
3	92.40	0.435
4	95.15	0.492
5	95.26	0.223
6	97.10	0.820
7	99.85	2.127
8	103.12	3.069
9	104.03	2.562
10	106.78	1.188
11	107.82	0.829
12	108.62	0.149
13	114.75	0.024
14	116.59	0.034
15	119.34	0.044

−11 −10 −9 −8 −7 −6 −5 −4 −3 −2 −1 0 +1 +2 +3 +4 +5 +6 +7 +8 +9 +10 +11

3D-56

J_{AB}	J_{AC}	J_{BC}
12	12	4

Maximum summed intensity = 3.676

LINE	FREQ	INTEN
1	80.95	0.085
2	84.51	0.049
3	89.04	0.012
4	93.24	0.217
5	94.66	0.144
6	97.77	0.821
7	101.33	2.830
8	102.28	3.710
9	103.39	2.771
10	106.95	0.903
11	111.01	0.106
12	111.48	0.168
13	114.57	0.000
14	119.10	0.170
15	124.73	0.014

−11 −10 −9 −8 −7 −6 −5 −4 −3 −2 −1 0 +1 +2 +3 +4 +5 +6 +7 +8 +9 +10 +11

3D-57

J_{AB}	J_{AC}	J_{BC}
4	4	18

Maximum summed intensity = 3.091

LINE	FREQ	INTEN
1	77.83	0.001
2	84.77	0.015
3	89.49	0.038
4	92.29	0.389
5	95.14	0.503
6	97.01	0.982
7	99.85	2.123
8	103.20	3.092
9	103.94	2.596
10	106.79	1.341
11	107.92	0.856
12	114.31	0.013
13	114.86	0.010
14	122.38	0.021
15	125.22	0.021

−11 −10 −9 −8 −7 −6 −5 −4 −3 −2 −1 0 +1 +2 +3 +4 +5 +6 +7 +8 +9 +10 +11

3D-58

J_{AB}	J_{AC}	J_{BC}
18	18	4

Maximum summed intensity = 3.799

LINE	FREQ	INTEN
1	72.15	0.044
2	76.47	0.025
3	85.99	0.000
4	87.79	0.049
5	91.76	0.079
6	97.31	0.977
7	101.63	2.914
8	102.28	3.852
9	103.09	2.877
10	107.41	0.999
11	113.60	0.052
12	116.93	0.035
13	117.92	0.013
14	127.44	0.073
15	133.22	0.010

−11 −10 −9 −8 −7 −6 −5 −4 −3 −2 −1 0 +1 +2 +3 +4 +5 +6 +7 +8 +9 +10 +11

3D-59

J_{AB}	J_{AC}	J_{BC}
6	6	9

Maximum summed intensity = 3.389

LINE	FREQ	INTEN
1	85.74	0.004
2	89.43	0.192
3	92.79	0.144
4	93.22	0.267
5	96.72	1.060
6	100.09	0.005
7	100.51	2.480
8	102.71	3.393
9	103.78	2.664
10	104.21	0.004
11	107.57	1.180
12	110.00	0.451
13	113.69	0.080
14	117.06	0.007
15	117.49	0.070

3D-60

J_{AB}	J_{AC}	J_{BC}
9	9	6

Maximum summed intensity =3.611

LINE	FREQ	INTEN
1	85.26	0.129
2	86.77	0.025
3	90.18	0.093
4	94.19	0.136
5	96.13	0.853
6	99.54	0.186
7	101.05	2.728
8	102.41	3.615
9	103.55	2.734
10	105.06	0.280
11	108.46	0.834
12	111.76	0.099
13	113.27	0.113
14	116.68	0.158
15	120.69	0.015

3D-61

J_{AB}	J_{AC}	J_{BC}
6	6	12

Maximum summed intensity = 3.311

LINE	FREQ	INTEN
1	82.94	0.002
2	89.00	0.053
3	90.29	0.250
4	93.17	0.275
5	96.35	0.783
6	97.65	0.256
7	100.52	2.479
8	102.77	3.420
9	103.71	2.698
10	106.59	0.410
11	107.88	0.795
12	110.12	0.480
13	116.18	0.057
14	117.48	0.001
15	120.35	0.041

−11 −10 −9 −8 −7 −6 −5 −4 −3 −2 −1 0 +1 +2 +3 +4 +5 +6 +7 +8 +9 +10 +11

3D-62

J_{AB}	J_{AC}	J_{BC}
12	12	6

Maximum summed intensity = 3.575

LINE	FREQ	INTEN
1	80.94	0.085
2	84.20	0.043
3	87.51	0.020
4	92.74	0.100
5	94.78	0.407
6	98.08	0.624
7	101.34	2.835
8	102.34	3.752
9	103.32	2.815
10	106.58	0.708
11	109.88	0.363
12	112.91	0.069
13	116.18	0.006
14	119.48	0.159
15	124.72	0.014

−11 −10 −9 −8 −7 −6 −5 −4 −3 −2 −1 0 +1 +2 +3 +4 +5 +6 +7 +8 +9 +10 +11

3D-63

J_{AB}	J_{AC}	J_{BC}
6	6	18

Maximum summed intensity = 3.318

LINE	FREQ	INTEN
1	77.14	0.001
2	83.75	0.011
3	89.62	0.262
4	91.15	0.055
5	93.14	0.284
6	97.02	0.963
7	100.54	2.477
8	102.83	3.442
9	103.63	2.727
10	107.14	1.188
11	110.23	0.504
12	113.02	0.032
13	116.84	0.019
14	122.72	0.016
15	126.23	0.020

−11 −10 −9 −8 −7 −6 −5 −4 −3 −2 −1 0 +1 +2 +3 +4 +5 +6 +7 +8 +9 +10 +11

3D-64

J_{AB}	J_{AC}	J_{BC}
18	18	6

Maximum summed intensity = 3.865

LINE	FREQ	INTEN
1	72.14	0.044
2	76.46	0.026
3	84.10	0.000
4	89.69	0.068
5	89.81	0.059
6	97.33	0.954
7	101.65	2.918
8	102.31	3.871
9	103.04	2.897
10	107.36	0.980
11	115.00	0.054
12	115.54	0.037
13	119.85	0.007
14	127.50	0.074
15	133.21	0.010

−11 −10 −9 −8 −7 −6 −5 −4 −3 −2 −1 0 +1 +2 +3 +4 +5 +6 +7 +8 +9 +10 +11

3D-65

J_{AB}	J_{AC}	J_{BC}
9	9	12

Maximum summed intensity = 3.617

LINE	FREQ	INTEN
1	81.70	0.004
2	85.14	0.104
3	88.46	0.086
4	89.58	0.122
5	96.63	1.036
6	99.95	0.000
7	101.08	2.733
8	102.52	3.683
9	103.40	2.809
10	104.52	0.008
11	107.84	1.096
12	114.02	0.226
13	117.46	0.042
14	120.78	0.008
15	121.91	0.040

−11 −10 −9 −8 −7 −6 −5 −4 −3 −2 −1 0 +1 +2 +3 +4 +5 +6 +7 +8 +9 +10 +11

3D-66

J_{AB}	J_{AC}	J_{BC}
12	12	9

Maximum summed intensity = 3.776

LINE	FREQ	INTEN
1	80.92	0.082
2	82.75	0.019
3	86.11	0.047
4	89.83	0.068
5	96.17	0.861
6	99.53	0.164
7	101.36	2.840
8	102.39	3.784
9	103.25	2.850
10	105.08	0.212
11	108.44	0.858
12	115.81	0.042
13	117.64	0.070
14	121.00	0.091
15	124.72	0.013

−11 −10 −9 −8 −7 −6 −5 −4 −3 −2 −1 0 +1 +2 +3 +4 +5 +6 +7 +8 +9 +10 +11

3D-67

J_{AB}	J_{AC}	J_{BC}
9	9	18

Maximum summed intensity = 3.619

LINE	FREQ	INTEN
1	75.92	0.002
2	82.15	0.003
3	85.52	0.165
4	89.50	0.129
5	93.74	0.131
6	97.11	0.885
7	101.09	2.735
8	102.57	3.701
9	103.33	2.832
10	107.32	1.008
11	110.69	0.110
12	114.16	0.247
13	120.39	0.025
14	123.76	0.008
15	127.74	0.018

−11 −10 −9 −8 −7 −6 −5 −4 −3 −2 −1 0 +1 +2 +3 +4 +5 +6 +7 +8 +9 +10 +11

3D-68

J_{AB}	J_{AC}	J_{BC}
18	18	9

Maximum summed intensity = 3.471

LINE	FREQ	INTEN
1	72.13	0.043
2	76.34	0.026
3	81.32	0.001
4	86.87	0.041
5	92.48	0.138
6	97.46	0.879
7	101.66	2.923
8	102.34	3.889
9	103.00	2.916
10	107.21	0.912
11	112.19	0.122
12	118.47	0.024
13	122.68	0.001
14	127.66	0.076
15	133.20	0.009

−11 −10 −9 −8 −7 −6 −5 −4 −3 −2 −1 0 +1 +2 +3 +4 +5 +6 +7 +8 +9 +10 +11

3D-69

J_{AB}	J_{AC}	J_{BC}
12	12	18

Maximum summed intensity = 3.635

LINE	FREQ	INTEN
1	74.58	0.002
2	80.07	0.011
3	81.78	0.102
4	85.52	0.068
5	95.95	0.613
6	97.66	0.402
7	101.39	2.845
8	102.46	3.816
9	103.15	2.887
10	106.88	0.461
11	108.59	0.609
12	118.34	0.137
13	123.83	0.028
14	125.54	0.000
15	129.27	0.018

3D-70

J_{AB}	J_{AC}	J_{BC}
18	18	12

Maximum summed intensity = 3.653

LINE	FREQ	INTEN
1	72.12	0.043
2	75.87	0.023
3	78.87	0.005
4	83.91	0.031
5	94.93	0.405
6	97.93	0.608
7	101.68	2.925
8	102.35	3.899
9	102.97	2.926
10	106.72	0.644
11	109.72	0.390
12	121.41	0.018
13	125.16	0.003
14	128.16	0.072
15	133.20	0.009

3D-71

J_{AB}	J_{AC}	J_{BC}
1	2	4

Maximum summed intensity = 2.580

LINE	FREQ	INTEN
1	91.15	0.003
2	95.37	0.696
3	96.60	0.942
4	97.12	0.928
5	98.35	1.415
6	99.59	0.254
7	100.82	0.333
8	102.56	0.017
9	103.61	2.118
10	104.84	1.308
11	105.04	2.050
12	106.79	1.363
13	109.06	0.296
14	110.81	0.278
15	113.28	0.001

3D-72

J_{AB}	J_{AC}	J_{BC}
1	4	2

Maximum summed intensity = 2.089

LINE	FREQ	INTEN
1	91.74	0.014
2	94.08	0.557
3	95.34	0.711
4	97.79	0.964
5	99.05	1.657
6	101.15	0.370
7	101.40	0.099
8	102.41	0.704
9	103.19	2.095
10	104.45	0.913
11	104.76	2.073
12	106.80	0.560
13	108.47	0.851
14	110.50	0.430
15	113.87	0.002

3D-73

J_{AB}	J_{AC}	J_{BC}
2	1	4

Maximum summed intensity = 3.126

LINE	FREQ	INTEN
1	91.26	0.000
2	95.29	0.587
3	96.39	0.777
4	97.21	1.151
5	98.32	1.449
6	99.38	0.520
7	101.31	0.094
8	102.34	0.036
9	103.35	2.115
10	105.28	1.306
11	105.33	1.893
12	106.44	1.493
13	109.30	0.334
14	110.41	0.245
15	113.40	0.000

−11 −10 −9 −8 −7 −6 −5 −4 −3 −2 −1 0 +1 +2 +3 +4 +5 +6 +7 +8 +9 +10 +11

3D-74

J_{AB}	J_{AC}	J_{BC}
2	4	1

Maximum summed intensity = 1.959

LINE	FREQ	INTEN
1	92.08	0.008
2	93.53	0.481
3	95.61	0.790
4	97.29	0.787
5	99.37	1.859
6	100.82	0.079
7	101.47	0.705
8	102.63	2.019
9	103.55	0.739
10	104.71	0.604
11	105.00	1.815
12	106.16	0.836
13	108.76	0.737
14	109.92	0.537
15	114.10	0.004

−11 −10 −9 −8 −7 −6 −5 −4 −3 −2 −1 0 +1 +2 +3 +4 +5 +6 +7 +8 +9 +10 +11

3D-75

J_{AB}	J_{AC}	J_{BC}
4	1	2

Maximum summed intensity = 2.058

LINE	FREQ	INTEN
1	92.40	0.006
2	93.85	0.397
3	94.99	0.488
4	97.73	1.299
5	98.87	1.730
6	100.32	0.079
7	100.41	1.032
8	102.38	2.076
9	104.30	0.075
10	105.74	1.571
11	106.27	0.890
12	106.88	1.322
13	107.72	0.653
14	108.86	0.380
15	114.28	0.000

−11 −10 −9 −8 −7 −6 −5 −4 −3 −2 −1 0 +1 +2 +3 +4 +5 +6 +7 +8 +9 +10 +11

3D-76

J_{AB}	J_{AC}	J_{BC}
4	2	1

Maximum summed intensity = 2.031

LINE	FREQ	INTEN
1	92.68	0.001
2	93.38	0.395
3	95.18	0.478
4	97.41	1.239
5	99.22	1.881
6	99.92	0.008
7	100.94	1.095
8	102.10	2.031
9	104.98	0.399
10	105.68	1.511
11	106.14	0.479
12	106.84	0.848
13	107.48	0.993
14	108.64	0.640
15	114.40	0.002

−11 −10 −9 −8 −7 −6 −5 −4 −3 −2 −1 0 +1 +2 +3 +4 +5 +6 +7 +8 +9 +10 +11

3D-77

J_{AB}	J_{AC}	J_{BC}
2	4	6

Maximum summed intensity = 2.705

LINE	FREQ	INTEN
1	89.11	0.009
2	93.51	0.496
3	96.29	0.852
4	96.59	0.701
5	97.16	0.088
6	99.37	1.857
7	99.94	0.302
8	103.30	2.706
9	103.76	0.091
10	104.33	2.416
11	106.08	0.979
12	107.41	1.188
13	110.47	0.145
14	113.55	0.164
15	114.12	0.006

-11 -10 -9 -8 -7 -6 -5 -4 -3 -2 -1 0 +1 +2 +3 +4 +5 +6 +7 +8 +9 +10 +11

3D-78

J_{AB}	J_{AC}	J_{BC}
2	6	4

Maximum summed intensity = 2.780

LINE	FREQ	INTEN
1	89.73	0.027
2	92.07	0.395
3	95.00	0.625
4	96.95	0.616
5	98.83	0.102
6	99.87	2.082
7	101.75	0.597
8	102.22	0.265
9	103.03	2.859
10	104.10	2.503
11	105.95	0.669
12	108.30	0.212
13	108.97	0.788
14	113.17	0.249
15	115.05	0.010

-11 -10 -9 -8 -7 -6 -5 -4 -3 -2 -1 0 +1 +2 +3 +4 +5 +6 +7 +8 +9 +10 +11

3D-79

J_{AB}	J_{AC}	J_{BC}
4	2	6

Maximum summed intensity = 2.776

LINE	FREQ	INTEN
1	89.44	0.000
2	93.17	0.301
3	95.43	0.551
4	97.01	1.107
5	97.14	0.480
6	99.28	1.880
7	100.98	0.004
8	103.00	0.162
9	103.03	2.668
10	104.70	2.220
11	106.87	1.009
12	106.97	1.296
13	110.59	0.211
14	112.86	0.111
15	114.56	0.000

3D-80

J_{AB}	J_{AC}	J_{BC}
4	6	2

Maximum summed intensity = 2.759

LINE	FREQ	INTEN
1	90.77	0.027
2	90.91	0.301
3	95.27	0.708
4	95.89	0.386
5	99.79	0.410
6	100.25	2.341
7	100.39	0.250
8	102.46	2.875
9	104.15	0.642
10	104.29	2.288
11	106.82	0.281
12	106.96	0.453
13	109.27	0.645
14	111.93	0.378
15	115.84	0.014

3D-81

J_{AB}	J_{AC}	J_{BC}
6	2	4

Maximum summed intensity = 2.585

LINE	FREQ	INTEN
1	90.79	0.011
2	91.59	0.229
3	94.02	0.343
4	97.20	1.071
5	98.50	0.730
6	99.63	2.080
7	100.43	0.266
8	102.46	2.688
9	104.11	0.026
10	104.91	2.042
11	107.33	1.203
12	108.07	0.812
13	108.88	0.392
14	111.30	0.108
15	115.78	0.000

3D-82

J_{AB}	J_{AC}	J_{BC}
6	4	2

Maximum summed intensity = 2.641

LINE	FREQ	INTEN
1	90.71	0.246
2	91.75	0.012
3	93.85	0.279
4	96.95	1.095
5	99.05	0.071
6	99.55	0.727
7	100.09	2.304
8	102.17	2.736
9	104.74	2.027
10	105.78	0.341
11	107.36	0.560
12	107.89	0.897
13	108.40	0.247
14	110.51	0.449
15	116.20	0.007

3D-83

J_{AB}	J_{AC}	J_{BC}
1	1	-1

Maximum summed intensity = 1.966

LINE	FREQ	INTEN
1	92.83	0.000
2	95.94	0.763
3	96.92	1.031
4	96.95	0.910
5	97.93	1.293
6	101.04	0.002
7	101.99	0.927
8	102.98	0.590
9	102.98	1.399
10	103.97	1.086
11	106.09	1.366
12	107.08	0.837
13	107.10	1.117
14	108.09	0.678
15	113.13	0.000

3D-84

J_{AB}	J_{AC}	J_{BC}
1	-1	1

Maximum summed intensity = 1.859

LINE	FREQ	INTEN
1	92.82	0.002
2	95.99	0.773
3	96.92	0.892
4	96.94	1.036
5	97.88	1.274
6	101.05	0.023
7	102.01	1.019
8	102.97	0.487
9	102.99	1.314
10	103.94	1.200
11	106.14	1.404
12	107.07	1.089
13	107.11	0.764
14	108.05	0.721
15	113.14	0.000

3D- 85

J_{AB}	J_{AC}	J_{BC}
-1	1	1

Maximum summed intensity =1.902

LINE	FREQ	INTEN
1	92.82	0.001
2	95.95	0.752
3	96.93	1.044
4	96.94	0.919
5	97.92	1.277
6	101.04	0.007
7	102.00	0.954
8	102.97	0.552
9	102.98	1.373
10	103.96	1.127
11	106.10	1.404
12	107.09	0.792
13	107.09	1.090
14	108.08	0.708
15	113.13	0.000

-11 -10 -9 -8 -7 -6 -5 -4 -3 -2 -1 0 +1 +2 +3 +4 +5 +6 +7 +8 +9 +10 +11

3D- 86

J_{AB}	J_{AC}	J_{BC}
1	1	-2

Maximum summed intensity = 1.846

LINE	FREQ	INTEN
1	92.47	0.000
2	95.94	0.765
3	96.91	1.021
4	96.96	0.913
5	97.93	1.297
6	101.33	0.695
7	101.39	0.004
8	102.30	0.413
9	103.31	1.627
10	104.28	1.269
11	105.76	1.602
12	106.78	1.290
13	107.75	0.609
14	108.77	0.496
15	113.13	0.000

-11 -10 -9 -8 -7 -6 -5 -4 -3 -2 -1 0 +1 +2 +3 +4 +5 +6 +7 +8 +9 +10 +11

3D-87

J_{AB}	J_{AC}	J_{BC}
1	-2	1

Maximum summed intensity = 1.621

LINE	FREQ	INTEN
1	92.65	0.006
2	95.45	0.697
3	96.37	0.917
4	97.34	0.948
5	98.26	1.372
6	101.06	0.061
7	102.03	1.095
8	102.95	0.397
9	102.99	1.254
10	103.92	1.308
11	105.75	1.551
12	106.71	0.775
13	107.63	0.957
14	108.60	0.662
15	113.29	0.001

−11 −10 −9 −8 −7 −6 −5 −4 −3 −2 −1 0 +1 +2 +3 +4 +5 +6 +7 +8 +9 +10 +11

3D-88

J_{AB}	J_{AC}	J_{BC}
-2	1	1

Maximum summed intensity = 1.839

LINE	FREQ	INTEN
1	92.82	0.003
2	95.33	0.616
3	96.32	0.749
4	97.30	1.171
5	98.29	1.445
6	100.81	0.016
7	101.62	1.094
8	102.60	1.538
9	103.59	0.400
10	104.57	0.982
11	106.11	1.429
12	107.08	0.768
13	107.10	1.078
14	108.08	0.712
15	113.38	0.000

−11 −10 −9 −8 −7 −6 −5 −4 −3 −2 −1 0 +1 +2 +3 +4 +5 +6 +7 +8 +9 +10 +11

3D-89

J_{AB}	J_{AC}	J_{BC}
1	1	-4

Maximum summed intensity = 1.873

LINE	FREQ	INTEN
1	91.29	0.000
2	95.94	0.766
3	96.89	1.004
4	96.97	0.908
5	97.92	1.313
6	99.74	0.411
7	100.70	0.182
8	102.58	0.009
9	103.73	1.915
10	104.68	1.501
11	105.35	1.902
12	106.38	1.505
13	109.33	0.319
14	110.36	0.265
15	113.14	0.001

−11 −10 −9 −8 −7 −6 −5 −4 −3 −2 −1 0 +1 +2 +3 +4 +5 +6 +7 +8 +9 +10 +11

3D-90

J_{AB}	J_{AC}	J_{BC}
1	-4	1

Maximum summed intensity = 1.787

LINE	FREQ	INTEN
1	92.04	0.020
2	94.24	0.544
3	95.10	0.705
4	98.03	1.033
5	98.88	1.500
6	101.09	0.202
7	102.06	1.240
8	102.92	0.215
9	102.99	1.163
10	103.85	1.560
11	105.12	1.814
12	106.05	0.735
13	108.91	0.727
14	109.84	0.538
15	113.87	0.003

−11 −10 −9 −8 −7 −6 −5 −4 −3 −2 −1 0 +1 +2 +3 +4 +5 +6 +7 +8 +9 +10 +11

3D-91

J_{AB}	J_{AC}	J_{BC}
-4	1	1

Maximum summed intensity = 1.906

LINE	FREQ	INTEN
1	92.77	0.018
2	93.93	0.387
3	94.89	0.484
4	97.85	1.367
5	98.81	1.627
6	99.96	0.116
7	101.08	1.313
8	102.04	1.797
9	105.00	0.091
10	105.96	0.896
11	106.15	1.542
12	107.11	1.054
13	107.11	0.587
14	108.07	0.719
15	114.27	0.000

3D-92

J_{AB}	J_{AC}	J_{BC}
1	1	-6

Maximum summed intensity = 2.329

LINE	FREQ	INTEN
1	89.73	0.000
2	95.94	0.767
3	96.89	0.992
4	96.96	0.813
5	97.90	1.364
6	97.99	0.367
7	98.94	0.031
8	103.95	2.052
9	104.11	0.067
10	104.90	1.614
11	105.15	1.992
12	106.16	1.606
13	111.11	0.181
14	112.12	0.150
15	113.16	0.004

3D-93

J_{AB}	J_{AC}	J_{BC}
1	-6	1

Maximum summed intensity = 1.953

LINE	FREQ	INTEN
1	91.08	0.038
2	92.88	0.405
3	93.66	0.536
4	98.56	1.078
5	99.33	1.509
6	101.13	0.439
7	102.10	1.373
8	102.87	0.071
9	103.00	1.105
10	103.77	1.846
11	104.67	2.001
12	105.57	0.618
13	110.35	0.549
14	111.25	0.425
15	114.78	0.006

3D-94

J_{AB}	J_{AC}	J_{BC}
-6	1	1

Maximum summed intensity = 2.167

LINE	FREQ	INTEN
1	92.09	0.225
2	92.97	0.044
3	93.25	0.315
4	98.20	1.488
5	98.49	0.250
6	99.36	1.678
7	100.73	1.454
8	101.68	1.961
9	105.96	0.756
10	106.84	0.756
11	106.91	1.281
12	107.12	1.033
13	107.79	0.034
14	108.07	0.724
15	115.55	0.000

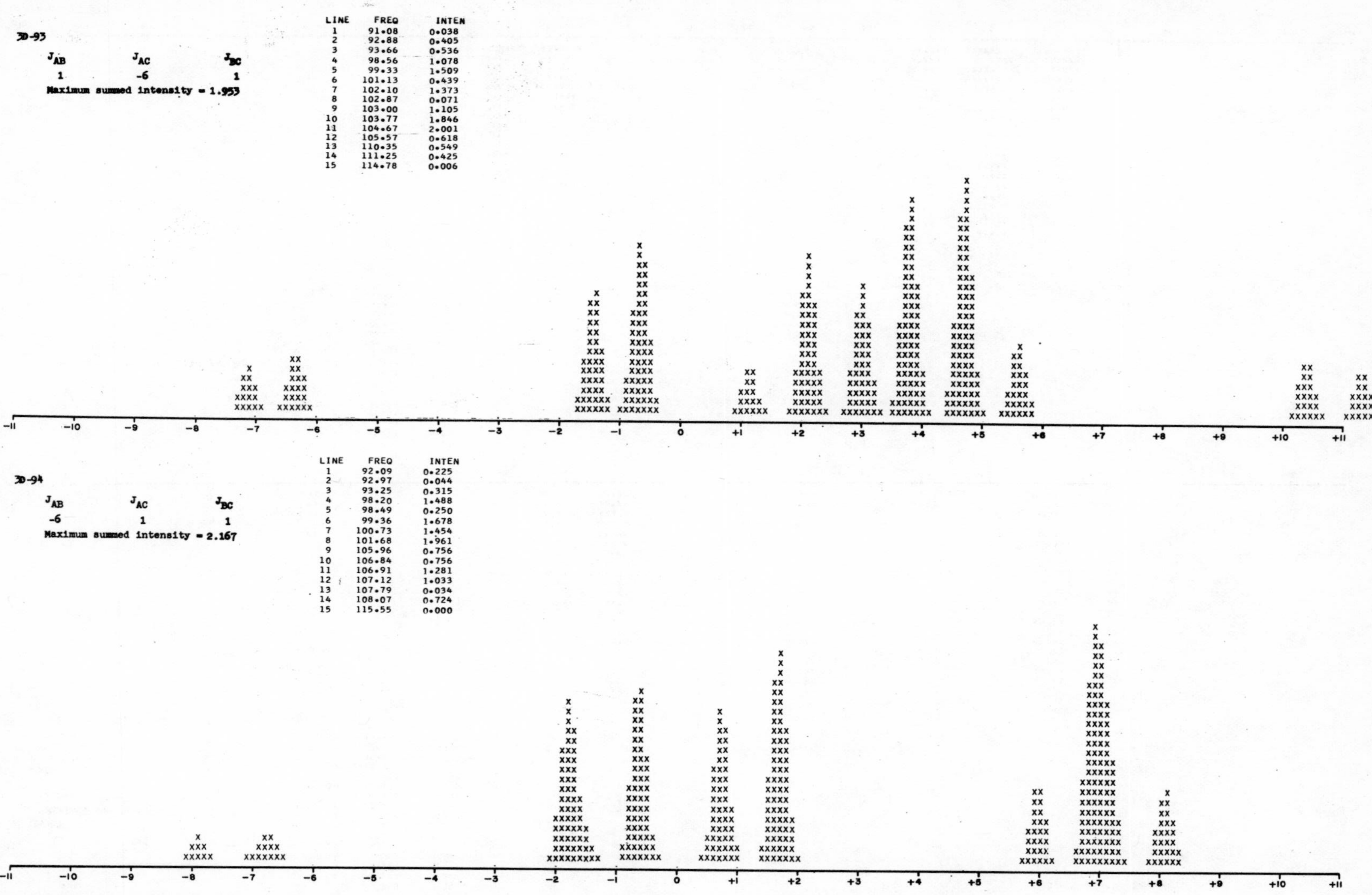

3D-95

J_{AB}	J_{AC}	J_{BC}
2	2	-2

Maximum summed intensity = 1.890

LINE	FREQ	INTEN
1	92.31	0.000
2	94.77	0.585
3	96.65	0.975
4	96.82	0.794
5	98.69	1.618
6	101.02	0.885
7	101.16	0.031
8	102.89	0.251
9	102.94	1.737
10	104.81	1.156
11	105.36	1.731
12	107.28	0.679
13	107.41	1.132
14	109.33	0.426
15	113.53	0.002

−11 −10 −9 −8 −7 −6 −5 −4 −3 −2 −1 0 +1 +2 +3 +4 +5 +6 +7 +8 +9 +10 +11

3D-96

J_{AB}	J_{AC}	J_{BC}
2	-2	2

Maximum summed intensity = 1.551

LINE	FREQ	INTEN
1	92.19	0.027
2	95.15	0.599
3	96.62	0.693
4	96.80	1.028
5	98.28	1.331
6	101.15	1.207
7	101.23	0.328
8	102.80	0.041
9	102.97	1.474
10	104.62	1.573
11	105.76	1.647
12	107.23	1.100
13	107.58	0.399
14	109.05	0.549
15	113.58	0.005

−11 −10 −9 −8 −7 −6 −5 −4 −3 −2 −1 0 +1 +2 +3 +4 +5 +6 +7 +8 +9 +10 +11

3D-97

J_{AB}	J_{AC}	J_{BC}
-2	2	2

Maximum summed intensity = 1.707

LINE	FREQ	INTEN
1	92.28	0.015
2	94.86	0.534
3	96.68	1.025
4	96.78	0.824
5	98.60	1.498
6	101.05	0.964
7	101.18	0.104
8	102.87	0.140
9	102.95	1.664
10	104.77	1.322
11	105.45	1.835
12	107.35	0.502
13	107.37	1.061
14	109.27	0.512
15	113.54	0.000

3D-98

J_{AB}	J_{AC}	J_{BC}
2	2	-4

Maximum summed intensity = 2.413

LINE	FREQ	INTEN
1	91.11	0.000
2	94.78	0.587
3	96.58	0.934
4	96.87	0.778
5	98.67	1.641
6	99.48	0.573
7	101.28	0.069
8	102.34	0.064
9	103.37	2.062
10	104.95	2.064
11	105.18	1.356
12	107.04	1.291
13	108.85	0.351
14	110.94	0.226
15	113.55	0.004

3D-99

J_{AB}	J_{AC}	J_{BC}
2	-4	2

Maximum summed intensity = 2.250

LINE	FREQ	INTEN
1	91.46	0.061
2	94.14	0.456
3	95.55	0.784
4	97.24	0.691
5	98.65	1.223
6	101.29	1.482
7	101.33	0.798
8	102.69	0.004
9	102.98	1.310
10	104.39	1.928
11	105.37	1.675
12	107.07	0.288
13	108.47	0.826
14	110.17	0.461
15	114.21	0.013

−11 −10 −9 −8 −7 −6 −5 −4 −3 −2 −1 0 +1 +2 +3 +4 +5 +6 +7 +8 +9 +10 +11

3D-100

J_{AB}	J_{AC}	J_{BC}
-4	2	2

Maximum summed intensity = 1.909

LINE	FREQ	INTEN
1	92.11	0.060
2	93.55	0.300
3	95.36	0.528
4	97.19	1.170
5	99.00	1.481
6	100.45	0.462
7	100.54	1.160
8	102.37	1.952
9	104.18	0.009
10	105.63	1.821
11	106.01	1.280
12	107.43	1.009
13	107.46	0.248
14	109.27	0.520
15	114.44	0.001

−11 −10 −9 −8 −7 −6 −5 −4 −3 −2 −1 0 +1 +2 +3 +4 +5 +6 +7 +8 +9 +10 +11

3D-101

J_{AB}	J_{AC}	J_{BC}
2	2	-6

Maximum summed intensity = 2.324

LINE	FREQ	INTEN
1	89.54	0.000
2	94.78	0.589
3	96.55	0.908
4	96.79	0.525
5	97.81	0.671
6	98.57	1.607
7	99.59	0.031
8	103.61	2.215
9	103.80	0.393
10	104.82	1.914
11	105.38	1.453
12	106.84	1.362
13	110.62	0.196
14	112.63	0.114
15	113.65	0.022

-11 -10 -9 -8 -7 -6 -5 -4 -3 -2 -1 0 +1 +2 +3 +4 +5 +6 +7 +8 +9 +10 +11

3D-102

J_{AB}	J_{AC}	J_{BC}
2	-6	2

Maximum summed intensity = 2.997

LINE	FREQ	INTEN
1	90.39	0.087
2	92.97	0.326
3	94.12	0.590
4	97.70	0.659
5	98.86	1.013
6	101.41	1.726
7	101.44	1.346
8	102.57	0.084
9	102.99	1.202
10	104.15	2.226
11	105.15	1.554
12	106.73	0.183
13	109.89	0.615
14	111.47	0.367
15	115.17	0.022

-11 -10 -9 -8 -7 -6 -5 -4 -3 -2 -1 0 +1 +2 +3 +4 +5 +6 +7 +8 +9 +10 +11

3D-103

J_{AB}	J_{AC}	J_{BC}
-6	2	2

Maximum summed intensity = 2.168

LINE	FREQ	INTEN
1	91.27	0.177
2	92.74	0.062
3	93.74	0.341
4	97.53	1.254
5	98.53	0.422
6	100.00	1.745
7	100.21	1.286
8	102.00	2.133
9	105.00	0.818
10	106.47	0.928
11	106.79	1.329
12	107.47	0.966
13	108.26	0.011
14	109.26	0.526
15	115.73	0.001

-11 -10 -9 -8 -7 -6 -5 -4 -3 -2 -1 0 +1 +2 +3 +4 +5 +6 +7 +8 +9 +10 +11

3D-104

J_{AB}	J_{AC}	J_{BC}
4	4	-4

Maximum summed intensity = 2.165

LINE	FREQ	INTEN
1	90.35	0.000
2	92.24	0.356
3	95.42	0.677
4	96.51	0.534
5	99.40	0.907
6	99.69	2.119
7	101.57	0.332
8	102.58	0.005
9	102.85	2.202
10	104.46	2.193
11	106.03	1.199
12	107.91	0.442
13	108.73	0.875
14	112.18	0.140
15	115.07	0.018

-11 -10 -9 -8 -7 -6 -5 -4 -3 -2 -1 0 +1 +2 +3 +4 +5 +6 +7 +8 +9 +10 +11

3D-105

J_{AB}	J_{AC}	J_{BC}
4	-4	4

Maximum summed intensity = 2.000

LINE	FREQ	INTEN
1	89.67	0.081
2	94.31	0.377
3	95.12	0.254
4	96.37	0.952
5	97.18	0.613
6	100.19	1.717
7	101.81	1.756
8	102.25	0.353
9	102.94	1.571
10	105.00	2.000
11	106.88	0.867
12	107.69	1.029
13	109.63	0.048
14	110.45	0.348
15	115.51	0.034

-11 -10 -9 -8 -7 -6 -5 -4 -3 -2 -1 0 +1 +2 +3 +4 +5 +6 +7 +8 +9 +10 +11

3D-106

J_{AB}	J_{AC}	J_{BC}
-4	4	4

Maximum summed intensity = 2.000

LINE	FREQ	INTEN
1	90.13	0.071
2	92.67	0.189
3	95.54	0.789
4	96.27	0.640
5	99.13	1.377
6	99.60	1.032
7	101.67	0.935
8	102.46	0.211
9	102.87	2.068
10	105.00	2.000
11	105.73	1.552
12	108.27	0.088
13	108.60	0.756
14	111.87	0.292
15	115.20	0.001

-11 -10 -9 -8 -7 -6 -5 -4 -3 -2 -1 0 +1 +2 +3 +4 +5 +6 +7 +8 +9 +10 +11

3D-107

J_{AB}	J_{AC}	J_{BC}
4	4	-6

Maximum summed intensity = 2.645

LINE	FREQ	INTEN
1	88.77	0.001
2	92.24	0.358
3	95.31	0.636
4	96.35	0.275
5	97.93	0.963
6	99.42	1.770
7	101.00	0.333
8	102.89	1.002
9	103.11	2.404
10	104.47	1.766
11	106.18	1.260
12	108.58	0.897
13	109.65	0.238
14	113.76	0.056
15	115.34	0.041

3D-108

J_{AB}	J_{AC}	J_{BC}
4	-6	4

Maximum summed intensity = 2.407

LINE	FREQ	INTEN
1	88.52	0.095
2	93.41	0.284
3	95.00	0.710
4	95.41	0.213
5	97.00	0.421
6	100.55	2.029
7	101.89	2.322
8	102.14	0.510
9	102.97	1.379
10	104.55	2.263
11	107.04	0.657
12	109.03	0.758
13	109.45	0.027
14	111.45	0.286
15	116.59	0.046

3D-109

J_{AB}	J_{AC}	J_{BC}
-6	4	4

Maximum summed intensity = 2.173

LINE	FREQ	INTEN
1	89.33	0.114
2	91.74	0.061
3	94.68	0.406
4	95.79	0.811
5	98.73	0.714
6	99.35	1.121
7	101.15	1.896
8	102.46	2.298
9	103.39	0.957
10	105.81	1.232
11	106.51	1.403
12	108.75	0.687
13	108.92	0.000
14	111.86	0.296
15	116.52	0.003

-11 -10 -9 -8 -7 -6 -5 -4 -3 -2 -1 0 +1 +2 +3 +4 +5 +6 +7 +8 +9 +10 +11

3D-110

J_{AB}	J_{AC}	J_{BC}
1	2	-1

Maximum summed intensity = 1.997

LINE	FREQ	INTEN
1	92.68	0.000
2	95.37	0.688
3	96.34	0.911
4	97.38	0.988
5	98.35	1.412
6	101.04	0.001
7	102.01	0.910
8	102.98	0.607
9	102.98	1.414
10	103.95	1.070
11	105.67	1.502
12	106.65	0.898
13	107.68	0.981
14	108.65	0.618
15	113.28	0.000

-11 -10 -9 -8 -7 -6 -5 -4 -3 -2 -1 0 +1 +2 +3 +4 +5 +6 +7 +8 +9 +10 +11

^{3}D-111

J_{AB}	J_{AC}	J_{BC}
2	1	-1

Maximum summed intensity = 1.959

LINE	FREQ	INTEN
1	92.81	0.001
2	95.33	0.638
3	96.34	0.729
4	97.28	1.143
5	98.29	1.468
6	100.81	0.021
7	101.64	1.130
8	102.60	1.502
9	103.59	0.395
10	104.55	0.993
11	106.11	1.338
12	107.07	0.860
13	107.12	1.137
14	108.07	0.645
15	113.38	0.001

^{3}D-112

J_{AB}	J_{AC}	J_{BC}
2	2	-1

Maximum summed intensity = 1.647

LINE	FREQ	INTEN
1	92.66	0.000
2	94.77	0.583
3	96.69	1.001
4	96.78	0.784
5	98.70	1.610
6	100.81	0.024
7	101.67	1.151
8	102.60	1.482
9	103.59	0.393
10	104.52	0.996
11	105.70	1.458
12	106.63	0.935
13	107.71	0.997
14	108.63	0.586
15	113.53	0.002

3D-113

J_{AB}	J_{AC}	J_{BC}
1	4	-1

Maximum summed intensity = 2.058

LINE	FREQ	INTEN
1	92.11	0.001
2	94.11	0.550
3	95.04	0.695
4	98.11	1.133
5	99.04	1.621
6	101.04	0.000
7	102.05	0.869
8	102.98	0.637
9	102.98	1.446
10	103.91	1.045
11	104.98	1.751
12	105.91	1.004
13	108.98	0.742
14	109.91	0.504
15	113.85	0.001

−11 −10 −9 −8 −7 −6 −5 −4 −3 −2 −1 0 +1 +2 +3 +4 +5 +6 +7 +8 +9 +10 +11

3D-114

J_{AB}	J_{AC}	J_{BC}
4	1	-1

Maximum summed intensity = 1.704

LINE	FREQ	INTEN
1	92.73	0.012
2	93.94	0.435
3	94.95	0.443
4	97.78	1.254
5	98.79	1.713
6	99.99	0.145
7	101.16	1.436
8	102.01	1.675
9	105.00	0.091
10	105.85	0.930
11	106.21	1.276
12	107.05	0.890
13	107.21	1.196
14	108.06	0.503
15	114.27	0.002

−11 −10 −9 −8 −7 −6 −5 −4 −3 −2 −1 0 +1 +2 +3 +4 +5 +6 +7 +8 +9 +10 +11

3D-115

J_{AB}	J_{AC}	J_{BC}
4	4	-1

Maximum summed intensity = 2.157

LINE	FREQ	INTEN
1	91.96	0.006
2	92.23	0.353
3	95.84	0.795
4	96.18	0.507
5	99.78	2.148
6	100.05	0.200
7	101.40	1.672
8	101.95	1.462
9	105.00	0.091
10	105.27	1.467
11	105.55	0.960
12	105.82	1.185
13	109.22	0.761
14	109.77	0.384
15	114.98	0.010

-11 -10 -9 -8 -7 -6 -5 -4 -3 -2 -1 0 +1 +2 +3 +4 +5 +6 +7 +8 +9 +10 +11

3D-116

J_{AB}	J_{AC}	J_{BC}
1	4	-2

Maximum summed intensity = 2.086

LINE	FREQ	INTEN
1	91.76	0.008
2	94.12	0.549
3	95.08	0.684
4	98.07	1.148
5	99.03	1.597
6	101.37	0.502
7	101.39	0.015
8	102.33	0.567
9	103.28	1.793
10	104.25	1.145
11	104.69	2.094
12	106.60	0.658
13	108.64	0.836
14	110.55	0.403
15	113.85	0.000

-11 -10 -9 -8 -7 -6 -5 -4 -3 -2 -1 0 +1 +2 +3 +4 +5 +6 +7 +8 +9 +10 +11

3D-117

J_{AB}	J_{AC}	J_{BC}
4	1	-2

Maximum summed intensity = 2.316

LINE	FREQ	INTEN
1	92.28	0.016
2	93.96	0.444
3	95.10	0.431
4	97.60	1.137
5	98.74	1.698
6	100.42	0.277
7	100.58	1.239
8	102.36	1.871
9	104.22	0.009
10	105.90	1.457
11	106.00	1.140
12	107.04	1.293
13	107.68	0.685
14	108.82	0.301
15	114.30	0.003

-11 -10 -9 -8 -7 -6 -5 -4 -3 -2 -1 0 +1 +2 +3 +4 +5 +6 +7 +8 +9 +10 +11

3D-118

J_{AB}	J_{AC}	J_{BC}
4	4	-2

Maximum summed intensity = 2.064

LINE	FREQ	INTEN
1	91.58	0.002
2	92.23	0.354
3	95.65	0.746
4	96.35	0.539
5	99.76	2.148
6	100.42	0.222
7	100.82	1.329
8	102.35	1.775
9	104.24	0.034
10	104.89	1.807
11	105.77	1.070
12	106.42	0.870
13	109.00	0.818
14	110.53	0.273
15	115.00	0.012

-11 -10 -9 -8 -7 -6 -5 -4 -3 -2 -1 0 +1 +2 +3 +4 +5 +6 +7 +8 +9 +10 +11

3D-119

J_{AB}	J_{AC}	J_{BC}
2	4	-1

Maximum summed intensity = 1.805

LINE	FREQ	INTEN
1	92.09	0.000
2	93.53	0.478
3	95.37	0.751
4	97.54	0.885
5	99.37	1.861
6	100.81	0.030
7	101.76	1.198
8	102.60	1.439
9	103.59	0.390
10	104.43	0.999
11	105.04	1.658
12	105.87	1.083
13	109.04	0.749
14	109.87	0.475
15	114.10	0.004

3D-120

J_{AB}	J_{AC}	J_{BC}
4	2	-1

Maximum summed intensity = 2.188

LINE	FREQ	INTEN
1	92.57	0.009
2	93.41	0.408
3	95.40	0.467
4	97.18	1.083
5	99.17	1.874
6	100.01	0.162
7	101.23	1.507
8	101.99	1.608
9	105.00	0.091
10	105.76	0.943
11	105.84	1.363
12	106.60	0.984
13	107.83	1.035
14	108.59	0.462
15	114.42	0.004

3D-121

J_{AB}	J_{AC}	J_{BC}
2	4	-2

Maximum summed intensity = 3.090

LINE	FREQ	INTEN
1	91.75	0.002
2	93.54	0.477
3	95.33	0.730
4	97.57	0.920
5	99.37	1.862
6	101.11	0.823
7	101.16	0.013
8	102.90	0.301
9	102.94	1.778
10	104.69	2.036
11	104.74	1.104
12	106.52	0.744
13	108.73	0.837
14	110.56	0.369
15	114.10	0.004

−11 −10 −9 −8 −7 −6 −5 −4 −3 −2 −1 0 +1 +2 +3 +4 +5 +6 +7 +8 +9 +10 +11

3D-122

J_{AB}	J_{AC}	J_{BC}
4	2	-2

Maximum summed intensity = 1.804

LINE	FREQ	INTEN
1	92.14	0.009
2	93.42	0.414
3	95.55	0.469
4	97.00	0.998
5	99.13	1.865
6	100.42	0.251
7	100.65	1.267
8	102.36	1.841
9	104.23	0.017
10	105.51	1.592
11	105.94	1.111
12	107.22	0.745
13	107.64	1.118
14	109.35	0.297
15	114.45	0.005

−11 −10 −9 −8 −7 −6 −5 −4 −3 −2 −1 0 +1 +2 +3 +4 +5 +6 +7 +8 +9 +10 +11

$^3\Sigma$-1

J_{AB}	J_{AC}	J_{BC}
1	1	1

Maximum summed intensity =2.081

LINE	FREQ	INTEN
1	87.88	0.000
2	92.94	0.773
3	93.93	0.896
4	93.95	1.063
5	94.93	1.268
6	98.99	0.960
7	100.00	0.000
8	100.00	1.371
9	100.00	0.709
10	101.01	0.960
11	105.07	1.268
12	106.05	1.063
13	106.07	0.896
14	107.06	0.773
15	112.12	0.000

−11 −10 −9 −8 −7 −6 −5 −4 −3 −2 −1 0 +1 +2 +3 +4 +5 +6 +7 +8 +9 +10 +11

$^3\Sigma$-2

J_{AB}	J_{AC}	J_{BC}
2	2	2

Maximum summed intensity = 2.295

LINE	FREQ	INTEN
1	87.51	0.001
2	91.78	0.593
3	93.68	0.759
4	93.83	1.093
5	95.73	1.552
6	97.95	0.854
7	100.00	1.793
8	100.00	0.002
9	100.00	0.500
10	102.05	0.854
11	104.27	1.552
12	106.17	1.093
13	106.32	0.759
14	108.22	0.593
15	112.49	0.001

−11 −10 −9 −8 −7 −6 −5 −4 −3 −2 −1 0 +1 +2 +3 +4 +5 +6 +7 +8 +9 +10 +11

3E-3

J_{AB}	J_{AC}	J_{BC}
3	3	3

Maximum summed intensity = 2.576

LINE	FREQ	INTEN
1	86.93	0.002
2	90.54	0.458
3	93.23	0.610
4	93.70	1.100
5	96.38	1.825
6	96.84	0.717
7	100.00	0.007
8	100.00	0.356
9	100.00	2.213
10	103.16	0.717
11	103.62	1.825
12	106.30	1.100
13	106.77	0.610
14	109.46	0.458
15	113.07	0.002

3E-4

J_{AB}	J_{AC}	J_{BC}
4	4	4

Maximum summed intensity = 2.857

LINE	FREQ	INTEN
1	86.16	0.004
2	89.24	0.358
3	92.58	0.472
4	93.58	1.095
5	95.67	0.581
6	96.91	2.061
7	100.00	0.014
8	100.00	2.585
9	100.00	0.259
10	103.09	2.061
11	104.33	0.581
12	106.42	1.095
13	107.42	0.472
14	110.76	0.358
15	113.84	0.004

3E- 5

J_{AB}	J_{AC}	J_{BC}
6	6	6

Maximum summed intensity = 3.291

LINE	FREQ	INTEN
1	84.20	0.009
2	86.53	0.229
3	90.80	0.272
4	93.13	0.368
5	93.40	1.074
6	97.66	2.403
7	100.00	0.022
8	100.00	0.146
9	100.00	3.122
10	102.34	2.403
11	106.60	1.074
12	106.87	0.368
13	109.20	0.272
14	113.47	0.229
15	115.80	0.009

3E- 6

J_{AB}	J_{AC}	J_{BC}
8	8	8

Maximum summed intensity =3.548

LINE	FREQ	INTEN
1	81.87	0.011
2	83.72	0.156
3	88.58	0.161
4	90.43	0.239
5	93.29	1.054
6	98.15	2.606
7	100.00	0.024
8	100.00	3.434
9	100.00	0.091
10	101.85	2.606
11	106.71	1.054
12	109.57	0.239
13	111.42	0.161
14	116.28	0.156
15	118.13	0.011

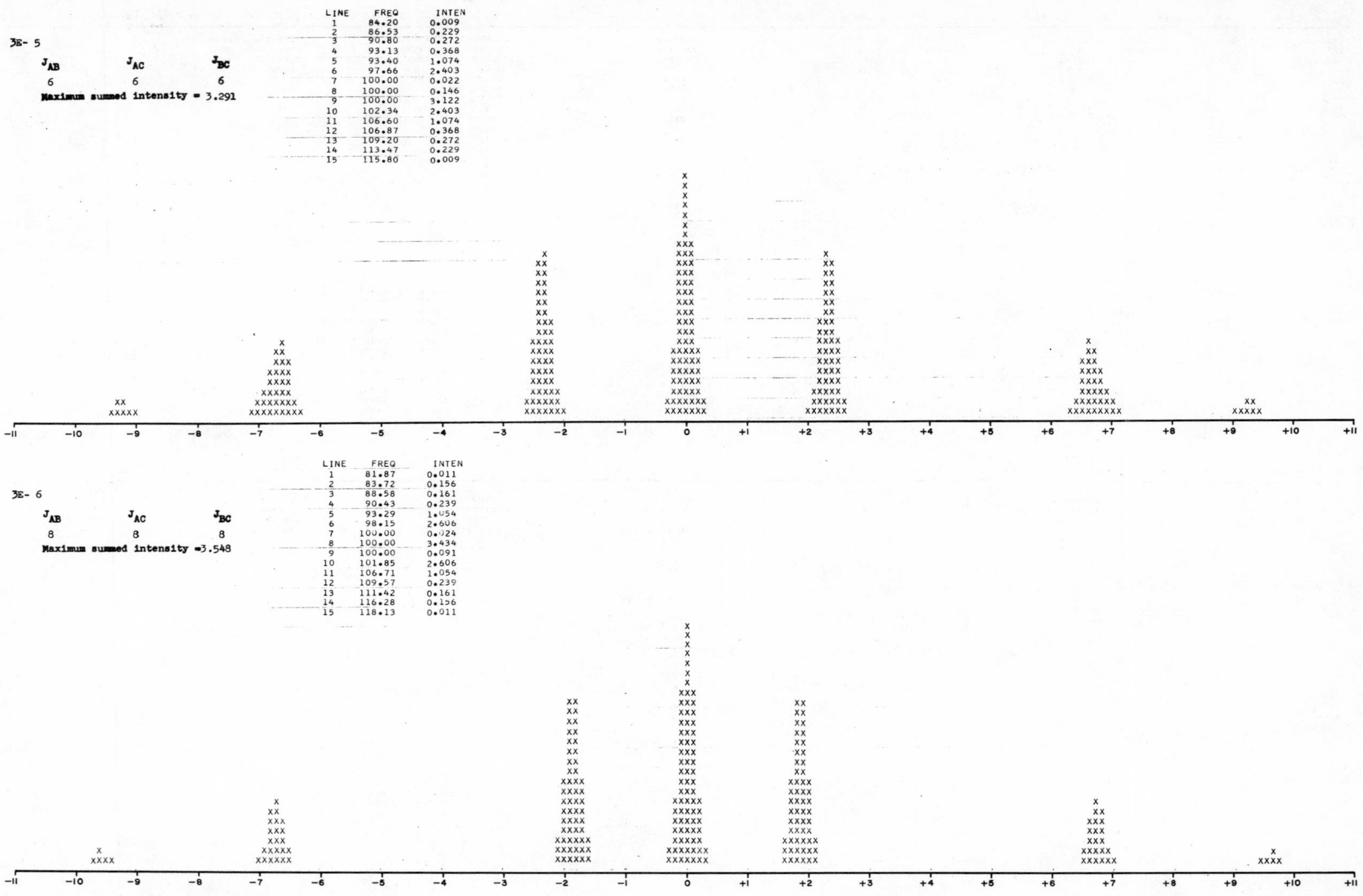

3E- 7

J_{AB}	J_{AC}	J_{BC}
10	10	10

Maximum summed intensity =3.696

LINE	FREQ	INTEN
1	79.33	0.011
2	80.85	0.111
3	86.11	0.101
4	87.63	0.162
5	93.23	1.040
6	98.48	2.726
7	100.00	0.022
8	100.00	3.614
9	100.00	0.060
10	101.52	2.726
11	106.77	1.040
12	112.37	0.162
13	113.89	0.101
14	119.15	0.111
15	120.67	0.011

−11 −10 −9 −8 −7 −6 −5 −4 −3 −2 −1 0 +1 +2 +3 +4 +5 +6 +7 +8 +9 +10 +11

3E- 8

J_{AB}	J_{AC}	J_{BC}
12	12	12

Maximum summed intensity =3.784

LINE	FREQ	INTEN
1	76.66	0.011
2	77.95	0.083
3	83.48	0.068
4	84.76	0.116
5	93.18	1.030
6	98.71	2.801
7	100.00	0.018
8	100.00	0.043
9	100.00	3.723
10	101.29	2.801
11	106.82	1.030
12	115.24	0.116
13	116.52	0.068
14	122.05	0.083
15	123.34	0.011

−11 −10 −9 −8 −7 −6 −5 −4 −3 −2 −1 0 +1 +2 +3 +4 +5 +6 +7 +8 +9 +10 +11

3E- 9

J_{AB}	J_{AC}	J_{BC}
15	15	15

Maximum summed intensity =3.860

LINE	FREQ	INTEN
1	72.51	0.009
2	73.55	0.057
3	79.36	0.041
4	80.41	0.075
5	93.15	1.021
6	98.96	2.867
7	100.00	0.014
8	100.00	0.027
9	100.00	3.818
10	101.04	2.867
11	106.85	1.021
12	119.59	0.075
13	120.64	0.041
14	126.45	0.057
15	127.49	0.009

-11 -10 -9 -8 -7 -6 -5 -4 -3 -2 -1 0 +1 +2 +3 +4 +5 +6 +7 +8 +9 +10 +11

3E- 10

J_{AB}	J_{AC}	J_{BC}
18	18	18

Maximum summed intensity =3.902

LINE	FREQ	INTEN
1	68.25	0.008
2	69.13	0.041
3	75.13	0.027
4	76.00	0.053
5	93.13	1.015
6	99.13	2.906
7	100.00	0.011
8	100.00	0.019
9	100.00	3.872
10	100.87	2.906
11	106.87	1.015
12	124.00	0.053
13	124.87	0.027
14	130.87	0.041
15	131.75	0.008

-11 -10 -9 -8 -7 -6 -5 -4 -3 -2 -1 0 +1 +2 +3 +4 +5 +6 +7 +8 +9 +10 +11

3E- 11

J_{AB}	J_{AC}	J_{BC}
1	1	2

Maximum summed intensity = 1.860

LINE	FREQ	INTEN
1	87.63	0.000
2	92.94	0.769
3	93.92	0.899
4	93.95	1.067
5	94.94	1.265
6	98.37	0.797
7	99.38	0.568
8	100.24	0.000
9	100.37	1.535
10	101.39	1.100
11	104.69	1.434
12	105.67	1.200
13	106.70	0.730
14	107.68	0.635
15	112.12	0.000

3E- 12

J_{AB}	J_{AC}	J_{BC}
1	2	1

Maximum summed intensity =2.191

LINE	FREQ	INTEN
1	87.75	0.000
2	92.39	0.716
3	93.41	0.961
4	94.35	0.943
5	95.37	1.376
6	98.98	0.908
7	100.00	1.432
8	100.00	0.004
9	100.00	0.754
10	101.02	0.908
11	104.63	1.376
12	105.65	0.943
13	106.59	0.961
14	107.61	0.716
15	112.25	0.000

3E-13

J_{AB}	J_{AC}	J_{BC}
2	1	1

Maximum summed intensity = 1.860

LINE	FREQ	INTEN
1	87.88	0.000
2	92.32	0.635
3	93.30	0.730
4	94.33	1.200
5	95.31	1.434
6	98.61	1.100
7	99.63	1.535
8	99.76	0.000
9	100.62	0.568
10	101.63	0.797
11	105.06	1.265
12	106.05	1.067
13	106.08	0.899
14	107.06	0.769
15	112.37	0.000

3E-14

J_{AB}	J_{AC}	J_{BC}
1	2	2

Maximum summed intensity = 1.658

LINE	FREQ	INTEN
1	87.51	0.001
2	92.39	0.716
3	93.44	0.965
4	94.31	0.938
5	95.37	1.375
6	98.34	0.725
7	99.40	0.633
8	100.24	0.006
9	100.36	1.620
10	101.42	1.027
11	104.27	1.558
12	106.20	1.083
13	106.29	0.755
14	108.22	0.598
15	112.25	0.000

3E- 15

J_{AB}	J_{AC}	J_{BC}
2	2	1

Maximum summed intensity =1.658

LINE	FREQ	INTEN
1	87.75	0.000
2	91.78	0.598
3	93.71	0.755
4	93.80	1.083
5	95.73	1.558
6	98.58	1.027
7	99.64	1.620
8	99.76	0.006
9	100.60	0.633
10	101.66	0.725
11	104.63	1.375
12	105.69	0.938
13	106.56	0.965
14	107.61	0.716
15	112.49	0.001

−11 −10 −9 −8 −7 −6 −5 −4 −3 −2 −1 0 +1 +2 +3 +4 +5 +6 +7 +8 +9 +10 +11

3E- 16

J_{AB}	J_{AC}	J_{BC}
2	1	2

Maximum summed intensity =2.111

LINE	FREQ	INTEN
1	87.63	0.000
2	92.32	0.624
3	93.32	0.741
4	94.32	1.204
5	95.32	1.428
6	98.00	0.947
7	100.00	0.003
8	100.00	1.688
9	100.00	0.420
10	102.00	0.947
11	104.68	1.428
12	105.68	1.204
13	106.68	0.741
14	107.68	0.624
15	112.37	0.000

−11 −10 −9 −8 −7 −6 −5 −4 −3 −2 −1 0 +1 +2 +3 +4 +5 +6 +7 +8 +9 +10 +11

3E- 17

J_{AB}	J_{AC}	J_{BC}
1	1	4

Maximum summed intensity = 1.852

LINE	FREQ	INTEN
1	86.75	0.000
2	92.94	0.756
3	93.91	0.908
4	93.96	1.075
5	94.94	1.260
6	96.92	0.547
7	97.95	0.343
8	100.92	1.789
9	101.13	0.001
10	101.95	1.322
11	104.14	1.697
12	105.11	1.414
13	108.14	0.471
14	109.11	0.417
15	112.13	0.000

−11 −10 −9 −8 −7 −6 −5 −4 −3 −2 −1 0 +1 +2 +3 +4 +5 +6 +7 +8 +9 +10 +11

3E- 18

J_{AB}	J_{AC}	J_{BC}
1	4	1

Maximum summed intensity = 2.425

LINE	FREQ	INTEN
1	87.26	0.002
2	91.15	0.602
3	92.20	0.772
4	95.06	1.014
5	96.11	1.586
6	98.95	0.812
7	100.00	0.027
8	100.00	1.571
9	100.00	0.828
10	101.05	0.812
11	103.89	1.586
12	104.94	1.014
13	107.80	0.772
14	108.85	0.602
15	112.74	0.002

−11 −10 −9 −8 −7 −6 −5 −4 −3 −2 −1 0 +1 +2 +3 +4 +5 +6 +7 +8 +9 +10 +11

3E- 19

J_{AB}	J_{AC}	J_{BC}
4	1	1

Maximum summed intensity =1.852

LINE	FREQ	INTEN
1	87.87	0.000
2	90.89	0.417
3	91.86	0.471
4	94.89	1.414
5	95.86	1.697
6	98.05	1.322
7	98.87	0.001
8	99.08	1.789
9	102.05	0.343
10	103.08	0.547
11	105.06	1.260
12	106.04	1.075
13	106.09	0.908
14	107.06	0.756
15	113.25	0.000

−11 −10 −9 −8 −7 −6 −5 −4 −3 −2 −1 0 +1 +2 +3 +4 +5 +6 +7 +8 +9 +10 +11

3E- 20

J_{AB}	J_{AC}	J_{BC}
1	4	4

Maximum summed intensity = 2.076

LINE	FREQ	INTEN
1	86.14	0.008
2	91.13	0.617
3	92.52	0.770
4	94.72	0.931
5	96.11	1.600
6	96.75	0.309
7	98.14	0.595
8	100.77	2.135
9	101.09	0.078
10	102.16	1.027
11	103.12	2.074
12	106.72	1.018
13	107.14	0.461
14	110.73	0.373
15	112.76	0.004

−11 −10 −9 −8 −7 −6 −5 −4 −3 −2 −1 0 +1 +2 +3 +4 +5 +6 +7 +8 +9 +10 +11

3E- 21

J_{AB}	J_{AC}	J_{BC}
4	4	1

Maximum summed intensity =2.076

LINE	FREQ	INTEN
1	87.24	0.004
2	89.27	0.373
3	92.86	0.461
4	93.28	1.018
5	96.88	2.074
6	97.84	1.027
7	98.91	0.078
8	99.23	2.135
9	101.86	0.595
10	103.25	0.309
11	103.89	1.600
12	105.28	0.931
13	107.48	0.770
14	108.87	0.617
15	113.86	0.008

−11 −10 −9 −8 −7 −6 −5 −4 −3 −2 −1 0 +1 +2 +3 +4 +5 +6 +7 +8 +9 +10 +11

3E- 22

J_{AB}	J_{AC}	J_{BC}
4	1	4

Maximum summed intensity =2.319

LINE	FREQ	INTEN
1	86.66	0.001
2	90.73	0.349
3	92.11	0.524
4	94.55	1.315
5	95.92	1.691
6	96.19	0.961
7	100.00	0.121
8	100.00	2.165
9	100.00	0.033
10	103.81	0.961
11	104.08	1.691
12	105.45	1.315
13	107.89	0.524
14	109.27	0.349
15	113.34	0.001

−11 −10 −9 −8 −7 −6 −5 −4 −3 −2 −1 0 +1 +2 +3 +4 +5 +6 +7 +8 +9 +10 +11

3E- 23

J_{AB}	J_{AC}	J_{BC}
1	1	6

Maximum summed intensity =1.927

LINE	FREQ	INTEN
1	85.47	0.000
2	92.93	0.724
3	93.90	0.916
4	93.96	1.095
5	94.94	1.257
6	95.29	0.411
7	96.32	0.181
8	101.28	1.949
9	102.32	1.467
10	102.40	0.008
11	103.78	1.865
12	104.76	1.543
13	109.77	0.307
14	110.75	0.276
15	112.13	0.001

−11 −10 −9 −8 −7 −6 −5 −4 −3 −2 −1 0 +1 +2 +3 +4 +5 +6 +7 +8 +9 +10 +11

3E- 24

J_{AB}	J_{AC}	J_{BC}
1	6	1

Maximum summed intensity =2.667

LINE	FREQ	INTEN
1	86.48	0.004
2	89.78	0.497
3	90.85	0.613
4	95.64	1.050
5	96.71	1.778
6	98.93	0.726
7	100.00	1.724
8	100.00	0.063
9	100.00	0.880
10	101.07	0.726
11	103.29	1.778
12	104.36	1.050
13	109.15	0.613
14	110.22	0.497
15	113.52	0.004

−11 −10 −9 −8 −7 −6 −5 −4 −3 −2 −1 0 +1 +2 +3 +4 +5 +6 +7 +8 +9 +10 +11

3E- 25

J_{AB}	J_{AC}	J_{BC}
6	1	1

Maximum summed intensity = 1.927

LINE	FREQ	INTEN
1	87.87	0.001
2	89.25	0.276
3	90.23	0.307
4	95.24	1.543
5	96.22	1.865
6	97.60	0.008
7	97.68	1.467
8	98.72	1.949
9	103.68	0.181
10	104.71	0.411
11	105.06	1.257
12	106.04	1.095
13	106.10	0.916
14	107.07	0.724
15	114.53	0.000

3E- 26

J_{AB}	J_{AC}	J_{BC}
1	6	6

Maximum summed intensity = 2.475

LINE	FREQ	INTEN
1	84.17	0.016
2	89.61	0.519
3	91.61	0.571
4	94.72	0.825
5	94.97	0.081
6	96.72	1.825
7	96.97	0.662
8	100.87	2.560
9	102.16	0.257
10	102.41	2.401
11	102.86	0.926
12	107.53	0.844
13	108.31	0.253
14	113.42	0.249
15	113.67	0.012

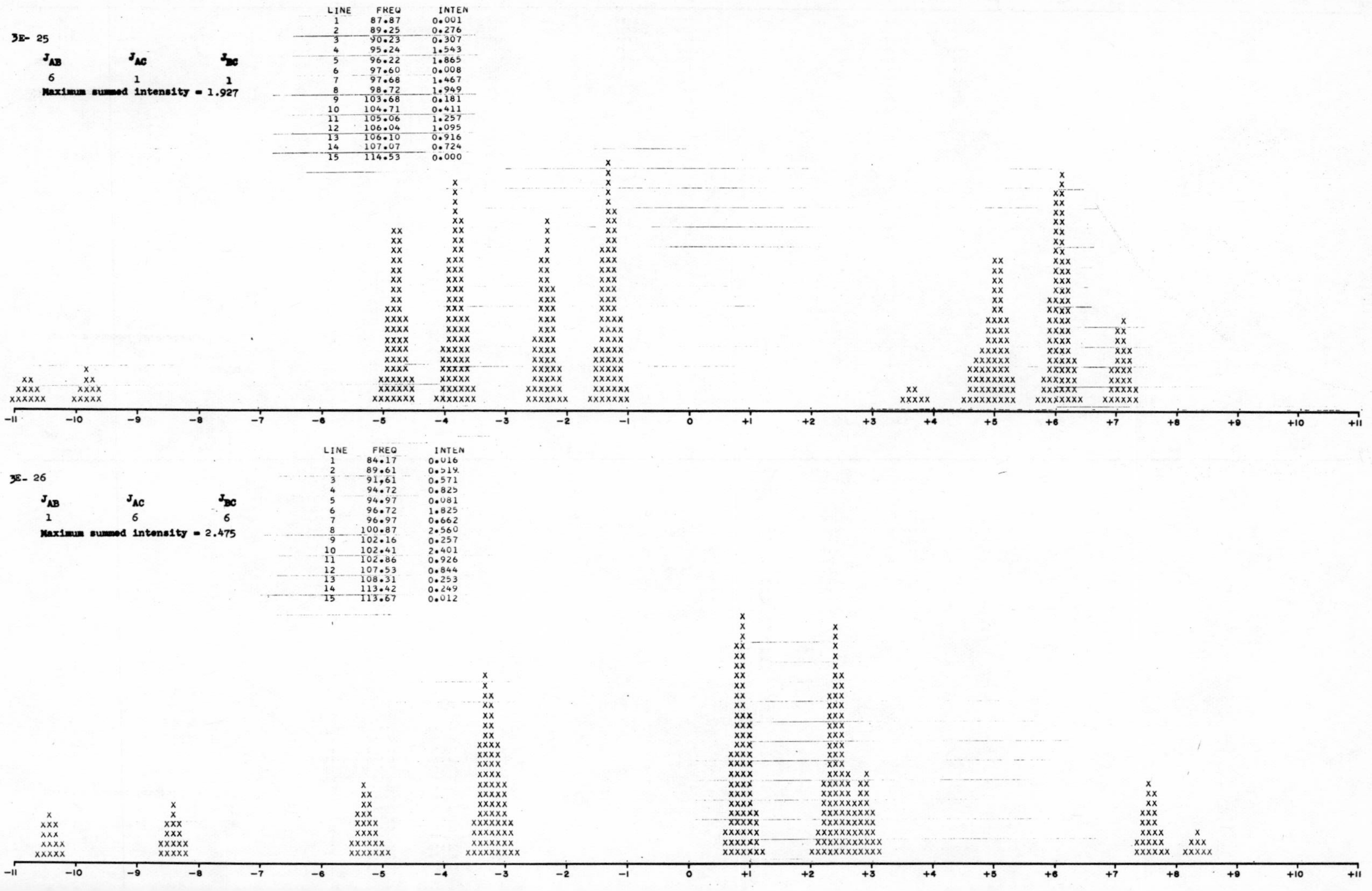

3E- 27

J_{AB}	J_{AC}	J_{BC}
6	6	1

Maximum summed intensity = 2.475

LINE	FREQ	INTEN
1	86.33	0.012
2	86.58	0.249
3	91.69	0.253
4	92.47	0.844
5	97.14	0.926
6	97.59	2.401
7	97.84	0.257
8	99.13	2.560
9	103.03	0.662
10	103.28	1.825
11	105.03	0.081
12	105.28	0.825
13	108.39	0.571
14	110.39	0.519
15	115.83	0.016

−11 −10 −9 −8 −7 −6 −5 −4 −3 −2 −1 0 +1 +2 +3 +4 +5 +6 +7 +8 +9 +10 +11

3E- 28

J_{AB}	J_{AC}	J_{BC}
6	1	6

Maximum summed intensity = 3.014

LINE	FREQ	INTEN
1	85.08	0.006
2	88.69	0.164
3	91.10	0.393
4	93.98	1.094
5	94.71	0.941
6	96.39	1.895
7	100.00	0.064
8	100.00	2.497
9	100.00	0.453
10	103.61	1.895
11	105.29	0.941
12	106.02	1.094
13	108.90	0.393
14	111.31	0.164
15	114.92	0.006

−11 −10 −9 −8 −7 −6 −5 −4 −3 −2 −1 0 +1 +2 +3 +4 +5 +6 +7 +8 +9 +10 +11

3E- 29

J_{AB}	J_{AC}	J_{BC}
1	1	9

Maximum summed intensity =2.072

LINE	FREQ	INTEN
1	83.14	0.000
2	92.50	0.000
3	93.05	0.995
4	93.54	0.612
5	93.90	0.926
6	94.09	0.548
7	94.94	1.254
8	101.61	2.079
9	102.65	1.586
10	103.45	2.005
11	104.30	1.344
12	104.85	0.316
13	112.01	0.039
14	112.56	0.136
15	113.41	0.160

-11 -10 -9 -8 -7 -6 -5 -4 -3 -2 -1 0 +1 +2 +3 +4 +5 +6 +7 +8 +9 +10 +11

3E- 30

J_{AB}	J_{AC}	J_{BC}
9	9	1

Maximum summed intensity = 2.944

LINE	FREQ	INTEN
1	82.39	0.150
2	84.12	0.028
3	89.92	0.093
4	90.66	0.504
5	96.03	0.718
6	96.47	0.604
7	98.20	2.642
8	99.23	3.011
9	102.58	2.131
10	104.31	0.826
11	105.77	0.611
12	107.50	0.000
13	110.11	0.304
14	113.30	0.358
15	119.41	0.020

-11 -10 -9 -8 -7 -6 -5 -4 -3 -2 -1 0 +1 +2 +3 +4 +5 +6 +7 +8 +9 +10 +11

3E- 31

J_{AB}	J_{AC}	J_{BC}
1	1	12

Maximum summed intensity = 2.139

LINE	FREQ	INTEN
1	80.54	0.000
2	89.78	0.077
3	90.83	0.141
4	92.96	0.848
5	93.89	0.933
6	94.01	0.960
7	94.94	1.252
8	101.81	2.142
9	102.85	1.647
10	103.25	2.075
11	104.19	1.705
12	107.36	0.009
13	112.10	0.002
14	115.28	0.108
15	116.21	0.101

−11 −10 −9 −8 −7 −6 −5 −4 −3 −2 −1 0 +1 +2 +3 +4 +5 +6 +7 +8 +9 +10 +11

3E- 32

J_{AB}	J_{AC}	J_{BC}
12	12	1

Maximum summed intensity = 3.270

LINE	FREQ	INTEN
1	78.09	0.099
2	81.02	0.031
3	88.25	0.263
4	88.39	0.036
5	94.84	0.529
6	95.61	0.839
7	98.55	2.755
8	99.38	3.310
9	102.07	2.371
10	105.01	0.931
11	106.61	0.427
12	109.54	0.019
13	112.37	0.150
14	116.91	0.226
15	123.36	0.019

−11 −10 −9 −8 −7 −6 −5 −4 −3 −2 −1 0 +1 +2 +3 +4 +5 +6 +7 +8 +9 +10 +11

3E- 33

J_{AB}	J_{AC}	J_{BC}
1	1	18

Maximum summed intensity = 3.545

LINE	FREQ	INTEN
1	74.98	0.000
2	84.01	0.046
3	85.06	0.057
4	92.95	0.816
5	93.89	0.942
6	94.00	0.992
7	94.94	1.249
8	102.03	2.196
9	103.04	2.138
10	103.07	1.702
11	103.97	1.759
12	112.11	0.000
13	112.91	0.001
14	121.05	0.052
15	121.99	0.050

3E- 34

J_{AB}	J_{AC}	J_{BC}
18	18	1

Maximum summed intensity = 3.609

LINE	FREQ	INTEN
1	69.33	0.052
2	73.46	0.022
3	82.66	0.086
4	85.62	0.002
5	92.23	0.285
6	94.82	0.992
7	98.95	2.860
8	99.62	3.639
9	101.44	2.662
10	105.56	0.990
11	108.82	0.208
12	112.95	0.043
13	117.72	0.049
14	125.11	0.098
15	131.72	0.013

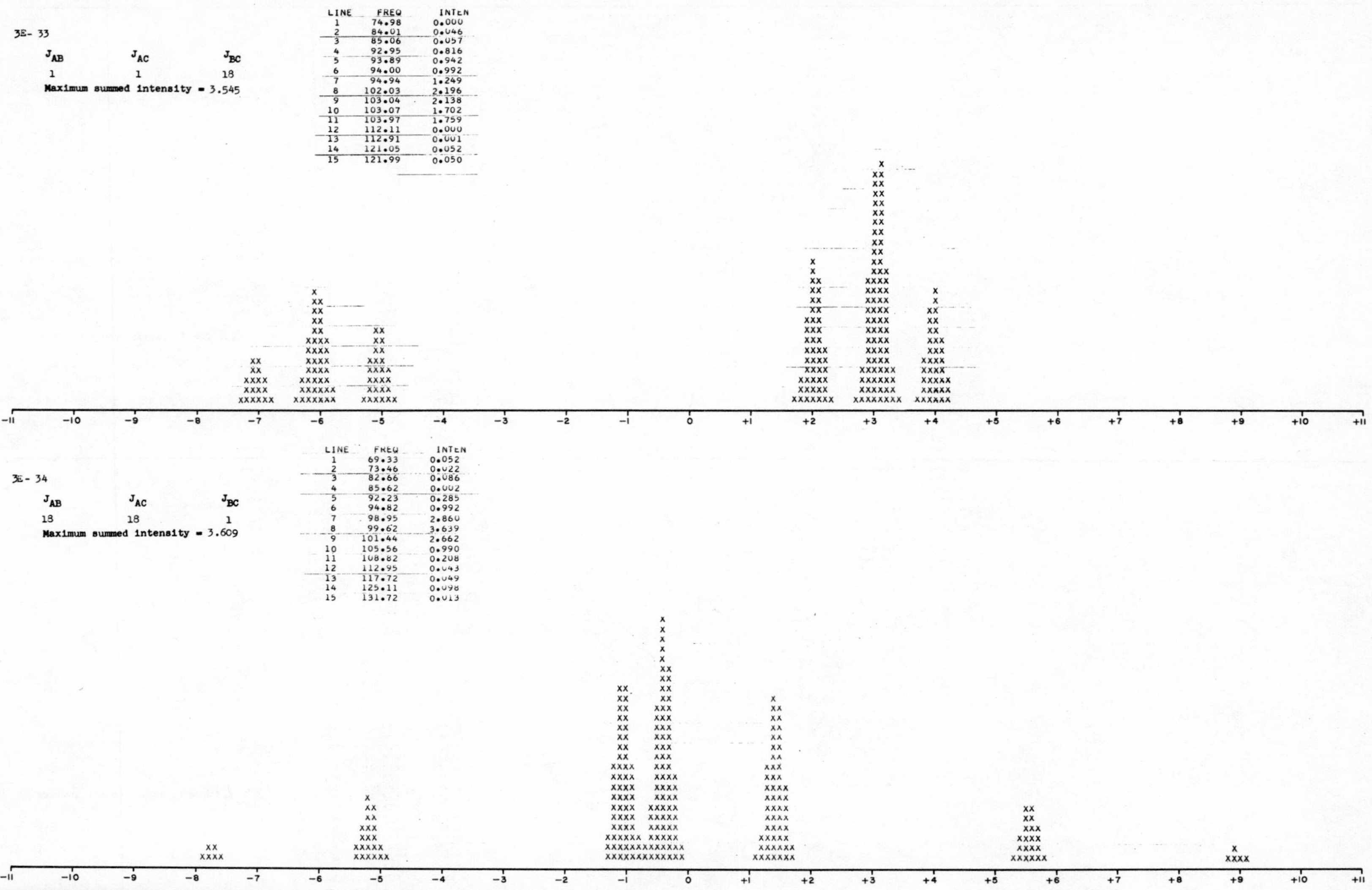

3E- 35

J_{AB}	J_{AC}	J_{BC}
2	2	4

Maximum summed intensity = 2.012

LINE	FREQ	INTEN
1	86.62	0.001
2	91.77	0.578
3	93.63	0.770
4	93.87	1.107
5	95.73	1.544
6	96.49	0.593
7	98.59	0.286
8	100.53	2.058
9	100.88	0.000
10	102.63	1.062
11	103.74	1.829
12	105.60	1.292
13	107.78	0.486
14	109.64	0.394
15	112.49	0.000

−11 −10 −9 −8 −7 −6 −5 −4 −3 −2 −1 0 +1 +2 +3 +4 +5 +6 +7 +8 +9 +10 +11

3E- 36

J_{AB}	J_{AC}	J_{BC}
2	4	2

Maximum summed intensity = 2.707

LINE	FREQ	INTEN
1	87.02	0.004
2	90.58	0.520
3	92.73	0.875
4	94.29	0.767
5	96.44	1.789
6	97.85	0.691
7	100.00	2.018
8	100.00	0.640
9	100.00	0.049
10	102.15	0.691
11	103.56	1.789
12	105.71	0.767
13	107.27	0.875
14	109.42	0.520
15	112.98	0.004

−11 −10 −9 −8 −7 −6 −5 −4 −3 −2 −1 0 +1 +2 +3 +4 +5 +6 +7 +8 +9 +10 +11

3E-37

J_{AB}	J_{AC}	J_{BC}
4	2	2

Maximum summed intensity = 2.012

LINE	FREQ	INTEN
1	87.51	0.000
2	90.36	0.394
3	92.22	0.486
4	94.40	1.292
5	96.26	1.829
6	97.37	1.062
7	99.12	0.000
8	99.47	2.058
9	101.41	0.286
10	103.51	0.593
11	104.27	1.544
12	106.13	1.107
13	106.37	0.770
14	108.23	0.578
15	113.38	0.001

−11 −10 −9 −8 −7 −6 −5 −4 −3 −2 −1 0 +1 +2 +3 +4 +5 +6 +7 +8 +9 +10 +11

3E-38

J_{AB}	J_{AC}	J_{BC}
2	4	4

Maximum summed intensity = 2.173

LINE	FREQ	INTEN
1	86.15	0.007
2	90.58	0.524
3	92.95	0.894
4	94.07	0.745
5	96.31	0.407
6	96.44	1.784
7	98.68	0.469
8	100.45	2.318
9	100.87	0.051
10	102.82	0.846
11	103.11	2.070
12	106.60	1.050
13	107.25	0.462
14	110.74	0.369
15	112.98	0.004

−11 −10 −9 −8 −7 −6 −5 −4 −3 −2 −1 0 +1 +2 +3 +4 +5 +6 +7 +8 +9 +10 +11

3E-39

J_{AB}	J_{AC}	J_{BC}
4	2	4

Maximum summed intensity = 2.430

LINE	FREQ	INTEN
1	86.58	0.000
2	90.29	0.359
3	92.29	0.516
4	94.29	1.270
5	96.00	0.818
6	96.29	1.823
7	100.00	2.307
8	100.00	0.033
9	100.00	0.090
10	103.71	1.823
11	104.00	0.818
12	105.71	1.270
13	107.71	0.516
14	109.71	0.359
15	113.42	0.000

−11 −10 −9 −8 −7 −6 −5 −4 −3 −2 −1 0 +1 +2 +3 +4 +5 +6 +7 +8 +9 +10 +11

3E-40

J_{AB}	J_{AC}	J_{BC}
4	4	2

Maximum summed intensity = 2.173

LINE	FREQ	INTEN
1	87.02	0.004
2	89.26	0.369
3	92.75	0.462
4	93.40	1.050
5	96.89	2.070
6	97.18	0.846
7	99.13	0.051
8	99.55	2.318
9	101.32	0.469
10	103.56	1.784
11	103.69	0.407
12	105.93	0.745
13	107.05	0.894
14	109.42	0.524
15	113.85	0.007

−11 −10 −9 −8 −7 −6 −5 −4 −3 −2 −1 0 +1 +2 +3 +4 +5 +6 +7 +8 +9 +10 +11

3E-41

J_{AB}	J_{AC}	J_{BC}
2	2	6

Maximum summed intensity = 2.157

LINE	FREQ	INTEN
1	85.34	0.001
2	91.75	0.544
3	93.61	0.783
4	93.88	1.126
5	94.85	0.451
6	95.74	1.538
7	96.98	0.135
8	100.87	2.221
9	102.15	0.009
10	103.00	1.200
11	103.39	2.005
12	105.25	1.408
13	109.41	0.316
14	111.26	0.262
15	112.51	0.000

−11 −10 −9 −8 −7 −6 −5 −4 −3 −2 −1 0 +1 +2 +3 +4 +5 +6 +7 +8 +9 +10 +11

3E-42

J_{AB}	J_{AC}	J_{BC}
2	6	2

Maximum summed intensity = 3.130

LINE	FREQ	INTEN
1	86.23	0.009
2	89.23	0.441
3	91.46	0.685
4	94.77	0.741
5	97.00	2.000
6	97.77	0.559
7	100.00	2.250
8	100.00	0.133
9	100.00	0.747
10	102.23	0.559
11	103.00	2.000
12	105.23	0.741
13	108.54	0.685
14	110.77	0.441
15	113.77	0.009

−11 −10 −9 −8 −7 −6 −5 −4 −3 −2 −1 0 +1 +2 +3 +4 +5 +6 +7 +8 +9 +10 +11

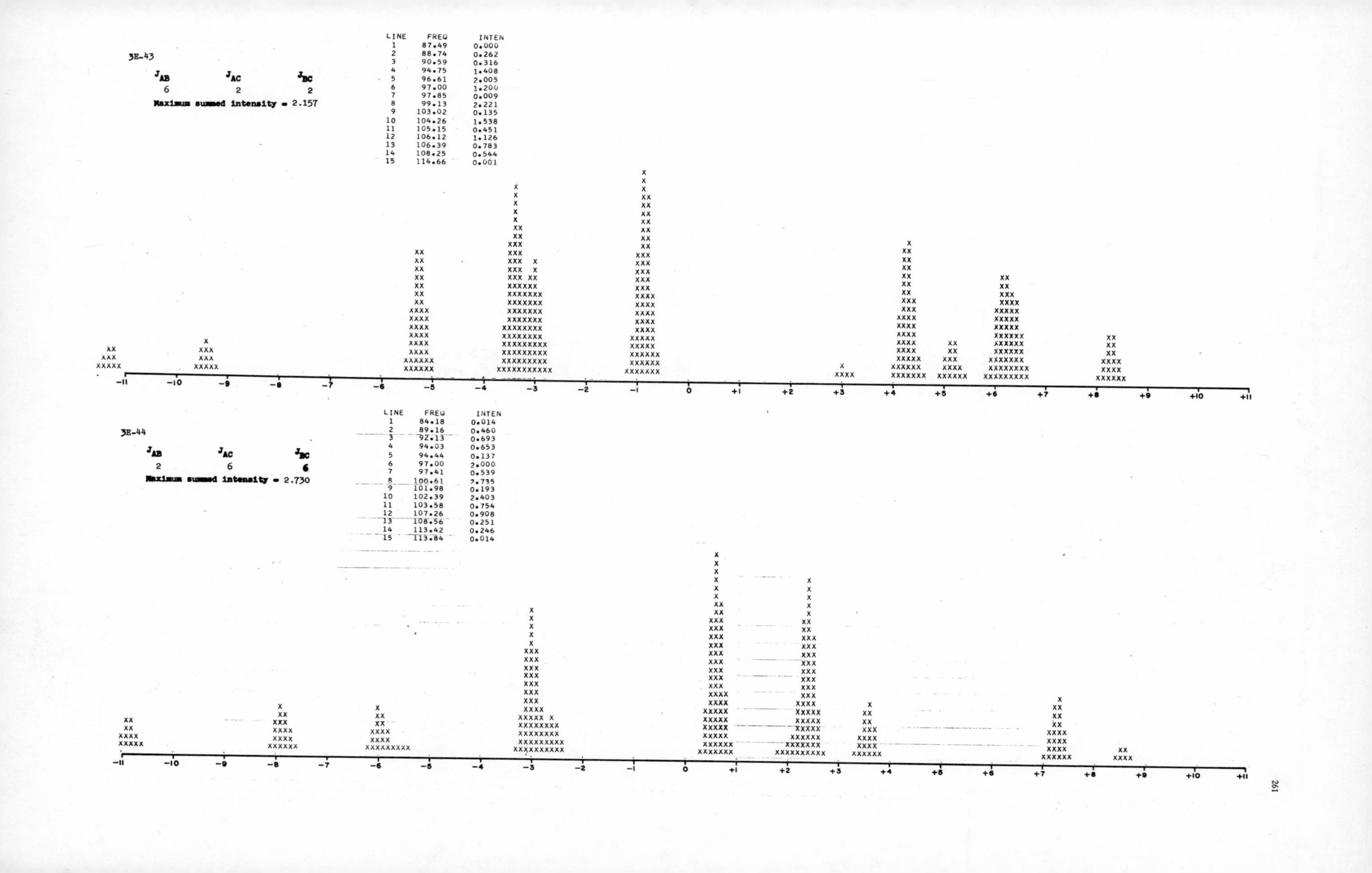

3E-43

J_{AB}	J_{AC}	J_{BC}
6	2	2

Maximum summed intensity = 2.157

LINE	FREQ	INTEN
1	87.49	0.000
2	88.74	0.262
3	90.59	0.316
4	94.75	1.408
5	96.61	2.005
6	97.00	1.200
7	97.85	0.009
8	99.13	2.221
9	103.02	0.135
10	104.26	1.538
11	105.15	0.451
12	106.12	1.126
13	106.39	0.783
14	108.25	0.544
15	114.66	0.001

−11 −10 −9 −8 −7 −6 −5 −4 −3 −2 −1 0 +1 +2 +3 +4 +5 +6 +7 +8 +9 +10 +11

3E-44

J_{AB}	J_{AC}	J_{BC}
2	6	6

Maximum summed intensity = 2.730

LINE	FREQ	INTEN
1	84.18	0.014
2	89.16	0.460
3	92.13	0.693
4	94.03	0.653
5	94.44	0.137
6	97.00	2.000
7	97.41	0.539
8	100.61	2.735
9	101.98	0.193
10	102.39	2.403
11	103.58	0.754
12	107.26	0.908
13	108.56	0.251
14	113.42	0.246
15	113.84	0.014

−11 −10 −9 −8 −7 −6 −5 −4 −3 −2 −1 0 +1 +2 +3 +4 +5 +6 +7 +8 +9 +10 +11

3E-45

J_{AB}	J_{AC}	J_{BC}
6	2	6

Maximum summed intensity = 2.914

LINE	FREQ	INTEN
1	85.09	0.001
2	88.37	0.183
3	91.06	0.377
4	94.03	1.164
5	94.34	0.797
6	96.72	2.020
7	100.00	0.256
8	100.00	0.017
9	100.00	2.641
10	103.28	2.020
11	105.66	0.797
12	105.97	1.164
13	108.94	0.377
14	111.63	0.183
15	114.91	0.001

-11 -10 -9 -8 -7 -6 -5 -4 -3 -2 -1 0 +1 +2 +3 +4 +5 +6 +7 +8 +9 +10 +11

3E-46

J_{AB}	J_{AC}	J_{BC}
6	6	2

Maximum summed intensity = 2.730

LINE	FREQ	INTEN
1	86.16	0.014
2	86.58	0.246
3	91.44	0.251
4	92.74	0.908
5	96.42	0.754
6	97.61	2.403
7	98.02	0.193
8	99.39	2.735
9	102.59	0.539
10	103.00	2.000
11	105.56	0.137
12	105.97	0.653
13	107.87	0.693
14	110.84	0.460
15	115.82	0.014

-11 -10 -9 -8 -7 -6 -5 -4 -3 -2 -1 0 +1 +2 +3 +4 +5 +6 +7 +8 +9 +10 +11

3E-47

J_{AB}	J_{AC}	J_{BC}
2	2	9

Maximum summed intensity = 2.334

LINE	FREQ	INTEN
1	83.01	0.001
2	91.54	0.165
3	92.39	0.664
4	93.59	0.799
5	93.69	1.069
6	94.55	0.063
7	95.74	1.531
8	101.18	2.352
9	103.07	2.152
10	103.34	1.316
11	104.27	0.432
12	105.12	1.085
13	111.87	0.143
14	112.72	0.037
15	113.92	0.153

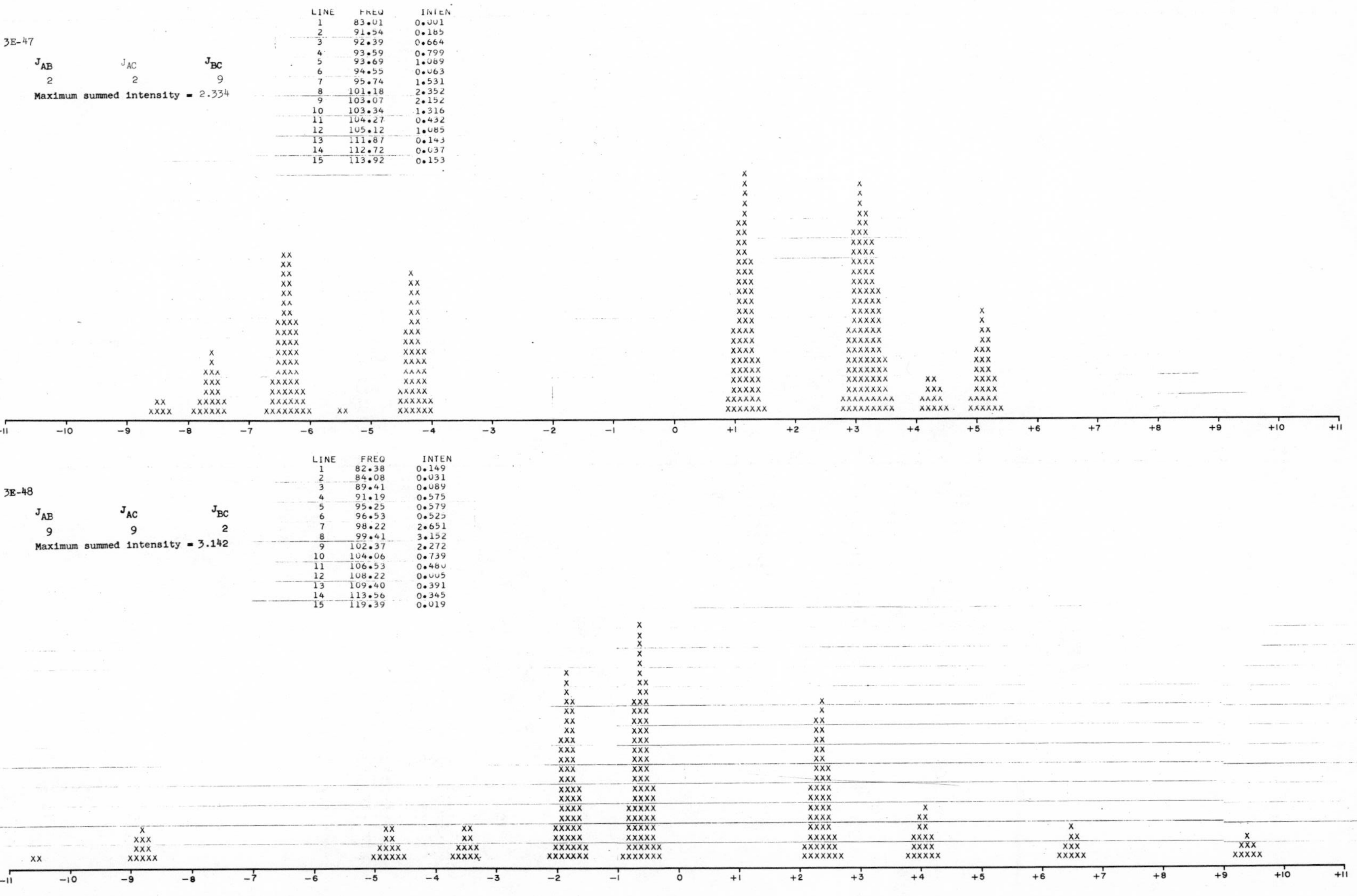

3E-48

J_{AB}	J_{AC}	J_{BC}
9	9	2

Maximum summed intensity = 3.142

LINE	FREQ	INTEN
1	82.38	0.149
2	84.08	0.031
3	89.41	0.089
4	91.19	0.575
5	95.25	0.579
6	96.53	0.525
7	98.22	2.651
8	99.41	3.152
9	102.37	2.272
10	104.06	0.739
11	106.53	0.480
12	108.22	0.005
13	109.40	0.391
14	113.56	0.345
15	119.39	0.019

3E-49

J_{AB}	J_{AC}	J_{BC}
2	2	12

Maximum summed intensity = 2.363

LINE	FREQ	INTEN
1	80.40	0.001
2	89.25	0.047
3	91.42	0.201
4	91.87	0.727
5	93.57	0.811
6	94.04	0.896
7	95.74	1.526
8	101.37	2.414
9	102.88	2.226
10	103.54	1.377
11	104.59	1.517
12	107.21	0.048
13	112.39	0.010
14	115.00	0.103
15	116.71	0.097

3E-50

J_{AB}	J_{AC}	J_{BC}
12	12	2

Maximum summed intensity = 3.405

LINE	FREQ	INTEN
1	78.08	0.099
2	81.06	0.035
3	87.68	0.027
4	88.98	0.299
5	94.00	0.429
6	95.60	0.792
7	98.58	2.765
8	99.51	3.411
9	101.92	2.473
10	104.89	0.891
11	107.42	0.337
12	110.40	0.009
13	111.52	0.190
14	117.02	0.226
15	123.34	0.018

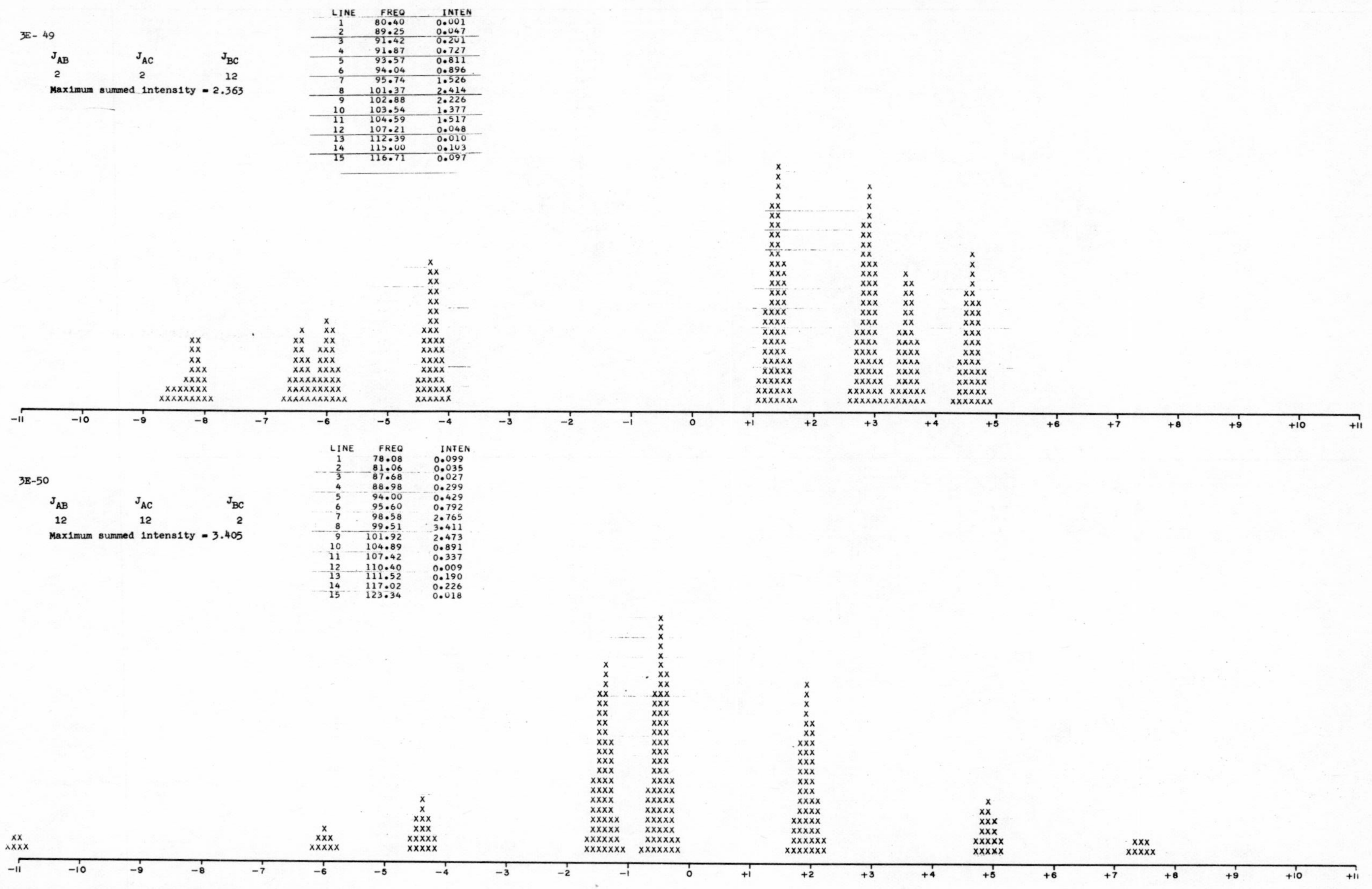

3E-51

J_{AB}	J_{AC}	J_{BC}
2	2	18

Maximum summed intensity = 2.445

LINE	FREQ	INTEN
1	74.84	0.000
2	83.51	0.041
3	85.69	0.064
4	91.82	0.666
5	93.57	0.827
6	94.00	0.983
7	95.75	1.520
8	101.58	2.466
9	102.67	2.293
10	103.76	1.432
11	104.41	1.599
12	112.43	0.003
13	112.73	0.006
14	120.75	0.052
15	122.49	0.048

−11 −10 −9 −8 −7 −6 −5 −4 −3 −2 −1 0 +1 +2 +3 +4 +5 +6 +7 +8 +9 +10 +11

3E-52

J_{AB}	J_{AC}	J_{BC}
18	18	2

Maximum summed intensity = 3.633

LINE	FREQ	INTEN
1	69.33	0.052
2	73.51	0.024
3	83.54	0.093
4	84.76	0.001
5	91.32	0.238
6	94.79	0.975
7	98.97	2.867
8	99.68	3.685
9	101.35	2.710
10	105.53	0.982
11	109.71	0.169
12	113.89	0.034
13	116.78	0.058
14	125.14	0.099
15	131.70	0.013

−11 −10 −9 −8 −7 −6 −5 −4 −3 −2 −1 0 +1 +2 +3 +4 +5 +6 +7 +8 +9 +10 +11

3E-53

J_{AB}	J_{AC}	J_{BC}
4	4	9

Maximum summed intensity = 2.757

LINE	FREQ	INTEN
1	82.55	0.003
2	89.09	0.246
3	91.41	0.378
4	92.39	0.506
5	93.64	1.138
6	95.96	0.001
7	96.94	2.046
8	100.56	2.867
9	102.50	2.376
10	103.48	0.062
11	105.11	0.812
12	105.80	1.244
13	111.65	0.179
14	113.97	0.000
15	114.95	0.141

3E-54

J_{AB}	J_{AC}	J_{BC}
9	9	4

Maximum summed intensity = 3.255

LINE	FREQ	INTEN
1	82.37	0.146
2	83.64	0.029
3	88.50	0.094
4	92.13	0.753
5	93.57	0.390
6	97.00	0.333
7	98.27	2.662
8	99.67	3.341
9	102.06	2.464
10	103.33	0.511
11	108.17	0.305
12	108.20	0.618
13	109.44	0.044
14	114.30	0.294
15	119.37	0.017

3B-55

J_{AB}	J_{AC}	J_{BC}
4	4	12

Maximum summed intensity = 2.857

LINE	FREQ	INTEN
1	79.95	0.002
2	88.00	0.000
3	89.68	0.551
4	92.35	0.521
5	92.59	0.512
6	94.27	0.576
7	96.95	2.040
8	100.73	2.925
9	102.32	2.449
10	105.00	0.980
11	105.32	0.869
12	106.68	0.368
13	113.38	0.059
14	115.05	0.056
15	117.73	0.090

3B-56

J_{AB}	J_{AC}	J_{BC}
12	12	4

Maximum summed intensity = 3.531

LINE	FREQ	INTEN
1	78.07	0.097
2	80.93	0.038
3	86.31	0.027
4	90.38	0.418
5	92.24	0.293
6	95.76	0.657
7	98.62	2.779
8	99.69	3.544
9	101.69	2.609
10	104.55	0.764
11	109.14	0.219
12	109.93	0.317
13	112.00	0.000
14	117.38	0.221
15	123.31	0.016

III-57

J_{AB}	J_{AC}	J_{BC}
4	4	18

Maximum summed intensity = 2.964

LINE	FREQ	INTEN
1	74.37	0.001
2	82.48	0.031
3	87.12	0.086
4	89.39	0.454
5	92.33	0.541
6	94.02	0.958
7	96.96	2.032
8	100.91	2.973
9	102.13	2.515
10	105.07	1.354
11	105.54	0.923
12	111.97	0.028
13	113.65	0.014
14	120.56	0.045
15	123.50	0.045

III-58

J_{AB}	J_{AC}	J_{BC}
18	18	4

Maximum summed intensity = 3.655

LINE	FREQ	INTEN
1	69.32	0.052
2	73.55	0.026
3	83.01	0.001
4	85.32	0.117
5	89.46	0.172
6	94.77	0.938
7	99.00	2.879
8	99.77	3.750
9	101.22	2.777
10	105.46	0.958
11	111.54	0.117
12	114.91	0.082
13	115.77	0.021
14	125.23	0.100
15	131.68	0.012

3E-59

J_{AB}	J_{AC}	J_{BC}
6	6	9

Maximum summed intensity = 3.188

LINE	FREQ	INTEN
1	81.90	0.005
2	86.45	0.195
3	90.47	0.277
4	90.61	0.290
5	93.52	1.110
6	97.54	0.019
7	97.69	2.400
8	100.22	3.233
9	102.09	2.528
10	102.24	0.003
11	106.26	1.172
12	107.30	0.466
13	111.85	0.164
14	115.87	0.004
15	116.01	0.134

−11 −10 −9 −8 −7 −6 −5 −4 −3 −2 −1 0 +1 +2 +3 +4 +5 +6 +7 +8 +9 +10 +11

3E-60

J_{AB}	J_{AC}	J_{BC}
9	9	6

Maximum summed intensity = 3.281

LINE	FREQ	INTEN
1	82.35	0.142
2	82.71	0.021
3	87.86	0.108
4	91.79	0.280
5	92.78	0.920
6	97.93	0.156
7	98.30	2.668
8	99.84	3.449
9	101.86	2.578
10	102.23	0.280
11	107.38	0.847
12	109.91	0.205
13	110.28	0.111
14	115.43	0.221
15	119.36	0.015

−11 −10 −9 −8 −7 −6 −5 −4 −3 −2 −1 0 +1 +2 +3 +4 +5 +6 +7 +8 +9 +10 +11

3E-61

J_{AB}	J_{AC}	J_{BC}
6	6	12

Maximum summed intensity = 3.095

LINE	FREQ	INTEN
1	79.30	0.004
2	86.06	0.073
3	88.00	0.333
4	90.53	0.303
5	93.24	0.982
6	95.17	0.100
7	97.71	2.397
8	100.36	3.286
9	101.94	2.593
10	104.47	0.242
11	106.41	0.971
12	107.53	0.517
13	114.29	0.109
14	116.23	0.002
15	118.76	0.085

3E-62

J_{AB}	J_{AC}	J_{BC}
12	12	6

Maximum summed intensity = 3.612

LINE	FREQ	INTEN
1	78.05	0.096
2	80.46	0.034
3	85.11	0.035
4	90.41	0.213
5	91.59	0.610
6	96.25	0.453
7	98.65	2.788
8	99.81	3.622
9	101.54	2.691
10	103.95	0.556
11	108.60	0.524
12	110.94	0.151
13	113.35	0.012
14	118.00	0.200
15	123.29	0.015

3E-63

J_{AB}	J_{AC}	J_{BC}
6	6	18

Maximum summed intensity = 3.325

LINE	FREQ	INTEN
1	73.73	0.002
2	81.43	0.020
3	86.81	0.326
4	88.69	0.125
5	90.47	0.321
6	94.06	0.915
7	97.73	2.392
8	100.51	3.331
9	101.76	2.654
10	105.43	1.174
11	107.76	0.565
12	110.80	0.071
13	115.47	0.027
14	120.84	0.034
15	124.51	0.043

−11 −10 −9 −8 −7 −6 −5 −4 −3 −2 −1 0 +1 +2 +3 +4 +5 +6 +7 +8 +9 +10 +11

3E-64

J_{AB}	J_{AC}	J_{BC}
18	18	6

Maximum summed intensity = 3.642

LINE	FREQ	INTEN
1	69.31	0.051
2	73.51	0.028
3	81.26	0.001
4	87.09	0.158
5	87.56	0.130
6	94.83	0.887
7	99.03	2.887
8	99.84	3.790
9	101.13	2.819
10	105.34	0.917
11	113.08	0.123
12	113.41	0.085
13	117.61	0.011
14	125.35	0.102
15	131.66	0.012

−11 −10 −9 −8 −7 −6 −5 −4 −3 −2 −1 0 +1 +2 +3 +4 +5 +6 +7 +8 +9 +10 +11

3E-65

J_{AB}	J_{AC}	J_{BC}
9	9	12

Maximum summed intensity = 3.580

LINE	FREQ	INTEN
1	78.10	0.007
2	82.16	0.105
3	86.29	0.170
4	87.16	0.138
5	93.35	1.074
6	97.48	0.001
7	98.36	2.676
8	100.10	3.580
9	101.55	2.724
10	102.42	0.006
11	106.55	1.099
12	111.29	0.243
13	115.35	0.090
14	119.48	0.006
15	120.36	0.082

−11 −10 −9 −8 −7 −6 −5 −4 −3 −2 −1 0 +1 +2 +3 +4 +5 +6 +7 +8 +9 +10 +11

3E-66

J_{AB}	J_{AC}	J_{BC}
12	12	9

Maximum summed intensity = 3.611

LINE	FREQ	INTEN
1	78.02	0.091
2	78.95	0.020
3	83.97	0.054
4	87.60	0.147
5	92.74	0.904
6	97.76	0.148
7	98.69	2.796
8	99.93	3.688
9	101.39	2.762
10	102.32	0.212
11	107.34	0.866
12	113.72	0.095
13	114.65	0.068
14	119.67	0.136
15	123.29	0.013

−11 −10 −9 −8 −7 −6 −5 −4 −3 −2 −1 0 +1 +2 +3 +4 +5 +6 +7 +8 +9 +10 +11

3E-67

J_{AB}	J_{AC}	J_{BC}
9	9	18

Maximum summed intensity = 3.603

LINE	FREQ	INTEN
1	72.56	0.003
2	79.69	0.003
3	82.91	0.224
4	87.02	0.150
5	91.06	0.298
6	94.27	0.739
7	98.39	2.677
8	100.21	3.620
9	101.40	2.773
10	105.52	0.883
11	108.73	0.249
12	111.58	0.283
13	118.71	0.042
14	121.92	0.015
15	126.04	0.040

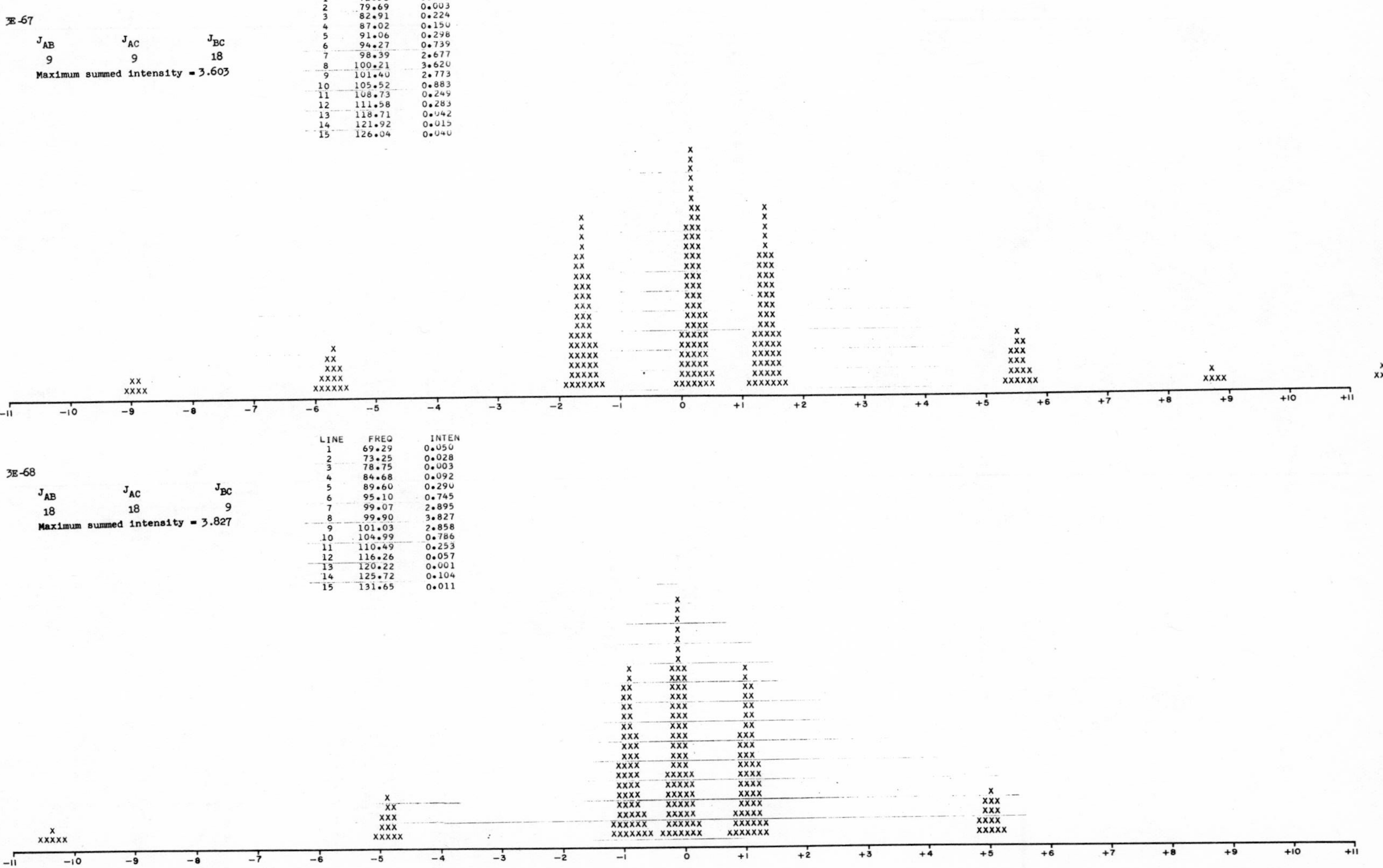

3E-68

J_{AB}	J_{AC}	J_{BC}
18	18	9

Maximum summed intensity = 3.827

LINE	FREQ	INTEN
1	69.29	0.050
2	73.25	0.028
3	78.75	0.003
4	84.68	0.092
5	89.60	0.290
6	95.10	0.745
7	99.07	2.895
8	99.90	3.827
9	101.03	2.858
10	104.99	0.786
11	110.49	0.253
12	116.26	0.057
13	120.22	0.001
14	125.72	0.104
15	131.65	0.011

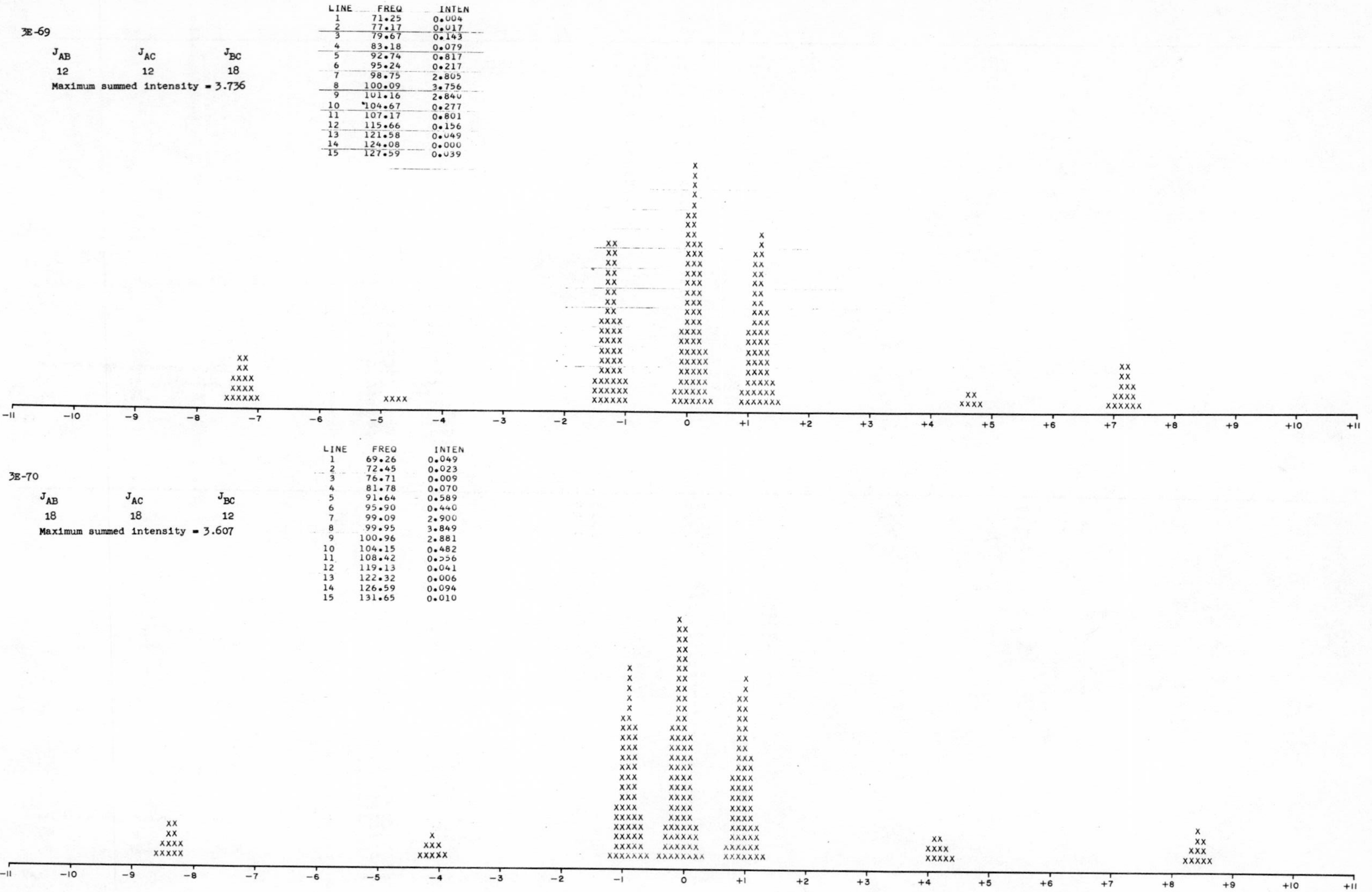

3E-69

J_{AB}	J_{AC}	J_{BC}
12	12	18

Maximum summed intensity = 3.736

LINE	FREQ	INTEN
1	71.25	0.004
2	77.17	0.017
3	79.67	0.143
4	83.18	0.079
5	92.74	0.817
6	95.24	0.217
7	98.75	2.805
8	100.09	3.756
9	101.16	2.840
10	104.67	0.277
11	107.17	0.801
12	115.66	0.156
13	121.58	0.049
14	124.08	0.000
15	127.59	0.039

3E-70

J_{AB}	J_{AC}	J_{BC}
18	18	12

Maximum summed intensity = 3.607

LINE	FREQ	INTEN
1	69.26	0.049
2	72.45	0.023
3	76.71	0.009
4	81.78	0.070
5	91.64	0.589
6	95.90	0.440
7	99.09	2.900
8	99.95	3.849
9	100.96	2.881
10	104.15	0.482
11	108.42	0.556
12	119.13	0.041
13	122.32	0.006
14	126.59	0.094
15	131.65	0.010

3E-71

J_{AB}	J_{AC}	J_{BC}
1	2	4

Maximum summed intensity = 1.867

LINE	FREQ	INTEN
1	86.63	0.002
2	92.39	0.719
3	93.53	0.969
4	94.22	0.930
5	95.37	1.374
6	96.86	0.449
7	98.00	0.435
8	100.88	1.900
9	101.12	0.007
10	102.02	1.220
11	103.76	1.832
12	105.59	1.284
13	107.78	0.473
14	109.61	0.406
15	112.25	0.000

−11 −10 −9 −8 −7 −6 −5 −4 −3 −2 −1 0 +1 +2 +3 +4 +5 +6 +7 +8 +9 +10 +11

3E-72

J_{AB}	J_{AC}	J_{BC}
1	4	2

Maximum summed intensity = 1.806

LINE	FREQ	INTEN
1	87.02	0.004
2	91.15	0.606
3	92.29	0.774
4	94.96	0.983
5	96.11	1.592
6	98.29	0.601
7	99.44	0.740
8	100.24	0.044
9	100.33	1.806
10	101.47	0.890
11	103.56	1.793
12	105.60	0.783
13	107.38	0.863
14	109.42	0.518
15	112.74	0.002

−11 −10 −9 −8 −7 −6 −5 −4 −3 −2 −1 0 +1 +2 +3 +4 +5 +6 +7 +8 +9 +10 +11

3E-73

J_{AB}	J_{AC}	J_{BC}
2	1	4

Maximum summed intensity = 1.843

LINE	FREQ	INTEN
1	86.73	0.000
2	92.29	0.588
3	93.36	0.764
4	94.25	1.205
5	95.32	1.419
6	96.60	0.717
7	98.56	0.194
8	100.56	1.931
9	100.88	0.024
10	102.52	1.182
11	104.12	1.695
12	105.19	1.394
13	108.08	0.488
14	109.15	0.399
15	112.39	0.001

3E-74

J_{AB}	J_{AC}	J_{BC}
2	4	1

Maximum summed intensity = 1.806

LINE	FREQ	INTEN
1	87.26	0.002
2	90.58	0.518
3	92.62	0.863
4	94.40	0.783
5	96.44	1.793
6	98.53	0.890
7	99.67	1.806
8	99.76	0.044
9	100.56	0.740
10	101.71	0.601
11	103.89	1.592
12	105.04	0.983
13	107.71	0.774
14	108.85	0.606
15	112.98	0.004

3E-75

J_{AB}	J_{AC}	J_{BC}
4	1	2

Maximum summed intensity = 1.843

LINE	FREQ	INTEN
1	87.61	0.001
2	90.85	0.399
3	91.92	0.488
4	94.81	1.394
5	95.88	1.695
6	97.48	1.182
7	99.12	0.024
8	99.44	1.931
9	101.44	0.194
10	103.40	0.717
11	104.68	1.419
12	105.75	1.205
13	106.64	0.764
14	107.71	0.588
15	113.27	0.000

−11 −10 −9 −8 −7 −6 −5 −4 −3 −2 −1 0 +1 +2 +3 +4 +5 +6 +7 +8 +9 +10 +11

3E-76

J_{AB}	J_{AC}	J_{BC}
4	2	1

Maximum summed intensity = 1.867

LINE	FREQ	INTEN
1	87.75	0.000
2	90.39	0.406
3	92.22	0.473
4	94.41	1.284
5	96.24	1.832
6	97.98	1.220
7	98.88	0.007
8	99.12	1.900
9	102.00	0.435
10	103.14	0.449
11	104.63	1.374
12	105.78	0.930
13	106.47	0.969
14	107.61	0.719
15	113.37	0.002

−11 −10 −9 −8 −7 −6 −5 −4 −3 −2 −1 0 +1 +2 +3 +4 +5 +6 +7 +8 +9 +10 +11

3E-77

J_{AB}	J_{AC}	J_{BC}
2	4	6

Maximum summed intensity = 2.399

LINE	FREQ	INTEN
1	84.91	0.007
2	90.58	0.531
3	93.14	0.901
4	93.88	0.735
5	94.60	0.240
6	96.44	1.781
7	97.16	0.352
8	100.73	2.487
9	102.11	0.051
10	102.83	2.229
11	103.30	0.960
12	106.13	1.175
13	108.97	0.288
14	112.27	0.259
15	112.99	0.005

−11 −10 −9 −8 −7 −6 −5 −4 −3 −2 −1 0 +1 +2 +3 +4 +5 +6 +7 +8 +9 +10 +11

3E-78

J_{AB}	J_{AC}	J_{BC}
2	6	4

Maximum summed intensity = 2.545

LINE	FREQ	INTEN
1	85.38	0.014
2	89.20	0.449
3	91.82	0.698
4	94.38	0.683
5	96.18	0.284
6	97.00	2.000
7	98.80	0.621
8	100.38	2.569
9	100.82	0.166
10	102.62	2.267
11	103.00	0.667
12	106.82	0.420
13	107.80	0.817
14	112.00	0.333
15	113.80	0.011

−11 −10 −9 −8 −7 −6 −5 −4 −3 −2 −1 0 +1 +2 +3 +4 +5 +6 +7 +8 +9 +10 +11

III-79

J_{AB}	J_{AC}	J_{BC}
4	2	6

Maximum summed intensity = 2.329

LINE	FREQ	INTEN
1	85.26	0.000
2	90.17	0.299
3	92.39	0.545
4	94.09	1.223
5	94.50	0.685
6	96.31	1.817
7	98.43	0.006
8	100.36	2.470
9	101.22	0.117
10	103.33	2.015
11	104.28	0.954
12	105.55	1.291
13	109.18	0.345
14	111.41	0.229
15	113.52	0.002

III-80

J_{AB}	J_{AC}	J_{BC}
4	6	2

Maximum summed intensity = 2.545

LINE	FREQ	INTEN
1	86.20	0.011
2	88.00	0.333
3	92.20	0.817
4	93.18	0.420
5	97.00	0.667
6	97.38	2.267
7	99.18	0.166
8	99.62	2.569
9	101.20	0.621
10	103.00	2.000
11	103.82	0.284
12	105.62	0.683
13	108.18	0.698
14	110.80	0.449
15	114.62	0.014

XE-81

J_{AB}	J_{AC}	J_{BC}
6	2	4

Maximum summed intensity = 2.329

LINE	FREQ	INTEN
1	86.48	0.002
2	88.59	0.229
3	90.82	0.345
4	94.45	1.291
5	95.72	0.954
6	96.67	2.015
7	98.78	0.117
8	99.64	2.470
9	101.57	0.006
10	103.69	1.817
11	105.50	0.685
12	105.91	1.223
13	107.61	0.545
14	109.83	0.299
15	114.74	0.000

XE-82

J_{AB}	J_{AC}	J_{BC}
6	4	2

Maximum summed intensity = 2.339

LINE	FREQ	INTEN
1	87.01	0.005
2	87.73	0.259
3	91.03	0.288
4	93.87	1.175
5	96.70	0.960
6	97.17	2.229
7	97.89	0.051
8	99.27	2.487
9	102.84	0.352
10	103.56	1.781
11	105.40	0.240
12	106.12	0.735
13	106.86	0.901
14	109.42	0.531
15	115.09	0.007

3E-83

J_{AB}	J_{AC}	J_{BC}
1	1	-1

Maximum summed intensity = 1.976

LINE	FREQ	INTEN
1	87.87	0.000
2	92.94	0.778
3	93.93	1.053
4	93.94	0.892
5	94.93	1.276
6	99.01	1.015
7	100.00	0.002
8	100.00	1.316
9	100.00	0.659
10	100.99	1.012
11	105.07	1.261
12	106.06	0.906
13	106.07	1.066
14	107.06	0.765
15	112.13	0.000

3E-84

J_{AB}	J_{AC}	J_{BC}
1	-1	1

Maximum summed intensity = 1.880

LINE	FREQ	INTEN
1	87.87	0.000
2	92.97	0.786
3	93.93	0.877
4	93.95	1.053
5	94.90	1.274
6	99.02	1.069
7	100.00	1.267
8	100.00	0.010
9	100.00	0.603
10	100.98	1.069
11	105.10	1.274
12	106.05	1.053
13	106.07	0.877
14	107.03	0.786
15	112.13	0.000

3E-85

J_{AB}	J_{AC}	J_{BC}
-1	1	1

Maximum summed intensity = 1.976

LINE	FREQ	INTEN
1	87.87	0.000
2	92.94	0.765
3	93.93	1.066
4	93.94	0.906
5	94.93	1.261
6	99.01	1.012
7	100.00	0.002
8	100.00	1.316
9	100.00	0.659
10	100.99	1.015
11	105.07	1.276
12	106.06	0.892
13	106.07	1.053
14	107.06	0.778
15	112.13	0.000

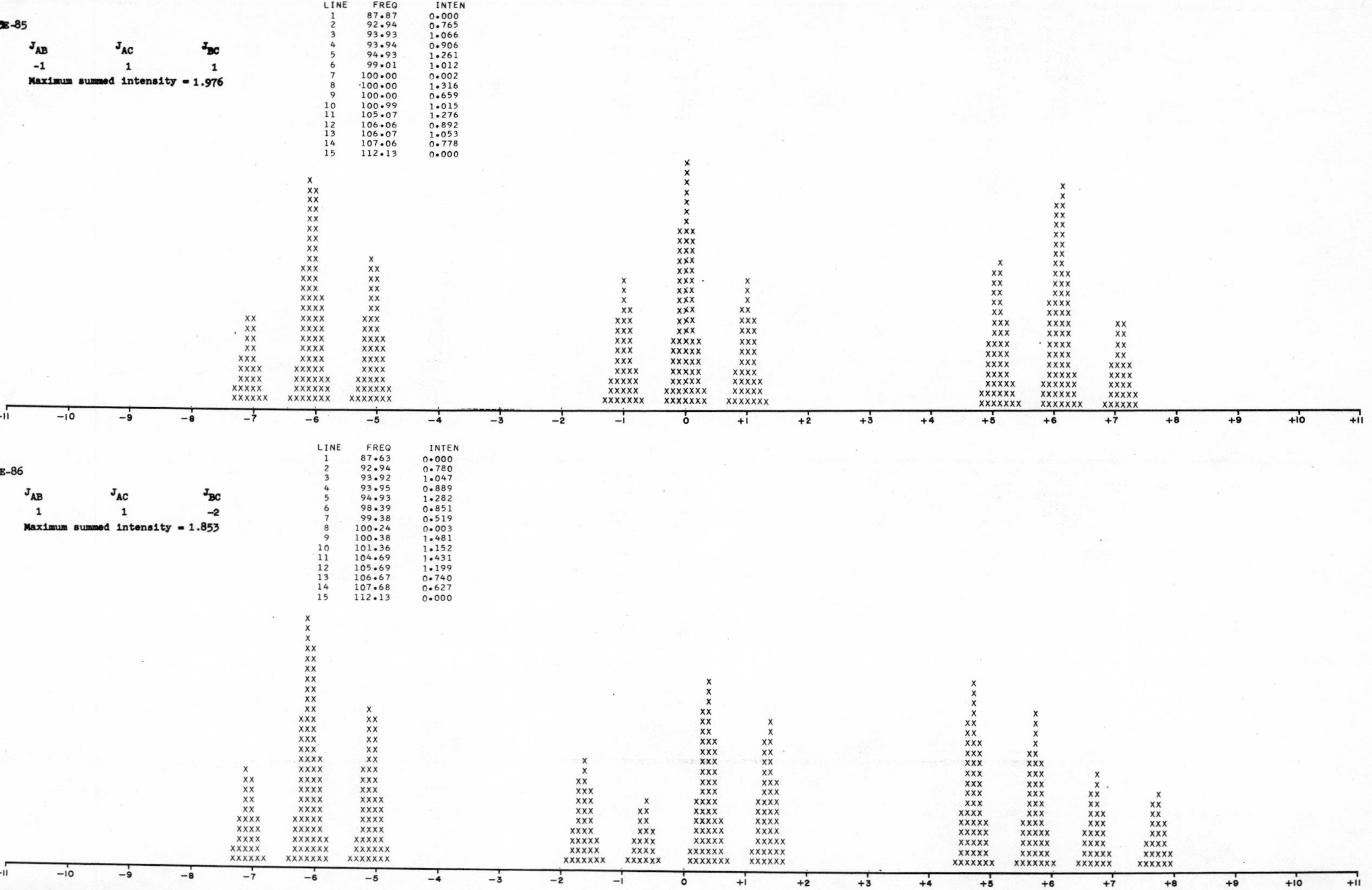

3E-86

J_{AB}	J_{AC}	J_{BC}
1	1	-2

Maximum summed intensity = 1.853

LINE	FREQ	INTEN
1	87.63	0.000
2	92.94	0.780
3	93.92	1.047
4	93.95	0.889
5	94.93	1.282
6	98.39	0.851
7	99.38	0.519
8	100.24	0.003
9	100.38	1.481
10	101.36	1.152
11	104.69	1.431
12	105.69	1.199
13	106.67	0.740
14	107.68	0.627
15	112.13	0.000

3E-87

J_{AB}	J_{AC}	J_{BC}
1	-2	1

Maximum summed intensity = 1.793

LINE	FREQ	INTEN
1	87.74	0.001
2	92.43	0.726
3	93.39	0.952
4	94.35	0.922
5	95.32	1.376
6	99.04	1.127
7	100.00	0.024
8	100.00	0.544
9	100.00	1.224
10	100.96	1.127
11	104.68	1.376
12	105.65	0.922
13	106.61	0.952
14	107.57	0.726
15	112.26	0.001

−11 −10 −9 −8 −7 −6 −5 −4 −3 −2 −1 0 +1 +2 +3 +4 +5 +6 +7 +8 +9 +10 +11

3E-88

J_{AB}	J_{AC}	J_{BC}
-2	1	1

Maximum summed intensity = 1.853

LINE	FREQ	INTEN
1	87.87	0.000
2	92.32	0.627
3	93.33	0.740
4	94.31	1.199
5	95.31	1.431
6	98.64	1.152
7	99.62	1.481
8	99.76	0.003
9	100.62	0.519
10	101.61	0.851
11	105.07	1.282
12	106.05	0.889
13	106.08	1.047
14	107.06	0.780
15	112.37	0.000

−11 −10 −9 −8 −7 −6 −5 −4 −3 −2 −1 0 +1 +2 +3 +4 +5 +6 +7 +8 +9 +10 +11

3E-89

J_{AB}	J_{AC}	J_{BC}
1	1	-4

Maximum summed intensity = 1.881

LINE	FREQ	INTEN
1	86.74	0.000
2	92.94	0.783
3	93.91	1.033
4	93.96	0.872
5	94.92	1.304
6	96.96	0.607
7	97.93	0.292
8	100.94	1.739
9	101.12	0.010
10	101.91	1.371
11	104.13	1.696
12	105.14	1.404
13	108.11	0.478
14	109.12	0.410
15	112.13	0.001

3E-90

J_{AB}	J_{AC}	J_{BC}
1	-4	1

Maximum summed intensity = 1.652

LINE	FREQ	INTEN
1	87.25	0.004
2	91.22	0.606
3	92.16	0.766
4	95.09	0.987
5	96.03	1.564
6	99.07	1.247
7	100.00	0.077
8	100.00	0.419
9	100.00	1.157
10	100.93	1.247
11	103.97	1.564
12	104.91	0.987
13	107.84	0.766
14	108.78	0.606
15	112.75	0.004

III-91

J_{AB}	J_{AC}	J_{BC}
-4	1	1

Maximum summed intensity = 1.821

LINE	FREQ	INTEN
1	87.87	0.001
2	90.88	0.410
3	91.89	0.478
4	94.86	1.404
5	95.87	1.696
6	98.09	1.371
7	98.88	0.010
8	99.06	1.739
9	102.07	0.292
10	103.04	0.607
11	105.08	1.304
12	106.04	0.872
13	106.09	1.033
14	107.06	0.783
15	113.26	0.000

III-92

J_{AB}	J_{AC}	J_{BC}
1	1	-6

Maximum summed intensity = 1.899

LINE	FREQ	INTEN
1	85.47	0.000
2	92.94	0.785
3	93.91	1.020
4	93.94	0.780
5	94.90	1.367
6	95.35	0.532
7	96.31	0.100
8	101.31	1.903
9	102.27	1.512
10	102.38	0.053
11	103.79	1.829
12	104.79	1.533
13	109.75	0.312
14	110.74	0.267
15	112.15	0.005

3E-93

J_{AB}	J_{AC}	J_{BC}
1	-6	1

Maximum summed intensity = 1.705

LINE	FREQ	INTEN
1	86.46	0.007
2	89.87	0.495
3	90.78	0.611
4	95.68	1.017
5	96.59	1.715
6	99.10	1.373
7	100.00	0.295
8	100.00	1.109
9	100.00	0.163
10	100.90	1.373
11	103.41	1.715
12	104.32	1.017
13	109.22	0.611
14	110.13	0.495
15	113.54	0.007

-11 -10 -9 -8 -7 -6 -5 -4 -3 -2 -1 0 +1 +2 +3 +4 +5 +6 +7 +8 +9 +10 +11

3E-94

J_{AB}	J_{AC}	J_{BC}
-6	1	1

Maximum summed intensity = 1.899

LINE	FREQ	INTEN
1	87.85	0.005
2	89.26	0.267
3	90.25	0.312
4	95.21	1.533
5	96.21	1.829
6	97.62	0.053
7	97.73	1.512
8	98.69	1.903
9	103.69	0.100
10	104.65	0.532
11	105.10	1.367
12	106.06	0.780
13	106.09	1.020
14	107.06	0.785
15	114.53	0.000

-11 -10 -9 -8 -7 -6 -5 -4 -3 -2 -1 0 +1 +2 +3 +4 +5 +6 +7 +8 +9 +10 +11

3E-95

J_{AB}	J_{AC}	J_{BC}
2	2	-2

Maximum summed intensity = 1.948

LINE	FREQ	INTEN
1	87.50	0.000
2	91.79	0.608
3	93.71	1.039
4	93.79	0.744
5	95.71	1.585
6	98.08	1.060
7	100.00	0.333
8	100.00	0.026
9	100.00	1.588
10	101.92	1.042
11	104.29	1.523
12	106.21	0.804
13	106.29	1.081
14	108.21	0.563
15	112.50	0.003

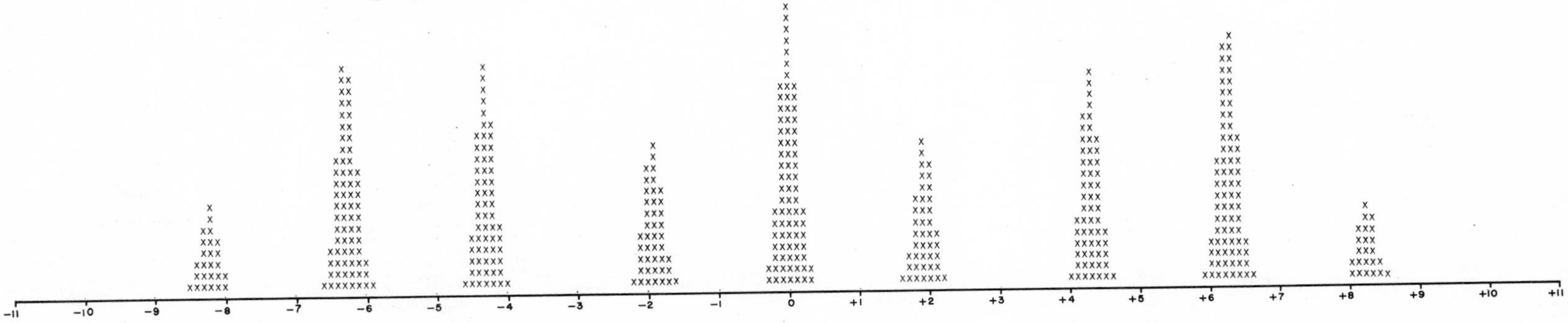

−11 −10 −9 −8 −7 −6 −5 −4 −3 −2 −1 0 +1 +2 +3 +4 +5 +6 +7 +8 +9 +10 +11

3E-96

J_{AB}	J_{AC}	J_{BC}
2	-2	2

Maximum summed intensity = 1.751

LINE	FREQ	INTEN
1	87.46	0.006
2	91.98	0.632
3	93.65	0.670
4	93.81	1.063
5	95.48	1.486
6	98.17	1.266
7	100.00	0.148
8	100.00	0.178
9	100.00	1.425
10	101.83	1.266
11	104.52	1.486
12	106.19	1.063
13	106.35	0.670
14	108.02	0.632
15	112.54	0.006

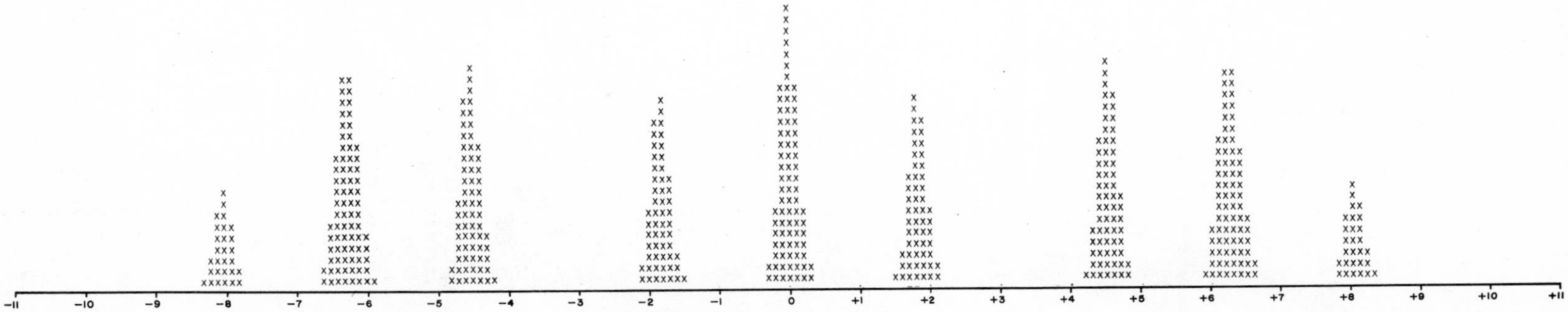

−11 −10 −9 −8 −7 −6 −5 −4 −3 −2 −1 0 +1 +2 +3 +4 +5 +6 +7 +8 +9 +10 +11

3E-97

J_{AB}	J_{AC}	J_{BC}
-2	2	2

Maximum summed intensity = 1.948

LINE	FREQ	INTEN
1	87.50	0.003
2	91.79	0.563
3	93.71	1.081
4	93.79	0.804
5	95.71	1.523
6	98.08	1.042
7	100.00	0.333
8	100.00	0.026
9	100.00	1.588
10	101.92	1.060
11	104.29	1.585
12	106.21	0.744
13	106.29	1.039
14	108.21	0.608
15	112.50	0.000

−11 −10 −9 −8 −7 −6 −5 −4 −3 −2 −1 0 +1 +2 +3 +4 +5 +6 +7 +8 +9 +10 +11

3E-98

J_{AB}	J_{AC}	J_{BC}
2	2	-4

Maximum summed intensity = 1.840

LINE	FREQ	INTEN
1	86.60	0.000
2	91.79	0.612
3	93.66	1.006
4	93.81	0.702
5	95.68	1.621
6	96.69	0.815
7	98.55	0.132
8	100.57	1.871
9	100.87	0.065
10	102.44	1.241
11	103.75	1.800
12	105.77	1.247
13	107.63	0.517
14	109.65	0.364
15	112.53	0.006

−11 −10 −9 −8 −7 −6 −5 −4 −3 −2 −1 0 +1 +2 +3 +4 +5 +6 +7 +8 +9 +10 +11

3E-99

J_{AB}	J_{AC}	J_{BC}
2	-4	2

Maximum summed intensity = 1.740

LINE	FREQ	INTEN
1	86.92	0.016
2	90.89	0.534
3	92.60	0.849
4	94.31	0.654
5	96.02	1.580
6	98.29	1.497
7	100.00	1.299
8	100.00	0.383
9	100.00	0.058
10	101.71	1.497
11	103.98	1.580
12	105.69	0.654
13	107.40	0.849
14	109.11	0.534
15	113.08	0.016

3E-100

J_{AB}	J_{AC}	J_{BC}
-4	2	2

Maximum summed intensity = 1.840

LINE	FREQ	INTEN
1	87.47	0.006
2	90.35	0.364
3	92.37	0.517
4	94.23	1.247
5	96.25	1.800
6	97.56	1.241
7	99.13	0.065
8	99.43	1.871
9	101.45	0.132
10	103.31	0.815
11	104.32	1.621
12	106.19	0.702
13	106.34	1.006
14	108.21	0.612
15	113.40	0.000

3E-101

J_{AB}	J_{AC}	J_{BC}
2	2	-6

Maximum summed intensity = 1.913

LINE	FREQ	INTEN
1	85.32	0.000
2	91.79	0.615
3	93.63	0.979
4	93.74	0.489
5	95.16	0.846
6	95.58	1.652
7	97.00	0.000
8	100.95	2.050
9	102.05	0.291
10	102.78	1.368
11	103.48	1.780
12	105.42	1.348
13	109.26	0.335
14	111.21	0.220
15	112.63	0.027

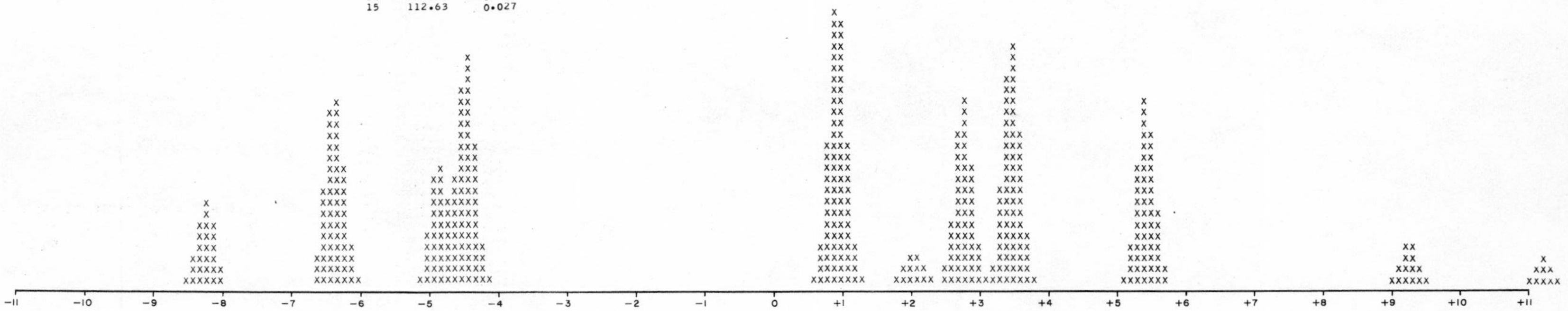

3E-102

J_{AB}	J_{AC}	J_{BC}
2	-6	2

Maximum summed intensity = 1.925

LINE	FREQ	INTEN
1	86.07	0.027
2	89.65	0.434
3	91.24	0.670
4	94.83	0.606
5	96.42	1.576
6	98.41	1.724
7	100.00	1.209
8	100.00	0.713
9	100.00	0.003
10	101.59	1.724
11	103.58	1.576
12	105.17	0.606
13	108.76	0.670
14	110.35	0.434
15	113.93	0.027

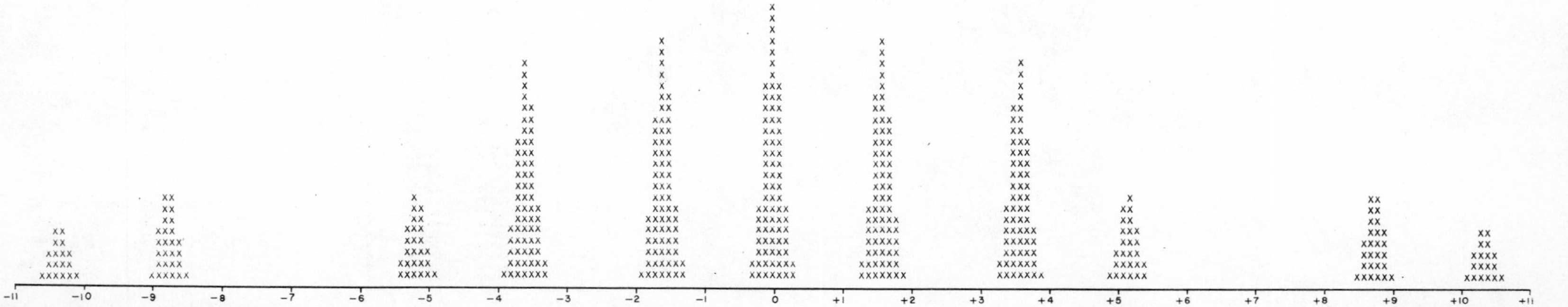

3E-103

J_{AB}	J_{AC}	J_{BC}
-6	2	2

Maximum summed intensity = 1.913

LINE	FREQ	INTEN
1	87.37	0.027
2	88.79	0.220
3	90.74	0.335
4	94.58	1.348
5	96.52	1.780
6	97.22	1.366
7	97.95	0.291
8	99.05	2.050
9	103.00	0.000
10	104.42	1.652
11	104.84	0.846
12	106.26	0.489
13	106.37	0.979
14	108.21	0.615
15	114.68	0.000

-11 -10 -9 -8 -7 -6 -5 -4 -3 -2 -1 0 +1 +2 +3 +4 +5 +6 +7 +8 +9 +10 +11

3E-104

J_{AB}	J_{AC}	J_{BC}
4	4	-4

Maximum summed intensity = 2.799

LINE	FREQ	INTEN
1	85.99	0.000
2	89.28	0.385
3	92.71	0.829
4	93.28	0.410
5	96.57	1.205
6	96.71	2.067
7	100.00	0.333
8	100.00	2.000
9	100.00	0.000
10	103.29	1.837
11	103.43	1.104
12	106.72	0.615
13	107.29	0.933
14	110.72	0.257
15	114.01	0.025

-11 -10 -9 -8 -7 -6 -5 -4 -3 -2 -1 0 +1 +2 +3 +4 +5 +6 +7 +8 +9 +10 +11

E-105

J_{AB}	J_{AC}	J_{BC}
4	-4	4

Maximum summed intensity = 2.985

LINE	FREQ	INTEN
1	85.62	0.043
2	90.60	0.422
3	92.21	0.231
4	93.41	1.018
5	95.02	1.043
6	97.20	1.752
7	100.00	1.287
8	100.00	1.553
9	100.00	0.145
10	102.80	1.752
11	104.98	1.043
12	106.59	1.018
13	107.79	0.231
14	109.40	0.422
15	114.38	0.043

E-106

J_{AB}	J_{AC}	J_{BC}
-4	4	4

Maximum summed intensity = 2.799

LINE	FREQ	INTEN
1	85.99	0.025
2	89.28	0.257
3	92.71	0.933
4	93.28	0.615
5	96.57	1.104
6	96.71	1.837
7	100.00	0.333
8	100.00	2.000
9	100.00	0.000
10	103.29	2.067
11	103.43	1.205
12	106.72	0.410
13	107.29	0.829
14	110.72	0.385
15	114.01	0.000

3E-107

J_{AB}	J_{AC}	J_{BC}
4	4	-6

Maximum summed intensity = 2.218

LINE	FREQ	INTEN
1	84.68	0.001
2	89.29	0.388
3	92.58	0.778
4	93.13	0.212
5	95.27	1.180
6	96.43	1.846
7	98.56	0.177
8	100.40	2.220
9	101.03	0.830
10	103.17	1.611
11	103.70	1.199
12	107.01	0.977
13	108.31	0.392
14	112.15	0.135
15	114.29	0.055

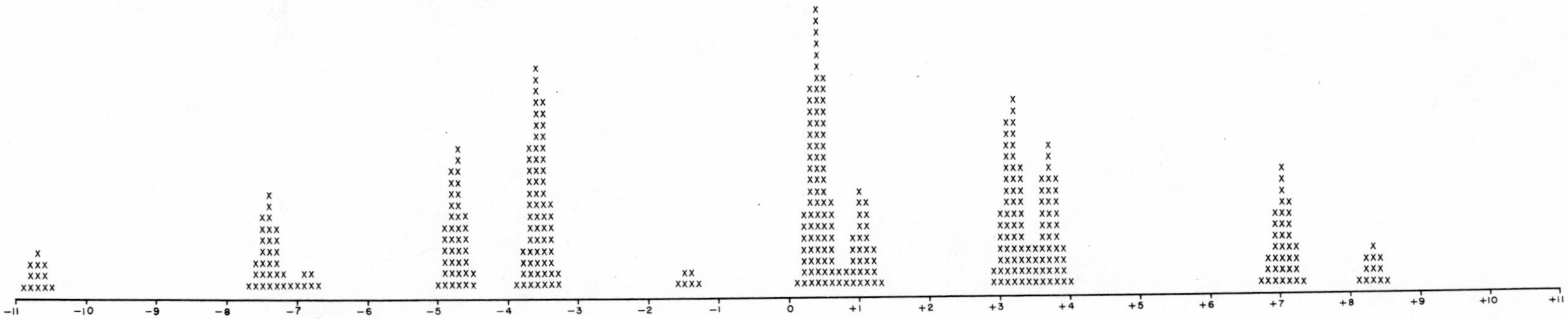

−11 −10 −9 −8 −7 −6 −5 −4 −3 −2 −1 0 +1 +2 +3 +4 +5 +6 +7 +8 +9 +10 +11

3E-108

J_{AB}	J_{AC}	J_{BC}
4	-6	4

Maximum summed intensity = 3.515

LINE	FREQ	INTEN
1	84.64	0.059
2	89.65	0.346
3	92.10	0.797
4	92.54	0.183
5	94.99	0.837
6	97.56	2.020
7	100.00	1.836
8	100.00	0.286
9	100.00	1.392
10	102.44	2.020
11	105.01	0.837
12	107.46	0.183
13	107.90	0.797
14	110.35	0.346
15	115.36	0.059

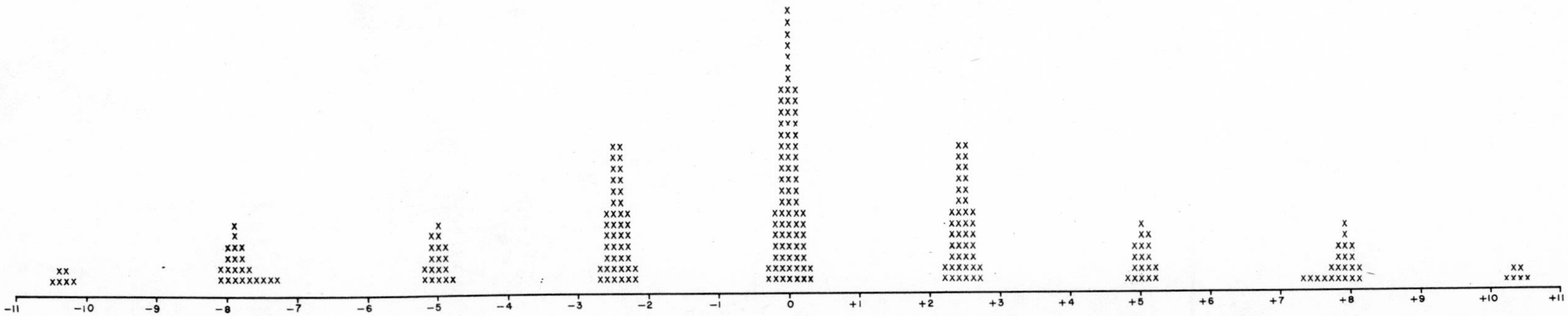

−11 −10 −9 −8 −7 −6 −5 −4 −3 −2 −1 0 +1 +2 +3 +4 +5 +6 +7 +8 +9 +10 +11

3E-109

J_{AB}	J_{AC}	J_{BC}
-6	4	4

Maximum summed intensity = 2.218

LINE	FREQ	INTEN
1	85.71	0.055
2	87.85	0.135
3	91.69	0.392
4	92.99	0.977
5	96.30	1.199
6	96.83	1.611
7	98.97	0.830
8	99.60	2.220
9	101.44	0.177
10	103.57	1.846
11	104.73	1.180
12	106.87	0.212
13	107.42	0.778
14	110.71	0.388
15	115.32	0.001

−11 −10 −9 −8 −7 −6 −5 −4 −3 −2 −1 0 +1 +2 +3 +4 +5 +6 +7 +8 +9 +10 +11

3E-110

J_{AB}	J_{AC}	J_{BC}
1	2	-1

Maximum summed intensity =1.976

LINE	FREQ	INTEN
1	87.75	0.000
2	92.39	0.715
3	93.37	0.952
4	94.39	0.954
5	95.37	1.379
6	99.02	1.016
7	100.00	0.002
8	100.00	0.659
9	100.00	1.316
10	100.98	1.011
11	104.63	1.362
12	105.61	0.969
13	106.63	0.963
14	107.61	0.703
15	112.25	0.000

−11 −10 −9 −8 −7 −6 −5 −4 −3 −2 −1 0 +1 +2 +3 +4 +5 +6 +7 +8 +9 +10 +11

3E-111

J_{AB}	J_{AC}	J_{BC}
2	1	-1

Maximum summed intensity = 1.911

LINE	FREQ	INTEN
1	87.87	0.000
2	92.34	0.651
3	93.32	0.711
4	94.31	1.177
5	95.29	1.450
6	98.66	1.205
7	99.61	1.433
8	99.76	0.011
9	100.63	0.476
10	101.59	0.897
11	105.10	1.244
12	106.05	0.916
13	106.08	1.074
14	107.03	0.754
15	112.37	0.001

−11 −10 −9 −8 −7 −6 −5 −4 −3 −2 −1 0 +1 +2 +3 +4 +5 +6 +7 +8 +9 +10 +11

3E-112

J_{AB}	J_{AC}	J_{BC}
2	2	-1

Maximum summed intensity = 1.666

LINE	FREQ	INTEN
1	87.74	0.000
2	91.79	0.605
3	93.74	1.056
4	93.76	0.750
5	95.72	1.574
6	98.68	1.236
7	99.61	1.409
8	99.76	0.017
9	100.63	0.456
10	101.56	0.915
11	104.67	1.336
12	105.60	0.986
13	106.65	0.970
14	107.58	0.689
15	112.50	0.002

−11 −10 −9 −8 −7 −6 −5 −4 −3 −2 −1 0 +1 +2 +3 +4 +5 +6 +7 +8 +9 +10 +11

3E-113

J_{AB}	J_{AC}	J_{BC}
1	4	-1

Maximum summed intensity = 1.976

LINE	FREQ	INTEN
1	87.27	0.000
2	91.16	0.596
3	92.11	0.764
4	95.16	1.071
5	96.11	1.568
6	99.06	1.017
7	100.00	0.002
8	100.00	1.316
9	100.00	0.659
10	100.94	1.009
11	103.89	1.550
12	104.84	1.088
13	107.89	0.774
14	108.84	0.586
15	112.73	0.001

-11 -10 -9 -8 -7 -6 -5 -4 -3 -2 -1 0 +1 +2 +3 +4 +5 +6 +7 +8 +9 +10 +11

3E-114

J_{AB}	J_{AC}	J_{BC}
4	1	-1

Maximum summed intensity = 1.934

LINE	FREQ	INTEN
1	87.84	0.001
2	90.94	0.444
3	91.86	0.438
4	94.87	1.369
5	95.79	1.696
6	98.17	1.491
7	98.89	0.053
8	99.01	1.625
9	102.10	0.206
10	102.94	0.728
11	105.20	1.203
12	106.04	0.931
13	106.11	1.098
14	106.96	0.715
15	113.27	0.002

-11 -10 -9 -8 -7 -6 -5 -4 -3 -2 -1 0 +1 +2 +3 +4 +5 +6 +7 +8 +9 +10 +11

3E-115

J_{AB}	J_{AC}	J_{BC}
4	4	-1

Maximum summed intensity = 1.979

LINE	FREQ	INTEN
1	87.19	0.001
2	89.27	0.379
3	93.02	0.939
4	93.09	0.464
5	96.84	2.084
6	98.38	1.705
7	98.92	0.144
8	98.95	1.450
9	102.13	0.132
10	102.70	0.845
11	104.21	1.367
12	104.78	1.171
13	108.03	0.785
14	108.60	0.523
15	113.89	0.012

−11 −10 −9 −8 −7 −6 −5 −4 −3 −2 −1 0 +1 +2 +3 +4 +5 +6 +7 +8 +9 +10 +11

3E-116

J_{AB}	J_{AC}	J_{BC}
1	4	-2

Maximum summed intensity = 1.761

LINE	FREQ	INTEN
1	87.03	0.002
2	91.17	0.593
3	92.11	0.759
4	95.15	1.093
5	96.10	1.552
6	98.44	0.759
7	99.39	0.593
8	100.24	0.001
9	100.37	1.552
10	101.32	1.093
11	103.52	1.793
12	105.46	0.854
13	107.51	0.854
14	109.45	0.500
15	112.73	0.001

−11 −10 −9 −8 −7 −6 −5 −4 −3 −2 −1 0 +1 +2 +3 +4 +5 +6 +7 +8 +9 +10 +11

Æ-117

J_{AB}	J_{AC}	J_{BC}
4	1	-2

Maximum summed intensity = 1.784

LINE	FREQ	INTEN
1	87.56	0.003
2	90.97	0.454
3	91.91	0.418
4	94.79	1.313
5	95.74	1.691
6	97.63	1.358
7	99.15	0.124
8	99.40	1.767
9	101.45	0.090
10	103.23	0.904
11	104.86	1.330
12	105.81	1.219
13	106.63	0.779
14	107.58	0.547
15	113.30	0.003

-11 -10 -9 -8 -7 -6 -5 -4 -3 -2 -1 0 +1 +2 +3 +4 +5 +6 +7 +8 +9 +10 +11

Æ-118

J_{AB}	J_{AC}	J_{BC}
4	4	-2

Maximum summed intensity = 2.077

LINE	FREQ	INTEN
1	86.92	0.000
2	89.28	0.382
3	92.90	0.899
4	93.19	0.462
5	96.81	2.086
6	97.84	1.497
7	99.17	0.185
8	99.37	1.659
9	101.46	0.065
10	103.00	0.949
11	103.82	1.575
12	105.35	0.959
13	107.73	0.849
14	109.26	0.418
15	113.91	0.014

-11 -10 -9 -8 -7 -6 -5 -4 -3 -2 -1 0 +1 +2 +3 +4 +5 +6 +7 +8 +9 +10 +11

3E-119

J_{AB}	J_{AC}	J_{BC}
2	4	-1

Maximum summed intensity = 1.741

LINE	FREQ	INTEN
1	87.26	0.000
2	90.58	0.516
3	92.47	0.836
4	94.55	0.818
5	96.43	1.804
6	98.75	1.304
7	99.60	1.361
8	99.76	0.031
9	100.64	0.419
10	101.49	0.942
11	103.96	1.495
12	104.81	1.122
13	107.93	0.778
14	108.78	0.569
15	112.98	0.005

-11 -10 -9 -8 -7 -6 -5 -4 -3 -2 -1 0 +1 +2 +3 +4 +5 +6 +7 +8 +9 +10 +11

3E-120

J_{AB}	J_{AC}	J_{BC}
4	2	-1

Maximum summed intensity = 1.820

LINE	FREQ	INTEN
1	87.71	0.001
2	90.42	0.424
3	92.30	0.449
4	94.30	1.213
5	96.18	1.835
6	98.23	1.559
7	98.90	0.082
8	98.99	1.567
9	102.11	0.176
10	102.87	0.774
11	104.83	1.272
12	105.59	1.009
13	106.71	0.989
14	107.47	0.645
15	113.40	0.004

-11 -10 -9 -8 -7 -6 -5 -4 -3 -2 -1 0 +1 +2 +3 +4 +5 +6 +7 +8 +9 +10 +11

^{3}E-121

J_{AB}	J_{AC}	J_{BC}
2	4	-2

Maximum summed intensity = 1.948

LINE	FREQ	INTEN
1	87.02	0.001
2	90.58	0.516
3	92.43	0.821
4	94.58	0.830
5	96.43	1.812
6	98.15	1.066
7	100.00	0.026
8	100.00	1.588
9	100.00	0.333
10	101.85	1.033
11	103.57	1.741
12	105.42	0.896
13	107.57	0.854
14	109.42	0.477
15	112.98	0.005

-11 -10 -9 -8 -7 -6 -5 -4 -3 -2 -1 0 +1 +2 +3 +4 +5 +6 +7 +8 +9 +10 +11

^{3}E-122

J_{AB}	J_{AC}	J_{BC}
4	2	-2

Maximum summed intensity = 1.748

LINE	FREQ	INTEN
1	87.42	0.002
2	90.43	0.431
3	92.37	0.434
4	94.21	1.162
5	96.14	1.833
6	97.68	1.402
7	99.15	0.145
8	99.39	1.731
9	101.46	0.080
10	103.16	0.923
11	104.47	1.424
12	106.17	0.838
13	106.40	1.087
14	108.11	0.501
15	113.42	0.007

-11 -10 -9 -8 -7 -6 -5 -4 -3 -2 -1 0 +1 +2 +3 +4 +5 +6 +7 +8 +9 +10 +11

4

The AB_3 *Case*

The simplest case of the spin coupling of four protons is the AB_3 case in which three of the protons are identical. In most AB_3 cases, the three A-B coupling constants are identical, there are only two parameters, J_{AB} and $\Delta\nu_{AB}$, and the spectrum is a function of the ratio of these two quantities.

The effect of the ratio $J_{AB}/\Delta\nu_{AB}$ on the spectral transitions is shown in Spectra 4-1 through 4-12. The value of ν_B is fairly readily determined since it is given as the average of two sets of lines of the B part of the spectrum. The value of J_{AB} may also be determined directly from the spectrum since it is given as the separation of two of the lines of the A part of the spectrum. With these values, ν_A may be obtained by a detailed comparison of the observed spectrum with those given here.

4-1

J=0

Maximum summed intensity is 24.000

LINE	FREQ	INTEN	LINE	FREQ	INTEN	LINE	FREQ	INTEN	LINE	FREQ	INTEN
1	97.00	1.000	15	97.00	1.000	29	103.00	1.000	43	103.00	1.000
2	97.00	1.000	16	97.00	0.	30	103.00	0.	44	103.00	1.000
3	97.00	0.	17	97.00	0.	31	103.00	1.000	45	103.00	1.000
4	97.00	0.	18	97.00	0.	32	103.00	0.	46	103.00	1.000
5	97.00	0.	19	97.00	1.000	33	103.00	1.000	47	103.00	1.000
6	97.00	1.000	20	97.00	1.000	34	103.00	1.000	48	103.00	1.000
7	97.00	0.	21	103.00	0.	35	103.00	1.000	49	103.00	1.000
8	97.00	0.	22	103.00	1.000	36	103.00	1.000	50	103.00	1.000
9	97.00	0.	23	103.00	0.	37	103.00	1.000	51	109.00	0.
10	97.00	1.000	24	103.00	1.000	38	103.00	1.000	52	109.00	0.
11	97.00	1.000	25	103.00	1.000	39	103.00	1.000	53	109.00	0.
12	97.00	0.	26	103.00	1.000	40	103.00	1.000	54	109.00	0.
13	97.00	0.	27	103.00	1.000	41	103.00	0.	55	109.00	0.
14	97.00	0.	28	103.00	0.	42	103.00	1.000	56	109.00	0.

4-2

J=0.5

Maximum summed intensity is 12.368

LINE	FREQ	INTEN	LINE	FREQ	INTEN	LINE	FREQ	INTEN	LINE	FREQ	INTEN
1	96.22	0.780	15	97.21	0.000	29	102.76	0.271	43	103.26	0.688
2	96.68	0.891	16	97.24	0.812	30	102.76	4.329	44	103.26	0.688
3	96.71	0.000	17	97.24	0.271	31	102.77	0.000	45	103.26	0.229
4	96.71	0.000	18	97.24	0.271	32	102.77	0.000	46	103.27	0.000
5	96.71	0.000	19	97.24	0.812	33	102.78	3.220	47	103.27	0.000
6	96.71	0.000	20	97.72	1.282	34	102.79	0.000	48	103.28	2.718
7	96.74	0.688	21	102.73	0.000	35	102.79	0.000	49	103.29	0.000
8	96.74	0.229	22	102.73	0.000	36	103.23	0.000	50	103.29	0.000
9	96.74	0.229	23	102.74	3.282	37	103.23	0.000	51	108.79	0.000
10	96.74	0.688	24	102.75	0.000	38	103.24	2.780	52	108.79	0.000
11	97.17	1.047	25	102.75	0.000	39	103.25	0.000	53	108.83	0.000
12	97.21	0.000	26	102.76	0.271	40	103.25	0.000	54	109.29	0.000
13	97.21	0.000	27	102.76	0.812	41	103.26	3.671	55	109.29	0.000
14	97.21	0.000	28	102.76	0.812	42	103.26	0.229	56	109.32	0.000

4-3

J=1.0

Maximum summed intensity is 12.398

LINE	FREQ	INTEN	LINE	FREQ	INTEN	LINE	FREQ	INTEN	LINE	FREQ	INTEN
1	95.39	0.613	15	97.34	0.000	29	102.54	0.291	43	103.54	0.209
2	96.23	0.755	16	97.46	0.873	30	102.56	4.632	44	103.54	0.209
3	96.34	0.000	17	97.46	0.291	31	102.60	0.000	45	103.54	0.627
4	96.34	0.000	18	97.46	0.291	32	102.60	0.000	46	103.56	0.000
5	96.35	0.000	19	97.46	0.873	33	102.61	3.387	47	103.56	0.000
6	96.35	0.000	20	98.35	1.622	34	102.66	0.000	48	103.65	2.378
7	96.46	0.627	21	102.44	0.000	35	102.66	0.000	49	103.66	0.000
8	96.46	0.209	22	102.44	0.000	36	103.40	0.000	50	103.66	0.000
9	96.46	0.209	23	102.48	3.621	37	103.40	0.000	51	108.69	0.000
10	96.46	0.627	24	102.50	0.000	38	103.44	2.613	52	108.69	0.000
11	97.19	1.011	25	102.50	0.000	39	103.50	0.000	53	108.81	0.001
12	97.31	0.000	26	102.54	0.291	40	103.50	0.000	54	109.65	0.000
13	97.31	0.000	27	102.54	0.873	41	103.52	3.367	55	109.65	0.000
14	97.34	0.000	28	102.54	0.873	42	103.54	0.627	56	109.77	0.000

4-4

J=2.0

Maximum summed intensity is 10.941

LINE	FREQ	INTEN	LINE	FREQ	INTEN	LINE	FREQ	INTEN	LINE	FREQ	INTEN
1	93.64	0.394	15	97.39	0.000	29	102.16	1.217	43	104.16	0.171
2	95.04	0.498	16	97.84	0.986	30	102.25	5.107	44	104.16	0.512
3	95.39	0.000	17	97.84	0.330	31	102.36	3.606	45	104.16	0.171
4	95.39	0.000	18	97.84	0.330	32	102.48	0.000	46	104.20	0.
5	95.48	0.000	19	97.84	0.986	33	102.48	0.000	47	104.20	0.000
6	95.48	0.000	20	99.35	2.378	34	102.61	0.000	48	104.61	0.000
7	95.84	0.052	21	101.80	0.000	35	102.61	0.000	49	104.61	0.000
8	95.84	0.632	22	101.80	0.000	36	103.52	0.000	50	104.65	1.622
9	95.84	0.632	23	102.00	0.000	37	103.52	0.000	51	108.81	0.000
10	95.84	0.052	24	102.00	0.000	38	103.75	2.392	52	108.81	0.000
11	96.75	0.741	25	102.04	4.369	39	103.96	2.881	53	109.25	0.009
12	97.19	0.000	26	102.16	1.217	40	104.00	0.000	54	110.52	0.000
13	97.19	0.000	27	102.16	0.099	41	104.00	0.000	55	110.52	0.000
14	97.39	0.000	28	102.16	0.099	42	104.16	0.512	56	110.96	0.002

4-5

J=3.0

Maximum summed intensity is 8.515

LINE	FREQ	INTEN	LINE	FREQ	INTEN	LINE	FREQ	INTEN	LINE	FREQ	INTEN
1	91.80	0.268	15	97.26	0.000	29	101.85	0.362	43	104.84	0.000
2	93.56	0.322	16	98.15	1.077	30	102.05	5.410	44	104.85	0.239
3	94.26	0.000	17	98.15	0.370	31	102.20	3.732	45	104.85	0.314
4	94.26	0.000	18	98.15	0.370	32	102.65	0.000	46	104.85	0.239
5	94.45	0.000	19	98.15	1.077	33	102.65	0.000	47	104.85	0.314
6	94.45	0.000	20	100.00	3.000	34	102.74	0.000	48	105.74	0.000
7	95.15	0.531	21	101.16	0.000	35	102.74	0.000	49	105.74	0.000
8	95.15	0.022	22	101.16	0.000	36	103.35	0.000	50	106.00	1.000
9	95.15	0.022	23	101.50	0.000	37	103.35	0.000	51	109.35	0.000
10	95.15	0.531	24	101.50	0.000	38	103.95	2.264	52	109.35	0.000
11	95.76	0.439	25	101.76	4.975	39	104.24	2.561	53	110.24	0.025
12	96.65	0.000	26	101.85	0.362	40	104.50	0.000	54	111.55	0.000
13	96.65	0.000	27	101.85	1.086	41	104.50	0.000	55	111.55	0.000
14	97.26	0.000	28	101.85	1.086	42	104.84	0.000	56	112.44	0.004

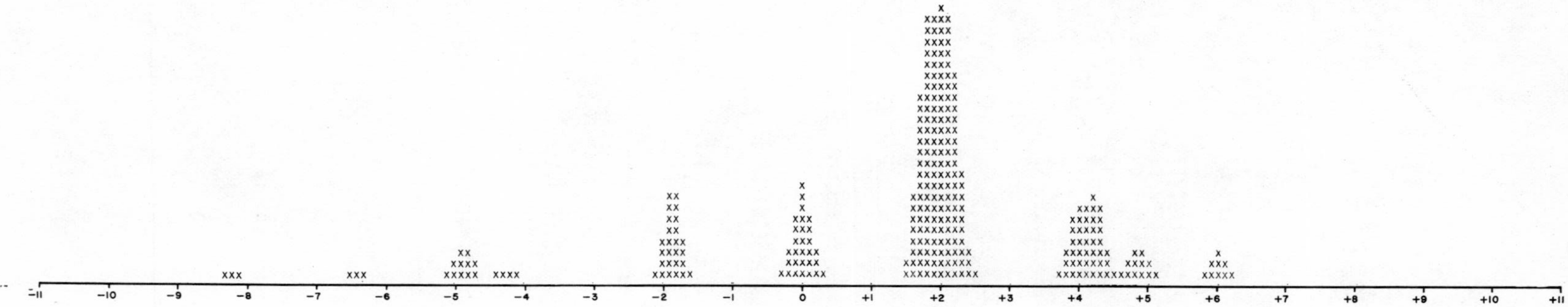

4-6

J=4.0

Maximum summed intensity is 8.708

LINE	FREQ	INTEN	LINE	FREQ	INTEN	LINE	FREQ	INTEN	LINE	FREQ	INTEN
1	89.92	0.192	15	97.00	0.000	29	101.61	0.388	43	105.48	0.000
2	91.92	0.214	16	98.39	1.140	30	101.92	5.595	44	105.61	0.118
3	93.00	0.000	17	98.39	0.414	31	102.08	3.808	45	105.61	0.328
4	93.00	0.000	18	98.39	0.414	32	103.00	0.000	46	105.61	0.328
5	93.31	0.000	19	98.39	1.140	33	103.00	0.000	47	105.61	0.118
6	93.31	0.000	20	100.39	3.387	34	103.00	0.000	48	107.00	0.000
7	94.39	0.248	21	100.52	0.000	35	103.00	0.000	49	107.00	0.000
8	94.39	0.112	22	100.52	0.000	36	103.00	0.000	50	107.61	0.613
9	94.39	0.333	23	101.00	0.000	37	103.00	0.000	51	110.21	0.000
10	94.39	0.333	24	101.00	0.000	38	104.08	2.186	52	110.21	0.000
11	94.39	0.112	25	101.61	5.352	39	104.39	2.365	53	111.61	0.035
12	95.79	0.000	26	101.61	0.388	40	105.00	0.000	54	112.69	0.000
13	95.79	0.000	27	101.61	1.167	41	105.00	0.000	55	112.69	0.000
14	97.00	0.000	28	101.61	1.167	42	105.48	0.000	56	114.08	0.005

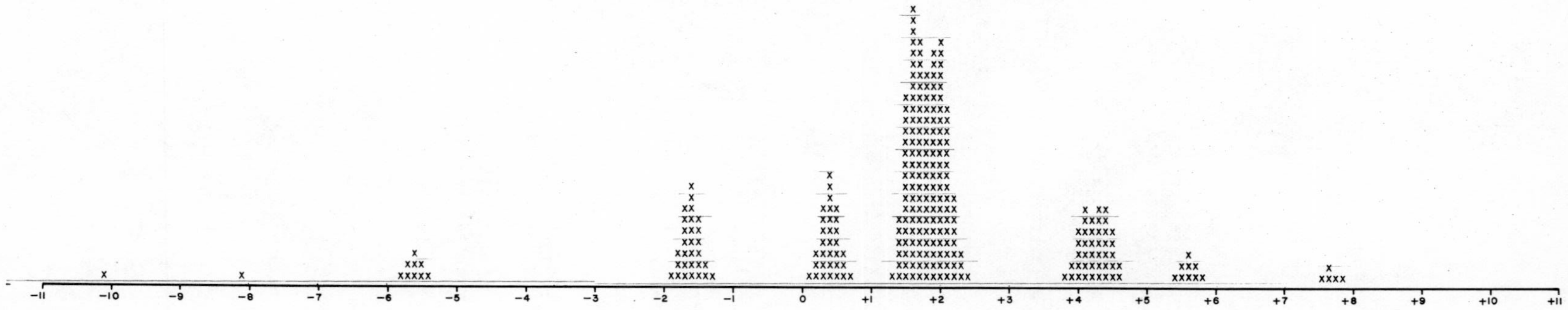

4-7

J=6.0

Maximum summed intensity is 8.095

LINE	FREQ	INTEN	LINE	FREQ	INTEN	LINE	FREQ	INTEN	LINE	FREQ	INTEN
1	86.06	0.110	15	96.29	0.000	29	101.49	5.697	43	106.69	0.000
2	88.35	0.107	16	98.76	1.459	30	101.77	5.783	44	107.24	0.043
3	90.29	0.000	17	98.76	0.249	31	101.94	3.890	45	107.24	0.250
4	90.29	0.000	18	98.76	0.249	32	102.05	0.000	46	107.24	0.250
5	90.82	0.000	19	98.76	1.459	33	102.05	0.000	47	107.24	0.043
6	90.82	0.000	20	99.31	0.000	34	103.71	0.000	48	109.71	0.000
7	91.10	0.092	21	99.31	0.000	35	103.71	0.000	49	109.71	0.000
8	92.76	0.073	22	100.00	0.000	36	103.95	0.000	50	111.20	0.268
9	92.76	0.220	23	100.00	0.000	37	103.95	0.000	51	112.44	0.000
10	92.76	0.220	24	100.80	3.732	38	104.23	2.105	52	112.44	0.000
11	92.76	0.073	25	101.24	1.283	39	104.51	2.176	53	114.90	0.035
12	93.56	0.000	26	101.24	0.424	40	106.00	0.	54	115.18	0.000
13	93.56	0.000	27	101.24	0.424	41	106.00	0.000	55	115.18	0.000
14	96.29	0.000	28	101.24	1.283	42	106.69	0.000	56	117.65	0.006

−11 −10 −9 −8 −7 −6 −5 −4 −3 −2 −1 0 +1 +2 +3 +4 +5 +6 +7 +8 +9 +10 +11

4-8

J=8.0

Maximum summed intensity is 8.779

LINE	FREQ	INTEN	LINE	FREQ	INTEN	LINE	FREQ	INTEN	LINE	FREQ	INTEN
1	82.15	0.071	15	95.46	0.000	29	101.00	0.444	43	107.85	0.000
2	84.61	0.061	16	98.15	0.000	30	101.00	3.857	44	109.00	0.010
3	87.46	0.043	17	98.15	0.000	31	101.46	5.830	45	109.00	0.190
4	87.46	0.000	18	99.00	1.295	32	101.70	5.868	46	109.00	0.010
5	87.46	0.000	19	99.00	0.505	33	101.85	3.929	47	109.00	0.190
6	88.15	0.000	20	99.00	0.505	34	104.30	2.066	48	112.54	0.000
7	88.15	0.000	21	99.00	1.295	35	104.54	2.100	49	112.54	0.000
8	91.00	0.000	22	99.00	0.000	36	104.54	0.000	50	115.00	0.000
9	91.00	0.000	23	99.00	0.000	37	104.54	0.000	51	115.00	0.000
10	91.00	0.014	24	101.00	0.000	38	105.00	0.000	52	115.00	0.143
11	91.00	0.186	25	101.00	0.000	39	105.00	0.000	53	117.85	0.000
12	91.00	0.186	26	101.00	0.444	40	107.00	0.000	54	117.85	0.000
13	91.00	0.014	27	101.00	1.356	41	107.00	0.000	55	118.54	0.028
14	95.46	0.000	28	101.00	1.356	42	107.85	0.000	56	121.39	0.005

−11 −10 −9 −8 −7 −6 −5 −4 −3 −2 −1 0 +1 +2 +3 +4 +5 +6 +7 +8 +9 +10 +11

4-9

J=10.0

Maximum summed intensity is 9.657

LINE	FREQ	INTEN	LINE	FREQ	INTEN	LINE	FREQ	INTEN	LINE	FREQ	INTEN
1	78.21	0.049	15	94.56	0.000	29	100.83	0.341	43	108.96	0.
2	80.77	0.039	16	97.04	0.000	30	101.11	3.913	44	110.83	0.037
3	83.67	0.024	17	97.04	0.000	31	101.45	5.892	45	110.83	0.105
4	84.56	0.000	18	98.00	0.000	32	101.65	5.911	46	110.83	0.037
5	84.56	0.000	19	98.00	0.000	33	101.79	3.951	47	110.83	0.105
6	85.38	0.000	20	99.17	0.642	34	104.35	2.045	48	115.44	0.000
7	85.38	0.000	21	99.17	1.216	35	104.55	2.063	49	115.44	0.000
8	88.28	0.000	22	99.17	1.216	36	105.44	0.000	50	117.72	0.000
9	88.28	0.000	23	99.17	0.642	37	105.44	0.000	51	117.72	0.000
10	89.17	0.105	24	99.94	0.000	38	106.06	0.000	52	118.89	0.087
11	89.17	0.037	25	99.94	0.000	39	106.06	0.000	53	120.62	0.000
12	89.17	0.037	26	100.83	0.341	40	108.00	0.000	54	120.62	0.000
13	89.17	0.105	27	100.83	1.517	41	108.00	0.000	55	122.33	0.021
14	94.56	0.000	28	100.83	1.517	42	108.96	0.000	56	125.23	0.004

4-10

J=12.0

Maximum summed intensity is 10.784

LINE	FREQ	INTEN	LINE	FREQ	INTEN	LINE	FREQ	INTEN	LINE	FREQ	INTEN
1	74.25	0.036	15	93.63	0.000	29	100.71	1.755	43	110.04	0.000
2	76.88	0.027	16	95.96	0.000	30	101.18	3.941	44	112.71	0.061
3	79.81	0.015	17	95.96	0.000	31	101.45	5.925	45	112.71	0.044
4	81.63	0.000	18	97.00	0.000	32	101.62	5.937	46	112.71	0.044
5	81.63	0.000	19	97.00	0.000	33	101.75	3.964	47	112.71	0.061
6	82.54	0.000	20	98.89	0.000	34	104.38	2.033	48	118.37	0.000
7	82.54	0.000	21	98.89	0.000	35	104.55	2.044	49	118.37	0.000
8	85.48	0.000	22	99.29	0.934	36	106.37	0.000	50	120.52	0.000
9	85.48	0.000	23	99.29	0.960	37	106.37	0.000	51	120.52	0.000
10	87.29	0.013	24	99.29	0.934	38	107.11	0.000	52	122.82	0.059
11	87.29	0.092	25	99.29	0.960	39	107.11	0.000	53	123.46	0.000
12	87.29	0.092	26	100.71	1.755	40	109.00	0.000	54	123.46	0.000
13	87.29	0.013	27	100.71	0.140	41	109.00	0.000	55	126.19	0.016
14	93.63	0.000	28	100.71	0.140	42	110.04	0.000	56	129.12	0.003

4-11

J=15.0

Maximum summed intensity is 11.903

LINE	FREQ	INTEN	LINE	FREQ	INTEN	LINE	FREQ	INTEN	LINE	FREQ	INTEN
1	68.30	0.024	15	92.20	0.000	29	100.58	0.127	43	111.63	0.000
2	71.00	0.017	16	94.37	0.000	30	101.25	3.964	44	115.58	0.048
3	73.96	0.009	17	94.37	0.000	31	101.45	5.953	45	115.58	0.024
4	77.20	0.000	18	95.50	0.000	32	101.59	5.959	46	115.58	0.048
5	77.20	0.000	19	95.50	0.000	33	101.70	3.976	47	115.58	0.024
6	78.22	0.000	20	97.33	0.000	34	104.41	2.022	48	122.80	0.000
7	78.22	0.000	21	97.33	0.000	35	104.55	2.027	49	122.80	0.000
8	81.17	0.000	22	99.42	1.813	36	107.80	0.000	50	124.83	0.000
9	81.17	0.000	23	99.42	0.115	37	107.80	0.000	51	124.83	0.000
10	84.42	0.014	24	99.42	1.813	38	108.67	0.000	52	127.78	0.000
11	84.42	0.058	25	99.42	0.115	39	108.67	0.000	53	127.78	0.000
12	84.42	0.058	26	100.58	0.127	40	110.50	0.000	54	128.75	0.036
13	84.42	0.014	27	100.58	1.802	41	110.50	0.000	55	132.04	0.011
14	92.20	0.000	28	100.58	1.802	42	111.63	0.000	56	135.00	0.003

4-12

J=18.0

Maximum summed intensity is 13.313

LINE	FREQ	INTEN	LINE	FREQ	INTEN	LINE	FREQ	INTEN	LINE	FREQ	INTEN
1	62.33	0.018	15	90.75	0.000	29	100.49	0.353	43	113.19	0.000
2	65.08	0.012	16	92.81	0.000	30	101.30	3.976	44	118.49	0.026
3	68.05	0.005	17	92.81	0.000	31	101.45	5.967	45	118.49	0.026
4	72.75	0.000	18	94.00	0.000	32	101.58	5.971	46	118.49	0.025
5	72.75	0.000	19	94.00	0.000	33	101.67	3.982	47	118.49	0.025
6	73.84	0.000	20	95.78	0.000	34	104.42	2.015	48	127.25	0.000
7	73.84	0.000	21	95.78	0.000	35	104.54	2.019	49	127.25	0.000
8	76.81	0.000	22	99.51	0.573	36	109.25	0.000	50	129.19	0.000
9	76.81	0.000	23	99.51	1.376	37	109.25	0.000	51	129.19	0.
10	81.51	0.049	24	99.51	0.573	38	110.22	0.000	52	132.16	0.000
11	81.51	0.003	25	99.51	1.376	39	110.22	0.000	53	132.16	0.000
12	81.51	0.003	26	100.49	0.353	40	112.00	0.000	54	134.70	0.024
13	81.51	0.049	27	100.49	1.596	41	112.00	0.000	55	137.95	0.008
14	90.75	0.000	28	100.49	1.596	42	113.19	0.	56	140.92	0.002

5

The A_2B_2 Case

The spin coupling of two sets of identical protons leads to the A_2B_2 case. Besides the chemical shift, there are four coupling constants, $J_{AA'}$, J_{AB}, $J_{AB'}$, and $J_{BB'}$. Because of symmetry, $J_{A'B} = J_{AB'}$ and $J_{A'B'} = J_{AB}$. For convenience in the following discussion, we shall define four new quantities: $K = J_{AA'} + J_{BB'}$; $L = J_{AB} - J_{AB'}$; $M = J_{AA'} - J_{BB'}$; and $N = J_{AB} + J_{AB'}$.

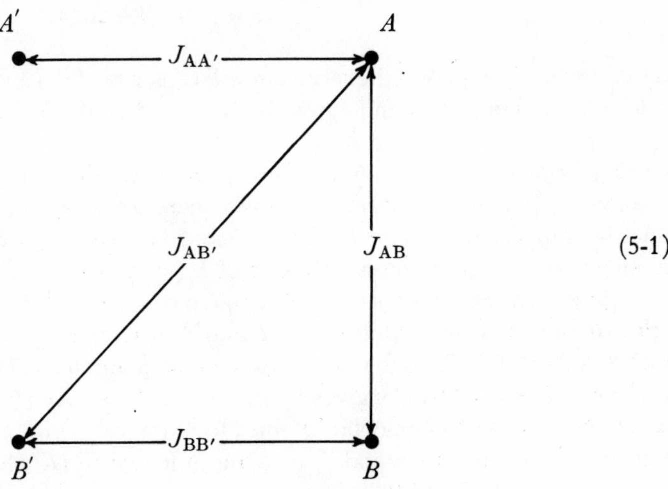

(5-1)

* H. M. McConnell, A. D. McLean, and C. A. Reilly, *J. Chem. Phys.*, **23**, 1152 (1955).

A simpler subcase of A_2B_2 is A_2X_2 in which the chemical shift between A and X is large compared to the coupling constants. The A and X parts of the spectrum will now be identical, and each part will be symmetrical about its center. There will be ten lines in each of the two parts. The line positions and intensities are given in Table 5-1. It can be seen from

Table 5-1 Line Positions and Intensities for the A_2X_2 Case[a]

Transition	Position relative to ν_A or ν_X	Relative intensity
1	$\frac{1}{2}N$	1
2	$\frac{1}{2}N$	1
3	$-\frac{1}{2}N$	1
4	$-\frac{1}{2}N$	1
5	$\frac{1}{2}K + \frac{1}{2}(K^2 + L^2)^{1/2}$	$\sin^2 \theta_s$
6	$-\frac{1}{2}K + \frac{1}{2}(K^2 + L^2)^{1/2}$	$\cos^2 \theta_s$
7	$\frac{1}{2}K - \frac{1}{2}(K^2 + L^2)^{1/2}$	$\cos^2 \theta_s$
8	$-\frac{1}{2}K - \frac{1}{2}(K^2 + L^2)^{1/2}$	$\sin^2 \theta_s$
9	$\frac{1}{2}M + \frac{1}{2}(M^2 + L^2)^{1/2}$	$\sin^2 \theta_a$
10	$-\frac{1}{2}M + \frac{1}{2}(M^2 + L^2)^{1/2}$	$\cos^2 \theta_a$
11	$\frac{1}{2}M - \frac{1}{2}(M^2 + L^2)^{1/2}$	$\cos^2 \theta_a$
12	$-\frac{1}{2}M - \frac{1}{2}(M^2 + L^2)^{1/2}$	$\sin^2 \theta_a$

$$\theta_s = \tfrac{1}{2} \cos^{-1} [K/(K^2 + L^2)^{1/2}]$$
$$\theta_a = \tfrac{1}{2} \cos^{-1} [M/(M^2 + L^2)^{1/2}]$$

[a] J. A. Pople, W. G. Schneider, and H. J. Bernstein, *High-Resolution Nuclear Magnetic Resonance*, McGraw-Hill, New York, 1959, p. 141.

this table that each part of the spectrum will consist of: (1) a strong doublet formed from lines 1, 2, 3, and 4, which is centered on the frequency ν_A (or ν_X). The separation will be $N = J_{AX} + J_{AX'}$; and (2) two symmetrical quartets formed from lines 5, 6, 7, 8 and 9, 10, 11, 12 which are centered on ν_A (or ν_X). Taking the outermost line as 5, one does not know which of the inner lines to assign as 6 and 7, and as 10 and 11. However, only one assignment will lead to a consistent value of L (see below).

These features of the spectrum may often be seen, and this will permit a determination of the magnitudes of L and N separately, and the magnitude of K and M. The difference between lines 5 and 6 (or 7 and 8) will be given as K, and M will be given by the difference between lines 9 and 10 (or 11 and 12). Then L may be obtained from the value of K and from the difference between lines 5 and 7, or 6 and 8 [equal to $(K^2 + L^2)^{1/2}$], and from the value of M and the difference between lines 9 and 11, or 10 and 12 [equal to $(M^2 + L^2)^{1/2}$]. It is not possible to decide which quartet should be assigned as 5, 6, 7, 8 and which should be assigned 9, 10, 11, 12.

As a result, one cannot differentiate between K and M. Since these quantities and L appear as their squares in the expressions for transitions 5-12, it is not possible to determine the relative signs of these quantities.

Although the analysis permits one to obtain a set of four coupling constants, it can be seen that one cannot distinguish between $J_{AA'}$ and $J_{XX'}$, nor between J_{AX} and $J_{AX'}$. It is often possible to assign individual values to these constants based on the geometry of the molecule and on knowledge concerning the effect of geometry on coupling constants.

In order to facilitate the assignment of parameters for this case, Fig. 5-1a and b shows the effect of changes in the coupling constants on the appearance of the A part of the spectrum. It may be noted that, if $J_{AX} = J_{AX'}$, lines 5, 8, 9, and 12 will have zero intensity, and lines 6, 7, 10, and 11 will appear at ν_A (or ν_X). Thus, the spectrum will be independent of $J_{AA'}$ and $J_{XX'}$. Also, even when $J_{AX} \neq J_{AX'}$, the A and X parts of the spectrum may still be triplets if $J_{AA'} \gg |J_{AX} - J_{AX'}| + J_{XX'}$. The observation of a triplet does not demonstrate that the two A-X coupling constants are equal.

Having considered the A_2X_2 case, it is important to see how the spectrum changes as the chemical shift between A and X is decreased. Some typical spectra are shown in Fig. 5-2. In each case, the coupling constants are: $J_{AA'} = 3.0$; $J_{AX} = 1.0$; $J_{AX'} = 9.0$; and $J_{XX'} = 7.0$. The zero point is taken as the transition frequency for the A proton (ν_A), which is the left-hand part of the whole spectrum. Only this half of the spectrum is shown.

In the true A_2X_2 case where the chemical shift is very large, both the A part and the X part of the spectrum are symmetrical about the respective transition frequencies. The frequencies and relative intensities for the A part are given in Table 5-2.

Table 5-2 Frequencies and Intensities for the A Part

Frequency	Intensity	Frequency	Intensity
−11.40	0.22	1.40	1.78
−6.47	0.55	2.47	1.45
−5.00	4.00	5.00	4.00
−2.47	1.45	6.47	0.55
−1.40	1.78	11.40	0.22

For the spectra shown in Fig. 5-2, the chemical shifts between A and X are given in Table 5-3. It can be seen that, in the first case, where the chemical shift is ten times as large as the largest coupling constant, the spectrum is only slightly displaced from the true A_2X_2 case, and the intensity distribution is nearly symmetrical. All the lines have been shifted away from the X proton lines by approximately the same amount, 0.20 ±

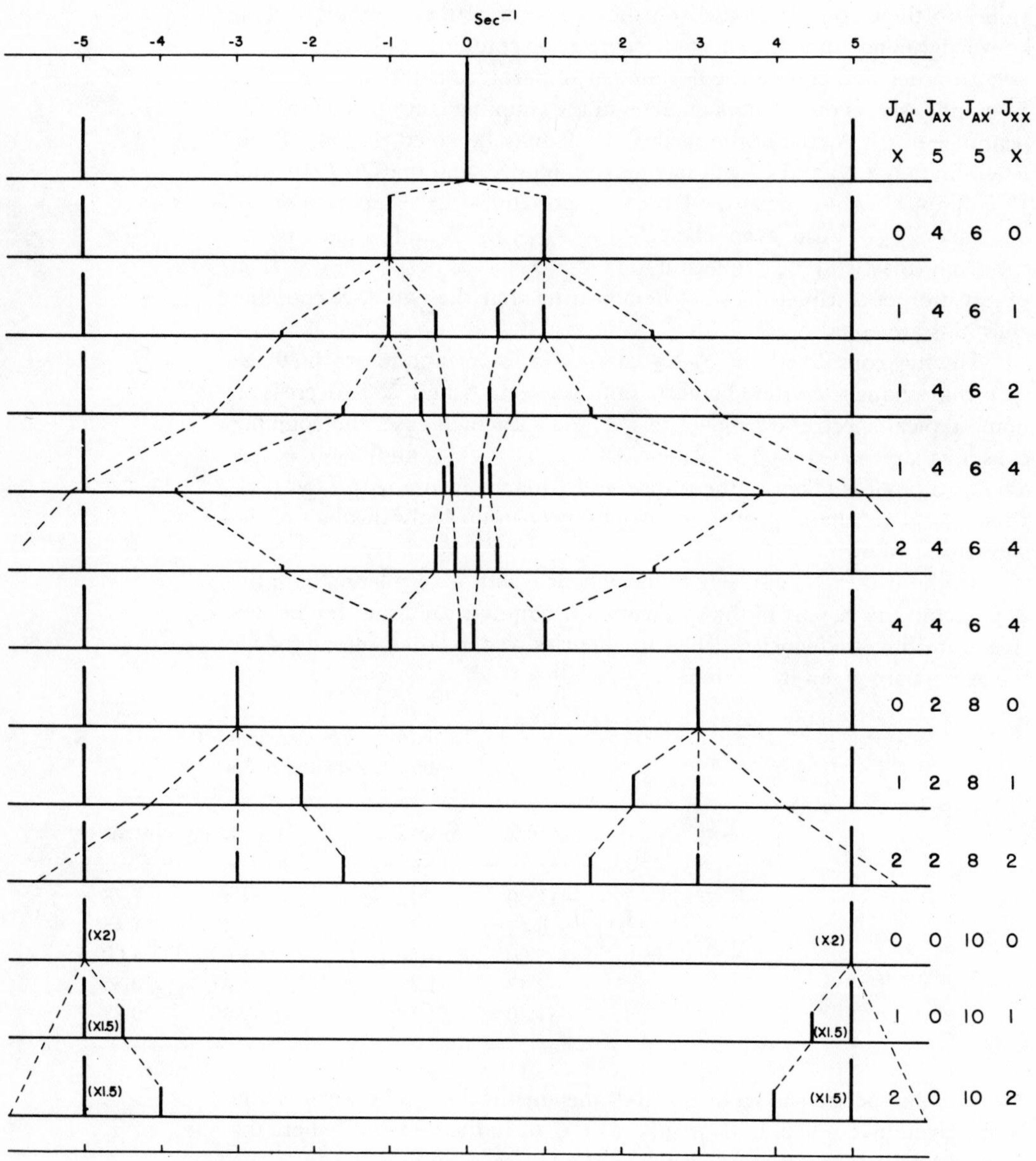

Fig. 5-1a Effect of coupling constants on the A part of an A_2X_2 spectrum, with the parameter N kept constant and equal to 10 sec^{-1}.

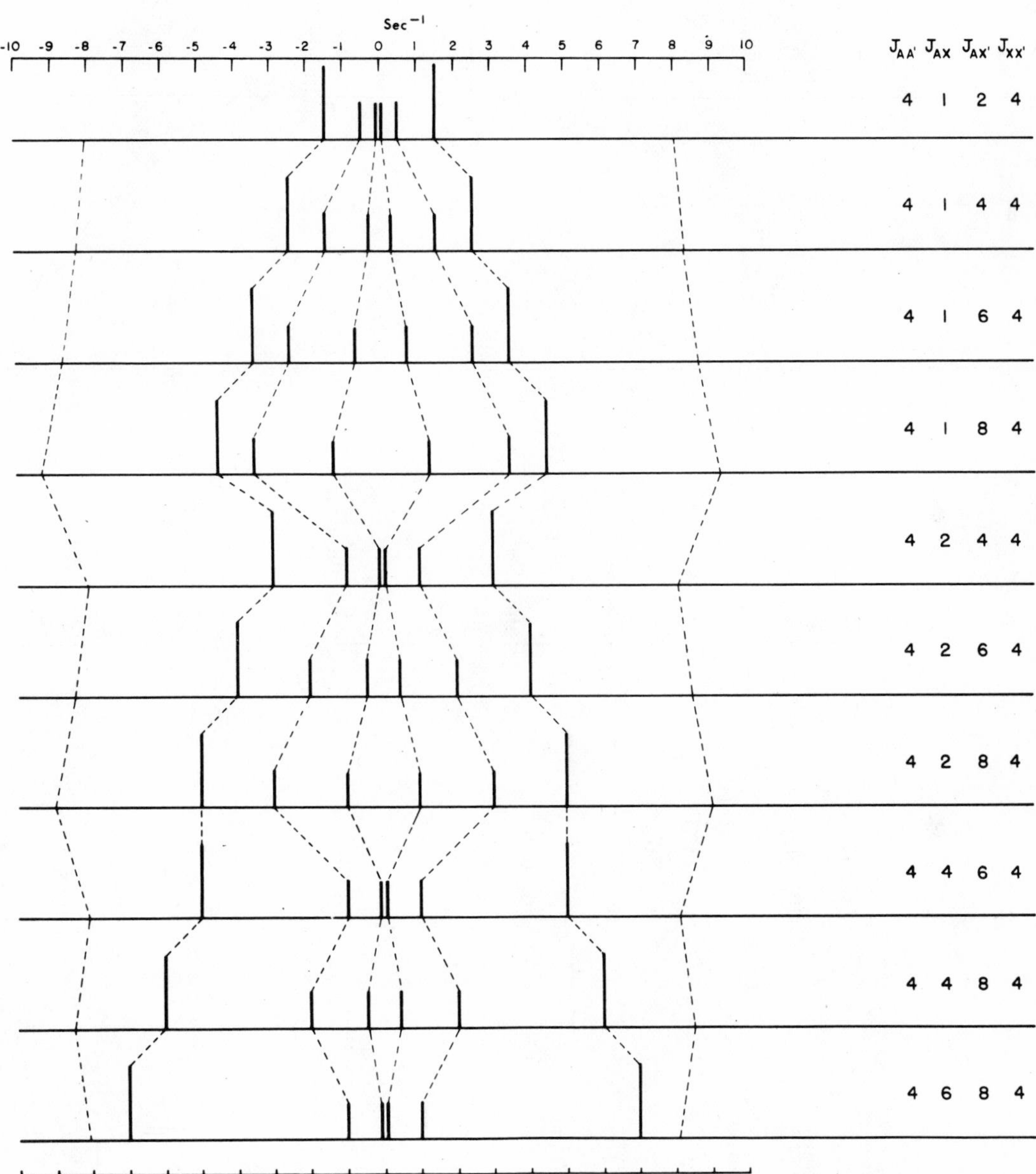

Fig. 5-1b Effect of coupling constants on the A part of an A_2X_2 spectrum with $J_{AA'} = J_{XX'} = 4\ \text{sec}^{-1}$.

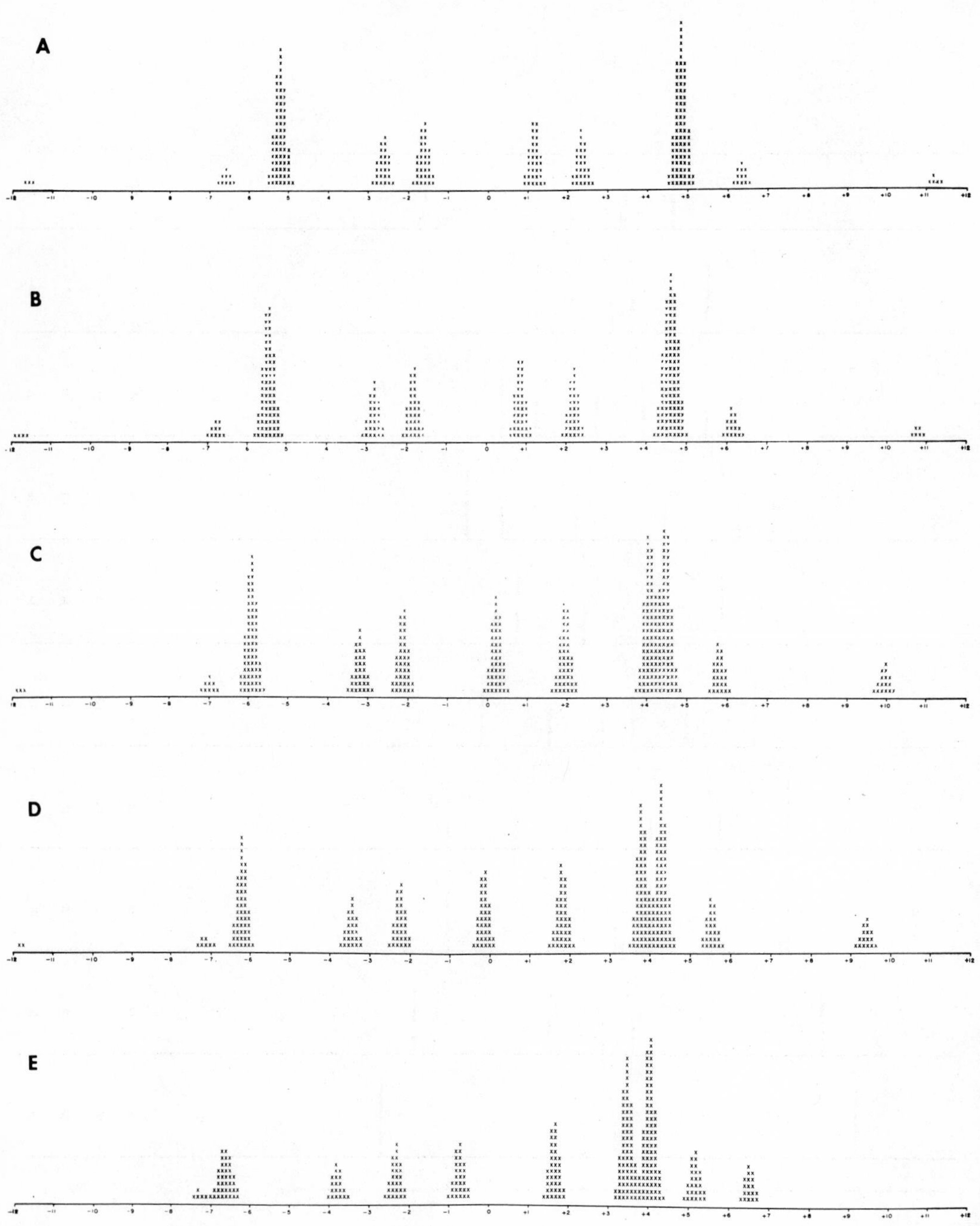

Fig. 5-2 Typical spectra of the A_2X_2 case.

0.05 sec^{-1}. As the chemical shift is decreased further, the effect becomes more pronounced, and the intensity distribution begins to favor the part of the spectrum nearest the X proton band. The most characteristic change is the splitting of the line originally at +5.0 sec^{-1} into two parts.

The exact nature of these changes will, of course, be a function of the coupling constants that apply in the particular case. However, if the features shown above can be recognized, estimates of the magnitudes of the coupling constants may be obtained, and this greatly simplifies the interpretation of the A_2B_2 spectra.

Table 5-3 Chemical Shifts between A and X

Spectrum	Chemical shift, sec^{-1}
A	100
B	50
C	25
D	20
E	15

In order to obtain the values of the coupling constants, one may compare the observed spectra with the theoretical A_2B_2 spectra. These spectra are arranged in several groups and are shown in Table 5-4. The arrangement is designed to facilitate the determination of the appropriate ranges of coupling constants by comparing the observed spectrum with the groups one at a time. The first group may give one an idea of

Table 5-4 Grouping of Spectra

Group	Spectra	Type
I	1–12	$J_{AB} = J_{AB'}$. These spectra are independent of the values of $J_{AA'}$ and $J_{BB'}$.
II	13–96	Two different values of coupling constants; all positive.
III	97–127	Two different values of coupling constants; one negative.
IV	128–158	Two different values of coupling constants; two negative.
V	159–310	Three different values of coupling constants; all positive.
VI	311–439	Three different values of coupling constants; one negative.
VII	440–490	Three different values of coupling constants; two negative.

the magnitude of J_{AB} and $J_{AB'}$; the next three groups may indicate the range of values of the several coupling constants and may suggest whether all the coupling constants have the same sign. The estimates thus obtained may be further refined using the spectra of groups V through VII.

Because of the large number of possible combinations, no spectra arising from four different values of coupling constants are given. This is not too severe a limitation, for most common A_2B_2 cases have at least two coupling constants with the same or similar values. The calculated spectra permit one to make a fairly good estimate of the values of the chemical shifts and coupling constants. The final parameters are best checked by calculating the spectral transitions, which should be found based on these values, and by comparing the result with the observed spectrum. This may be done by evaluating the following energies:

$$\begin{aligned}
E_1 &= \nu_A + \nu_B + \tfrac{1}{2}N \\
E_2 &= \tfrac{1}{2}(\nu_A + \nu_B) - \tfrac{1}{2}(\Delta\nu^2 + N^2)^{1/2} \\
E_3 &= \tfrac{1}{2}(\nu_A + \nu_B) + \tfrac{1}{2}(\Delta\nu^2 + N^2)^{1/2} \\
E_8 &= -E_2 \\
E_9 &= -E_3 \\
E_{10} &= -(\nu_A + \nu_B) + \tfrac{1}{2}N \\
E_{11} &= \tfrac{1}{2}(\nu_A + \nu_B) - \tfrac{1}{2}K - \tfrac{1}{2}[(\Delta\nu + M)^2 + L^2]^{1/2} \\
E_{12} &= \tfrac{1}{2}(\nu_A + \nu_B) - \tfrac{1}{2}K + \tfrac{1}{2}[(\Delta\nu + M)^2 + L^2]^{1/2} \\
E_{13} &= -\tfrac{1}{2}K + \tfrac{1}{2}(M^2 + L^2)^{1/2} \\
E_{14} &= -\tfrac{1}{2}K - \tfrac{1}{2}(M^2 + L^2)^{1/2} \\
E_{15} &= -\tfrac{1}{2}(\nu_A + \nu_B) - \tfrac{1}{2}K + \tfrac{1}{2}[(\Delta\nu - M)^2 + L^2]^{1/2} \\
E_{16} &= -\tfrac{1}{2}(\nu_A + \nu_B) - \tfrac{1}{2}K - \tfrac{1}{2}[(\Delta\nu - M)^2 + L^2]^{1/2}
\end{aligned} \tag{5-2}$$

The remaining energies E_4, E_5, E_6, and E_7 are given as roots of the determinant, Eq. (5-3).

$$\begin{vmatrix}
-\nu_A + \nu_B - \tfrac{1}{2}N - E & 0 & \tfrac{1}{2}L & \tfrac{1}{2}N \\
0 & \nu_A - \nu_B - \tfrac{1}{2}N - E & \tfrac{1}{2}L & \tfrac{1}{2}N \\
\tfrac{1}{2}L & \tfrac{1}{2}L & -K - E & -\tfrac{1}{2}L \\
\tfrac{1}{2}N & \tfrac{1}{2}N & -\tfrac{1}{2}L & -E
\end{vmatrix} = 0 \tag{5-3}$$

There are a total of 28 possible transitions between these levels. Four of them are almost forbidden, and lead to very weak lines. Of the remaining 24, half are in the A part and half are in the B part. Therefore one need only consider the 12 A lines, and the B lines will be related to these as the mirror images. The A lines are given as the following transitions:

$$\begin{array}{lll}
E_2 \rightarrow E_1 & E_8 \rightarrow E_5 & E_{13} \rightarrow E_{12} \\
E_4 \rightarrow E_2 & E_9 \rightarrow E_6 & E_{14} \rightarrow E_{12} \\
E_6 \rightarrow E_3 & E_9 \rightarrow E_7 & E_{16} \rightarrow E_{13} \\
E_7 \rightarrow E_3 & E_{10} \rightarrow E_8 & E_{16} \rightarrow E_{14}
\end{array}$$

The relative intensities may also be calculated, but may often be estimated with sufficient accuracy by comparison with a spectrum given here that has similar coupling constants (after correction for the difference in $\Delta\nu_{AB}$ between the observed and calculated spectra).

There are some features of the A_2B_2 spectra that deserve special comment. First, all structure is rapidly washed out if J_{AB} or $J_{AB'}$ becomes comparable to $\Delta\nu_{AB}$ and large compared to the other coupling constants (Spectrum 5-166). This is, however, not the case if $J_{AA'}$ or $J_{BB'}$ becomes too large with respect to the other constants (Spectrum 5-160). In the former case, it is not possible to evaluate the coupling constants.

Second, one may note the difference between spectra arising from coupling constants having the same sign, and those for which one coupling constant has a different sign than the others. As an example, one may compare Spectra 5-14 and 5-99. A negative J_{AB} generally leads to a significant increase in intensity at the center of the band system, as compared to cases having all constants positive.

It is important to observe the relatively small effect of $J_{AA'}$ and $J_{BB'}$ on most of the spectra. If $J_{AB} = J_{AB'}$, the spectrum is independent of $J_{AA'}$ and $J_{BB'}$. When J_{AB} and $J_{AB'}$ are not very different, the spectrum is almost independent of $J_{AA'}$ and $J_{BB'}$ so long as the last two are not large compared to the first two. This may be seen in comparisons of Spectra 5-42 and 5-217, and of the series 5-189 to 5-194.

If the difference between J_{AB} and $J_{AB'}$ is large, the effect of $J_{AA'}$ and $J_{BB'}$ is more marked as shown in Spectra 5-220, 5-221, 5-222, 5-251, and 5-269. On the other hand, if $J_{AA'}$ or $J_{BB'}$ is large compared to $|J_{AB} - J_{AB'}|$, the spectrum has the appearance of one in which $J_{AB} = J_{AB'}$. This may be seen in Spectrum 5-160. If both $J_{AA'}$ and $J_{BB'}$ are large compared to $|J_{AB} - J_{AB'}|$, the spectrum has a more complex appearance (Spectrum 5-263).

5-1

$J_{AB} = J_{AB'} = 0$

Maximum summed intensity = 16.0

LINE	FREQ	INTEN	LINE	FREQ	INTEN	LINE	FREQ	INTEN	LINE	FREQ	INTEN
1	91.00	0.	15	97.00	0.	29	103.00	1.000	43	103.00	0.
2	91.00	0.	16	97.00	1.000	30	103.00	1.000	44	103.00	0.
3	91.00	0.	17	97.00	1.000	31	103.00	1.000	45	103.00	1.000
4	91.00	0.	18	97.00	0.	32	103.00	0.	46	103.00	1.000
5	97.00	1.000	19	97.00	0.	33	103.00	1.000	47	103.00	1.000
6	97.00	1.000	20	97.00	1.000	34	103.00	0.	48	103.00	1.000
7	97.00	1.000	21	97.00	1.000	35	103.00	0.	49	103.00	1.000
8	97.00	1.000	22	97.00	0.	36	103.00	1.000	50	103.00	1.000
9	97.00	0.	23	97.00	0.	37	103.00	0.	51	103.00	1.000
10	97.00	1.000	24	97.00	1.000	38	103.00	1.000	52	103.00	1.000
11	97.00	0.	25	97.00	1.000	39	103.00	1.000	53	109.00	0.
12	97.00	1.000	26	97.00	1.000	40	103.00	0.	54	109.00	0.
13	97.00	0.	27	97.00	1.000	41	103.00	1.000	55	109.00	0.
14	97.00	1.000	28	97.00	1.000	42	103.00	0.	56	109.00	0.

−11 −10 −9 −8 −7 −6 −5 −4 −3 −2 −1 0 +1 +2 +3 +4 +5 +6 +7 +8 +9 +10 +11

5-2

$J_{AB} = J_{AB'} = 0.5$

Maximum summed intensity = 7.717

LINE	FREQ	INTEN	LINE	FREQ	INTEN	LINE	FREQ	INTEN	LINE	FREQ	INTEN
1	90.42	0.000	15	96.96	0.000	29	102.00	0.000	43	103.05	0.000
2	90.95	0.000	16	96.97	1.966	30	102.04	0.000	44	103.05	1.952
3	90.96	0.000	17	97.00	2.000	31	102.50	0.000	45	103.49	0.000
4	91.41	0.000	18	97.00	0.000	32	102.50	2.377	46	103.50	1.706
5	95.96	0.000	19	97.00	2.000	33	102.51	0.000	47	103.50	0.000
6	96.00	0.000	20	97.00	0.000	34	102.54	0.000	48	103.54	0.000
7	96.46	0.000	21	97.46	0.000	35	102.54	0.000	49	103.54	0.000
8	96.46	0.000	22	97.46	0.000	36	102.54	2.329	50	103.54	1.671
9	96.46	1.671	23	97.46	2.329	37	103.00	0.000	51	104.00	0.000
10	96.50	0.000	24	97.49	0.000	38	103.00	2.000	52	104.04	0.000
11	96.50	1.706	25	97.50	2.377	39	103.00	0.000	53	108.59	0.000
12	96.51	0.000	26	97.50	0.000	40	103.00	2.000	54	109.04	0.000
13	96.95	1.952	27	97.96	0.000	41	103.03	1.966	55	109.05	0.000
14	96.95	0.000	28	98.00	0.000	42	103.04	0.000	56	109.58	0.000

−11 −10 −9 −8 −7 −6 −5 −4 −3 −2 −1 0 +1 +2 +3 +4 +5 +6 +7 +8 +9 +10 +11

5-3

$J_{AB} = J_{AB'} = 1.0$

Maximum summed intensity = 6.009

LINE	FREQ	INTEN	LINE	FREQ	INTEN	LINE	FREQ	INTEN	LINE	FREQ	INTEN
1	89.70	0.000	15	96.86	0.000	29	101.00	0.000	43	103.20	0.000
2	90.80	0.000	16	96.89	1.890	30	101.16	0.000	44	103.22	1.794
3	90.86	0.000	17	97.00	1.793	31	102.00	0.000	45	103.95	0.000
4	91.64	0.001	18	97.00	0.207	32	102.03	2.838	46	103.98	1.477
5	94.84	0.000	19	97.00	1.793	33	102.05	0.000	47	104.00	0.000
6	95.00	0.000	20	97.00	0.207	34	102.16	0.000	48	104.16	0.000
7	95.84	0.000	21	97.84	0.000	35	102.16	0.000	49	104.16	0.000
8	95.84	0.000	22	97.84	0.000	36	102.16	2.632	50	104.16	1.368
9	95.84	1.368	23	97.84	2.632	37	103.00	0.207	51	105.00	0.000
10	96.00	0.000	24	97.95	0.000	38	103.00	1.793	52	105.16	0.000
11	96.02	1.477	25	97.97	2.838	39	103.00	0.207	53	108.36	0.001
12	96.05	0.000	26	98.00	0.000	40	103.00	1.793	54	109.14	0.000
13	96.78	1.794	27	98.84	0.000	41	103.11	1.890	55	109.20	0.000
14	96.80	0.000	28	99.00	0.000	42	103.14	0.000	56	110.30	0.000

5-4

$J_{AB} = J_{AB'} = 2.0$

Maximum summed intensity = 4.394

LINE	FREQ	INTEN	LINE	FREQ	INTEN	LINE	FREQ	INTEN	LINE	FREQ	INTEN
1	87.90	0.001	15	96.51	0.000	29	100.39	0.000	43	103.88	0.000
2	90.12	0.000	16	96.78	1.730	30	101.00	0.000	44	103.99	1.231
3	90.51	0.000	17	97.00	0.015	31	101.00	0.000	45	104.61	0.000
4	91.52	0.008	18	97.00	1.985	32	101.27	3.877	46	104.88	1.153
5	92.39	0.000	19	97.00	0.015	33	101.39	0.000	47	105.00	0.000
6	93.00	0.000	20	97.00	1.985	34	101.61	0.000	48	105.61	0.000
7	94.39	0.000	21	98.39	0.000	35	101.61	0.000	49	105.61	0.000
8	94.39	0.000	22	98.39	0.000	36	101.61	3.109	50	105.61	0.891
9	94.39	0.891	23	98.39	3.109	37	103.00	1.985	51	107.00	0.000
10	95.00	0.000	24	98.61	0.000	38	103.00	0.015	52	107.61	0.000
11	95.12	1.153	25	98.73	3.877	39	103.00	1.985	53	108.48	0.008
12	95.39	0.000	26	99.00	0.000	40	103.00	0.015	54	109.49	0.000
13	96.01	1.231	27	99.00	0.000	41	103.22	1.730	55	109.88	0.000
14	96.12	0.000	28	99.61	0.000	42	103.49	0.000	56	112.10	0.001

5-5

$J_{AB} = J_{AB'} = 3.0$

Maximum summed intensity = 4.715

LINE	FREQ	INTEN	LINE	FREQ	INTEN	LINE	FREQ	INTEN	LINE	FREQ	INTEN
1	85.79	0.002	15	96.03	0.000	29	100.00	0.000	43	104.93	0.000
2	88.96	0.000	16	96.83	1.632	30	100.80	4.707	44	105.04	0.000
3	89.76	0.000	17	97.00	1.249	31	101.07	0.000	45	105.32	0.705
4	90.03	0.000	18	97.00	0.751	32	101.24	0.000	46	105.73	0.934
5	90.71	0.020	19	97.00	1.249	33	101.24	0.000	47	106.00	0.000
6	91.00	0.000	20	97.00	0.751	34	101.24	3.414	48	107.24	0.000
7	92.76	0.000	21	97.00	0.000	35	101.76	0.000	49	107.24	0.000
8	92.76	0.000	22	98.24	0.000	36	103.00	0.751	50	107.24	0.586
9	92.76	0.586	23	98.76	0.000	37	103.00	1.249	51	109.00	0.000
10	94.00	0.000	24	98.76	0.000	38	103.00	0.751	52	109.29	0.020
11	94.27	0.934	25	98.76	3.414	39	103.00	1.249	53	109.97	0.000
12	94.68	0.705	26	98.93	0.000	40	103.00	0.000	54	110.24	0.000
13	94.96	0.000	27	99.20	4.707	41	103.17	1.632	55	111.04	0.000
14	95.07	0.000	28	100.00	0.000	42	103.97	0.000	56	114.21	0.002

5-6

$J_{AB} = J_{AB'} = 4.0$

Maximum summed intensity = 5.600

LINE	FREQ	INTEN	LINE	FREQ	INTEN	LINE	FREQ	INTEN	LINE	FREQ	INTEN
1	83.46	0.002	15	95.00	0.000	29	100.54	5.198	43	105.00	0.000
2	87.00	0.000	16	95.46	0.000	30	101.00	0.000	44	106.54	0.000
3	87.46	0.000	17	97.00	1.600	31	101.00	0.000	45	106.54	0.775
4	89.00	0.000	18	97.00	1.561	32	101.00	0.000	46	107.00	0.400
5	89.46	0.025	19	97.00	0.439	33	101.00	0.000	47	107.00	0.000
6	89.46	0.000	20	97.00	1.561	34	101.00	3.600	48	109.00	0.000
7	91.00	0.000	21	97.00	0.439	35	103.00	1.561	49	109.00	0.000
8	91.00	0.000	22	97.00	0.000	36	103.00	0.439	50	109.00	0.400
9	91.00	0.400	23	99.00	0.000	37	103.00	0.000	51	110.54	0.000
10	93.00	0.400	24	99.00	0.000	38	103.00	1.600	52	110.54	0.025
11	93.00	0.000	25	99.00	0.000	39	103.00	0.439	53	111.00	0.000
12	93.46	0.000	26	99.00	0.000	40	103.00	1.561	54	112.54	0.000
13	93.46	0.775	27	99.00	3.600	41	104.54	0.000	55	113.00	0.000
14	95.00	0.000	28	99.46	5.198	42	105.00	0.000	56	116.54	0.002

5-7

$J_{AB} = J_{AB'} = 6.0$

Maximum summed intensity = 5.624

LINE	FREQ	INTEN	LINE	FREQ	INTEN	LINE	FREQ	INTEN	LINE	FREQ	INTEN
1	78.40	0.001	15	94.11	0.000	29	100.31	5.628	43	108.18	0.553
2	81.29	0.000	16	94.71	0.000	30	100.71	0.000	44	109.00	0.000
3	83.98	0.000	17	95.13	0.000	31	100.71	0.000	45	109.00	0.000
4	85.00	0.000	18	97.00	0.052	32	100.71	3.789	46	110.02	0.000
5	86.27	0.023	19	97.00	1.948	33	101.13	0.000	47	110.84	0.160
6	87.29	0.000	20	97.00	0.052	34	102.57	1.636	48	111.89	0.000
7	87.29	0.000	21	97.00	1.948	35	103.00	1.948	49	112.71	0.000
8	87.29	0.211	22	97.00	0.000	36	103.00	0.052	50	112.71	0.000
9	88.11	0.000	23	97.43	1.636	37	103.00	0.000	51	112.71	0.211
10	89.16	0.160	24	98.87	0.000	38	103.00	0.052	52	113.73	0.023
11	89.98	0.000	25	99.29	0.000	39	103.00	1.948	53	115.00	0.000
12	91.00	0.000	26	99.29	0.000	40	104.87	0.000	54	116.02	0.000
13	91.00	0.000	27	99.29	3.789	41	105.29	0.000	55	118.71	0.000
14	91.82	0.553	28	99.69	5.628	42	105.89	0.000	56	121.60	0.001

5-8

$J_{AB} = J_{AB'} = 8.0$

Maximum summed intensity = 5.873

LINE	FREQ	INTEN	LINE	FREQ	INTEN	LINE	FREQ	INTEN	LINE	FREQ	INTEN
1	73.05	0.001	15	92.54	0.000	29	100.22	5.789	43	109.87	0.408
2	75.46	0.000	16	92.59	0.000	30	100.54	0.000	44	111.00	0.000
3	80.24	0.000	17	95.00	0.000	31	100.54	0.000	45	113.00	0.000
4	81.00	0.000	18	95.35	0.000	32	100.54	3.873	46	113.41	0.000
5	82.70	0.017	19	97.00	1.512	33	101.35	0.000	47	113.76	0.000
6	83.46	0.000	20	97.00	0.488	34	102.19	1.703	48	114.89	0.083
7	83.46	0.000	21	97.00	1.512	35	103.00	0.488	49	116.54	0.000
8	83.46	0.127	22	97.00	0.488	36	103.00	1.512	50	116.54	0.000
9	85.11	0.083	23	97.81	1.703	37	103.00	0.488	51	116.54	0.127
10	86.24	0.000	24	98.65	0.000	38	103.00	1.512	52	117.30	0.017
11	86.59	0.000	25	99.46	0.000	39	104.65	0.000	53	119.00	0.000
12	87.00	0.000	26	99.46	0.000	40	105.00	0.000	54	119.76	0.000
13	89.00	0.000	27	99.46	3.873	41	107.41	0.000	55	124.54	0.000
14	90.13	0.408	28	99.78	5.789	42	107.46	0.000	56	126.95	0.001

5-9

$J_{AB} = J_{AB'} = 10.0$

Maximum summed intensity = 6.407

LINE	FREQ	INTEN	LINE	FREQ	INTEN	LINE	FREQ	INTEN	LINE	FREQ	INTEN
1	67.50	0.000	15	90.44	0.000	29	100.17	5.865	43	111.61	0.309
2	69.56	0.000	16	90.95	0.000	30	100.44	0.000	44	113.00	0.000
3	76.39	0.000	17	93.00	0.000	31	100.44	0.000	45	115.05	0.000
4	77.00	0.	18	95.55	0.000	32	100.44	3.916	46	117.00	0.000
5	78.95	0.012	19	97.00	1.648	33	101.55	0.000	47	117.61	0.000
6	79.56	0.000	20	97.00	0.352	34	101.89	1.764	48	118.99	0.050
7	79.56	0.000	21	97.00	1.648	35	103.00	0.352	49	120.44	0.000
8	79.56	0.084	22	97.00	0.352	36	103.00	1.648	50	120.44	0.000
9	81.01	0.050	23	98.11	1.764	37	103.00	0.352	51	120.44	0.084
10	82.39	0.000	24	98.45	0.000	38	103.00	1.648	52	121.05	0.012
11	83.00	0.000	25	99.56	0.000	39	104.45	0.000	53	123.00	0.000
12	84.95	0.000	26	99.56	0.000	40	107.00	0.000	54	123.61	0.000
13	87.00	0.000	27	99.56	3.916	41	109.06	0.000	55	130.44	0.000
14	88.39	0.309	28	99.83	5.865	42	109.56	0.000	56	132.50	0.000

−11 −10 −9 −8 −7 −6 −5 −4 −3 −2 −1 0 +1 +2 +3 +4 +5 +6 +7 +8 +9 +10 +11

5-10

$J_{AB} = J_{AB'} = 12.0$

Maximum summed intensity = 7.221

LINE	FREQ	INTEN	LINE	FREQ	INTEN	LINE	FREQ	INTEN	LINE	FREQ	INTEN
1	61.85	0.000	15	88.37	0.000	29	100.13	5.906	43	113.41	0.239
2	63.63	0.000	16	89.22	0.000	30	100.37	0.000	44	115.00	0.000
3	72.50	0.000	17	91.00	0.000	31	100.37	0.000	45	116.78	0.000
4	73.00	0.000	18	95.72	0.000	32	100.37	3.940	46	121.00	0.000
5	75.13	0.009	19	97.00	0.028	33	101.65	1.812	47	121.50	0.000
6	75.63	0.000	20	97.00	1.972	34	101.72	0.000	48	123.09	0.034
7	75.63	0.000	21	97.00	0.028	35	103.00	1.972	49	124.37	0.000
8	75.63	0.060	22	97.00	1.972	36	103.00	0.028	50	124.37	0.000
9	76.91	0.034	23	98.28	0.000	37	103.00	0.028	51	124.37	0.060
10	78.50	0.000	24	98.35	1.812	38	103.00	1.972	52	124.87	0.009
11	79.00	0.000	25	99.63	0.000	39	104.28	0.000	53	127.00	0.000
12	83.22	0.000	26	99.63	0.000	40	109.00	0.000	54	127.50	0.000
13	85.00	0.000	27	99.63	3.940	41	110.78	0.000	55	136.37	0.000
14	86.59	0.239	28	99.87	5.906	42	111.63	0.000	56	138.15	0.000

−11 −10 −9 −8 −7 −6 −5 −4 −3 −2 −1 0 +1 +2 +3 +4 +5 +6 +7 +8 +9 +10 +11

5-11

$J_{AB} = J_{AB'} = 15.00$

Maximum summed intensity = 9.001

LINE	FREQ	INTEN	LINE	FREQ	INTEN	LINE	FREQ	INTEN	LINE	FREQ	INTEN
1	53.22	0.000	15	85.30	0.000	29	100.10	5.940	43	116.18	0.170
2	54.70	0.000	16	86.52	0.000	30	100.30	0.000	44	118.00	0.000
3	66.60	0.000	17	88.00	0.000	31	100.30	0.000	45	119.48	0.000
4	67.00	0.000	18	95.92	0.000	32	100.30	3.961	46	127.00	0.000
5	69.30	0.006	19	97.00	1.179	33	101.37	1.863	47	127.40	0.000
6	69.70	0.000	20	97.00	0.821	34	101.92	0.000	48	129.22	0.021
7	69.70	0.000	21	97.00	0.821	35	103.00	0.821	49	130.30	0.000
8	69.70	0.039	22	97.00	1.179	36	103.00	1.179	50	130.30	0.000
9	70.78	0.021	23	98.08	0.000	37	103.00	1.179	51	130.30	0.039
10	72.60	0.000	24	98.63	1.863	38	103.00	0.821	52	130.70	0.006
11	73.00	0.000	25	99.70	0.000	39	104.08	0.000	53	133.00	0.000
12	80.52	0.000	26	99.70	0.000	40	112.00	0.000	54	133.40	0.000
13	82.00	0.000	27	99.70	3.961	41	113.48	0.000	55	145.30	0.000
14	83.82	0.170	28	99.90	5.940	42	114.70	0.000	56	146.78	0.000

−11 −10 −9 −8 −7 −6 −5 −4 −3 −2 −1 0 +1 +2 +3 +4 +5 +6 +7 +8 +9 +10 +11

5-12

$J_{AB} = J_{AB'} = 18.0$

Maximum summed intensity = 10.675

LINE	FREQ	INTEN	LINE	FREQ	INTEN	LINE	FREQ	INTEN	LINE	FREQ	INTEN
1	44.49	0.000	15	82.25	0.000	29	100.09	5.958	43	119.01	0.125
2	45.75	0.000	16	83.74	0.000	30	100.25	0.000	44	121.00	0.000
3	60.67	0.000	17	85.00	0.000	31	100.25	0.000	45	122.26	0.000
4	61.00	0.000	18	96.07	0.000	32	100.25	3.973	46	133.00	0.000
5	63.42	0.004	19	97.00	1.442	33	101.17	1.897	47	133.33	0.000
6	63.75	0.000	20	97.00	0.558	34	102.07	0.000	48	135.32	0.014
7	63.75	0.000	21	97.00	0.558	35	103.00	0.558	49	136.25	0.000
8	63.75	0.027	22	97.00	1.442	36	103.00	1.442	50	136.25	0.000
9	64.68	0.014	23	97.93	0.000	37	103.00	1.442	51	136.25	0.027
10	66.67	0.000	24	98.83	1.897	38	103.00	0.558	52	136.58	0.004
11	67.00	0.000	25	99.75	0.000	39	103.93	0.000	53	139.00	0.000
12	77.74	0.000	26	99.75	0.000	40	115.00	0.000	54	139.33	0.000
13	79.00	0.000	27	99.75	3.973	41	116.26	0.000	55	154.25	0.000
14	80.99	0.125	28	99.91	5.958	42	117.75	0.000	56	155.51	0.000

−11 −10 −9 −8 −7 −6 −5 −4 −3 −2 −1 0 +1 +2 +3 +4 +5 +6 +7 +8 +9 +10 +11

5-13

$J_{AA'}$	J_{AB}	$J_{AB'}$	$J_{BB'}$
1	1	2	1
1	2	1	1

The maximum summed intensity is 4.290.

LINE	FREQ	INTEN	LINE	FREQ	INTEN	LINE	FREQ	INTEN	LINE	FREQ	INTEN
1	88.79	0.000	15	96.46	0.836	29	100.54	0.	43	103.54	0.836
2	90.10	0.000	16	96.61	1.510	30	101.26	0.214	44	103.82	0.000
3	90.97	0.000	17	96.68	1.626	31	101.63	3.327	45	103.85	0.000
4	91.66	0.002	18	97.05	0.000	32	101.85	0.000	46	104.01	0.000
5	94.46	0.	19	97.15	0.000	33	101.85	2.894	47	104.14	0.000
6	94.55	0.057	20	97.46	1.164	34	101.95	0.000	48	104.50	1.263
7	95.15	0.000	21	97.46	1.164	35	102.08	0.000	49	104.85	0.000
8	95.15	1.106	22	97.92	0.000	36	102.54	1.164	50	104.85	1.106
9	95.50	1.263	23	98.05	0.000	37	102.54	1.164	51	105.45	0.057
10	95.86	0.000	24	98.15	0.000	38	102.85	0.000	52	105.54	0.
11	95.99	0.000	25	98.15	2.894	39	102.95	0.000	53	108.34	0.002
12	96.15	0.000	26	98.37	3.327	40	103.32	1.626	54	109.03	0.000
13	96.18	0.000	27	98.74	0.214	41	103.39	1.510	55	109.90	0.000
14	96.46	0.836	28	99.46	0.	42	103.54	0.836	56	111.21	0.000

5-14

$J_{AA'}$	J_{AB}	$J_{AB'}$	$J_{BB'}$
1	1	4	1
1	4	1	1

The maximum summed intensity is 5.111.

LINE	FREQ	INTEN	LINE	FREQ	INTEN	LINE	FREQ	INTEN	LINE	FREQ	INTEN
1	86.37	0.000	15	95.59	0.000	29	100.15	0.000	43	104.81	0.000
2	87.92	0.000	16	95.64	0.860	30	101.08	4.156	44	104.85	0.553
3	90.66	0.000	17	96.55	0.930	31	101.18	0.991	45	104.85	0.553
4	91.11	0.008	18	96.59	0.000	32	101.41	0.000	46	105.08	0.000
5	93.15	0.000	19	97.37	0.000	33	101.41	3.280	47	105.37	0.000
6	93.37	0.194	20	98.11	0.000	34	101.63	0.000	48	105.82	0.860
7	93.59	0.000	21	98.15	1.447	35	101.85	1.447	49	106.41	0.000
8	93.59	0.720	22	98.15	1.447	36	101.85	1.447	50	106.41	0.720
9	94.18	0.860	23	98.37	0.000	37	101.89	0.000	51	106.63	0.194
10	94.63	0.000	24	98.59	0.000	38	102.63	0.000	52	106.85	0.000
11	94.92	0.000	25	98.59	3.280	39	103.41	0.000	53	108.89	0.008
12	95.15	0.553	26	98.82	0.991	40	103.45	0.930	54	109.34	0.000
13	95.15	0.553	27	98.92	4.156	41	104.36	0.860	55	112.08	0.000
14	95.19	0.000	28	99.85	0.000	42	104.41	0.000	56	113.63	0.000

5-15

$J_{AA'}$	J_{AB}	$J_{AB'}$	$J_{BB'}$
1	1	6	1
1	6	1	1

The maximum summed intensity is 5.038.

LINE	FREQ	INTEN	LINE	FREQ	INTEN	LINE	FREQ	INTEN	LINE	FREQ	INTEN
1	83.40	0.000	15	93.89	0.000	29	100.59	0.000	43	106.13	0.000
2	85.11	0.	16	94.17	0.458	30	100.76	4.729	44	106.41	0.360
3	89.73	0.000	17	96.61	0.602	31	101.01	1.435	45	106.41	0.360
4	90.02	0.013	18	96.89	0.000	32	101.11	0.000	46	106.51	0.000
5	91.59	0.000	19	97.54	0.000	33	101.11	3.519	47	107.08	0.000
6	91.79	0.188	20	98.32	0.000	34	101.30	0.000	48	107.38	0.576
7	91.89	0.000	21	98.59	1.640	35	101.41	1.640	49	108.11	0.000
8	91.89	0.481	22	98.59	1.640	36	101.41	1.640	50	108.11	0.481
9	92.62	0.576	23	98.70	0.000	37	101.68	0.000	51	108.21	0.188
10	92.92	0.000	24	98.89	0.000	38	102.46	0.000	52	108.41	0.000
11	93.49	0.000	25	98.89	3.519	39	103.11	0.000	53	109.98	0.013
12	93.59	0.360	26	98.99	1.435	40	103.39	0.602	54	110.27	0.000
13	93.59	0.360	27	99.24	4.729	41	105.83	0.458	55	114.89	0.000
14	93.87	0.000	28	99.41	0.000	42	106.11	0.000	56	116.60	0.000

5-16

$J_{AA'}$	J_{AB}	$J_{AB'}$	$J_{BB'}$
1	1	9	1
1	9	1	1

The maximum summed intensity is 7.089.

LINE	FREQ	INTEN	LINE	FREQ	INTEN	LINE	FREQ	INTEN	LINE	FREQ	INTEN
1	78.35	0.000	15	91.47	0.000	29	100.49	5.231	43	108.83	0.000
2	80.18	0.000	16	91.64	0.214	30	100.79	1.723	44	109.00	0.200
3	87.67	0.000	17	96.70	0.354	31	100.83	0.000	45	109.00	0.200
4	87.84	0.015	18	97.17	0.000	32	100.83	3.715	46	109.04	0.000
5	89.00	0.000	19	97.67	0.000	33	100.96	0.000	47	109.82	0.000
6	89.13	0.130	20	98.53	0.000	34	101.00	1.800	48	109.99	0.333
7	89.17	0.000	21	99.00	1.800	35	101.00	1.800	49	110.83	0.000
8	89.17	0.285	22	99.00	1.800	36	101.00	0.000	50	110.83	0.285
9	90.01	0.333	23	99.00	0.	37	101.47	0.000	51	110.87	0.130
10	90.18	0.000	24	99.04	0.000	38	102.33	0.000	52	111.00	0.000
11	90.96	0.000	25	99.17	0.000	39	102.83	0.000	53	112.16	0.015
12	91.00	0.200	26	99.17	3.715	40	103.30	0.354	54	112.33	0.000
13	91.00	0.200	27	99.21	1.723	41	108.36	0.214	55	119.82	0.000
14	91.17	0.000	28	99.51	5.231	42	108.53	0.000	56	121.65	0.000

5-17

$J_{AA'}$	J_{AB}	$J_{AB'}$	$J_{BB'}$
1	1	12	1
1	12	1	1

The maximum summed intensity is 8.715.

LINE	FREQ	INTEN	LINE	FREQ	INTEN	LINE	FREQ	INTEN	LINE	FREQ	INTEN
1	72.92	0.000	15	88.81	0.000	29	100.36	5.497	43	111.66	0.000
2	74.82	0.000	16	88.92	0.118	30	100.64	1.842	44	111.76	0.122
3	85.22	0.000	17	96.76	0.230	31	100.66	0.000	45	111.76	0.122
4	85.33	0.013	18	97.34	0.000	32	100.66	3.816	46	111.78	0.000
5	86.24	0.000	19	97.75	0.000	33	100.75	0.000	47	112.65	0.000
6	86.32	0.088	20	98.66	0.000	34	100.76	1.878	48	112.76	0.210
7	86.34	0.000	21	98.76	0.000	35	100.76	1.878	49	113.66	0.000
8	86.34	0.184	22	99.24	1.878	36	101.24	0.000	50	113.66	0.184
9	87.24	0.210	23	99.24	1.878	37	101.34	0.000	51	113.68	0.088
10	87.35	0.000	24	99.25	0.000	38	102.25	0.000	52	113.76	0.000
11	88.22	0.000	25	99.34	0.000	39	102.66	0.000	53	114.67	0.013
12	88.24	0.122	26	99.34	3.816	40	103.24	0.230	54	114.78	0.000
13	88.24	0.122	27	99.36	1.842	41	111.08	0.118	55	125.18	0.000
14	88.34	0.000	28	99.64	5.497	42	111.19	0.000	56	127.08	0.000

−11 −10 −9 −8 −7 −6 −5 −4 −3 −2 −1 0 +1 +2 +3 +4 +5 +6 +7 +8 +9 +10 +11

5-18

$J_{AA'}$	J_{AB}	$J_{AB'}$	$J_{BB'}$
1	1	15	1
1	15	1	1

The maximum summed intensity is 9.198

LINE	FREQ	INTEN	LINE	FREQ	INTEN	LINE	FREQ	INTEN	LINE	FREQ	INTEN
1	67.30	0.000	15	86.04	0.000	29	100.27	5.650	43	114.54	0.000
2	69.23	0.000	16	86.11	0.074	30	100.53	1.900	44	114.62	0.081
3	82.57	0.000	17	96.80	0.160	31	100.54	0.000	45	114.62	0.081
4	82.64	0.011	18	97.46	0.000	32	100.54	3.873	46	114.63	0.000
5	83.38	0.000	19	97.80	0.000	33	100.61	0.000	47	115.54	0.000
6	83.45	0.062	20	98.62	0.000	34	100.62	1.919	48	115.61	0.143
7	83.46	0.000	21	98.73	0.000	35	100.62	1.919	49	116.54	0.000
8	83.46	0.127	22	99.38	1.919	36	101.27	0.000	50	116.54	0.127
9	84.39	0.143	23	99.38	1.919	37	101.38	0.000	51	116.55	0.062
10	84.46	0.000	24	99.39	0.000	38	102.20	0.000	52	116.62	0.000
11	85.37	0.000	25	99.46	0.000	39	102.54	0.000	53	117.36	0.011
12	85.38	0.081	26	99.46	3.873	40	103.20	0.160	54	117.43	0.000
13	85.38	0.081	27	99.47	1.900	41	113.89	0.074	55	130.77	0.000
14	85.46	0.000	28	99.73	5.650	42	113.96	0.000	56	132.70	0.000

−11 −10 −9 −8 −7 −6 −5 −4 −3 −2 −1 0 +1 +2 +3 +4 +5 +6 +7 +8 +9 +10 +11

5-19

$J_{AA'}$	J_{AB}	$J_{AB'}$	$J_{BB'}$
1	1	18	1
1	18	1	1

The maximum summed intensity is 9.946.

LINE	FREQ	INTEN	LINE	FREQ	INTEN	LINE	FREQ	INTEN	LINE	FREQ	INTEN
1	61.56	0.000	15	83.19	0.000	29	100.22	5.744	43	117.46	0.000
2	63.51	0.000	16	83.24	0.050	30	100.46	1.932	44	117.51	0.057
3	79.80	0.000	17	96.83	0.118	31	100.46	0.000	45	117.51	0.057
4	79.85	0.009	18	97.54	0.000	32	100.46	3.907	46	117.52	0.000
5	80.49	0.000	19	97.83	0.000	33	100.51	0.000	47	118.46	0.000
6	80.53	0.046	20	98.51	0.000	34	100.51	1.943	48	118.51	0.103
7	80.54	0.000	21	98.78	0.000	35	100.51	1.943	49	119.46	0.000
8	80.54	0.093	22	99.49	1.943	36	101.22	0.000	50	119.46	0.093
9	81.49	0.103	23	99.49	1.943	37	101.49	0.000	51	119.47	0.046
10	81.54	0.000	24	99.49	0.000	38	102.17	0.000	52	119.51	0.000
11	82.48	0.000	25	99.54	0.000	39	102.46	0.000	53	120.15	0.009
12	82.49	0.057	26	99.54	3.907	40	103.17	0.118	54	120.20	0.000
13	82.49	0.057	27	99.54	1.932	41	116.76	0.050	55	136.49	0.000
14	82.54	0.000	28	99.76	5.744	42	116.81	0.000	56	138.44	0.000

5-20

$J_{AA'}$	J_{AB}	$J_{AB'}$	$J_{BB'}$
1	2	1	2
1	1	2	2
2	2	1	1
2	1	2	1

The maximum summed intensity is 4.505.

LINE	FREQ	INTEN	LINE	FREQ	INTEN	LINE	FREQ	INTEN	LINE	FREQ	INTEN
1	88.78	0.000	15	96.57	1.541	29	99.68	0.142	43	103.94	0.000
2	89.98	0.000	16	96.73	1.708	30	100.32	0.142	44	103.97	0.000
3	91.08	0.000	17	96.74	1.555	31	101.01	0.000	45	104.15	0.000
4	91.66	0.002	18	97.05	0.000	32	101.15	0.000	46	104.24	0.200
5	93.61	0.021	19	97.17	1.800	33	101.63	3.332	47	104.52	1.253
6	94.44	0.000	20	97.44	0.000	34	101.84	0.445	48	104.85	1.106
7	94.45	0.000	21	98.00	0.000	35	101.85	2.894	49	105.07	0.000
8	95.04	0.000	22	98.15	2.894	36	102.12	0.000	50	105.56	0.000
9	95.15	1.106	23	98.16	0.445	37	102.56	0.000	51	106.39	0.021
10	95.48	1.253	24	98.37	3.332	38	102.83	1.800	52	106.54	0.000
11	95.76	0.200	25	98.85	0.000	39	102.83	0.000	53	108.34	0.002
12	95.85	0.000	26	98.87	0.000	40	103.26	1.555	54	109.03	0.000
13	95.92	0.000	27	99.46	0.000	41	103.27	1.708	55	109.91	0.000
14	96.18	0.000	28	99.55	0.000	42	103.43	1.541	56	111.22	0.000

5-21

$J_{AA'}$	J_{AB}	$J_{AB'}$	$J_{BB'}$
1	4	1	4
1	1	4	4
4	4	1	1
4	1	4	1

The maximum summed intensity is 4.375.

LINE	FREQ	INTEN	LINE	FREQ	INTEN	LINE	FREQ	INTEN	LINE	FREQ	INTEN
1	86.08	0.000	15	95.76	1.000	29	100.00	1.000	43	104.28	0.000
2	87.80	0.000	16	95.96	1.013	30	100.24	0.000	44	104.48	0.000
3	90.37	0.000	17	96.23	1.324	31	100.26	0.000	45	105.34	0.000
4	91.13	0.010	18	96.47	0.000	32	100.72	0.000	46	106.11	0.735
5	91.28	0.042	19	97.12	0.000	33	100.91	0.650	47	106.41	0.720
6	91.47	0.000	20	97.28	0.000	34	101.06	4.226	48	106.86	0.106
7	92.88	0.000	21	97.38	1.894	35	101.41	3.280	49	107.06	0.000
8	92.89	0.000	22	97.57	0.000	36	102.38	0.000	50	108.53	0.000
9	93.14	0.106	23	98.59	3.280	37	102.62	1.894	51	108.72	0.042
10	93.59	0.720	24	98.94	4.226	38	102.77	0.000	52	108.87	0.010
11	93.89	0.735	25	99.09	0.650	39	103.53	0.000	53	109.58	0.000
12	94.61	0.000	26	99.28	0.000	40	103.77	1.324	54	109.74	0.000
13	95.57	0.000	27	99.81	0.000	41	104.04	1.013	55	112.25	0.
14	95.72	0.000	28	100.00	1.000	42	104.24	1.000	56	113.92	0.000

−11 −10 −9 −8 −7 −6 −5 −4 −3 −2 −1 0 +1 +2 +3 +4 +5 +6 +7 +8 +9 +10 +11

5-22

$J_{AA'}$	J_{AB}	$J_{AB'}$	$J_{BB'}$
1	6	1	6
1	1	6	6
6	6	1	1
6	1	6	1

The maximum summed intensity is 5.005.

LINE	FREQ	INTEN	LINE	FREQ	INTEN	LINE	FREQ	INTEN	LINE	FREQ	INTEN
1	82.47	0.000	15	95.04	0.600	29	100.60	0.000	43	105.70	0.000
2	85.14	0.000	16	95.35	0.000	30	100.71	4.873	44	106.09	0.445
3	88.03	0.000	17	95.43	0.000	31	100.96	0.000	45	106.27	0.000
4	88.35	0.000	18	95.55	0.000	32	100.99	1.555	46	108.11	0.481
5	89.35	0.045	19	95.74	1.056	33	101.11	3.519	47	108.32	0.386
6	90.07	0.018	20	96.50	0.000	34	101.43	1.022	48	108.59	0.000
7	90.42	0.064	21	97.22	0.000	35	102.43	0.000	49	109.58	0.064
8	90.45	0.	22	97.49	1.936	36	102.51	1.936	50	109.93	0.018
9	90.81	0.000	23	97.57	0.000	37	102.89	0.000	51	110.65	0.045
10	91.68	0.386	24	98.57	1.022	38	103.38	0.000	52	111.37	0.000
11	91.89	0.481	25	98.89	3.519	39	104.26	1.056	53	111.65	0.000
12	93.12	0.	26	99.01	1.555	40	104.57	0.000	54	113.04	0.000
13	93.91	0.445	27	99.29	4.873	41	104.65	0.000	55	115.47	0.000
14	94.91	0.000	28	100.01	0.000	42	104.96	0.600	56	117.53	0.000

−11 −10 −9 −8 −7 −6 −5 −4 −3 −2 −1 0 +1 +2 +3 +4 +5 +6 +7 +8 +9 +10 +11

5-23

$J_{AA'}$	J_{AB}	$J_{AB'}$	$J_{BB'}$
1	9	1	9
1	1	9	9
9	9	1	1
9	1	9	1

The maximum summed intensity is 5.196.

LINE	FREQ	INTEN	LINE	FREQ	INTEN	LINE	FREQ	INTEN	LINE	FREQ	INTEN
1	76.21	0.000	15	93.43	0.000	29	100.44	5.404	43	107.14	0.000
2	80.67	0.000	16	93.51	0.000	30	100.83	3.715	44	108.26	0.000
3	82.92	0.000	17	94.12	0.000	31	101.53	1.857	45	109.78	0.143
4	83.51	0.000	18	94.38	0.000	32	101.61	1.298	46	110.51	0.000
5	85.88	0.000	19	94.83	0.000	33	101.68	0.000	47	110.83	0.285
6	86.28	0.035	20	95.03	0.793	34	101.94	0.000	48	112.10	0.021
7	86.73	0.043	21	95.17	0.000	35	102.41	1.965	49	112.13	0.173
8	87.80	0.000	22	96.79	0.000	36	103.93	0.000	50	113.27	0.043
9	87.87	0.173	23	97.59	1.965	37	104.83	0.000	51	113.72	0.035
10	87.90	0.021	24	98.39	1.298	38	104.90	0.000	52	115.39	0.000
11	89.17	0.285	25	98.47	1.857	39	104.97	0.793	53	116.49	0.000
12	90.22	0.143	26	99.17	3.715	40	105.17	0.000	54	118.06	0.000
13	91.16	0.000	27	99.56	5.404	41	106.49	0.000	55	121.02	0.000
14	93.31	0.268	28	100.01	0.000	42	106.69	0.268	56	123.79	0.000

−11 −10 −9 −8 −7 −6 −5 −4 −3 −2 −1 0 +1 +2 +3 +4 +5 +6 +7 +8 +9 +10 +11

5-24

$J_{AA'}$	J_{AB}	$J_{AB'}$	$J_{BB'}$
1	12	1	12
1	1	12	12
12	12	1	1
12	1	12	1

The maximum summed intensity is 5.718.

LINE	FREQ	INTEN	LINE	FREQ	INTEN	LINE	FREQ	INTEN	LINE	FREQ	INTEN
1	69.55	0.000	15	91.56	0.000	29	100.30	5.649	43	108.62	0.130
2	75.91	0.000	16	91.75	0.000	30	100.66	3.816	44	111.08	0.000
3	77.17	0.000	17	92.09	0.000	31	101.55	1.451	45	112.34	0.000
4	78.56	0.000	18	92.88	0.000	32	101.74	1.936	46	113.66	0.184
5	80.96	0.	19	93.04	0.	33	102.35	1.978	47	113.82	0.064
6	82.10	0.022	20	94.12	0.000	34	102.88	0.000	48	114.62	0.018
7	83.87	0.095	21	94.31	0.619	35	103.83	0.000	49	115.87	0.038
8	84.13	0.038	22	96.16	0.000	36	105.09	0.000	50	116.13	0.095
9	84.84	0.000	23	97.65	1.978	37	105.69	0.619	51	117.90	0.022
10	85.38	0.018	24	98.26	1.936	38	105.88	0.000	52	120.00	0.000
11	86.18	0.064	25	98.45	1.451	39	106.66	0.000	53	121.44	0.000
12	86.34	0.184	26	98.99	0.000	40	107.12	0.000	54	123.12	0.000
13	89.25	0.000	27	99.34	3.816	41	107.92	0.000	55	126.91	0.000
14	91.38	0.130	28	99.70	5.649	42	108.44	0.000	56	130.45	0.000

−11 −10 −9 −8 −7 −6 −5 −4 −3 −2 −1 0 +1 +2 +3 +4 +5 +6 +7 +8 +9 +10 +11

5-25

$J_{AA'}$	J_{AB}	$J_{AB'}$	$J_{BB'}$
1	15	1	15
1	1	15	15
15	15	1	1
15	1	15	1

The maximum summed intensity is 5.732.

LINE	FREQ	INTEN	LINE	FREQ	INTEN	LINE	FREQ	INTEN	LINE	FREQ	INTEN
1	62.73	0.000	15	89.56	0.000	29	100.23	5.772	43	110.62	0.069
2	71.02	0.000	16	89.77	0.000	30	100.54	3.873	44	113.99	0.000
3	71.21	0.000	17	89.96	0.	31	101.43	1.560	45	114.18	0.000
4	73.56	0.000	18	90.64	0.000	32	101.84	1.965	46	116.54	0.127
5	75.94	0.000	19	92.06	0.	33	102.31	1.985	47	117.32	0.015
6	77.89	0.015	20	93.36	0.000	34	103.79	0.000	48	117.96	0.035
7	79.82	0.060	21	93.53	0.492	35	106.09	0.000	49	118.52	0.032
8	81.48	0.032	22	95.43	0.000	36	106.28	0.000	50	120.18	0.060
9	81.87	0.000	23	97.69	1.985	37	106.47	0.492	51	122.11	0.015
10	82.04	0.035	24	97.86	0.000	38	106.64	0.000	52	124.84	0.000
11	82.68	0.015	25	98.16	1.965	39	108.52	0.000	53	126.44	0.000
12	83.46	0.127	26	98.57	1.560	40	108.71	0.000	54	128.21	0.000
13	87.34	0.000	27	99.46	3.873	41	109.36	0.000	55	132.93	0.000
14	89.38	0.069	28	99.77	5.772	42	110.44	0.000	56	137.27	0.000

5-26

$J_{AA'}$	J_{AB}	$J_{AB'}$	$J_{BB'}$
1	18	1	18
1	1	18	18
18	18	1	1
18	1	18	1

The maximum summed intensity is 6.328.

LINE	FREQ	INTEN	LINE	FREQ	INTEN	LINE	FREQ	INTEN	LINE	FREQ	INTEN
1	55.82	0.000	15	87.46	0.	29	100.18	5.840	43	112.63	0.039
2	65.15	0.000	16	87.52	0.000	30	100.46	3.907	44	116.06	0.000
3	66.05	0.000	17	88.11	0.000	31	101.30	1.643	45	116.96	0.000
4	68.52	0.000	18	88.44	0.000	32	101.90	1.978	46	119.46	0.093
5	70.88	0.000	19	91.12	0.000	33	102.28	1.989	47	120.11	0.012
6	73.68	0.011	20	92.56	0.000	34	104.70	0.000	48	121.22	0.027
7	75.74	0.041	21	92.70	0.397	35	107.30	0.397	49	122.15	0.022
8	77.85	0.022	22	94.65	0.000	36	107.44	0.000	50	124.26	0.041
9	78.78	0.027	23	96.71	0.000	37	107.46	0.000	51	126.32	0.011
10	78.86	0.000	24	97.72	1.989	38	108.36	0.000	52	129.77	0.000
11	79.89	0.012	25	98.10	1.978	39	109.52	0.000	53	131.48	0.000
12	80.54	0.093	26	98.70	1.643	40	110.42	0.000	54	133.30	0.000
13	85.40	0.000	27	99.54	3.907	41	111.56	0.000	55	139.02	0.000
14	87.37	0.039	28	99.82	5.840	42	112.48	0.000	56	144.18	0.000

5-27

$J_{AA'}$	J_{AB}	$J_{AB'}$	$J_{BB'}$
2	2	1	2
2	1	2	2

The maximum summed intensity is 4.249.

LINE	FREQ	INTEN	LINE	FREQ	INTEN	LINE	FREQ	INTEN	LINE	FREQ	INTEN
1	88.76	0.000	15	96.46	0.836	29	100.46	0.000	43	103.54	0.836
2	89.98	0.000	16	96.54	1.549	30	100.64	0.125	44	103.94	0.000
3	91.07	0.000	17	96.75	1.742	31	100.85	0.000	45	104.53	1.236
4	91.66	0.003	18	97.15	0.000	32	101.05	0.000	46	104.85	0.000
5	92.66	0.010	19	97.46	1.164	33	101.15	0.000	47	104.85	1.106
6	93.46	0.000	20	97.46	1.164	34	101.63	3.335	48	104.94	0.000
7	94.15	0.000	21	98.15	0.000	35	101.85	0.000	49	105.03	0.000
8	94.97	0.000	22	98.15	2.894	36	101.85	2.894	50	105.85	0.000
9	95.06	0.000	23	98.37	3.335	37	102.54	1.164	51	106.54	0.000
10	95.15	0.000	24	98.85	0.000	38	102.54	1.164	52	107.34	0.010
11	95.15	1.106	25	98.95	0.000	39	102.85	0.000	53	108.34	0.003
12	95.47	1.236	26	99.15	0.000	40	103.25	1.742	54	108.93	0.000
13	96.06	0.000	27	99.36	0.125	41	103.46	1.549	55	110.02	0.000
14	96.46	0.836	28	99.54	0.000	42	103.54	0.836	56	111.24	0.000

5-28

$J_{AA'}$	J_{AB}	$J_{AB'}$	$J_{BB'}$
2	2	4	2
2	4	2	2

The maximum summed intensity is 4.634.

LINE	FREQ	INTEN	LINE	FREQ	INTEN	LINE	FREQ	INTEN	LINE	FREQ	INTEN
1	85.50	0.001	15	95.84	0.684	29	100.16	0.367	43	104.44	0.000
2	88.58	0.000	16	95.84	0.684	30	100.82	4.672	44	104.96	0.704
3	89.78	0.000	17	96.10	0.000	31	101.08	0.000	45	105.10	0.000
4	90.70	0.018	18	96.48	1.365	32	101.24	0.000	46	105.24	0.000
5	91.68	0.038	19	96.76	0.000	33	101.24	3.414	47	105.24	0.000
6	91.84	0.000	20	97.84	1.316	34	101.84	0.000	48	106.01	0.836
7	92.76	0.000	21	97.84	1.316	35	101.88	0.000	49	107.24	0.000
8	92.76	0.586	22	98.12	0.000	36	102.16	1.316	50	107.24	0.586
9	93.99	0.836	23	98.16	0.000	37	102.16	1.316	51	108.16	0.000
10	94.76	0.000	24	98.76	0.000	38	103.24	0.000	52	108.32	0.038
11	94.76	0.000	25	98.76	3.414	39	103.52	1.365	53	109.30	0.018
12	94.90	0.000	26	98.92	0.000	40	103.90	0.000	54	110.22	0.000
13	95.04	0.704	27	99.18	4.672	41	104.16	0.684	55	111.42	0.000
14	95.56	0.000	28	99.84	0.367	42	104.16	0.684	56	114.50	0.001

5-29

$J_{AA'}$	J_{AB}	$J_{AB'}$	$J_{BB'}$
2	2	6	2
2	6	2	2

The maximum summed intensity is 5.730.

LINE	FREQ	INTEN	LINE	FREQ	INTEN	LINE	FREQ	INTEN	LINE	FREQ	INTEN
1	82.50	0.000	15	94.95	0.000	29	100.49	1.012	43	105.56	0.372
2	85.89	0.000	16	95.00	0.000	30	100.57	5.136	44	105.61	0.445
3	88.82	0.000	17	95.00	0.000	31	101.00	0.000	45	105.61	0.445
4	89.43	0.022	18	95.56	0.798	32	101.00	3.600	46	106.12	0.000
5	90.39	0.000	19	96.03	0.000	33	101.09	0.000	47	106.89	0.000
6	90.49	0.092	20	97.61	0.000	34	101.61	1.555	48	107.50	0.569
7	91.00	0.000	21	97.83	0.000	35	101.61	1.555	49	109.00	0.000
8	91.00	0.400	22	98.39	1.555	36	102.17	0.000	50	109.00	0.400
9	92.50	0.569	23	98.39	1.555	37	102.39	0.000	51	109.51	0.092
10	93.11	0.000	24	98.91	0.000	38	103.97	0.000	52	109.61	0.000
11	93.88	0.000	25	99.00	0.000	39	104.44	0.798	53	110.57	0.022
12	94.39	0.445	26	99.00	3.600	40	105.00	0.000	54	111.18	0.000
13	94.39	0.445	27	99.43	5.136	41	105.00	0.000	55	114.11	0.000
14	94.44	0.372	28	99.51	1.012	42	105.05	0.000	56	117.50	0.000

5-30

$J_{AA'}$	J_{AB}	$J_{AB'}$	$J_{BB'}$
2	2	9	2
2	9	2	2

The maximum summed intensity is 6.099.

LINE	FREQ	INTEN	LINE	FREQ	INTEN	LINE	FREQ	INTEN	LINE	FREQ	INTEN
1	77.42	0.000	15	93.03	0.000	29	100.38	5.498	43	107.76	0.000
2	81.07	0.000	16	93.38	0.327	30	100.58	1.565	44	108.11	0.241
3	86.74	0.000	17	94.09	0.162	31	100.76	0.000	45	108.11	0.241
4	87.09	0.020	18	95.24	0.000	32	100.76	3.756	46	108.30	0.000
5	87.89	0.000	19	95.96	0.000	33	100.92	0.000	47	109.71	0.000
6	88.05	0.096	20	97.11	0.000	34	101.11	1.759	48	110.05	0.332
7	88.24	0.000	21	97.75	0.000	35	101.11	1.759	49	111.76	0.000
8	88.24	0.244	22	98.89	1.759	36	102.25	0.000	50	111.76	0.244
9	89.95	0.332	23	98.89	1.759	37	102.89	0.000	51	111.95	0.096
10	90.29	0.000	24	99.08	0.000	38	104.04	0.000	52	112.11	0.000
11	91.70	0.000	25	99.24	0.000	39	104.76	0.000	53	112.91	0.020
12	91.89	0.241	26	99.24	3.756	40	105.91	0.162	54	113.26	0.000
13	91.89	0.241	27	99.42	1.565	41	106.62	0.327	55	118.93	0.000
14	92.24	0.000	28	99.62	5.498	42	106.97	0.000	56	122.58	0.000

5-31

$J_{AA'}$	J_{AB}	$J_{AB'}$	$J_{BB'}$
2	2	12	2
2	12	2	2

The maximum summed intensity is 6.320.

LINE	FREQ	INTEN	LINE	FREQ	INTEN	LINE	FREQ	INTEN	LINE	FREQ	INTEN
1	71.97	0.000	15	90.57	0.000	29	100.28	5.677	43	110.62	0.000
2	75.75	0.000	16	90.78	0.161	30	100.53	1.774	44	110.83	0.143
3	84.27	0.000	17	93.99	0.088	31	100.62	0.000	45	110.83	0.143
4	84.49	0.016	18	95.38	0.000	32	100.62	3.838	46	110.91	0.000
5	85.17	0.000	19	95.93	0.000	33	100.75	0.000	47	112.59	0.000
6	85.30	0.073	20	96.83	0.000	34	100.83	1.857	48	112.80	0.210
7	85.38	0.000	21	97.77	0.000	35	100.83	1.857	49	114.62	0.000
8	85.38	0.162	22	99.17	1.857	36	102.23	0.000	50	114.62	0.162
9	87.20	0.210	23	99.17	1.857	37	103.17	0.000	51	114.70	0.073
10	87.41	0.000	24	99.25	0.000	38	104.07	0.000	52	114.83	0.000
11	89.09	0.000	25	99.38	0.000	39	104.62	0.000	53	115.51	0.016
12	89.17	0.143	26	99.38	3.838	40	106.01	0.088	54	115.73	0.000
13	89.17	0.143	27	99.47	1.774	41	109.22	0.161	55	124.25	0.000
14	89.38	0.000	28	99.72	5.677	42	109.43	0.000	56	128.03	0.000

−11 −10 −9 −8 −7 −6 −5 −4 −3 −2 −1 0 +1 +2 +3 +4 +5 +6 +7 +8 +9 +10 +11

5-32

$J_{AA'}$	J_{AB}	$J_{AB'}$	$J_{BB'}$
2	2	15	2
2	15	2	2

The maximum summed intensity is 7.969.

LINE	FREQ	INTEN	LINE	FREQ	INTEN	LINE	FREQ	INTEN	LINE	FREQ	INTEN
1	66.33	0.000	15	87.80	0.000	29	100.22	5.777	43	113.51	0.000
2	70.19	0.	16	88.02	0.093	30	100.47	1.865	44	113.66	0.092
3	81.60	0.000	17	93.95	0.055	31	100.51	0.000	45	113.66	0.092
4	81.75	0.013	18	95.49	0.000	32	100.51	3.886	46	113.70	0.000
5	82.34	0.000	19	95.92	0.000	33	100.62	0.000	47	115.50	0.000
6	82.44	0.054	20	96.66	0.000	34	100.66	1.908	48	115.64	0.143
7	82.49	0.000	21	97.80	0.000	35	100.66	1.908	49	117.51	0.000
8	82.49	0.114	22	99.34	1.908	36	102.20	0.000	50	117.51	0.114
9	84.36	0.143	23	99.34	1.908	37	103.34	0.000	51	117.56	0.054
10	84.50	0.000	24	99.38	0.000	38	104.08	0.000	52	117.66	0.000
11	86.30	0.000	25	99.49	0.000	39	104.51	0.000	53	118.25	0.013
12	86.34	0.092	26	99.49	3.886	40	106.05	0.055	54	118.40	0.000
13	86.34	0.092	27	99.53	1.865	41	111.98	0.093	55	129.81	0.000
14	86.49	0.000	28	99.78	5.777	42	112.12	0.000	56	133.67	0.000

−11 −10 −9 −8 −7 −6 −5 −4 −3 −2 −1 0 +1 +2 +3 +4 +5 +6 +7 +8 +9 +10 +11

5-33

$J_{AA'}$	J_{AB}	$J_{AB'}$	$J_{BB'}$
2	2	18	2
2	18	2	2

The maximum summed intensity is 9.036.

LINE	FREQ	INTEN	LINE	FREQ	INTEN	LINE	FREQ	INTEN	LINE	FREQ	INTEN
1	60.59	0.000	15	85.08	0.000	29	100.18	5.837	43	116.44	0.000
2	64.48	0.	16	85.18	0.060	30	100.41	1.912	44	116.54	0.064
3	78.83	0.000	17	93.94	0.038	31	100.44	0.000	45	116.54	0.064
4	78.94	0.010	18	95.56	0.000	32	100.44	3.916	46	116.57	0.000
5	79.46	0.000	19	95.92	0.000	33	100.52	0.000	47	118.43	0.000
6	79.53	0.041	20	96.54	0.	34	100.54	1.936	48	118.53	0.102
7	79.56	0.000	21	97.83	0.000	35	100.54	1.936	49	120.44	0.000
8	79.56	0.084	22	99.46	1.936	36	102.17	0.000	50	120.44	0.084
9	81.47	0.102	23	99.46	1.936	37	103.46	0.	51	120.47	0.041
10	81.57	0.000	24	99.48	0.000	38	104.08	0.000	52	120.54	0.000
11	83.43	0.000	25	99.56	0.000	39	104.44	0.000	53	121.06	0.010
12	83.46	0.064	26	99.56	3.916	40	106.06	0.038	54	121.17	0.000
13	83.46	0.064	27	99.59	1.912	41	114.82	0.060	55	135.52	0.
14	83.56	0.000	28	99.82	5.837	42	114.92	0.000	56	139.41	0.000

5-34

$J_{AA'}$	J_{AB}	$J_{AB'}$	$J_{BB'}$
2	4	2	4
2	2	4	4
4	4	2	2
4	2	4	2

The maximum summed intensity is 5.330.

LINE	FREQ	INTEN	LINE	FREQ	INTEN	LINE	FREQ	INTEN	LINE	FREQ	INTEN
1	85.37	0.001	15	94.94	0.000	29	99.91	0.000	43	105.10	0.721
2	87.82	0.000	16	96.07	0.000	30	100.17	0.000	44	105.54	0.143
3	89.94	0.013	17	96.24	0.000	31	100.81	4.680	45	105.82	0.000
4	90.38	0.000	18	96.35	1.316	32	100.82	0.684	46	105.83	0.000
5	90.70	0.018	19	96.61	1.494	33	101.24	3.414	47	106.14	0.776
6	91.34	0.000	20	97.29	1.857	34	101.58	0.298	48	106.94	0.000
7	91.76	0.000	21	97.34	0.000	35	101.88	0.000	49	107.24	0.586
8	92.76	0.586	22	98.42	0.298	36	101.98	0.000	50	108.66	0.000
9	93.73	0.000	23	98.70	0.000	37	102.66	0.000	51	109.30	0.018
10	93.86	0.776	24	98.76	3.414	38	102.71	1.857	52	110.06	0.013
11	94.17	0.000	25	99.18	0.684	39	103.26	0.	53	110.12	0.000
12	94.46	0.143	26	99.19	4.680	40	103.39	1.494	54	110.29	0.000
13	94.85	0.000	27	99.42	0.000	41	103.65	1.316	55	111.51	0.
14	94.90	0.721	28	99.83	0.000	42	104.38	0.000	56	114.63	0.001

5-35

$J_{AA'}$	J_{AB}	$J_{AB'}$	$J_{BB'}$
2	6	2	6
2	2	6	6
6	6	2	2
6	2	6	2

The maximum summed intensity is 6.301.

LINE	FREQ	INTEN	LINE	FREQ	INTEN	LINE	FREQ	INTEN	LINE	FREQ	INTEN
1	81.84	0.000	15	94.24	0.000	29	100.44	0.000	43	106.17	0.000
2	85.05	0.000	16	94.69	0.000	30	100.56	5.160	44	106.33	0.418
3	87.92	0.022	17	94.94	0.684	31	100.59	1.316	45	107.33	0.000
4	88.17	0.000	18	95.82	0.000	32	101.00	3.600	46	108.16	0.418
5	88.60	0.000	19	96.17	0.000	33	101.83	0.000	47	108.21	0.081
6	89.44	0.023	20	96.33	1.259	34	102.08	0.700	48	108.46	0.000
7	89.76	0.000	21	97.44	1.919	35	102.56	1.919	49	109.00	0.400
8	91.00	0.400	22	97.69	0.000	36	102.61	0.000	50	110.56	0.023
9	91.79	0.081	23	97.92	0.700	37	102.71	0.000	51	111.80	0.000
10	91.84	0.418	24	98.17	0.000	38	103.67	1.259	52	111.83	0.000
11	91.94	0.000	25	99.00	3.600	39	103.78	0.000	53	112.08	0.022
12	93.07	0.000	26	99.16	0.000	40	103.83	0.000	54	113.39	0.000
13	93.67	0.418	27	99.41	1.316	41	104.91	0.000	55	114.55	0.000
14	93.83	0.000	28	99.44	5.160	42	105.06	0.684	56	118.16	0.000

5-36

$J_{AA'}$	J_{AB}	$J_{AB'}$	$J_{BB'}$
2	9	2	9
2	2	9	9
9	9	2	2
9	2	9	2

The maximum summed intensity is 5.424.

LINE	FREQ	INTEN	LINE	FREQ	INTEN	LINE	FREQ	INTEN	LINE	FREQ	INTEN
1	75.60	0.000	15	92.54	0.000	29	100.37	5.532	43	108.35	0.198
2	80.48	0.000	16	93.18	0.000	30	100.62	0.000	44	108.49	0.200
3	83.29	0.000	17	93.54	0.000	31	100.76	3.756	45	108.60	0.000
4	83.83	0.000	18	94.29	0.000	32	101.41	1.800	46	110.30	0.000
5	85.32	0.026	19	95.25	0.000	33	102.15	1.046	47	111.76	0.244
6	85.46	0.000	20	95.54	0.000	34	102.43	1.958	48	111.87	0.184
7	87.10	0.022	21	95.82	0.000	35	103.62	0.000	49	112.33	0.042
8	87.67	0.042	22	95.82	0.993	36	103.96	0.000	50	112.90	0.022
9	88.13	0.184	23	97.57	1.958	37	104.18	0.993	51	114.68	0.026
10	88.24	0.244	24	97.85	1.046	38	104.18	0.000	52	115.67	0.000
11	89.20	0.	25	98.59	1.800	39	105.25	0.000	53	116.71	0.000
12	90.90	0.000	26	99.24	3.756	40	105.71	0.000	54	118.38	0.000
13	91.51	0.200	27	99.63	5.532	41	106.82	0.000	55	120.01	0.000
14	91.65	0.198	28	99.88	0.000	42	106.95	0.000	56	124.40	0.000

5-37

$J_{AA'}$	J_{AB}	$J_{AB'}$	$J_{BB'}$
2	12	2	12
2	2	12	12
12	12	2	2
12	2	12	2

The maximum summed intensity is 5.706.

LINE	FREQ	INTEN	LINE	FREQ	INTEN	LINE	FREQ	INTEN	LINE	FREQ	INTEN
1	68.94	0.000	15	91.39	0.	29	100.27	5.709	43	109.55	0.000
2	75.68	0.000	16	92.00	0.000	30	100.62	3.838	44	110.45	0.103
3	78.17	0.000	17	92.31	0.000	31	101.69	1.919	45	112.05	0.000
4	78.31	0.000	18	92.46	0.000	32	102.00	1.250	46	112.46	0.081
5	80.61	0.	19	93.18	0.000	33	102.36	1.974	47	114.62	0.162
6	82.77	0.026	20	93.54	0.000	34	102.77	0.000	48	115.50	0.018
7	83.49	0.026	21	94.55	0.000	35	104.57	0.	49	115.82	0.100
8	84.18	0.100	22	95.22	0.794	36	104.78	0.794	50	116.51	0.026
9	84.50	0.018	23	97.64	1.974	37	105.27	0.000	51	117.23	0.026
10	85.38	0.162	24	98.00	1.250	38	106.46	0.000	52	120.27	0.
11	86.40	0.000	25	98.31	1.919	39	107.01	0.000	53	121.69	0.000
12	87.54	0.081	26	98.78	0.000	40	107.54	0.000	54	123.43	0.000
13	88.94	0.000	27	99.38	3.838	41	107.69	0.000	55	125.87	0.000
14	89.55	0.103	28	99.73	5.709	42	109.50	0.000	56	131.06	0.000

5-38

$J_{AA'}$	J_{AB}	$J_{AB'}$	$J_{BB'}$
2	15	2	15
2	2	15	15
15	15	2	2
15	2	15	2

The maximum summed intensity is 6.010.

LINE	FREQ	INTEN	LINE	FREQ	INTEN	LINE	FREQ	INTEN	LINE	FREQ	INTEN
1	62.11	0.000	15	90.29	0.000	29	100.21	5.804	43	112.34	0.000
2	70.77	0.000	16	90.31	0.000	30	100.51	3.886	44	112.56	0.058
3	72.24	0.000	17	90.38	0.000	31	101.79	1.400	45	113.82	0.000
4	73.29	0.000	18	90.79	0.	32	101.81	1.958	46	116.57	0.042
5	75.62	0.000	19	91.32	0.000	33	102.32	1.983	47	117.51	0.114
6	79.30	0.017	20	91.68	0.000	34	105.08	0.000	48	118.24	0.014
7	80.14	0.062	21	93.79	0.000	35	105.47	0.637	49	119.82	0.025
8	80.18	0.025	22	94.53	0.637	36	105.49	0.000	50	119.86	0.062
9	81.76	0.014	23	97.57	0.000	37	106.56	0.000	51	120.70	0.017
10	82.49	0.114	24	97.68	1.983	38	108.32	0.000	52	125.11	0.000
11	83.43	0.042	25	98.19	1.958	39	108.68	0.000	53	126.71	0.000
12	83.53	0.000	26	98.21	1.400	40	108.86	0.000	54	128.51	0.000
13	87.01	0.000	27	99.49	3.886	41	109.71	0.000	55	131.88	0.000
14	87.44	0.058	28	99.79	5.804	42	110.34	0.000	56	137.89	0.000

5-39

$J_{AA'}$	J_{AB}	$J_{AB'}$	$J_{BB'}$
2	18	2	18
2	2	18	18
18	18	2	2
18	2	18	2

The maximum summed intensity is 6.456.

LINE	FREQ	INTEN	LINE	FREQ	INTEN	LINE	FREQ	INTEN	LINE	FREQ	INTEN
1	55.20	0.000	15	88.25	0.000	29	100.17	5.859	43	114.66	0.035
2	65.79	0.000	16	88.43	0.000	30	100.44	3.916	44	115.22	0.000
3	66.20	0.000	17	88.53	0.000	31	101.59	1.517	45	115.63	0.000
4	68.25	0.000	18	89.13	0.000	32	101.88	1.974	46	120.44	0.084
5	70.57	0.000	19	89.43	0.000	33	102.29	1.988	47	120.75	0.026
6	75.08	0.012	20	90.87	0.000	34	106.22	0.513	48	121.05	0.011
7	76.08	0.043	21	92.99	0.000	35	106.40	0.000	49	122.47	0.022
8	77.53	0.022	22	93.76	0.513	36	107.40	0.000	50	123.92	0.043
9	78.95	0.011	23	96.35	0.000	37	107.82	0.000	51	124.92	0.012
10	79.25	0.026	24	97.71	1.988	38	109.13	0.000	52	130.05	0.000
11	79.56	0.084	25	98.12	1.974	39	110.76	0.000	53	131.75	0.000
12	80.61	0.000	26	98.41	1.517	40	110.87	0.000	54	133.60	0.000
13	85.07	0.000	27	99.56	3.916	41	111.18	0.000	55	137.96	0.000
14	85.34	0.035	28	99.83	5.859	42	111.75	0.000	56	144.80	0.000

−11 −10 −9 −8 −7 −6 −5 −4 −3 −2 −1 0 +1 +2 +3 +4 +5 +6 +7 +8 +9 +10 +11

5-40

$J_{AA'}$	J_{AB}	$J_{AB'}$	$J_{BB'}$
4	4	1	4
4	1	4	4

The maximum summed intensity is 4.044.

LINE	FREQ	INTEN	LINE	FREQ	INTEN	LINE	FREQ	INTEN	LINE	FREQ	INTEN
1	85.36	0.000	15	95.15	0.553	29	100.30	0.000	43	104.85	0.553
2	87.70	0.000	16	95.75	1.009	30	100.49	0.000	44	105.59	0.000
3	89.23	0.014	17	96.44	1.484	31	101.04	4.257	45	106.22	0.000
4	89.91	0.000	18	96.62	0.000	32	101.41	0.000	46	106.41	0.000
5	90.15	0.000	19	96.85	0.000	33	101.41	3.280	47	106.41	0.720
6	90.59	0.000	20	97.04	0.772	34	101.59	0.000	48	106.83	0.453
7	91.15	0.011	21	98.15	1.447	35	101.85	1.447	49	107.01	0.000
8	92.99	0.000	22	98.15	1.447	36	101.85	1.447	50	108.85	0.011
9	93.17	0.453	23	98.41	0.000	37	102.96	0.772	51	109.41	0.000
10	93.59	0.000	24	98.59	0.000	38	103.15	0.000	52	109.85	0.000
11	93.59	0.720	25	98.59	3.280	39	103.38	0.000	53	110.09	0.000
12	93.78	0.000	26	98.96	4.257	40	103.56	1.484	54	110.77	0.014
13	94.41	0.000	27	99.51	0.000	41	104.25	1.009	55	112.30	0.000
14	95.15	0.553	28	99.70	0.000	42	104.85	0.553	56	114.64	0.000

−11 −10 −9 −8 −7 −6 −5 −4 −3 −2 −1 0 +1 +2 +3 +4 +5 +6 +7 +8 +9 +10 +11

5-41

$J_{AA'}$	J_{AB}	$J_{AB'}$	$J_{BB'}$
4	4	2	4
4	2	4	4

The maximum summed intensity is 4.670.

LINE	FREQ	INTEN	LINE	FREQ	INTEN	LINE	FREQ	INTEN	LINE	FREQ	INTEN
1	85.09	0.000	15	95.84	0.684	29	100.08	0.000	43	105.16	0.723
2	87.78	0.000	16	95.84	0.684	30	100.31	0.000	44	105.89	0.000
3	88.28	0.006	17	96.16	0.000	31	100.76	0.000	45	106.25	0.000
4	89.84	0.000	18	96.50	0.000	32	100.81	4.685	46	106.42	0.629
5	90.17	0.000	19	96.67	1.545	33	101.24	0.000	47	106.64	0.000
6	90.70	0.018	20	96.77	0.394	34	101.24	3.414	48	107.24	0.000
7	90.76	0.000	21	97.84	1.316	35	102.16	1.316	49	107.24	0.586
8	92.76	0.000	22	97.84	1.316	36	102.16	1.316	50	109.24	0.000
9	92.76	0.586	23	98.76	0.000	37	103.23	0.394	51	109.30	0.018
10	93.36	0.000	24	98.76	3.414	38	103.33	1.545	52	109.83	0.000
11	93.58	0.629	25	99.19	4.685	39	103.50	0.000	53	110.16	0.000
12	93.75	0.000	26	99.24	0.000	40	103.84	0.000	54	111.72	0.006
13	94.11	0.000	27	99.69	0.000	41	104.16	0.684	55	112.22	0.000
14	94.84	0.723	28	99.92	0.000	42	104.16	0.684	56	114.91	0.000

−11 −10 −9 −8 −7 −6 −5 −4 −3 −2 −1 0 +1 +2 +3 +4 +5 +6 +7 +8 +9 +10 +11

5-42

$J_{AA'}$	J_{AB}	$J_{AB'}$	$J_{BB'}$
4	4	6	4
4	6	4	4

The maximum summed intensity is 5.478.

LINE	FREQ	INTEN	LINE	FREQ	INTEN	LINE	FREQ	INTEN	LINE	FREQ	INTEN
1	80.60	0.001	15	94.16	0.000	29	100.40	5.467	43	106.41	0.000
2	86.37	0.006	16	95.70	0.000	30	100.64	0.000	44	106.96	0.000
3	86.61	0.000	17	95.84	0.684	31	100.83	0.000	45	107.07	0.000
4	87.27	0.000	18	95.84	0.684	32	100.83	3.715	46	107.74	0.565
5	87.84	0.000	19	97.03	1.500	33	101.97	0.195	47	108.69	0.242
6	87.94	0.025	20	97.17	0.000	34	102.03	0.000	48	108.83	0.000
7	89.17	0.000	21	97.84	1.316	35	102.16	1.316	49	110.83	0.000
8	89.17	0.285	22	97.84	1.316	36	102.16	1.316	50	110.83	0.285
9	91.17	0.000	23	97.97	0.000	37	102.83	0.000	51	112.06	0.025
10	91.31	0.242	24	98.03	0.195	38	102.97	1.500	52	112.16	0.000
11	92.26	0.565	25	99.17	0.000	39	104.16	0.684	53	112.73	0.000
12	92.93	0.000	26	99.17	3.715	40	104.16	0.684	54	113.39	0.000
13	93.04	0.000	27	99.36	0.000	41	104.30	0.000	55	113.63	0.006
14	93.59	0.000	28	99.60	5.467	42	105.84	0.000	56	119.40	0.001

−11 −10 −9 −8 −7 −6 −5 −4 −3 −2 −1 0 +1 +2 +3 +4 +5 +6 +7 +8 +9 +10 +11

5-43

$J_{AA'}$	J_{AB}	$J_{AB'}$	$J_{BB'}$
4	4	9	4
4	9	4	4

The maximum summed intensity is 5.814.

LINE	FREQ	INTEN	LINE	FREQ	INTEN	LINE	FREQ	INTEN	LINE	FREQ	INTEN
1	75.51	0.000	15	93.41	0.000	29	100.18	0.000	43	107.54	0.000
2	82.76	0.000	16	93.59	0.360	30	100.29	5.675	44	107.63	0.000
3	84.65	0.000	17	93.59	0.360	31	100.57	0.887	45	108.66	0.000
4	85.12	0.030	18	94.34	0.000	32	100.66	0.000	46	109.43	0.000
5	85.40	0.020	19	95.48	0.000	33	100.66	3.816	47	110.17	0.331
6	85.59	0.000	20	96.23	0.946	34	101.41	1.640	48	110.55	0.110
7	86.34	0.000	21	96.71	0.000	35	101.41	1.640	49	113.66	0.000
8	86.34	0.184	22	98.59	1.640	36	103.29	0.000	50	113.66	0.184
9	89.45	0.110	23	98.59	1.640	37	103.77	0.946	51	114.41	0.000
10	89.83	0.331	24	99.34	0.000	38	104.52	0.000	52	114.60	0.020
11	90.57	0.000	25	99.34	3.816	39	105.66	0.000	53	114.88	0.030
12	91.34	0.000	26	99.43	0.887	40	106.41	0.360	54	115.35	0.000
13	92.37	0.000	27	99.71	5.675	41	106.41	0.360	55	117.24	0.
14	92.46	0.000	28	99.82	0.000	42	106.59	0.000	56	124.49	0.000

5-44

$J_{AA'}$	J_{AB}	$J_{AB'}$	$J_{BB'}$
4	4	12	4
4	12	4	4

The maximum summed intensity is 6.775.

LINE	FREQ	INTEN	LINE	FREQ	INTEN	LINE	FREQ	INTEN	LINE	FREQ	INTEN
1	70.04	0.000	15	91.46	0.000	29	100.05	1.490	43	109.00	0.200
2	77.58	0.000	16	91.46	0.000	30	100.22	5.782	44	109.00	0.200
3	82.23	0.000	17	92.23	0.000	31	100.50	0.000	45	109.50	0.000
4	82.69	0.016	18	93.00	0.000	32	100.54	0.000	46	111.39	0.047
5	82.96	0.044	19	93.85	0.000	33	100.54	3.873	47	112.42	0.000
6	83.00	0.000	20	94.30	0.412	34	101.00	1.800	48	112.88	0.209
7	83.46	0.000	21	96.15	0.000	35	101.00	1.800	49	116.54	0.000
8	83.46	0.127	22	99.00	1.800	36	103.85	0.000	50	116.54	0.127
9	87.12	0.209	23	99.00	1.800	37	105.70	0.412	51	117.00	0.000
10	87.58	0.000	24	99.46	0.000	38	106.15	0.000	52	117.04	0.044
11	88.61	0.047	25	99.46	3.873	39	107.00	0.000	53	117.31	0.016
12	90.50	0.000	26	99.50	0.000	40	107.77	0.000	54	117.77	0.000
13	91.00	0.200	27	99.78	5.782	41	108.54	0.000	55	122.42	0.000
14	91.00	0.200	28	99.95	1.490	42	108.54	0.000	56	129.96	0.000

5-45

$J_{AA'}$	J_{AB}	$J_{AB'}$	$J_{BB'}$
4	4	15	4
4	15	4	4

The maximum summed intensity is 8.024.

LINE	FREQ	INTEN	LINE	FREQ	INTEN	LINE	FREQ	INTEN	LINE	FREQ	INTEN
1	64.38	0.000	15	88.54	0.000	29	100.18	5.844	43	111.71	0.024
2	72.08	0.	16	91.49	0.000	30	100.23	1.745	44	111.76	0.122
3	79.59	0.000	17	91.54	0.000	31	100.46	0.000	45	111.76	0.122
4	79.89	0.012	18	91.79	0.193	32	100.46	3.907	46	112.00	0.000
5	80.24	0.000	19	92.12	0.000	33	100.53	0.000	47	115.39	0.000
6	80.30	0.040	20	92.76	0.	34	100.76	1.878	48	115.69	0.142
7	80.54	0.000	21	95.98	0.000	35	100.76	1.878	49	119.46	0.000
8	80.54	0.093	22	99.24	1.878	36	104.02	0.000	50	119.46	0.093
9	84.31	0.142	23	99.24	1.878	37	107.24	0.000	51	119.70	0.040
10	84.61	0.000	24	99.47	0.000	38	107.88	0.000	52	119.76	0.000
11	88.00	0.000	25	99.54	0.000	39	108.21	0.193	53	120.11	0.012
12	88.24	0.122	26	99.54	3.907	40	108.46	0.000	54	120.41	0.000
13	88.24	0.122	27	99.77	1.745	41	108.51	0.000	55	127.92	0.000
14	88.29	0.024	28	99.82	5.844	42	111.46	0.000	56	135.62	0.000

−11 −10 −9 −8 −7 −6 −5 −4 −3 −2 −1 0 +1 +2 +3 +4 +5 +6 +7 +8 +9 +10 +11

5-46

$J_{AA'}$	J_{AB}	$J_{AB'}$	$J_{BB'}$
4	4	18	4
4	18	4	4

The maximum summed intensity is 8.327.

LINE	FREQ	INTEN	LINE	FREQ	INTEN	LINE	FREQ	INTEN	LINE	FREQ	INTEN
1	58.62	0.000	15	88.15	0.014	29	100.15	5.883	43	114.40	0.000
2	66.41	0.000	16	88.84	0.000	30	100.27	1.852	44	114.62	0.081
3	76.83	0.000	17	89.05	0.106	31	100.40	0.000	45	114.62	0.081
4	77.04	0.010	18	91.60	0.000	32	100.40	3.930	46	114.74	0.000
5	77.38	0.000	19	92.06	0.000	33	100.49	0.000	47	118.36	0.000
6	77.47	0.032	20	92.62	0.000	34	100.62	1.919	48	118.57	0.102
7	77.60	0.000	21	95.93	0.000	35	100.62	1.919	49	122.40	0.000
8	77.60	0.070	22	99.38	1.919	36	104.07	0.000	50	122.40	0.070
9	81.43	0.102	23	99.38	1.919	37	107.38	0.000	51	122.53	0.032
10	81.64	0.000	24	99.51	0.000	38	107.94	0.000	52	122.62	0.000
11	85.26	0.000	25	99.60	0.000	39	108.40	0.000	53	122.96	0.010
12	85.38	0.081	26	99.60	3.930	40	110.95	0.106	54	123.17	0.000
13	85.38	0.081	27	99.73	1.852	41	111.16	0.000	55	133.59	0.000
14	85.60	0.000	28	99.85	5.883	42	111.85	0.014	56	141.38	0.000

−11 −10 −9 −8 −7 −6 −5 −4 −3 −2 −1 0 +1 +2 +3 +4 +5 +6 +7 +8 +9 +10 +11

5-47

$J_{AA'}$	J_{AB}	$J_{AB'}$	$J_{BB'}$
4	6	4	6
4	4	6	6
6	6	4	4
6	4	6	4

The maximum summed intensity is 5.482.

LINE	FREQ	INTEN	LINE	FREQ	INTEN	LINE	FREQ	INTEN	LINE	FREQ	INTEN
1	80.41	0.001	15	93.48	0.000	29	100.40	5.467	43	105.88	0.000
2	84.61	0.003	16	93.79	0.000	30	100.44	0.000	44	107.92	0.505
3	84.64	0.000	17	94.46	0.143	31	100.58	0.000	45	108.69	0.000
4	87.75	0.000	18	96.27	0.214	32	100.82	0.684	46	108.75	0.244
5	87.76	0.000	19	96.35	1.316	33	100.83	3.715	47	109.00	0.000
6	87.94	0.025	20	97.08	1.541	34	102.04	0.000	48	109.42	0.000
7	89.01	0.000	21	97.29	1.857	35	102.25	0.000	49	110.83	0.285
8	89.17	0.285	22	97.67	0.000	36	102.71	1.857	50	112.06	0.025
9	90.58	0.000	23	97.75	0.000	37	102.92	1.541	51	112.25	0.000
10	91.25	0.244	24	99.17	3.715	38	103.65	1.316	52	112.88	0.000
11	92.08	0.505	25	99.18	0.684	39	103.73	0.214	53	113.47	0.000
12	92.24	0.000	26	99.42	0.000	40	104.32	0.000	54	114.12	0.000
13	92.89	0.000	27	99.60	5.467	41	104.63	0.000	55	115.39	0.003
14	93.20	0.000	28	99.85	0.000	42	105.54	0.143	56	119.59	0.001

5-48

$J_{AA'}$	J_{AB}	$J_{AB'}$	$J_{BB'}$
4	9	4	9
4	4	9	9
9	9	4	4
9	4	9	4

The maximum summed intensity is 5.710.

LINE	FREQ	INTEN	LINE	FREQ	INTEN	LINE	FREQ	INTEN	LINE	FREQ	INTEN
1	74.35	0.000	15	91.56	0.000	29	99.85	0.000	43	109.58	0.064
2	80.01	0.000	16	92.10	0.000	30	100.28	5.677	44	110.12	0.000
3	81.99	0.008	17	93.10	0.000	31	100.66	3.816	45	110.39	0.000
4	82.81	0.000	18	93.91	0.445	32	100.99	1.555	46	111.26	0.131
5	84.45	0.000	19	95.81	0.000	33	102.51	1.936	47	111.34	0.212
6	85.40	0.021	20	96.31	0.573	34	102.88	0.000	48	111.39	0.000
7	85.45	0.000	21	96.94	1.378	35	103.06	1.378	49	113.66	0.184
8	86.34	0.184	22	97.12	0.000	36	103.64	0.000	50	114.60	0.021
9	88.66	0.212	23	97.49	1.936	37	103.69	0.573	51	116.49	0.000
10	88.74	0.131	24	98.20	0.000	38	104.19	0.000	52	117.19	0.000
11	89.55	0.000	25	98.31	0.000	39	104.95	0.000	53	118.01	0.008
12	89.88	0.000	26	99.01	1.555	40	105.95	0.000	54	118.04	0.000
13	90.42	0.064	27	99.34	3.816	41	106.09	0.445	55	119.04	0.
14	90.55	0.000	28	99.72	5.677	42	106.96	0.	56	125.65	0.000

5-49

$J_{AA'}$	J_{AB}	$J_{AB'}$	$J_{BB'}$
4	12	4	12
4	4	12	12
12	12	4	4
12	4	12	4

The maximum summed intensity is 5.843

LINE	FREQ	INTEN	LINE	FREQ	INTEN	LINE	FREQ	INTEN	LINE	FREQ	INTEN
1	67.70	0.000	15	89.11	0.000	29	100.22	5.785	43	110.89	0.000
2	75.17	0.000	16	90.22	0.143	30	100.28	0.000	44	111.91	0.000
3	77.80	0.000	17	91.30	0.000	31	100.54	3.873	45	112.64	0.000
4	79.61	0.011	18	92.03	0.000	32	101.53	1.857	46	113.71	0.077
5	79.88	0.000	19	93.80	0.000	33	102.41	1.965	47	113.72	0.035
6	80.12	0.000	20	94.89	0.000	34	103.30	0.802	48	115.21	0.111
7	82.69	0.016	21	95.78	0.000	35	103.38	1.199	49	116.54	0.127
8	83.46	0.127	22	96.62	1.199	36	105.11	0.000	50	117.31	0.016
9	84.79	0.111	23	96.70	0.802	37	105.23	0.000	51	120.39	0.011
10	86.28	0.035	24	97.59	1.965	38	106.20	0.000	52	120.89	0.000
11	86.29	0.077	25	98.47	1.857	39	106.96	0.000	53	122.20	0.000
12	88.12	0.000	26	98.71	0.000	40	107.69	0.000	54	123.81	0.000
13	88.37	0.000	27	99.46	3.873	41	107.94	0.	55	124.06	0.000
14	89.10	0.000	28	99.78	5.785	42	109.78	0.143	56	132.30	0.000

5-50

$J_{AA'}$	J_{AB}	$J_{AB'}$	$J_{BB'}$
4	15	4	15
4	4	15	15
15	15	4	4
15	4	15	4

The maximum summed intensity is 6.304.

LINE	FREQ	INTEN	LINE	FREQ	INTEN	LINE	FREQ	INTEN	LINE	FREQ	INTEN
1	60.87	0.000	15	87.04	0.000	29	100.18	5.847	43	113.46	0.000
2	70.23	0.000	16	88.32	0.000	30	100.46	3.907	44	113.60	0.000
3	72.76	0.000	17	90.48	0.000	31	101.74	1.936	45	113.82	0.064
4	74.29	0.000	18	90.62	0.000	32	102.35	1.978	46	116.10	0.048
5	74.96	0.000	19	91.76	0.000	33	102.70	0.000	47	117.90	0.022
6	77.20	0.012	20	92.68	0.000	34	102.88	0.993	48	119.20	0.068
7	79.90	0.013	21	93.21	0.000	35	103.83	1.019	49	119.46	0.093
8	80.54	0.093	22	96.17	1.019	36	106.76	0.000	50	120.10	0.013
9	80.80	0.068	23	97.12	0.993	37	107.32	0.000	51	122.80	0.012
10	82.10	0.022	24	97.32	0.000	38	108.24	0.000	52	125.68	0.000
11	83.90	0.048	25	97.65	1.978	39	108.88	0.000	53	127.24	0.000
12	86.18	0.064	26	98.26	1.936	40	109.41	0.000	54	129.12	0.000
13	86.38	0.000	27	99.54	3.907	41	109.54	0.000	55	129.79	0.000
14	86.51	0.000	28	99.82	5.847	42	111.68	0.000	56	139.13	0.000

5-51

$J_{AA'}$	J_{AB}	$J_{AB'}$	$J_{BB'}$
4	18	4	18
4	4	18	18
18	18	4	4
18	4	18	4

The maximum summed intensity is 6.713.

LINE	FREQ	INTEN	LINE	FREQ	INTEN	LINE	FREQ	INTEN	LINE	FREQ	INTEN
1	53.95	0.000	15	86.06	0.	29	100.15	5.886	43	114.49	0.000
2	65.24	0.000	16	87.50	0.000	30	100.40	3.930	44	115.09	0.000
3	67.70	0.000	17	89.05	0.000	31	101.84	1.965	45	117.96	0.035
4	68.29	0.000	18	89.65	0.000	32	102.31	1.985	46	118.42	0.031
5	69.94	0.	19	89.70	0.000	33	102.48	1.166	47	122.11	0.015
6	74.71	0.013	20	90.50	0.000	34	104.38	0.849	48	122.40	0.070
7	76.75	0.045	21	90.68	0.	35	105.18	0.000	49	122.95	0.010
8	77.05	0.010	22	95.62	0.849	36	108.23	0.000	50	123.25	0.045
9	77.60	0.070	23	95.92	0.000	37	109.50	0.000	51	125.29	0.013
10	77.89	0.015	24	97.52	1.166	38	109.79	0.	52	130.61	0.000
11	81.58	0.031	25	97.69	1.985	39	110.30	0.000	53	132.30	0.000
12	82.04	0.035	26	98.16	1.965	40	111.44	0.000	54	134.21	0.
13	83.81	0.000	27	99.60	3.930	41	112.04	0.000	55	135.85	0.000
14	84.41	0.000	28	99.85	5.886	42	112.50	0.000	56	146.05	0.000

5-52

$J_{AA'}$	J_{AB}	$J_{AB'}$	$J_{BB'}$
6	6	1	6
6	1	6	6

The maximum summed intensity is 4.925.

LINE	FREQ	INTEN	LINE	FREQ	INTEN	LINE	FREQ	INTEN	LINE	FREQ	INTEN
1	80.25	0.000	15	93.80	0.000	29	100.69	4.916	43	106.41	0.360
2	84.79	0.000	16	94.41	0.000	30	101.11	0.000	44	106.41	0.360
3	86.59	0.	17	94.53	0.588	31	101.11	3.519	45	107.40	0.000
4	86.89	0.000	18	94.76	0.000	32	101.23	0.000	46	108.11	0.000
5	86.95	0.000	19	96.11	0.000	33	101.41	1.640	47	108.11	0.481
6	87.10	0.014	20	96.25	1.325	34	101.41	1.640	48	109.04	0.000
7	89.47	0.141	21	96.32	0.997	35	101.61	0.000	49	109.91	0.019
8	90.09	0.019	22	98.39	0.000	36	103.68	0.997	50	110.53	0.141
9	90.96	0.000	23	98.59	1.640	37	103.75	1.325	51	112.90	0.014
10	91.89	0.000	24	98.59	1.640	38	103.89	0.000	52	113.05	0.000
11	91.89	0.481	25	98.77	0.000	39	105.24	0.000	53	113.11	0.000
12	92.60	0.000	26	98.89	0.000	40	105.47	0.588	54	113.41	0.
13	93.59	0.360	27	98.89	3.519	41	105.59	0.000	55	115.21	0.000
14	93.59	0.360	28	99.31	4.916	42	106.20	0.000	56	119.75	0.000

5-53

$J_{AA'}$	J_{AB}	$J_{AB'}$	$J_{BB'}$
6	6	2	6
6	2	6	6

The maximum summed intensity is 4.940.

LINE	FREQ	INTEN	LINE	FREQ	INTEN	LINE	FREQ	INTEN	LINE	FREQ	INTEN
1	80.25	0.000	15	93.61	0.000	29	100.38	0.000	43	106.59	0.421
2	84.84	0.000	16	94.39	0.445	30	100.56	5.171	44	106.83	0.000
3	85.77	0.009	17	94.39	0.445	31	100.81	0.000	45	107.95	0.000
4	86.39	0.000	18	94.86	0.000	32	101.00	0.000	46	108.02	0.000
5	87.00	0.000	19	95.77	0.780	33	101.00	3.600	47	109.00	0.000
6	87.65	0.000	20	96.59	1.414	34	101.61	1.555	48	109.00	0.400
7	89.44	0.024	21	97.00	0.000	35	101.61	1.555	49	109.75	0.183
8	90.25	0.183	22	98.39	1.555	36	103.00	0.000	50	110.56	0.024
9	91.00	0.000	23	98.39	1.555	37	103.41	1.414	51	112.35	0.000
10	91.00	0.400	24	99.00	0.000	38	104.23	0.780	52	113.00	0.000
11	91.98	0.000	25	99.00	3.600	39	105.14	0.000	53	113.61	0.000
12	92.05	0.000	26	99.19	0.000	40	105.61	0.445	54	114.23	0.009
13	93.17	0.000	27	99.44	5.171	41	105.61	0.445	55	115.16	0.000
14	93.41	0.421	28	99.62	0.000	42	106.39	0.000	56	119.75	0.000

-11 -10 -9 -8 -7 -6 -5 -4 -3 -2 -1 0 +1 +2 +3 +4 +5 +6 +7 +8 +9 +10 +11

5-54

$J_{AA'}$	J_{AB}	$J_{AB'}$	$J_{BB'}$
6	6	4	6
6	4	6	6

The maximum summed intensity is 5.480.

LINE	FREQ	INTEN	LINE	FREQ	INTEN	LINE	FREQ	INTEN	LINE	FREQ	INTEN
1	79.99	0.000	15	93.78	0.000	29	100.10	0.000	43	107.84	0.000
2	83.06	0.003	16	94.72	0.334	30	100.40	5.468	44	108.27	0.000
3	84.61	0.000	17	94.98	0.	31	100.83	0.000	45	108.35	0.365
4	85.84	0.000	18	95.84	0.684	32	100.83	3.715	46	108.77	0.244
5	87.17	0.000	19	95.84	0.684	33	101.17	0.000	47	109.07	0.000
6	87.94	0.025	20	97.11	1.561	34	101.95	0.000	48	110.83	0.000
7	88.66	0.000	21	97.84	1.316	35	102.16	1.316	49	110.83	0.285
8	89.17	0.000	22	97.84	1.316	36	102.16	1.316	50	111.34	0.000
9	89.17	0.285	23	98.05	0.000	37	102.89	1.561	51	112.06	0.025
10	90.93	0.000	24	98.83	0.000	38	104.16	0.684	52	112.83	0.000
11	91.23	0.244	25	99.17	0.000	39	104.16	0.684	53	114.16	0.000
12	91.65	0.365	26	99.17	3.715	40	105.02	0.000	54	115.39	0.000
13	91.73	0.000	27	99.60	5.468	41	105.28	0.334	55	116.94	0.003
14	92.16	0.000	28	99.90	0.000	42	106.22	0.000	56	120.01	0.000

-11 -10 -9 -8 -7 -6 -5 -4 -3 -2 -1 0 +1 +2 +3 +4 +5 +6 +7 +8 +9 +10 +11

5-55

$J_{AA'}$	J_{AB}	$J_{AB'}$	$J_{BB'}$
6	6	9	6
6	9	6	6

The maximum summed intensity is 5.613.

LINE	FREQ	INTEN	LINE	FREQ	INTEN	LINE	FREQ	INTEN	LINE	FREQ	INTEN
1	73.56	0.000	15	91.26	0.000	29	100.23	5.760	43	109.01	0.000
2	80.54	0.003	16	95.15	0.553	30	100.58	0.000	44	110.15	0.000
3	82.33	0.000	17	95.15	0.553	31	100.58	3.857	45	110.29	0.335
4	83.15	0.000	18	96.21	0.000	32	101.85	1.447	46	110.96	0.000
5	83.61	0.018	19	96.42	0.000	33	101.85	1.447	47	112.58	0.000
6	84.28	0.000	20	96.69	0.232	34	102.03	0.000	48	113.64	0.094
7	84.42	0.000	21	97.09	0.000	35	102.52	1.558	49	115.58	0.000
8	84.42	0.143	22	97.48	1.558	36	102.91	0.000	50	115.58	0.143
9	86.36	0.094	23	97.97	0.000	37	103.31	0.232	51	115.72	0.000
10	87.42	0.000	24	98.15	1.447	38	103.58	0.000	52	116.39	0.018
11	89.04	0.000	25	98.15	1.447	39	103.79	0.000	53	116.85	0.000
12	89.71	0.335	26	99.42	0.000	40	104.85	0.553	54	117.67	0.000
13	89.85	0.000	27	99.42	3.857	41	104.85	0.553	55	119.46	0.003
14	90.99	0.000	28	99.77	5.760	42	108.74	0.000	56	126.44	0.000

−11 −10 −9 −8 −7 −6 −5 −4 −3 −2 −1 0 +1 +2 +3 +4 +5 +6 +7 +8 +9 +10 +11

5-56

$J_{AA'}$	J_{AB}	$J_{AB'}$	$J_{BB'}$
6	6	12	6
6	12	6	6

The maximum summed intensity is 6.173.

LINE	FREQ	INTEN	LINE	FREQ	INTEN	LINE	FREQ	INTEN	LINE	FREQ	INTEN
1	68.08	0.000	15	90.83	0.000	29	100.19	5.832	43	110.76	0.000
2	79.33	0.000	16	92.76	0.293	30	100.49	0.000	44	111.43	0.000
3	79.59	0.013	17	92.76	0.293	31	100.49	3.897	45	112.19	0.000
4	80.08	0.000	18	93.51	0.000	32	100.69	0.000	46	112.49	0.000
5	80.76	0.000	19	95.44	0.000	33	101.24	1.707	47	112.94	0.210
6	80.84	0.014	20	96.08	0.000	34	101.24	1.707	48	115.81	0.052
7	81.51	0.000	21	96.83	1.119	35	101.44	0.760	49	118.49	0.000
8	81.51	0.103	22	98.56	0.760	36	103.17	1.119	50	118.49	0.103
9	84.19	0.052	23	98.76	1.707	37	103.92	0.000	51	119.16	0.014
10	87.06	0.210	24	98.76	1.707	38	104.56	0.000	52	119.24	0.000
11	87.51	0.000	25	99.31	0.000	39	106.49	0.000	53	119.92	0.000
12	87.81	0.000	26	99.51	0.000	40	107.24	0.293	54	120.41	0.013
13	88.57	0.000	27	99.51	3.897	41	107.24	0.293	55	120.67	0.000
14	89.24	0.000	28	99.81	5.832	42	109.17	0.000	56	131.92	0.000

−11 −10 −9 −8 −7 −6 −5 −4 −3 −2 −1 0 +1 +2 +3 +4 +5 +6 +7 +8 +9 +10 +11

5-57

$J_{AA'}$	J_{AB}	$J_{AB'}$	$J_{BB'}$
6	6	15	6
6	15	6	6

The maximum summed intensity is 6.869.

LINE	FREQ	INTEN	LINE	FREQ	INTEN	LINE	FREQ	INTEN	LINE	FREQ	INTEN
1	62.42	0.000	15	89.25	0.000	29	100.07	0.000	43	111.09	0.000
2	73.93	0.000	16	90.09	0.168	30	100.16	5.876	44	111.67	0.000
3	77.51	0.000	17	90.09	0.168	31	100.42	0.000	45	112.42	0.000
4	77.74	0.023	18	90.58	0.000	32	100.42	3.923	46	115.25	0.000
5	78.00	0.011	19	94.51	0.000	33	100.42	1.390	47	115.74	0.142
6	78.09	0.000	20	94.67	0.000	34	100.91	1.832	48	117.00	0.024
7	78.58	0.000	21	95.16	0.534	35	100.91	1.832	49	121.42	0.000
8	78.58	0.077	22	99.09	1.832	36	104.84	0.534	50	121.42	0.07[illegible]
9	83.00	0.024	23	99.09	1.832	37	105.33	0.000	51	121.91	0.00[illegible]
10	84.26	0.142	24	99.58	1.390	38	105.49	0.000	52	122.00	0.01[illegible]
11	84.75	0.000	25	99.58	0.000	39	109.42	0.000	53	122.26	0.02[illegible]
12	87.58	0.000	26	99.58	3.923	40	109.91	0.168	54	122.49	0.000
13	88.33	0.000	27	99.84	5.876	41	109.91	0.168	55	126.07	0.000
14	88.91	0.000	28	99.93	0.000	42	110.75	0.000	56	137.58	0.000

```
                                                        X   X
                                                        X   X
                                                        XX  XX
                                                      XXXX XXXX
                                                      XXXX XXXX
                                                      XXXXXXXXX
                                                      XXXXXXXXX
                                                      XXXXXXXXX
                                                      XXXXXXXXX
                                                     XXXXXXXXXXX
                                                     XXXXXXXXXXX
                                                     XXXXXXXXXXX
                                                  X  XXXXXXXXXXX  X
                                                  X  XXXXXXXXXXX  X
                                                  X  XXXXXXXXXXX  X
                                                  XX XXXXXXXXXXX  XX
                                                 XXX XXXXXXXXXXX XXX
                                                 XXX XXXXXXXXXXXXX XXX
                                                 XXX XXXXXXXXXXXXX XXX
                                                 XXX XXXXXXXXXXXXX XXX
                                                 XXXXXXXXXXXXXXXXXXXXX
                                                 XXXXXXXXXXXXXXXXXXXXXXX
                                                XXXXXXXXXXXXXXXXXXXXXXXX
                      XX                        XXXXXXXXXXXXXXXXXXXXXXXX                      XX
  XXX                XXXX                      XXXXXXXXXXXXXXXXXXXXXXXXXX                    XXXX                       XXX
-11  -10  -9  -8  -7  -6  -5  -4  -3  -2  -1  0  +1  +2  +3  +4  +5  +6  +7  +8  +9  +10  +11
```

5-58

$J_{AA'}$	J_{AB}	$J_{AB'}$	$J_{BB'}$
6	6	18	6
6	18	6	6

The maximum summed intensity is 10.091.

LINE	FREQ	INTEN	LINE	FREQ	INTEN	LINE	FREQ	INTEN	LINE	FREQ	INTEN
1	56.66	0.000	15	87.63	0.000	29	100.04	1.708	43	112.71	0.106
2	68.32	0.000	16	87.63	0.000	30	100.14	5.905	44	112.71	0.106
3	74.79	0.000	17	88.20	0.000	31	100.30	0.000	45	113.11	0.000
4	75.13	0.009	18	88.71	0.000	32	100.37	0.000	46	117.49	0.011
5	75.23	0.024	19	92.42	0.000	33	100.37	3.940	47	118.27	0.000
6	75.29	0.000	20	92.76	0.241	34	100.71	1.894	48	118.61	0.102
7	75.63	0.000	21	94.17	0.000	35	100.71	1.894	49	124.37	0.000
8	75.63	0.060	22	99.29	1.894	36	105.83	0.000	50	124.37	0.060
9	81.39	0.102	23	99.29	1.894	37	107.24	0.241	51	124.71	0.000
10	81.73	0.000	24	99.63	0.000	38	107.58	0.000	52	124.77	0.024
11	82.51	0.011	25	99.63	3.940	39	111.29	0.000	53	124.87	0.009
12	86.89	0.000	26	99.70	0.000	40	111.80	0.000	54	125.21	0.000
13	87.29	0.106	27	99.86	5.905	41	112.37	0.000	55	131.68	0.000
14	87.29	0.106	28	99.96	1.708	42	112.37	0.000	56	143.34	0.000

```
                                                          X
                                                          X
                                                         XXX
                                                         XXX
                                                         XXX
                                                        XXXXX
                                                        XXXXX
                                                        XXXXX
                                                        XXXXX
                                                        XXXXX
                                                       XXXXXXX
                                                       XXXXXXX
                                                       XXXXXXX
                                                      XXXXXXXXX
                                                      XXXXXXXXX
                                                   X  XXXXXXXXX  X
                                                   X  XXXXXXXXX  X
                                                   XXXXXXXXXXXXXXX
                                                  XXXXXXXXXXXXXXXXX
                                                  XXXXXXXXXXXXXXXXX
                                                  XXXXXXXXXXXXXXXXX
                                                  XXXXXXXXXXXXXXXXX
                                                 XXXXXXXXXXXXXXXXXXX
                                                 XXXXXXXXXXXXXXXXXXX
               XX                                XXXXXXXXXXXXXXXXXXXX                            XX
-11  -10  -9  -8  -7  -6  -5  -4  -3  -2  -1  0  +1  +2  +3  +4  +5  +6  +7  +8  +9  +10  +11
```

5-59

$J_{AA'}$	J_{AB}	$J_{AB'}$	$J_{BB'}$
6	9	6	9
6	6	9	9
9	9	6	6
9	6	9	6

The maximum summed intensity is 6.198.

LINE	FREQ	INTEN	LINE	FREQ	INTEN	LINE	FREQ	INTEN	LINE	FREQ	INTEN
1	73.01	0.000	15	91.62	0.000	29	100.00	1.000	43	110.26	0.000
2	78.16	0.002	16	93.14	0.106	30	100.23	5.760	44	110.84	0.255
3	79.44	0.000	17	93.39	0.000	31	100.58	3.857	45	111.01	0.000
4	82.30	0.000	18	94.32	0.257	32	101.52	0.000	46	113.46	0.000
5	82.88	0.000	19	95.76	1.000	33	101.54	0.000	47	113.69	0.000
6	83.61	0.018	20	95.86	0.000	34	102.44	1.613	48	113.71	0.095
7	84.42	0.143	21	97.30	0.000	35	102.62	1.894	49	115.58	0.143
8	86.29	0.095	22	97.38	1.894	36	102.70	0.000	50	116.16	0.000
9	86.46	0.000	23	97.56	1.613	37	102.88	0.000	51	116.39	0.018
10	86.54	0.000	24	98.46	0.000	38	103.98	0.000	52	117.70	0.000
11	87.12	0.000	25	99.42	3.857	39	104.24	1.000	53	117.93	0.000
12	88.93	0.000	26	99.74	0.000	40	105.68	0.257	54	119.74	0.000
13	89.16	0.255	27	99.77	5.760	41	106.67	0.000	55	121.84	0.002
14	90.71	0.000	28	100.00	1.000	42	106.86	0.106	56	126.99	0.000

−11 −10 −9 −8 −7 −6 −5 −4 −3 −2 −1 0 +1 +2 +3 +4 +5 +6 +7 +8 +9 +10 +11

5-60

$J_{AA'}$	J_{AB}	$J_{AB'}$	$J_{BB'}$
6	12	6	12
6	6	12	12
12	12	6	6
12	6	12	6

The maximum summed intensity is 6.173.

LINE	FREQ	INTEN	LINE	FREQ	INTEN	LINE	FREQ	INTEN	LINE	FREQ	INTEN
1	66.44	0.000	15	89.05	0.051	29	99.81	5.832	43	111.29	0.000
2	74.62	0.000	16	91.25	0.000	30	100.19	5.832	44	112.35	0.000
3	75.87	0.003	17	91.36	0.000	31	100.49	3.897	45	114.24	0.000
4	77.27	0.000	18	92.76	0.293	32	101.24	1.707	46	114.59	0.124
5	79.00	0.000	19	94.85	0.445	33	102.47	1.949	47	115.68	0.000
6	80.84	0.014	20	95.27	0.000	34	102.53	1.519	48	116.45	0.062
7	81.51	0.103	21	96.24	0.000	35	103.76	0.000	49	118.49	0.103
8	81.92	0.000	22	97.36	0.000	36	104.67	0.000	50	119.16	0.014
9	83.55	0.062	23	97.47	1.519	37	104.73	0.000	51	121.68	0.000
10	85.00	0.000	24	97.53	1.949	38	105.04	0.000	52	121.78	0.000
11	85.41	0.124	25	98.76	1.707	39	105.15	0.445	53	122.73	0.000
12	85.76	0.000	26	98.93	0.000	40	107.24	0.293	54	124.13	0.003
13	87.92	0.000	27	99.04	0.000	41	108.37	0.000	55	124.71	0.000
14	88.03	0.000	28	99.51	3.897	42	110.95	0.051	56	133.56	0.000

−11 −10 −9 −8 −7 −6 −5 −4 −3 −2 −1 0 +1 +2 +3 +4 +5 +6 +7 +8 +9 +10 +11

5-61

$J_{AA'}$	J_{AB}	$J_{AB'}$	$J_{BB'}$
6	15	6	15
6	6	15	15
15	15	6	6
15	6	15	6

The maximum summed intensity is 6.551.

LINE	FREQ	INTEN	LINE	FREQ	INTEN	LINE	FREQ	INTEN	LINE	FREQ	INTEN
1	59.62	0.000	15	87.17	0.000	29	99.84	5.876	43	113.68	0.000
2	69.68	0.000	16	88.89	0.106	30	100.16	5.876	44	115.06	0.000
3	72.22	0.000	17	88.93	0.000	31	100.42	3.923	45	115.11	0.030
4	73.64	0.005	18	90.32	0.000	32	101.62	1.894	46	116.83	0.000
5	74.26	0.000	19	93.22	0.000	33	102.38	1.970	47	118.54	0.073
6	76.29	0.000	20	94.06	0.000	34	102.74	1.394	48	119.10	0.042
7	78.00	0.011	21	95.48	0.599	35	104.52	0.599	49	121.42	0.077
8	78.58	0.077	22	96.19	0.000	36	105.94	0.000	50	122.00	0.011
9	80.90	0.042	23	97.26	1.394	37	106.42	0.000	51	126.32	0.000
10	81.46	0.073	24	97.58	0.000	38	106.78	0.000	52	126.36	0.005
11	83.74	0.000	25	97.62	1.970	39	107.07	0.000	53	127.71	0.000
12	84.89	0.030	26	98.38	1.894	40	110.22	0.000	54	127.78	0.000
13	84.94	0.000	27	99.58	3.923	41	111.11	0.106	55	129.75	0.000
14	85.78	0.000	28	99.80	0.000	42	112.25	0.000	56	140.38	0.000

5-62

$J_{AA'}$	J_{AB}	$J_{AB'}$	$J_{BB'}$
6	18	6	18
6	6	18	18
18	18	6	6
18	6	18	6

The maximum summed intensity is 7.187.

LINE	FREQ	INTEN	LINE	FREQ	INTEN	LINE	FREQ	INTEN	LINE	FREQ	INTEN
1	52.70	0.000	15	84.81	0.051	29	100.14	5.905	43	115.19	0.051
2	64.68	0.000	16	86.31	0.000	30	100.37	3.940	44	115.88	0.000
3	67.15	0.000	17	86.48	0.000	31	101.78	1.949	45	117.80	0.000
4	69.29	0.000	18	89.02	0.000	32	102.33	1.981	46	119.30	0.019
5	70.36	0.000	19	91.15	0.000	33	102.44	0.000	47	121.67	0.029
6	71.36	0.006	20	91.88	0.000	34	103.07	1.246	48	122.57	0.049
7	75.13	0.009	21	93.45	0.000	35	103.90	0.756	49	124.37	0.060
8	75.63	0.060	22	95.99	0.000	36	108.12	0.000	50	124.67	0.009
9	77.43	0.049	23	96.10	0.756	37	108.12	0.000	51	128.64	0.006
10	78.33	0.029	24	96.93	1.246	38	108.85	0.000	52	131.21	0.000
11	80.70	0.019	25	97.67	1.981	39	109.41	0.000	53	132.85	0.000
12	82.71	0.000	26	98.22	1.949	40	112.12	0.000	54	133.75	0.000
13	83.77	0.000	27	99.63	3.940	41	113.18	0.000	55	134.82	0.000
14	84.12	0.000	28	99.86	5.905	42	115.09	0.000	56	147.30	0.000

5-63

$J_{AA'}$	J_{AB}	$J_{AB'}$	$J_{BB'}$
9	9	1	9
9	1	9	9

The maximum summed intensity is 5.858.

LINE	FREQ	INTEN	LINE	FREQ	INTEN	LINE	FREQ	INTEN	LINE	FREQ	INTEN
1	71.79	0.000	15	91.00	0.000	29	100.42	5.434	43	109.00	0.200
2	79.75	0.000	16	91.62	0.000	30	100.83	0.000	44	109.00	0.000
3	81.00	0.	17	92.21	0.268	31	100.83	3.715	45	110.25	0.000
4	81.17	0.000	18	92.83	0.000	32	101.00	1.800	46	110.83	0.000
5	81.62	0.000	19	94.09	0.000	33	101.00	1.800	47	110.83	0.285
6	83.45	0.049	20	95.91	0.000	34	102.04	0.000	48	112.04	0.000
7	84.26	0.013	21	95.92	1.010	35	103.87	1.204	49	112.08	0.022
8	87.92	0.022	22	96.13	1.204	36	104.08	1.010	50	115.74	0.013
9	87.96	0.000	23	97.96	0.000	37	104.09	0.000	51	116.55	0.049
10	89.17	0.000	24	99.00	1.800	38	105.91	0.000	52	118.38	0.000
11	89.17	0.285	25	99.00	1.800	39	107.17	0.000	53	118.83	0.000
12	89.75	0.000	26	99.17	0.000	40	107.79	0.268	54	119.00	0.000
13	91.00	0.200	27	99.17	3.715	41	108.38	0.000	55	120.25	0.000
14	91.00	0.200	28	99.58	5.434	42	109.00	0.200	56	128.21	0.000

5-64

$J_{AA'}$	J_{AB}	$J_{AB'}$	$J_{BB'}$
9	9	2	9
9	2	9	9

The maximum summed intensity is 5.373.

LINE	FREQ	INTEN	LINE	FREQ	INTEN	LINE	FREQ	INTEN	LINE	FREQ	INTEN
1	71.83	0.000	15	91.70	0.000	29	100.36	5.542	43	109.06	0.205
2	79.76	0.000	16	91.89	0.241	30	100.76	0.000	44	109.89	0.000
3	80.89	0.	17	91.89	0.241	31	100.76	3.756	45	110.81	0.
4	81.24	0.000	18	93.47	0.000	32	101.11	1.759	46	111.02	0.000
5	82.48	0.000	19	93.76	0.000	33	101.11	1.759	47	111.76	0.000
6	82.81	0.009	20	95.34	0.852	34	101.59	0.000	48	111.76	0.244
7	84.36	0.056	21	96.53	1.314	35	102.69	0.000	49	112.89	0.023
8	87.11	0.023	22	97.31	0.000	36	103.47	1.314	50	115.64	0.056
9	88.24	0.000	23	98.41	0.	37	104.66	0.852	51	117.19	0.009
10	88.24	0.244	24	98.89	1.759	38	106.24	0.000	52	117.52	0.000
11	88.98	0.000	25	98.89	1.759	39	106.53	0.000	53	118.76	0.000
12	89.19	0.000	26	99.24	0.000	40	108.11	0.241	54	119.11	0.
13	90.11	0.000	27	99.24	3.756	41	108.11	0.241	55	120.24	0.000
14	90.94	0.205	28	99.64	5.542	42	108.30	0.000	56	128.17	0.000

5-65

$J_{AA'}$	J_{AB}	$J_{AB'}$	$J_{BB'}$
9	9	4	9
9	4	9	9

The maximum summed intensity is 5.707.

LINE	FREQ	INTEN	LINE	FREQ	INTEN	LINE	FREQ	INTEN	LINE	FREQ	INTEN
1	71.85	0.000	15	91.92	0.000	29	100.23	0.000	43	108.58	0.000
2	79.65	0.000	16	91.96	0.000	30	100.28	5.678	44	111.48	0.134
3	79.71	0.004	17	93.59	0.360	31	100.66	0.000	45	111.59	0.000
4	80.59	0.000	18	93.59	0.360	32	100.66	3.816	46	112.54	0.000
5	81.34	0.000	19	94.03	0.581	33	100.77	0.000	47	113.66	0.000
6	84.11	0.000	20	95.66	0.000	34	101.41	1.640	48	113.66	0.184
7	85.40	0.021	21	97.16	1.503	35	101.41	1.640	49	113.83	0.079
8	86.17	0.079	22	98.59	1.640	36	102.84	1.503	50	114.60	0.021
9	86.34	0.000	23	98.59	1.640	37	104.34	0.000	51	115.89	0.000
10	86.34	0.184	24	99.23	0.000	38	105.97	0.581	52	118.66	0.000
11	87.46	0.000	25	99.34	0.000	39	106.41	0.360	53	119.41	0.000
12	88.41	0.000	26	99.34	3.816	40	106.41	0.360	54	120.29	0.004
13	88.52	0.134	27	99.72	5.678	41	108.04	0.000	55	120.35	0.000
14	91.42	0.000	28	99.77	0.000	42	108.08	0.000	56	128.15	0.000

−11 −10 −9 −8 −7 −6 −5 −4 −3 −2 −1 0 +1 +2 +3 +4 +5 +6 +7 +8 +9 +10 +11

5-66

$J_{AA'}$	J_{AB}	$J_{AB'}$	$J_{BB'}$
9	9	6	9
9	6	9	9

The maximum summed intensity is 5.616.

LINE	FREQ	INTEN	LINE	FREQ	INTEN	LINE	FREQ	INTEN	LINE	FREQ	INTEN
1	71.79	0.000	15	92.22	0.000	29	100.03	0.000	43	109.86	0.000
2	76.42	0.002	16	92.57	0.362	30	100.23	5.760	44	112.05	0.127
3	79.33	0.000	17	93.32	0.000	31	100.58	0.000	45	113.15	0.000
4	80.15	0.000	18	95.15	0.553	32	100.58	3.857	46	113.75	0.095
5	81.42	0.000	19	95.15	0.553	33	101.85	1.447	47	113.96	0.000
6	83.61	0.018	20	96.85	0.000	34	101.85	1.447	48	114.49	0.000
7	84.42	0.000	21	97.56	0.000	35	102.40	1.636	49	115.58	0.000
8	84.42	0.143	22	97.60	1.636	36	102.42	0.000	50	115.58	0.143
9	85.51	0.000	23	98.15	1.447	37	103.15	0.000	51	116.39	0.018
10	86.04	0.000	24	98.15	1.447	38	104.85	0.553	52	118.58	0.000
11	86.25	0.095	25	99.42	0.000	39	104.85	0.553	53	119.85	0.000
12	86.85	0.000	26	99.42	3.857	40	106.68	0.000	54	120.67	0.000
13	87.95	0.127	27	99.77	5.760	41	107.43	0.362	55	123.58	0.002
14	90.14	0.000	28	99.97	0.000	42	107.78	0.000	56	128.21	0.000

−11 −10 −9 −8 −7 −6 −5 −4 −3 −2 −1 0 +1 +2 +3 +4 +5 +6 +7 +8 +9 +10 +11

5-67

$J_{AA'}$	J_{AB}	$J_{AB'}$	$J_{BB'}$
9	9	12	9
9	12	9	9

The maximum summed intensity is 6.538.

LINE	FREQ	INTEN	LINE	FREQ	INTEN	LINE	FREQ	INTEN	LINE	FREQ	INTEN
1	65.12	0.000	15	88.52	0.000	29	100.16	5.877	43	111.81	0.000
2	71.95	0.001	16	93.79	0.124	30	100.42	0.000	44	113.04	0.216
3	76.57	0.000	17	95.15	0.553	31	100.42	3.923	45	116.15	0.000
4	77.15	0.005	18	95.15	0.553	32	101.85	1.447	46	116.72	0.000
5	78.00	0.011	19	95.23	0.000	33	101.85	1.447	47	118.32	0.000
6	78.58	0.000	20	96.58	0.000	34	101.93	1.726	48	118.42	0.000
7	78.58	0.077	21	96.63	0.000	35	103.34	0.000	49	119.91	0.045
8	80.09	0.045	22	96.66	0.000	36	103.37	0.000	50	121.42	0.000
9	81.58	0.000	23	98.07	1.726	37	103.42	0.000	51	121.42	0.077
10	81.68	0.000	24	98.15	1.447	38	104.77	0.000	52	122.00	0.011
11	83.28	0.000	25	98.15	1.447	39	104.85	0.553	53	122.85	0.000
12	83.85	0.000	26	99.58	0.000	40	104.85	0.553	54	123.43	0.000
13	86.96	0.216	27	99.58	3.923	41	106.21	0.124	55	128.05	0.001
14	88.39	0.000	28	99.84	5.877	42	111.48	0.000	56	134.88	0.000

5-68

$J_{AA'}$	J_{AB}	$J_{AB'}$	$J_{BB'}$
9	9	15	9
9	15	9	9

The maximum summed intensity is 7.212.

LINE	FREQ	INTEN	LINE	FREQ	INTEN	LINE	FREQ	INTEN	LINE	FREQ	INTEN
1	59.46	0.000	15	88.64	0.000	29	100.13	5.906	43	114.93	0.000
2	71.51	0.003	16	92.76	0.293	30	100.37	0.000	44	115.80	0.143
3	74.25	0.000	17	92.76	0.293	31	100.37	3.940	45	116.76	0.000
4	74.76	0.000	18	93.63	0.000	32	101.24	1.707	46	117.26	0.000
5	75.13	0.009	19	94.54	0.000	33	101.24	1.707	47	118.37	0.000
6	75.63	0.000	20	96.25	0.350	34	102.16	1.558	48	122.58	0.032
7	75.63	0.060	21	96.97	0.000	35	102.88	0.000	49	123.41	0.000
8	76.59	0.000	22	97.12	0.000	36	103.03	0.000	50	124.37	0.000
9	77.42	0.032	23	97.84	1.558	37	103.75	0.350	51	124.37	0.060
10	81.63	0.000	24	98.76	1.707	38	105.46	0.000	52	124.87	0.009
11	82.74	0.000	25	98.76	1.707	39	106.37	0.000	53	125.24	0.000
12	83.24	0.000	26	99.63	0.000	40	107.24	0.293	54	125.75	0.000
13	84.20	0.143	27	99.63	3.940	41	107.24	0.293	55	128.49	0.003
14	85.07	0.000	28	99.87	5.906	42	111.36	0.000	56	140.54	0.000

5-69

$J_{AA'}$	J_{AB}	$J_{AB'}$	$J_{BB'}$
9	9	18	9
9	18	9	9

The maximum summed intensity is 8.035.

LINE	FREQ	INTEN	LINE	FREQ	INTEN	LINE	FREQ	INTEN	LINE	FREQ	INTEN
1	53.69	0.000	15	87.98	0.000	29	100.12	5.926	43	117.09	0.000
2	70.56	0.008	16	90.09	0.168	30	100.33	0.000	44	117.54	0.000
3	71.11	0.000	17	90.09	0.168	31	100.33	3.952	45	118.07	0.000
4	71.64	0.000	18	90.67	0.000	32	100.91	1.832	46	118.33	0.000
5	72.09	0.000	19	92.74	0.000	33	100.91	1.832	47	118.65	0.103
6	72.22	0.007	20	96.45	0.000	34	101.21	0.000	48	124.68	0.019
7	72.67	0.000	21	97.02	1.086	35	101.79	0.852	49	127.33	0.000
8	72.67	0.048	22	98.21	0.852	36	102.98	1.086	50	127.33	0.048
9	75.32	0.019	23	98.79	0.000	37	103.55	0.000	51	127.78	0.007
10	81.35	0.103	24	99.09	1.832	38	107.26	0.000	52	127.91	0.000
11	81.67	0.000	25	99.09	1.832	39	109.33	0.000	53	128.36	0.000
12	81.93	0.000	26	99.67	0.000	40	109.91	0.168	54	128.89	0.
13	82.46	0.000	27	99.67	3.952	41	109.91	0.168	55	129.44	0.008
14	82.91	0.000	28	99.88	5.926	42	112.02	0.000	56	146.31	0.000

−11 −10 −9 −8 −7 −6 −5 −4 −3 −2 −1 0 +1 +2 +3 +4 +5 +6 +7 +8 +9 +10 +11

5-70

$J_{AA'}$	J_{AB}	$J_{AB'}$	$J_{BB'}$
9	12	9	12
9	9	12	12
12	12	9	9
12	9	12	9

The maximum summed intensity is 7.750.

LINE	FREQ	INTEN	LINE	FREQ	INTEN	LINE	FREQ	INTEN	LINE	FREQ	INTEN
1	64.47	0.000	15	88.93	0.000	29	100.00	1.000	43	113.69	0.158
2	69.63	0.001	16	91.47	0.164	30	100.16	5.877	44	113.69	0.000
3	73.68	0.000	17	93.14	0.106	31	100.42	3.923	45	116.26	0.000
4	76.46	0.000	18	93.17	0.000	32	101.70	0.000	46	118.86	0.000
5	76.88	0.000	19	93.77	0.000	33	101.91	1.743	47	119.30	0.000
6	78.00	0.011	20	95.76	1.000	34	102.54	0.000	48	119.45	0.000
7	78.58	0.077	21	97.38	1.894	35	102.62	1.894	49	119.93	0.045
8	80.07	0.045	22	97.46	0.000	36	103.26	0.000	50	121.42	0.077
9	80.70	0.000	23	98.09	1.743	37	103.61	0.000	51	122.00	0.011
10	81.12	0.000	24	98.30	0.000	38	104.21	0.000	52	123.54	0.000
11	83.17	0.000	25	99.36	0.000	39	104.24	1.000	53	123.70	0.000
12	83.77	0.000	26	99.58	3.923	40	106.86	0.106	54	125.74	0.000
13	86.31	0.158	27	99.84	5.877	41	108.53	0.164	55	130.37	0.001
14	88.01	0.000	28	100.00	1.000	42	109.37	0.000	56	135.53	0.000

−11 −10 −9 −8 −7 −6 −5 −4 −3 −2 −1 0 +1 +2 +3 +4 +5 +6 +7 +8 +9 +10 +11

5-71

$J_{AA'}$	J_{AB}	$J_{AB'}$	$J_{BB'}$
9	15	9	15
9	9	15	15
15	15	9	9
15	9	15	9

The maximum summed intensity is 7.213.

LINE	FREQ	INTEN	LINE	FREQ	INTEN	LINE	FREQ	INTEN	LINE	FREQ	INTEN
1	57.71	0.000	15	88.87	0.000	29	100.13	5.906	43	114.83	0.000
2	67.50	0.001	16	89.05	0.051	30	100.37	3.940	44	117.29	0.000
3	68.79	0.000	17	91.75	0.000	31	101.24	1.707	45	117.55	0.085
4	71.39	0.000	18	92.24	0.257	32	101.42	0.000	46	120.13	0.000
5	73.00	0.000	19	92.76	0.293	33	101.91	1.709	47	121.50	0.000
6	75.13	0.009	20	94.87	0.000	34	102.47	1.949	48	122.83	0.033
7	75.63	0.060	21	95.39	0.000	35	103.87	0.000	49	124.37	0.060
8	77.17	0.033	22	96.13	0.000	36	104.54	0.000	50	124.63	0.000
9	79.00	0.000	23	97.53	1.949	37	104.61	0.000	51	124.87	0.009
10	79.08	0.000	24	98.09	1.709	38	105.16	0.000	52	127.50	0.000
11	79.87	0.000	25	98.54	0.000	39	107.24	0.293	53	128.61	0.000
12	82.20	0.000	26	98.76	1.707	40	107.76	0.257	54	130.71	0.000
13	82.45	0.085	27	99.63	3.940	41	110.95	0.051	55	132.50	0.001
14	85.08	0.000	28	99.87	5.906	42	111.21	0.000	56	142.29	0.000

5-72

$J_{AA'}$	J_{AB}	$J_{AB'}$	$J_{BB'}$
9	18	9	18
9	9	18	18
18	18	9	9
18	9	18	9

The maximum summed intensity is 8.038.

LINE	FREQ	INTEN	LINE	FREQ	INTEN	LINE	FREQ	INTEN	LINE	FREQ	INTEN
1	50.80	0.000	15	84.89	0.030	29	99.88	5.926	43	116.00	0.000
2	63.81	0.000	16	88.00	0.000	30	100.12	5.926	44	118.25	0.000
3	65.42	0.001	17	88.89	0.106	31	100.33	3.952	45	120.97	0.000
4	66.31	0.000	18	89.58	0.000	32	101.62	1.894	46	121.54	0.054
5	68.26	0.	19	93.08	0.337	33	102.00	1.649	47	122.70	0.000
6	72.22	0.007	20	93.31	0.000	34	102.38	1.970	48	125.65	0.025
7	72.67	0.048	21	93.97	0.000	35	106.03	0.000	49	127.33	0.048
8	73.39	0.000	22	96.93	0.000	36	106.42	0.000	50	127.78	0.007
9	74.35	0.025	23	97.49	0.000	37	106.69	0.000	51	130.62	0.000
10	77.74	0.000	24	97.62	1.970	38	106.92	0.337	52	132.19	0.000
11	78.46	0.054	25	98.00	1.649	39	107.07	0.000	53	133.69	0.000
12	79.03	0.000	26	98.38	1.894	40	111.11	0.106	54	134.58	0.001
13	81.30	0.000	27	98.51	0.000	41	113.12	0.000	55	135.75	0.000
14	82.87	0.000	28	99.67	3.952	42	115.11	0.030	56	149.20	0.000

5-73

$J_{AA'}$	J_{AB}	$J_{AB'}$	$J_{BB'}$
12	12	1	12
12	1	12	12

The maximum summed intensity is 6.956.

LINE	FREQ	INTEN	LINE	FREQ	INTEN	LINE	FREQ	INTEN	LINE	FREQ	INTEN
1	63.07	0.000	15	88.24	0.122	29	100.29	5.665	43	111.76	0.122
2	74.28	0.000	16	88.49	0.000	30	100.66	0.000	44	112.24	0.
3	75.24	0.000	17	89.58	0.140	31	100.66	3.816	45	113.19	0.000
4	75.34	0.000	18	89.66	0.000	32	100.76	1.878	46	113.66	0.000
5	75.96	0.	19	93.16	0.000	33	100.76	1.878	47	113.66	0.184
6	77.39	0.025	20	94.31	0.000	34	102.48	0.000	48	114.61	0.020
7	81.42	0.011	21	95.73	0.988	35	103.90	1.151	49	115.01	0.000
8	84.99	0.000	22	96.10	1.151	36	104.27	0.988	50	118.58	0.011
9	85.39	0.020	23	97.52	0.000	37	105.69	0.000	51	122.61	0.025
10	86.34	0.000	24	99.24	1.878	38	106.84	0.000	52	124.04	0.000
11	86.34	0.184	25	99.24	1.878	39	110.34	0.000	53	124.66	0.000
12	86.81	0.000	26	99.34	0.000	40	110.42	0.140	54	124.76	0.
13	87.76	0.	27	99.34	3.816	41	111.51	0.000	55	125.72	0.000
14	88.24	0.122	28	99.71	5.665	42	111.76	0.122	56	136.93	0.000

−11 −10 −9 −8 −7 −6 −5 −4 −3 −2 −1 0 +1 +2 +3 +4 +5 +6 +7 +8 +9 +10 +11

5-74

$J_{AA'}$	J_{AB}	$J_{AB'}$	$J_{BB'}$
12	12	2	12
12	2	12	12

The maximum summed intensity is 5.663.

LINE	FREQ	INTEN	LINE	FREQ	INTEN	LINE	FREQ	INTEN	LINE	FREQ	INTEN
1	63.10	0.000	15	88.55	0.000	29	100.26	5.716	43	111.75	0.114
2	74.29	0.000	16	89.17	0.143	30	100.62	0.000	44	113.17	0.000
3	75.17	0.000	17	89.17	0.143	31	100.62	3.838	45	113.70	0.000
4	75.38	0.000	18	90.62	0.000	32	100.83	1.857	46	114.05	0.000
5	76.88	0.000	19	93.71	0.000	33	100.83	1.857	47	114.62	0.000
6	78.33	0.027	20	94.63	0.000	34	102.03	0.000	48	114.62	0.162
7	79.93	0.008	21	95.16	0.848	35	103.48	1.268	49	115.49	0.019
8	84.51	0.019	22	96.52	1.268	36	104.84	0.848	50	120.07	0.008
9	85.38	0.000	23	97.97	0.000	37	105.37	0.000	51	121.67	0.027
10	85.38	0.162	24	99.17	1.857	38	106.29	0.000	52	123.12	0.000
11	85.95	0.000	25	99.17	1.857	39	109.38	0.000	53	124.62	0.000
12	86.30	0.000	26	99.38	0.000	40	110.83	0.143	54	124.83	0.
13	86.83	0.000	27	99.38	3.838	41	110.83	0.143	55	125.71	0.000
14	88.25	0.114	28	99.74	5.716	42	111.45	0.000	56	136.90	0.000

−11 −10 −9 −8 −7 −6 −5 −4 −3 −2 −1 0 +1 +2 +3 +4 +5 +6 +7 +8 +9 +10 +11

5-75

$J_{AA'}$	J_{AB}	$J_{AB'}$	$J_{BB'}$
12	12	4	12
12	4	12	12

The maximum summed intensity is 5.851.

LINE	FREQ	INTEN	LINE	FREQ	INTEN	LINE	FREQ	INTEN	LINE	FREQ	INTEN
1	63.14	0.000	15	88.73	0.000	29	100.22	5.786	43	111.32	0.000
2	74.24	0.000	16	91.00	0.200	30	100.54	0.000	44	114.28	0.082
3	75.00	0.000	17	91.00	0.200	31	100.54	3.873	45	115.00	0.000
4	75.46	0.000	18	92.29	0.000	32	101.00	1.800	46	115.76	0.000
5	76.74	0.004	19	92.54	0.000	33	101.00	1.800	47	116.54	0.000
6	78.68	0.000	20	93.83	0.607	34	101.27	0.000	48	116.54	0.127
7	80.23	0.034	21	97.19	1.470	35	102.29	0.000	49	117.31	0.016
8	82.69	0.016	22	97.71	0.000	36	102.81	1.470	50	119.77	0.034
9	83.46	0.000	23	98.73	0.000	37	106.17	0.607	51	121.32	0.000
10	83.46	0.127	24	99.00	1.800	38	107.46	0.000	52	123.26	0.004
11	84.24	0.000	25	99.00	1.800	39	107.71	0.000	53	124.54	0.000
12	85.00	0.000	26	99.46	0.000	40	109.00	0.200	54	125.00	0.000
13	85.72	0.082	27	99.46	3.873	41	109.00	0.200	55	125.76	0.000
14	88.68	0.000	28	99.78	5.786	42	111.27	0.000	56	136.86	0.000

-11 -10 -9 -8 -7 -6 -5 -4 -3 -2 -1 0 +1 +2 +3 +4 +5 +6 +7 +8 +9 +10 +11

5-76

$J_{AA'}$	J_{AB}	$J_{AB'}$	$J_{BB'}$
12	12	6	12
12	9	12	12

The maximum summed intensity is 6.172.

LINE	FREQ	INTEN	LINE	FREQ	INTEN	LINE	FREQ	INTEN	LINE	FREQ	INTEN
1	63.15	0.000	15	90.59	0.000	29	100.19	5.833	43	111.12	0.000
2	73.35	0.002	16	90.91	0.000	30	100.49	0.000	44	116.64	0.063
3	74.08	0.000	17	92.32	0.426	31	100.49	3.897	45	116.76	0.000
4	74.76	0.000	18	92.76	0.293	32	100.61	0.000	46	117.43	0.000
5	75.51	0.000	19	92.76	0.293	33	100.92	0.000	47	117.88	0.044
6	80.40	0.000	20	94.49	0.000	34	101.24	1.707	48	118.49	0.000
7	80.84	0.014	21	97.66	1.619	35	101.24	1.707	49	118.49	0.103
8	81.51	0.000	22	98.76	1.707	36	102.34	1.619	50	119.16	0.014
9	81.51	0.103	23	98.76	1.707	37	105.51	0.000	51	119.60	0.000
10	82.12	0.044	24	99.08	0.000	38	107.24	0.293	52	124.49	0.000
11	82.57	0.000	25	99.39	0.000	39	107.24	0.293	53	125.24	0.000
12	83.24	0.000	26	99.51	0.000	40	107.68	0.426	54	125.92	0.000
13	83.36	0.063	27	99.51	3.897	41	109.09	0.000	55	126.65	0.002
14	88.88	0.000	28	99.81	5.833	42	109.41	0.000	56	136.85	0.000

-11 -10 -9 -8 -7 -6 -5 -4 -3 -2 -1 0 +1 +2 +3 +4 +5 +6 +7 +8 +9 +10 +11

5-77

$J_{AA'}$	J_{AB}	$J_{AB'}$	$J_{BB'}$
12	12	9	12
12	9	12	12

The maximum summed intensity is 6.538.

LINE	FREQ	INTEN	LINE	FREQ	INTEN	LINE	FREQ	INTEN	LINE	FREQ	INTEN
1	63.10	0.000	15	89.37	0.000	29	100.16	5.877	43	112.41	0.000
2	68.02	0.001	16	89.86	0.237	30	100.38	0.000	44	115.06	0.076
3	73.57	0.000	17	93.68	0.000	31	100.42	0.000	45	117.34	0.000
4	74.15	0.000	18	94.29	0.000	32	100.42	3.923	46	119.15	0.000
5	75.58	0.000	19	95.15	0.553	33	101.85	1.447	47	119.72	0.000
6	78.00	0.011	20	95.15	0.553	34	101.85	1.447	48	119.95	0.045
7	78.58	0.000	21	97.42	0.000	35	101.89	1.752	49	121.42	0.000
8	78.58	0.077	22	98.11	1.752	36	102.58	0.000	50	121.42	0.077
9	80.05	0.045	23	98.15	1.447	37	104.85	0.553	51	122.00	0.011
10	80.28	0.000	24	98.15	1.447	38	104.85	0.553	52	124.42	0.000
11	80.85	0.000	25	99.58	0.000	39	105.71	0.000	53	125.85	0.000
12	82.66	0.000	26	99.58	3.923	40	106.32	0.000	54	126.43	0.
13	84.94	0.076	27	99.62	0.000	41	110.14	0.237	55	131.98	0.001
14	87.59	0.000	28	99.84	5.877	42	110.63	0.000	56	136.90	0.000

5-78

$J_{AA'}$	J_{AB}	$J_{AB'}$	$J_{BB'}$
12	12	15	12
12	15	12	12

The maximum summed intensity is 8.046.

LINE	FREQ	INTEN	LINE	FREQ	INTEN	LINE	FREQ	INTEN	LINE	FREQ	INTEN
1	56.48	0.000	15	85.66	0.000	29	100.12	5.926	43	114.34	0.000
2	63.19	0.000	16	90.85	0.075	30	100.33	0.000	44	115.86	0.148
3	70.70	0.000	17	92.37	0.000	31	100.33	3.952	45	121.05	0.000
4	71.15	0.000	18	95.15	0.553	32	101.56	1.817	46	122.15	0.000
5	72.22	0.007	19	95.15	0.553	33	101.85	1.447	47	122.59	0.000
6	72.67	0.000	20	96.38	0.000	34	101.85	1.447	48	124.33	0.000
7	72.67	0.048	21	96.67	0.000	35	103.08	0.000	49	126.10	0.026
8	73.90	0.026	22	96.92	0.000	36	103.33	0.000	50	127.33	0.000
9	75.67	0.000	23	98.15	1.447	37	103.62	0.000	51	127.33	0.048
10	77.41	0.000	24	98.15	1.447	38	104.85	0.553	52	127.78	0.007
11	77.85	0.000	25	98.44	1.817	39	104.85	0.553	53	128.85	0.000
12	78.95	0.000	26	99.67	0.000	40	107.63	0.000	54	129.30	0.000
13	84.14	0.148	27	99.67	3.952	41	109.15	0.075	55	136.81	0.000
14	85.66	0.000	28	99.88	5.926	42	114.34	0.000	56	143.52	0.000

5-79

$J_{AA'}$	J_{AB}	$J_{AB'}$	$J_{BB'}$
12	12	18	12
12	18	12	12

The maximum summed intensity is 8.995.

LINE	FREQ	INTEN	LINE	FREQ	INTEN	LINE	FREQ	INTEN	LINE	FREQ	INTEN
1	50.72	0.000	15	86.01	0.000	29	100.10	5.940	43	117.74	0.000
2	62.95	0.001	16	92.76	0.293	30	100.30	0.000	44	118.69	0.104
3	68.36	0.000	17	92.76	0.293	31	100.30	3.961	45	122.76	0.000
4	68.76	0.000	18	93.55	0.172	32	101.24	1.707	46	123.16	0.000
5	69.30	0.006	19	93.70	0.000	33	101.24	1.707	47	124.30	0.000
6	69.70	0.000	20	94.09	0.000	34	101.63	1.757	48	126.23	0.000
7	69.70	0.039	21	94.49	0.000	35	102.57	0.000	49	128.97	0.021
8	71.03	0.021	22	97.43	0.000	36	105.51	0.000	50	130.30	0.000
9	73.77	0.000	23	98.37	1.757	37	105.91	0.000	51	130.30	0.039
10	75.70	0.000	24	98.76	1.707	38	106.30	0.000	52	130.70	0.006
11	76.84	0.000	25	98.76	1.707	39	106.45	0.172	53	131.24	0.000
12	77.24	0.	26	99.70	0.000	40	107.24	0.293	54	131.64	0.000
13	81.31	0.104	27	99.70	3.961	41	107.24	0.293	55	137.05	0.001
14	82.26	0.000	28	99.90	5.940	42	113.99	0.000	56	149.28	0.000

−11 −10 −9 −8 −7 −6 −5 −4 −3 −2 −1 0 +1 +2 +3 +4 +5 +6 +7 +8 +9 +10 +11

5-80

$J_{AA'}$	J_{AB}	$J_{AB'}$	$J_{BB'}$
12	15	12	15
12	12	15	15
15	15	12	12
15	12	15	12

The maximum summed intensity is 10.027

LINE	FREQ	INTEN	LINE	FREQ	INTEN	LINE	FREQ	INTEN	LINE	FREQ	INTEN
1	55.75	0.000	15	86.13	0.000	29	100.00	1.000	43	116.49	0.000
2	60.92	0.000	16	88.58	0.111	30	100.12	5.926	44	116.59	0.106
3	67.81	0.000	17	90.37	0.000	31	100.33	3.952	45	121.66	0.000
4	70.55	0.000	18	93.14	0.106	32	101.55	1.824	46	122.26	0.000
5	70.88	0.000	19	94.04	0.000	33	101.79	0.000	47	125.21	0.000
6	72.22	0.007	20	95.76	1.000	34	102.45	0.000	48	125.33	0.000
7	72.67	0.048	21	97.38	1.894	35	102.62	1.894	49	126.11	0.026
8	73.89	0.026	22	97.55	0.000	36	103.34	0.000	50	127.33	0.048
9	74.79	0.000	23	98.21	0.000	37	103.53	0.000	51	127.78	0.007
10	75.12	0.000	24	98.45	1.824	38	104.24	1.000	52	129.45	0.000
11	77.30	0.000	25	99.10	0.000	39	106.86	0.106	53	129.57	0.000
12	80.96	0.000	26	99.67	3.952	40	107.00	0.000	54	131.74	0.000
13	83.41	0.106	27	99.88	5.926	41	111.42	0.111	55	139.08	0.000
14	85.20	0.000	28	100.00	1.000	42	112.17	0.000	56	144.25	0.000

−11 −10 −9 −8 −7 −6 −5 −4 −3 −2 −1 0 +1 +2 +3 +4 +5 +6 +7 +8 +9 +10 +11

5-81

$J_{AA'}$	J_{AB}	$J_{AB'}$	$J_{BB'}$
12	18	12	18
12	12	18	18
18	18	12	12
18	12	18	12

The maximum summed intensity is 8.996.

LINE	FREQ	INTEN	LINE	FREQ	INTEN	LINE	FREQ	INTEN	LINE	FREQ	INTEN
1	48.89	0.000	15	86.18	0.000	29	100.10	5.940	43	117.53	0.000
2	58.88	0.000	16	89.05	0.051	30	100.30	3.961	44	120.51	0.062
3	62.89	0.000	17	89.48	0.160	31	101.24	1.707	45	123.29	0.000
4	65.46	0.000	18	92.06	0.000	32	101.53	1.811	46	126.05	0.000
5	67.00	0.000	19	92.18	0.000	33	102.47	1.949	47	127.40	0.000
6	69.30	0.006	20	92.76	0.293	34	103.95	0.000	48	127.52	0.000
7	69.70	0.039	21	95.46	0.000	35	104.11	0.000	49	129.07	0.021
8	70.93	0.021	22	96.05	0.000	36	104.23	0.000	50	130.30	0.039
9	73.00	0.000	23	97.53	1.949	37	104.54	0.000	51	130.70	0.006
10	73.95	0.000	24	98.23	0.000	38	105.48	0.000	52	133.40	0.000
11	76.19	0.000	25	98.47	1.811	39	107.24	0.293	53	134.54	0.000
12	76.31	0.000	26	98.76	1.707	40	110.52	0.160	54	136.71	0.000
13	79.49	0.062	27	99.70	3.961	41	110.95	0.051	55	141.12	0.000
14	82.19	0.000	28	99.90	5.940	42	114.10	0.000	56	151.11	0.000

5-82

$J_{AA'}$	J_{AB}	$J_{AB'}$	$J_{BB'}$
15	15	1	15
15	1	15	15

The maximum summed intensity is 7.399.

LINE	FREQ	INTEN	LINE	FREQ	INTEN	LINE	FREQ	INTEN	LINE	FREQ	INTEN
1	54.24	0.000	15	85.38	0.081	29	100.22	5.781	43	114.62	0.081
2	68.62	0.000	16	85.40	0.000	30	100.54	0.000	44	115.38	0.000
3	69.38	0.	17	86.54	0.000	31	100.54	3.873	45	116.15	0.000
4	69.46	0.000	18	86.82	0.082	32	100.62	1.919	46	116.54	0.000
5	70.17	0.000	19	90.30	0.000	33	100.62	1.919	47	116.54	0.127
6	71.33	0.015	20	94.47	0.000	34	102.75	0.000	48	117.31	0.016
7	78.54	0.010	21	95.63	0.970	35	103.91	1.127	49	117.98	0.000
8	82.02	0.000	22	96.09	1.127	36	104.37	0.970	50	121.46	0.010
9	82.69	0.016	23	97.25	0.000	37	105.53	0.000	51	128.67	0.015
10	83.46	0.000	24	99.38	1.919	38	109.70	0.000	52	129.83	0.000
11	83.46	0.127	25	99.38	1.919	39	113.18	0.082	53	130.54	0.000
12	83.85	0.000	26	99.46	0.000	40	113.46	0.000	54	130.62	0.000
13	84.62	0.000	27	99.46	3.873	41	114.60	0.000	55	131.38	0.000
14	85.38	0.081	28	99.78	5.781	42	114.62	0.081	56	145.76	0.000

5-83

$J_{AA'}$	J_{AB}	$J_{AB'}$	$J_{BB'}$
15	15	2	15
15	2	15	15

The maximum summed intensity is 6.570.

LINE	FREQ	INTEN	LINE	FREQ	INTEN	LINE	FREQ	INTEN	LINE	FREQ	INTEN
1	54.27	0.000	15	85.45	0.071	29	100.21	5.808	43	114.56	0.000
2	68.62	0.000	16	86.34	0.092	30	100.51	0.000	44	116.34	0.000
3	69.34	0.000	17	86.34	0.092	31	100.51	3.886	45	116.62	0.000
4	69.49	0.000	18	87.51	0.000	32	100.66	1.908	46	117.06	0.000
5	71.12	0.000	19	91.81	0.000	33	100.66	1.908	47	117.51	0.000
6	72.29	0.016	20	93.88	0.000	34	102.31	0.000	48	117.51	0.114
7	77.02	0.007	21	95.05	0.838	35	103.48	1.245	49	118.23	0.015
8	81.77	0.015	22	96.52	1.245	36	104.95	0.838	50	122.98	0.007
9	82.49	0.000	23	97.69	0.000	37	106.12	0.000	51	127.71	0.016
10	82.49	0.114	24	99.34	1.908	38	108.19	0.000	52	128.88	0.000
11	82.94	0.000	25	99.34	1.908	39	112.49	0.000	53	130.51	0.000
12	83.38	0.000	26	99.49	0.000	40	113.66	0.092	54	130.66	0.
13	83.66	0.000	27	99.49	3.886	41	113.66	0.092	55	131.38	0.
14	85.44	0.000	28	99.79	5.808	42	114.55	0.071	56	145.73	0.000

5-84

$J_{AA'}$	J_{AB}	$J_{AB'}$	$J_{BB'}$
15	15	4	15
15	4	15	4

The maximum summed intensity is 6.300.

LINE	FREQ	INTEN	LINE	FREQ	INTEN	LINE	FREQ	INTEN	LINE	FREQ	INTEN
1	54.30	0.000	15	85.90	0.000	29	100.18	5.848	43	114.47	0.000
2	68.59	0.	16	88.24	0.122	30	100.46	0.000	44	117.13	0.055
3	69.24	0.	17	88.24	0.122	31	100.46	3.907	45	118.24	0.000
4	69.54	0.000	18	89.46	0.000	32	100.76	1.878	46	118.88	0.000
5	73.00	0.000	19	92.50	0.000	33	100.76	1.878	47	119.46	0.000
6	73.80	0.004	20	93.73	0.609	34	101.57	0.000	48	119.46	0.093
7	74.22	0.019	21	94.97	0.000	35	102.80	1.452	49	120.10	0.013
8	79.90	0.013	22	97.20	1.452	36	105.03	0.000	50	125.78	0.019
9	80.54	0.000	23	98.43	0.000	37	106.27	0.609	51	126.20	0.004
10	80.54	0.093	24	99.24	1.878	38	107.50	0.000	52	127.00	0.000
11	81.12	0.000	25	99.24	1.878	39	110.54	0.000	53	130.46	0.000
12	81.76	0.000	26	99.54	0.000	40	111.76	0.122	54	130.76	0.000
13	82.87	0.055	27	99.54	3.907	41	111.76	0.122	55	131.41	0.000
14	85.53	0.000	28	99.82	5.848	42	114.10	0.000	56	145.70	0.000

5-85

$J_{AA'}$	J_{AB}	$J_{AB'}$	$J_{BB'}$
15	15	6	15
15	6	15	15

The maximum summed intensity is 6.548.

LINE	FREQ	INTEN	LINE	FREQ	INTEN	LINE	FREQ	INTEN	LINE	FREQ	INTEN
1	54.32	0.000	15	88.21	0.000	29	100.16	5.877	43	114.35	0.000
2	68.51	0.000	16	90.09	0.168	30	100.42	0.000	44	119.53	0.045
3	69.09	0.000	17	90.09	0.168	31	100.42	3.923	45	120.09	0.000
4	69.58	0.000	18	90.89	0.000	32	100.91	1.832	46	120.67	0.000
5	70.38	0.002	19	91.42	0.000	33	100.91	1.832	47	121.42	0.000
6	74.83	0.000	20	92.22	0.437	34	100.98	0.000	48	121.42	0.077
7	76.16	0.023	21	97.69	1.606	35	101.71	0.000	49	122.00	0.011
8	78.00	0.011	22	98.29	0.000	36	102.31	1.606	50	123.84	0.023
9	78.58	0.000	23	99.02	0.000	37	107.78	0.437	51	125.17	0.000
10	78.58	0.077	24	99.09	1.832	38	108.58	0.000	52	129.62	0.002
11	79.33	0.000	25	99.09	1.832	39	109.11	0.000	53	130.42	0.000
12	79.91	0.000	26	99.58	0.000	40	109.91	0.168	54	130.91	0.000
13	80.47	0.045	27	99.58	3.923	41	109.91	0.168	55	131.49	0.000
14	85.65	0.	28	99.84	5.877	42	111.79	0.000	56	145.68	0.000

5-86

$J_{AA'}$	J_{AB}	$J_{AB'}$	$J_{BB'}$
15	15	9	15
15	9	15	15

The maximum summed intensity is 7.214.

LINE	FREQ	INTEN	LINE	FREQ	INTEN	LINE	FREQ	INTEN	LINE	FREQ	INTEN
1	54.32	0.000	15	88.10	0.000	29	100.13	5.906	43	114.06	0.000
2	64.98	0.001	16	89.72	0.269	30	100.21	0.000	44	120.94	0.031
3	68.25	0.000	17	91.30	0.000	31	100.37	0.000	45	122.55	0.000
4	68.76	0.000	18	92.76	0.293	32	100.37	3.940	46	122.76	0.000
5	69.63	0.000	19	92.76	0.293	33	101.24	1.707	47	122.91	0.034
6	75.13	0.009	20	94.37	0.000	34	101.24	1.707	48	123.26	0.000
7	75.63	0.000	21	96.59	0.000	35	101.83	1.751	49	124.37	0.000
8	75.63	0.060	22	98.17	1.751	36	103.41	0.000	50	124.37	0.060
9	76.74	0.000	23	98.76	1.707	37	105.63	0.000	51	124.87	0.009
10	77.09	0.034	24	98.76	1.707	38	107.24	0.293	52	130.37	0.000
11	77.24	0.000	25	99.63	0.000	39	107.24	0.293	53	131.24	0.000
12	77.45	0.000	26	99.63	3.940	40	108.70	0.000	54	131.75	0.000
13	79.06	0.031	27	99.79	0.000	41	110.28	0.269	55	135.02	0.001
14	85.94	0.000	28	99.87	5.906	42	111.90	0.000	56	145.68	0.000

5-87

$J_{AA'}$	J_{AB}	$J_{AB'}$	$J_{BB'}$
15	15	12	15
15	12	15	15

The maximum summed intensity is 8.046.

LINE	FREQ	INTEN	LINE	FREQ	INTEN	LINE	FREQ	INTEN	LINE	FREQ	INTEN
1	54.28	0.000	15	86.46	0.000	29	100.12	5.926	43	115.12	0.000
2	59.41	0.000	16	87.06	0.163	30	100.33	0.000	44	118.06	0.050
3	67.70	0.000	17	91.59	0.000	31	100.33	3.952	45	120.25	0.000
4	68.15	0.000	18	93.94	0.000	32	100.64	0.000	46	125.15	0.000
5	69.67	0.000	19	95.15	0.553	33	101.54	1.827	47	125.59	0.000
6	72.22	0.007	20	95.15	0.553	34	101.85	1.447	48	126.12	0.026
7	72.67	0.000	21	97.33	0.000	35	101.85	1.447	49	127.33	0.000
8	72.67	0.048	22	98.15	1.447	36	102.67	0.000	50	127.33	0.048
9	73.88	0.026	23	98.15	1.447	37	104.85	0.553	51	127.78	0.007
10	74.41	0.000	24	98.46	1.827	38	104.85	0.553	52	130.33	0.000
11	74.85	0.000	25	99.36	0.000	39	106.06	0.000	53	131.85	0.000
12	79.75	0.000	26	99.67	0.000	40	108.41	0.000	54	132.30	0.000
13	81.94	0.050	27	99.67	3.952	41	112.94	0.163	55	140.59	0.000
14	84.88	0.000	28	99.88	5.926	42	113.54	0.000	56	145.72	0.000

−11 −10 −9 −8 −7 −6 −5 −4 −3 −2 −1 0 +1 +2 +3 +4 +5 +6 +7 +8 +9 +10 +11

5-88

$J_{AA'}$	J_{AB}	$J_{AB'}$	$J_{BB'}$
15	15	18	15
15	18	15	15

The maximum summed intensity is 9.875.

LINE	FREQ	INTEN	LINE	FREQ	INTEN	LINE	FREQ	INTEN	LINE	FREQ	INTEN
1	47.72	0.000	15	82.85	0.000	29	100.09	5.950	43	117.25	0.000
2	54.34	0.000	16	87.88	0.050	30	100.27	0.000	44	118.73	0.107
3	64.78	0.000	17	89.46	0.000	31	100.27	3.968	45	123.86	0.000
4	65.15	0.000	18	95.15	0.553	32	101.30	1.871	46	128.15	0.000
5	66.36	0.005	19	95.15	0.553	33	101.85	1.447	47	128.51	0.000
6	66.73	0.000	20	96.18	0.000	34	101.85	1.447	48	130.27	0.000
7	66.73	0.032	21	96.73	0.000	35	102.89	0.000	49	132.24	0.017
8	67.76	0.017	22	97.11	0.000	36	103.27	0.000	50	133.27	0.000
9	69.73	0.000	23	98.15	1.447	37	103.82	0.000	51	133.27	0.032
10	71.49	0.000	24	98.15	1.447	38	104.85	0.553	52	133.64	0.005
11	71.85	0.000	25	98.70	1.871	39	104.85	0.553	53	134.85	0.000
12	76.14	0.000	26	99.73	0.000	40	110.54	0.000	54	135.22	0.000
13	81.27	0.107	27	99.73	3.968	41	112.12	0.050	55	145.66	0.000
14	82.75	0.000	28	99.91	5.950	42	117.15	0.000	56	152.28	0.000

−11 −10 −9 −8 −7 −6 −5 −4 −3 −2 −1 0 +1 +2 +3 +4 +5 +6 +7 +8 +9 +10 +11

5-89

$J_{AA'}$	J_{AB}	$J_{AB'}$	$J_{BB'}$
15	18	15	18
15	15	18	18
18	18	15	15
18	15	18	15

The maximum summed intensity is 11.875.

LINE	FREQ	INTEN	LINE	FREQ	INTEN	LINE	FREQ	INTEN	LINE	FREQ	INTEN
1	46.95	0.000	15	83.27	0.000	29	100.00	1.000	43	119.35	0.000
2	52.12	0.000	16	85.66	0.079	30	100.09	5.950	44	119.51	0.075
3	61.89	0.000	17	87.51	0.000	31	100.27	3.968	45	124.53	0.000
4	64.61	0.000	18	93.14	0.106	32	101.30	1.873	46	128.26	0.000
5	64.88	0.000	19	94.23	0.000	33	101.85	0.000	47	131.15	0.000
6	66.36	0.005	20	95.76	1.000	34	102.39	0.000	48	131.24	0.000
7	66.73	0.032	21	97.38	1.894	35	102.62	1.894	49	132.25	0.017
8	67.75	0.017	22	97.61	0.000	36	103.15	0.000	50	133.27	0.032
9	68.85	0.000	23	98.15	0.000	37	103.72	0.000	51	133.64	0.005
10	69.12	0.000	24	98.70	1.873	38	104.24	1.000	52	135.39	0.000
11	71.38	0.000	25	98.90	0.000	39	106.86	0.106	53	135.49	0.000
12	78.10	0.000	26	99.73	3.968	40	109.86	0.000	54	137.74	0.000
13	80.49	0.075	27	99.91	5.950	41	114.34	0.079	55	147.88	0.000
14	82.34	0.000	28	100.00	1.000	42	115.04	0.000	56	153.05	0.000

5-90

$J_{AA'}$	J_{AB}	$J_{AB'}$	$J_{BB'}$
18	18	1	18
18	1	18	18

The maximum summed intensity is 7.856.

LINE	FREQ	INTEN	LINE	FREQ	INTEN	LINE	FREQ	INTEN	LINE	FREQ	INTEN
1	45.36	0.000	15	82.49	0.057	29	100.18	5.846	43	117.66	0.000
2	62.84	0.000	16	82.49	0.057	30	100.46	0.000	44	118.49	0.
3	63.49	0.	17	83.46	0.000	31	100.46	3.907	45	119.13	0.000
4	63.54	0.000	18	83.98	0.053	32	100.51	1.943	46	119.46	0.000
5	64.31	0.000	19	87.39	0.000	33	100.51	1.943	47	119.46	0.093
6	65.29	0.010	20	94.58	0.000	34	102.93	0.000	48	120.11	0.012
7	75.63	0.008	21	95.55	0.955	35	103.90	1.115	49	120.95	0.000
8	79.05	0.000	22	96.10	1.115	36	104.45	0.955	50	124.37	0.008
9	79.89	0.012	23	97.07	0.000	37	105.42	0.000	51	134.71	0.010
10	80.54	0.000	24	99.49	1.943	38	112.61	0.000	52	135.69	0.000
11	80.54	0.093	25	99.49	1.943	39	116.02	0.053	53	136.46	0.000
12	80.87	0.000	26	99.54	0.000	40	116.54	0.000	54	136.51	0.
13	81.51	0.	27	99.54	3.907	41	117.51	0.057	55	137.16	0.000
14	82.34	0.000	28	99.82	5.846	42	117.51	0.057	56	154.64	0.000

5-91

$J_{AA'}$	J_{AB}	$J_{AB'}$	$J_{BB'}$
18	18	2	18
18	2	18	18

The maximum summed intensity is 7.356.

LINE	FREQ	INTEN	LINE	FREQ	INTEN	LINE	FREQ	INTEN	LINE	FREQ	INTEN
1	45.38	0.000	15	82.59	0.048	29	100.17	5.862	43	117.64	0.000
2	62.85	0.	16	83.46	0.064	30	100.44	0.000	44	119.46	0.000
3	63.46	0.000	17	83.46	0.064	31	100.44	3.916	45	119.58	0.000
4	63.56	0.000	18	84.44	0.000	32	100.54	1.936	46	120.07	0.000
5	65.28	0.000	19	88.92	0.000	33	100.54	1.936	47	120.44	0.000
6	66.26	0.011	20	93.99	0.000	34	102.49	0.000	48	120.44	0.064
7	74.10	0.006	21	94.98	0.829	35	103.47	1.233	49	121.05	0.012
8	78.95	0.012	22	96.53	1.233	36	105.02	0.829	50	125.90	0.006
9	79.56	0.000	23	97.51	0.000	37	106.01	0.000	51	133.74	0.011
10	79.56	0.084	24	99.46	1.936	38	111.08	0.000	52	134.72	0.000
11	79.93	0.000	25	99.46	1.936	39	115.56	0.000	53	136.44	0.000
12	80.42	0.	26	99.56	0.000	40	116.54	0.064	54	136.54	0.
13	80.54	0.000	27	99.56	3.916	41	116.54	0.064	55	137.15	0.000
14	82.36	0.000	28	99.83	5.862	42	117.41	0.048	56	154.62	0.000

−11 −10 −9 −8 −7 −6 −5 −4 −3 −2 −1 0 +1 +2 +3 +4 +5 +6 +7 +8 +9 +10 +11

5-92

$J_{AA'}$	J_{AB}	$J_{AB'}$	$J_{BB'}$
18	18	4	18
18	4	18	18

The maximum summed intensity is 6.721.

LINE	FREQ	INTEN	LINE	FREQ	INTEN	LINE	FREQ	INTEN	LINE	FREQ	INTEN
1	45.41	0.000	15	83.00	0.000	29	100.15	5.887	43	117.58	0.000
2	62.83	0.000	16	85.38	0.081	30	100.40	0.000	44	120.02	0.039
3	63.38	0.000	17	85.38	0.081	31	100.40	3.930	45	121.38	0.
4	63.60	0.000	18	86.40	0.000	32	100.62	1.919	46	121.94	0.000
5	67.19	0.000	19	92.13	0.000	33	100.62	1.919	47	122.40	0.000
6	68.21	0.012	20	92.64	0.000	34	101.77	0.000	48	122.40	0.070
7	70.86	0.003	21	93.66	0.608	35	102.78	1.440	49	122.95	0.010
8	77.05	0.010	22	97.22	1.440	36	106.34	0.608	50	129.14	0.003
9	77.60	0.000	23	98.23	0.000	37	107.36	0.000	51	131.79	0.012
10	77.60	0.070	24	99.38	1.919	38	107.87	0.000	52	132.81	0.000
11	78.06	0.000	25	99.38	1.919	39	113.60	0.000	53	136.40	0.000
12	78.62	0.	26	99.60	0.000	40	114.62	0.081	54	136.62	0.
13	79.98	0.039	27	99.60	3.930	41	114.62	0.081	55	137.17	0.000
14	82.42	0.000	28	99.85	5.887	42	117.00	0.000	56	154.59	0.000

−11 −10 −9 −8 −7 −6 −5 −4 −3 −2 −1 0 +1 +2 +3 +4 +5 +6 +7 +8 +9 +10 +11

5-93

$J_{AA'}$	J_{AB}	$J_{AB'}$	$J_{BB'}$
18	18	6	18
18	6	18	18

The maximum summed intensity is 7.176.

LINE	FREQ	INTEN	LINE	FREQ	INTEN	LINE	FREQ	INTEN	LINE	FREQ	INTEN
1	45.43	0.000	15	85.37	0.000	29	100.13	5.906	43	117.50	0.000
2	62.79	0.000	16	87.29	0.106	30	100.37	0.000	44	122.45	0.033
3	63.29	0.	17	87.29	0.106	31	100.37	3.940	45	123.29	0.000
4	63.63	0.000	18	88.37	0.000	32	100.71	1.894	46	123.80	0.000
5	67.41	0.002	19	91.07	0.000	33	100.71	1.894	47	124.37	0.000
6	69.09	0.000	20	92.15	0.440	34	101.21	0.000	48	124.37	0.060
7	70.16	0.014	21	95.51	0.000	35	102.29	1.597	49	124.87	0.009
8	75.13	0.009	22	97.71	1.597	36	104.49	0.000	50	129.84	0.014
9	75.63	0.000	23	98.79	0.000	37	107.85	0.440	51	130.91	0.000
10	75.63	0.060	24	99.29	1.894	38	108.93	0.000	52	132.59	0.002
11	76.20	0.000	25	99.29	1.894	39	111.63	0.000	53	136.37	0.000
12	76.71	0.000	26	99.63	0.000	40	112.71	0.106	54	136.71	0.000
13	77.55	0.033	27	99.63	3.940	41	112.71	0.106	55	137.21	0.000
14	82.50	0.000	28	99.87	5.906	42	114.63	0.000	56	154.57	0.000

−11 −10 −9 −8 −7 −6 −5 −4 −3 −2 −1 0 +1 +2 +3 +4 +5 +6 +7 +8 +9 +10 +11

5-94

$J_{AA'}$	J_{AB}	$J_{AB'}$	$J_{BB'}$
18	18	9	18
18	9	18	18

The maximum summed intensity is 8.040.

LINE	FREQ	INTEN	LINE	FREQ	INTEN	LINE	FREQ	INTEN	LINE	FREQ	INTEN
1	45.44	0.000	15	88.41	0.000	29	100.12	5.926	43	117.32	0.000
2	61.99	0.001	16	88.63	0.000	30	100.33	0.000	44	125.87	0.026
3	62.64	0.000	17	89.65	0.276	31	100.33	3.952	45	126.09	0.000
4	63.09	0.000	18	90.09	0.168	32	100.55	0.000	46	126.54	0.000
5	63.67	0.000	19	90.09	0.168	33	100.77	0.000	47	126.90	0.018
6	71.86	0.000	20	91.33	0.000	34	100.91	1.832	48	127.33	0.000
7	72.22	0.007	21	98.21	1.747	35	100.91	1.832	49	127.33	0.048
8	72.67	0.000	22	99.09	1.832	36	101.79	1.747	50	127.78	0.007
9	72.67	0.048	23	99.09	1.832	37	108.67	0.000	51	128.14	0.000
10	73.10	0.018	24	99.23	0.000	38	109.91	0.168	52	136.33	0.000
11	73.46	0.000	25	99.45	0.000	39	109.91	0.168	53	136.91	0.000
12	73.91	0.000	26	99.67	0.000	40	110.35	0.276	54	137.36	0.000
13	74.13	0.026	27	99.67	3.952	41	111.37	0.000	55	138.01	0.001
14	82.68	0.000	28	99.88	5.926	42	111.59	0.000	56	154.56	0.000

−11 −10 −9 −8 −7 −6 −5 −4 −3 −2 −1 0 +1 +2 +3 +4 +5 +6 +7 +8 +9 +10 +11

5-95

$J_{AA'}$	J_{AB}	$J_{AB'}$	$J_{BB'}$
18	18	12	18
18	12	18	12

The maximum summed intensity is 8.996.

LINE	FREQ	INTEN	LINE	FREQ	INTEN	LINE	FREQ	INTEN	LINE	FREQ	INTEN
1	45.44	0.000	15	85.43	0.000	29	100.06	0.000	43	117.02	0.000
2	56.38	0.000	16	86.97	0.179	30	100.10	5.940	44	123.97	0.024
3	62.36	0.000	17	91.57	0.000	31	100.30	0.000	45	125.51	0.000
4	62.76	0.000	18	92.76	0.293	32	100.30	3.961	46	128.76	0.000
5	63.70	0.000	19	92.76	0.293	33	101.24	1.707	47	129.11	0.021
6	69.30	0.006	20	93.92	0.000	34	101.24	1.707	48	129.16	0.000
7	69.70	0.000	21	94.30	0.000	35	101.48	1.830	49	130.30	0.000
8	69.70	0.039	22	98.52	1.830	36	105.70	0.000	50	130.30	0.039
9	70.84	0.000	23	98.76	1.707	37	106.08	0.000	51	130.70	0.006
10	70.89	0.021	24	98.76	1.707	38	107.24	0.293	52	136.30	0.000
11	71.24	0.000	25	99.70	0.000	39	107.24	0.293	53	137.24	0.000
12	74.49	0.000	26	99.70	3.961	40	108.43	0.000	54	137.64	0.000
13	76.03	0.024	27	99.90	5.940	41	113.03	0.179	55	143.62	0.000
14	82.98	0.000	28	99.94	0.000	42	114.57	0.000	56	154.56	0.000

5-96

$J_{AA'}$	J_{AB}	$J_{AB'}$	$J_{BB'}$
18	18	15	18
18	15	18	18

The maximum summed intensity is 9.875.

LINE	FREQ	INTEN	LINE	FREQ	INTEN	LINE	FREQ	INTEN	LINE	FREQ	INTEN
1	45.40	0.000	15	83.53	0.000	29	100.09	5.950	43	117.91	0.000
2	50.67	0.000	16	84.21	0.117	30	100.27	0.000	44	121.06	0.035
3	61.78	0.000	17	88.80	0.000	31	100.27	3.968	45	123.18	0.000
4	62.15	0.000	18	94.13	0.000	32	100.83	0.000	46	131.15	0.000
5	63.73	0.000	19	95.15	0.553	33	101.29	1.875	47	131.51	0.000
6	66.36	0.005	20	95.15	0.553	34	101.85	1.447	48	132.25	0.017
7	66.73	0.000	21	97.27	0.000	35	101.85	1.447	49	133.27	0.000
8	66.73	0.032	22	98.15	1.447	36	102.73	0.000	50	133.27	0.032
9	67.75	0.017	23	98.15	1.447	37	104.85	0.553	51	133.64	0.005
10	68.49	0.000	24	98.71	1.875	38	104.85	0.553	52	136.27	0.000
11	68.85	0.000	25	99.17	0.000	39	105.87	0.000	53	137.85	0.000
12	76.82	0.000	26	99.73	0.000	40	111.20	0.000	54	138.22	0.000
13	78.94	0.035	27	99.73	3.968	41	115.79	0.117	55	149.33	0.000
14	82.09	0.000	28	99.91	5.950	42	116.47	0.000	56	154.60	0.000

5-97

$J_{AA'}$	J_{AB}	$J_{AB'}$	$J_{BB'}$
1	1	-1	1
1	-1	1	1

The maximum summed intensity is 5.731

LINE	FREQ	INTEN	LINE	FREQ	INTEN	LINE	FREQ	INTEN	LINE	FREQ	INTEN
1	89.71	0.000	15	96.87	1.887	29	100.71	0.781	43	103.25	1.732
2	90.75	0.001	16	97.00	0.000	30	101.00	0.000	44	103.41	1.487
3	90.87	0.000	17	97.00	0.000	31	101.75	0.000	45	103.96	0.000
4	91.59	0.000	18	97.00	2.000	32	101.87	0.000	46	104.16	0.684
5	94.71	0.157	19	97.00	2.000	33	102.09	0.000	47	104.16	0.684
6	95.00	0.000	20	97.41	1.956	34	102.16	1.316	48	104.16	0.000
7	95.43	0.000	21	97.84	1.316	35	102.16	1.316	49	104.45	0.000
8	95.55	0.000	22	97.84	1.316	36	102.16	0.000	50	104.57	0.000
9	95.84	0.684	23	97.84	0.000	37	102.59	1.956	51	105.00	0.000
10	95.84	0.684	24	97.91	0.000	38	103.00	0.000	52	105.29	0.157
11	95.84	0.000	25	98.13	0.000	39	103.00	0.000	53	108.41	0.000
12	96.04	0.000	26	98.25	0.000	40	103.00	2.000	54	109.13	0.000
13	96.59	1.487	27	99.00	0.000	41	103.00	2.000	55	109.25	0.001
14	96.75	1.732	28	99.29	0.781	42	103.13	1.887	56	110.29	0.000

5-98

$J_{AA'}$	J_{AB}	$J_{AB'}$	$J_{BB'}$
1	1	-2	1
1	-2	1	1

The maximum summed intensity is 2.846.

LINE	FREQ	INTEN	LINE	FREQ	INTEN	LINE	FREQ	INTEN	LINE	FREQ	INTEN
1	88.80	0.000	15	96.46	0.000	29	100.49	1.468	43	103.81	1.494
2	90.11	0.000	16	96.46	1.671	30	100.54	0.000	44	103.82	1.161
3	90.88	0.004	17	96.96	1.699	31	101.57	0.000	45	103.85	0.
4	91.57	0.	18	97.15	0.	32	101.72	0.	46	104.50	0.000
5	94.40	0.225	19	97.46	0.000	33	101.80	0.000	47	104.85	0.553
6	94.46	0.000	20	97.46	2.329	34	101.85	1.447	48	104.85	0.553
7	94.86	0.000	21	97.74	1.949	35	101.85	1.447	49	104.91	0.000
8	95.09	0.000	22	98.15	1.447	36	102.26	1.949	50	105.14	0.000
9	95.15	0.553	23	98.15	1.447	37	102.54	0.000	51	105.54	0.000
10	95.15	0.553	24	98.20	0.000	38	102.54	2.329	52	105.60	0.225
11	95.50	0.000	25	98.28	0.000	39	102.85	0.	53	108.43	0.000
12	96.15	0.	26	98.43	0.000	40	103.04	1.699	54	109.12	0.004
13	96.18	1.161	27	99.46	0.000	41	103.54	0.000	55	109.69	0.000
14	96.19	1.494	28	99.51	1.468	42	103.54	1.671	56	111.20	0.000

5-99

$J_{AA'}$	J_{AB}	$J_{AB'}$	$J_{BB'}$
1	1	-4	1
1	-4	1	1

The maximum summed intensity is 4.212.

LINE	FREQ	INTEN	LINE	FREQ	INTEN	LINE	FREQ	INTEN	LINE	FREQ	INTEN
1	86.38	0.000	15	95.15	1.106	29	100.15	0.000	43	104.85	1.106
2	87.93	-0.000	16	95.59	0.000	30	100.18	2.846	44	104.99	0.676
3	90.47	0.016	17	96.59	0.	31	101.27	0.000	45	105.37	0.931
4	90.92	0.000	18	97.17	1.372	32	101.27	0.000	46	105.81	0.000
5	93.15	0.000	19	98.15	0.000	33	101.41	1.640	47	106.08	0.000
6	93.46	0.000	20	98.15	2.894	34	101.41	1.640	48	106.41	0.360
7	93.47	0.237	21	98.27	0.000	35	101.72	1.921	49	106.41	0.360
8	93.59	0.360	22	98.26	1.921	36	101.73	0.000	50	106.53	0.237
9	93.59	0.360	23	98.59	1.640	37	101.85	0.000	51	106.54	0.000
10	93.92	0.000	24	98.59	1.640	38	101.85	2.894	52	106.85	0.000
11	94.19	0.000	25	98.73	0.000	39	102.83	1.372	53	109.08	0.000
12	94.63	0.931	26	98.73	0.000	40	103.41	0.000	54	109.53	0.016
13	95.01	0.676	27	99.82	2.846	41	104.41	0.000	55	112.07	0.000
14	95.15	0.000	28	99.85	0.000	42	104.85	0.000	56	113.62	0.000

−11 −10 −9 −8 −7 −6 −5 −4 −3 −2 −1 0 +1 +2 +3 +4 +5 +6 +7 +8 +9 +10 +11

5-100

$J_{AA'}$	J_{AB}	$J_{AB'}$	$J_{BB'}$
1	1	-6	1
1	-6	1	1

The maximum summed intensity is 7.725.

LINE	FREQ	INTEN	LINE	FREQ	INTEN	LINE	FREQ	INTEN	LINE	FREQ	INTEN
1	83.40	0.000	15	93.59	0.720	29	100.02	3.903	43	106.41	0.720
2	85.11	0.000	16	93.89	0.000	30	100.59	0.000	44	106.48	0.404
3	89.42	0.029	17	96.89	0.000	31	101.04	0.000	45	107.08	0.599
4	89.72	0.000	18	97.23	0.973	32	101.06	0.000	46	107.38	0.000
5	91.59	0.000	19	98.28	0.000	33	101.11	1.759	47	107.50	0.000
6	91.82	0.000	20	98.59	0.000	34	101.11	1.759	48	107.79	0.179
7	91.89	0.241	21	98.59	3.280	35	101.33	1.913	49	108.11	0.241
8	91.89	0.241	22	98.67	1.913	36	101.41	0.000	50	108.11	0.241
9	92.21	0.179	23	98.89	1.759	37	101.41	3.280	51	108.18	0.000
10	92.50	0.000	24	98.89	1.759	38	101.72	0.000	52	108.41	0.000
11	92.62	0.000	25	98.94	0.000	39	102.77	0.973	53	110.28	0.000
12	92.92	0.599	26	98.96	0.000	40	103.11	0.000	54	110.58	0.029
13	93.52	0.404	27	99.41	0.000	41	106.11	0.000	55	114.89	0.000
14	93.59	0.000	28	99.98	3.903	42	106.41	0.000	56	116.60	0.

−11 −10 −9 −8 −7 −6 −5 −4 −3 −2 −1 0 +1 +2 +3 +4 +5 +6 +7 +8 +9 +10 +11

5-101

$J_{AA'}$	J_{AB}	$J_{AB'}$	$J_{BB'}$
1	1	-9	1
1	-9	1	1

The maximum summed intensity is 8.213.

LINE	FREQ	INTEN	LINE	FREQ	INTEN	LINE	FREQ	INTEN	LINE	FREQ	INTEN
1	78.35	0.	15	91.00	0.400	29	100.07	4.827	43	109.00	0.400
2	80.18	0.000	16	91.17	0.000	30	100.80	0.000	44	109.03	0.211
3	87.22	0.034	17	97.17	0.000	31	100.83	1.857	45	109.82	0.339
4	87.39	0.000	18	97.22	0.561	32	100.83	1.857	46	109.90	0.000
5	89.00	0.000	19	98.24	0.000	33	100.95	0.000	47	109.99	0.000
6	89.14	0.000	20	99.00	0.000	34	100.97	1.925	48	110.07	0.103
7	89.17	0.143	21	99.00	3.600	35	101.00	0.000	49	110.83	0.143
8	89.17	0.143	22	99.00	0.000	36	101.00	0.000	50	110.83	0.143
9	89.93	0.103	23	99.03	1.925	37	101.00	3.600	51	110.86	0.000
10	90.01	0.000	24	99.05	0.000	38	101.76	0.000	52	111.00	0.000
11	90.10	0.000	25	99.17	1.857	39	102.78	0.561	53	112.61	0.000
12	90.18	0.339	26	99.17	1.857	40	102.83	0.000	54	112.78	0.034
13	90.97	0.211	27	99.20	0.000	41	108.83	0.000	55	119.82	0.000
14	91.00	0.000	28	99.93	4.827	42	109.00	0.000	56	121.65	0.

5-102

$J_{AA'}$	J_{AB}	$J_{AB'}$	$J_{BB'}$
2	2	-1	2
2	-1	2	2

The maximum summed intensity is 5.492.

LINE	FREQ	INTEN	LINE	FREQ	INTEN	LINE	FREQ	INTEN	LINE	FREQ	INTEN
1	88.90	0.000	15	96.46	0.000	29	100.46	0.000	43	103.54	1.671
2	89.54	0.003	16	96.46	1.671	30	100.79	1.157	44	104.38	1.009
3	91.21	0.001	17	97.29	2.159	31	100.85	0.000	45	104.39	0.000
4	91.23	0.000	18	97.46	0.000	32	100.85	0.000	46	104.85	0.553
5	93.13	0.071	19	97.46	2.096	33	101.52	0.000	47	104.85	0.553
6	93.46	0.000	20	97.46	2.329	34	101.85	1.447	48	105.19	0.000
7	94.15	0.000	21	97.94	0.000	35	101.85	1.447	49	105.85	0.000
8	94.15	0.000	22	98.15	1.447	36	102.06	0.000	50	105.85	0.000
9	94.81	0.000	23	98.15	1.447	37	102.54	0.000	51	106.54	0.000
10	95.15	0.553	24	98.48	0.000	38	102.54	2.096	52	106.87	0.071
11	95.15	0.553	25	99.15	0.000	39	102.54	2.329	53	108.77	0.000
12	95.61	0.000	26	99.15	0.000	40	102.71	2.159	54	108.79	0.001
13	95.62	1.009	27	99.21	1.157	41	103.54	1.504	55	110.46	0.003
14	96.46	1.504	28	99.54	0.000	42	103.54	0.000	56	111.10	0.000

5-103

$J_{AA'}$	J_{AB}	$J_{AB'}$	$J_{BB'}$
2	2	-2	2
2	-2	2	2

The maximum summed intensity is 4.007

LINE	FREQ	INTEN	LINE	FREQ	INTEN	LINE	FREQ	INTEN	LINE	FREQ	INTEN
1	87.97	0.000	15	96.58	1.663	29	100.73	1.907	43	103.80	1.298
2	89.50	0.010	16	97.00	0.000	30	100.80	0.000	44	104.50	0.793
3	90.58	0.002	17	97.00	0.000	31	101.00	0.000	45	104.82	0.000
4	90.90	0.000	18	97.00	2.000	32	101.61	1.555	46	105.33	0.000
5	93.00	0.000	19	97.00	2.000	33	101.61	1.555	47	105.61	0.445
6	93.27	0.104	20	97.80	2.223	34	101.61	0.000	48	105.61	0.445
7	93.59	0.000	21	98.11	0.000	35	101.88	0.000	49	105.61	0.000
8	94.39	0.445	22	98.12	0.000	36	101.89	0.000	50	106.41	0.000
9	94.39	0.445	23	98.39	1.555	37	102.20	2.223	51	106.73	0.104
10	94.39	0.000	24	98.39	1.555	38	103.00	0.000	52	107.00	0.000
11	94.67	0.000	25	98.39	0.000	39	103.00	0.000	53	109.10	0.000
12	95.18	0.000	26	99.00	0.000	40	103.00	2.000	54	109.42	0.002
13	95.50	0.793	27	99.20	0.000	41	103.00	2.000	55	110.50	0.010
14	96.20	1.298	28	99.27	1.907	42	103.42	1.663	56	112.03	0.000

−11 −10 −9 −8 −7 −6 −5 −4 −3 −2 −1 0 +1 +2 +3 +4 +5 +6 +7 +8 +9 +10 +11

5-104

$J_{AA'}$	J_{AB}	$J_{AB'}$	$J_{BB'}$
2	2	-4	2
2	-4	2	2

The maximum summed intensity is 3.230.

LINE	FREQ	INTEN	LINE	FREQ	INTEN	LINE	FREQ	INTEN	LINE	FREQ	INTEN
1	85.51	0.000	15	95.37	0.855	29	100.54	3.320	43	104.85	0.455
2	88.59	0.002	16	95.84	0.000	30	100.77	0.000	44	105.08	0.985
3	88.82	0.027	17	95.84	1.368	31	101.24	1.707	45	105.24	0.000
4	89.74	0.000	18	96.76	0.000	32	101.24	1.707	46	105.94	0.000
5	91.84	0.000	19	97.46	0.000	33	101.69	2.216	47	106.00	0.000
6	92.29	0.000	20	97.84	0.000	34	101.77	0.000	48	106.86	0.139
7	92.76	0.293	21	97.84	2.632	35	101.84	0.000	49	107.24	0.293
8	92.76	0.293	22	98.16	0.000	36	102.16	0.000	50	107.24	0.293
9	93.14	0.139	23	98.23	0.000	37	102.16	2.632	51	107.71	0.000
10	94.00	0.000	24	98.31	2.216	38	102.54	0.	52	108.16	0.000
11	94.06	0.000	25	98.76	1.707	39	103.24	0.000	53	110.26	0.000
12	94.76	0.	26	98.76	1.707	40	104.16	0.000	54	111.18	0.027
13	94.92	0.985	27	99.23	0.000	41	104.16	1.368	55	111.41	0.002
14	95.15	0.455	28	99.46	3.320	42	104.63	0.855	56	114.49	0.000

−11 −10 −9 −8 −7 −6 −5 −4 −3 −2 −1 0 +1 +2 +3 +4 +5 +6 +7 +8 +9 +10 +11

5-105

$J_{AA'}$	J_{AB}	$J_{AB'}$	$J_{BB'}$
2	2	-6	2
2	-6	2	2

The maximum summed intensity is 4.314.

LINE	FREQ	INTEN	LINE	FREQ	INTEN	LINE	FREQ	INTEN	LINE	FREQ	INTEN
1	82.50	0.000	15	94.39	0.891	29	100.39	4.318	43	105.61	0.891
2	85.90	0.001	16	94.85	0.268	30	100.74	0.000	44	105.87	0.523
3	87.64	0.036	17	95.00	0.000	31	101.00	1.800	45	106.89	0.617
4	88.24	0.000	18	95.00	0.000	32	101.00	1.800	46	107.00	0.000
5	90.39	0.000	19	97.00	0.000	33	101.34	2.111	47	107.50	0.000
6	90.74	0.000	20	97.61	0.000	34	101.61	0.000	48	107.61	0.127
7	91.00	0.200	21	98.24	0.000	35	101.61	3.109	49	109.00	0.200
8	91.00	0.200	22	98.39	0.000	36	101.76	0.000	50	109.00	0.200
9	92.39	0.127	23	98.39	3.109	37	102.39	0.000	51	109.26	0.000
10	92.50	0.000	24	98.66	2.111	38	103.00	0.000	52	109.61	0.000
11	93.00	0.000	25	99.00	1.800	39	105.00	0.000	53	111.76	0.000
12	93.11	0.617	26	99.00	1.800	40	105.00	0.000	54	112.36	0.036
13	94.13	0.523	27	99.26	0.000	41	105.15	0.268	55	114.10	0.001
14	94.39	0.000	28	99.61	4.318	42	105.61	0.000	56	117.50	0.000

−11 −10 −9 −8 −7 −6 −5 −4 −3 −2 −1 0 +1 +2 +3 +4 +5 +6 +7 +8 +9 +10 +11

5-106

$J_{AA'}$	J_{AB}	$J_{AB'}$	$J_{BB'}$
2	2	-9	2
2	-9	2	2

The maximum summed intensity is 5.127.

LINE	FREQ	INTEN	LINE	FREQ	INTEN	LINE	FREQ	INTEN	LINE	FREQ	INTEN
1	77.42	0.000	15	91.89	0.481	29	100.28	5.118	43	108.11	0.481
2	81.07	0.000	16	92.24	0.000	30	100.65	0.000	44	108.23	0.263
3	85.34	0.036	17	94.56	0.137	31	100.76	1.878	45	109.15	0.000
4	85.69	0.000	18	95.24	0.	32	100.76	1.878	46	109.50	0.084
5	87.89	0.000	19	96.62	0.000	33	100.99	2.019	47	109.71	0.343
6	88.12	0.000	20	97.11	0.000	34	101.11	0.000	48	110.05	0.000
7	88.24	0.122	21	98.22	0.000	35	101.11	3.519	49	111.76	0.122
8	88.24	0.122	22	98.89	0.000	36	101.78	0.000	50	111.76	0.122
9	89.95	0.000	23	98.89	3.519	37	102.89	0.000	51	111.88	0.000
10	90.29	0.343	24	99.01	2.019	38	103.38	0.000	52	112.11	0.000
11	90.50	0.084	25	99.24	1.878	39	104.76	0.	53	114.31	0.000
12	90.85	0.000	26	99.24	1.878	40	105.44	0.137	54	114.66	0.036
13	91.77	0.263	27	99.35	0.000	41	107.76	0.000	55	118.93	0.000
14	91.89	0.000	28	99.72	5.118	42	108.11	0.000	56	122.58	0.

−11 −10 −9 −8 −7 −6 −5 −4 −3 −2 −1 0 +1 +2 +3 +4 +5 +6 +7 +8 +9 +10 +11

5-107.

$J_{AA'}$	J_{AB}	$J_{AB'}$	$J_{BB'}$
4	4	-1	4
4	-1	4	4

The maximum summed intensity is 5.723.

LINE	FREQ	INTEN	LINE	FREQ	INTEN	LINE	FREQ	INTEN	LINE	FREQ	INTEN
1	85.32	0.003	15	95.15	1.106	29	100.74	0.000	43	104.85	1.106
2	86.86	0.000	16	96.00	1.326	30	101.41	1.640	44	105.33	0.000
3	88.77	0.000	17	96.58	0.000	31	101.41	1.640	45	105.46	0.000
4	90.15	0.000	18	96.85	0.000	32	101.59	0.000	46	106.41	0.360
5	90.59	0.000	19	97.29	1.910	33	101.85	0.000	47	106.41	0.360
6	91.09	0.036	20	97.65	0.000	34	101.85	2.894	48	107.98	0.242
7	91.41	0.000	21	97.80	1.537	35	101.88	2.945	49	108.55	0.000
8	91.45	0.000	22	98.12	2.945	36	102.20	1.537	50	108.59	0.000
9	92.02	0.242	23	98.15	0.000	37	102.35	0.000	51	108.91	0.036
10	93.59	0.360	24	98.15	2.894	38	102.71	1.910	52	109.41	0.000
11	93.59	0.360	25	98.41	0.000	39	103.15	0.000	53	109.85	0.000
12	94.54	0.000	26	98.59	1.640	40	103.42	0.000	54	111.23	0.000
13	94.67	0.000	27	98.59	1.640	41	104.00	1.326	55	113.14	0.000
14	95.15	0.000	28	99.26	0.000	42	104.85	0.000	56	114.68	0.003

5-108

$J_{AA'}$	J_{AB}	$J_{AB'}$	$J_{BB'}$
4	4	-2	4
4	-2	4	4

The maximum summed intensity is 4.866.

LINE	FREQ	INTEN	LINE	FREQ	INTEN	LINE	FREQ	INTEN	LINE	FREQ	INTEN
1	85.12	0.006	15	95.84	0.000	29	100.76	0.000	43	104.16	1.368
2	86.04	0.000	16	95.84	1.368	30	100.76	0.000	44	105.24	0.000
3	88.04	0.000	17	96.16	0.000	31	101.24	1.707	45	105.48	0.000
4	89.84	0.000	18	96.52	0.000	32	101.24	1.707	46	107.24	0.293
5	90.76	0.000	19	96.76	0.000	33	101.84	1.949	47	107.24	0.293
6	90.76	0.000	20	97.44	2.206	34	102.16	0.000	48	108.16	0.051
7	91.12	0.004	21	97.84	0.000	35	102.16	2.369	49	108.56	0.184
8	91.44	0.184	22	97.84	2.369	36	102.16	2.632	50	108.88	0.004
9	91.84	0.051	23	97.84	2.632	37	102.56	2.206	51	109.24	0.000
10	92.76	0.293	24	98.16	1.949	38	103.24	0.000	52	109.24	0.000
11	92.76	0.293	25	98.76	1.707	39	103.48	0.000	53	110.16	0.000
12	94.52	0.000	26	98.76	1.707	40	103.84	0.000	54	111.96	0.000
13	94.76	0.000	27	99.24	0.000	41	104.16	1.231	55	113.96	0.000
14	95.84	1.231	28	99.24	0.000	42	104.16	0.000	56	114.88	0.006

5-109

$J_{AA'}$	J_{AB}	$J_{AB'}$	$J_{BB'}$
4	4	-4	4
4	-4	4	4

The maximum summed intensity is 4.215

LINE	FREQ	INTEN	LINE	FREQ	INTEN	LINE	FREQ	INTEN	LINE	FREQ	INTEN
1	83.66	0.000	15	95.24	0.000	29	100.47	0.000	43	105.00	0.000
2	84.43	0.014	16	95.53	1.007	30	101.00	1.800	44	105.24	0.000
3	86.43	0.000	17	95.66	1.157	31	101.00	1.800	45	106.34	0.000
4	89.00	0.000	18	96.43	0.000	32	101.00	0.000	46	107.24	0.085
5	89.53	0.000	19	97.00	0.000	33	101.24	2.870	47	109.00	0.200
6	89.66	0.012	20	97.00	0.000	34	101.53	2.744	48	109.00	0.200
7	90.43	0.111	21	97.00	2.000	35	103.00	0.000	49	109.00	0.000
8	91.00	0.200	22	97.00	2.000	36	103.00	0.000	50	109.57	0.111
9	91.00	0.200	23	98.47	2.744	37	103.00	2.000	51	110.34	0.012
10	91.00	0.000	24	98.76	2.870	38	103.00	2.000	52	110.47	0.000
11	92.76	0.085	25	99.00	1.800	39	103.57	0.000	53	111.00	0.000
12	93.66	0.000	26	99.00	1.800	40	104.34	1.157	54	113.57	0.000
13	94.76	0.000	27	99.00	0.000	41	104.47	1.007	55	115.57	0.014
14	95.00	0.000	28	99.53	0.000	42	104.76	0.000	56	116.34	0.000

−11 −10 −9 −8 −7 −6 −5 −4 −3 −2 −1 0 +1 +2 +3 +4 +5 +6 +7 +8 +9 +10 +11

5-110

$J_{AA'}$	J_{AB}	$J_{AB'}$	$J_{BB'}$
4	4	-6	4
4	-6	4	4

The maximum summed intensity is 7.356.

LINE	FREQ	INTEN	LINE	FREQ	INTEN	LINE	FREQ	INTEN	LINE	FREQ	INTEN
1	80.64	0.000	15	94.16	0.000	29	100.10	0.000	43	105.84	0.
2	83.36	0.020	16	94.18	0.000	30	100.83	3.818	44	106.37	0.665
3	84.69	0.000	17	94.90	0.738	31	100.83	1.857	45	107.15	0.103
4	87.31	0.008	18	95.84	0.000	32	100.83	1.857	46	107.70	0.000
5	87.84	0.000	19	95.84	1.368	33	101.23	2.579	47	108.83	0.000
6	88.23	0.000	20	96.36	0.000	34	102.16	0.000	48	110.31	0.069
7	89.17	0.143	21	97.17	0.000	35	102.16	2.632	49	110.83	0.143
8	89.17	0.143	22	97.84	0.000	36	102.83	0.000	50	110.83	0.143
9	89.69	0.069	23	97.84	2.632	37	103.64	0.000	51	111.77	0.000
10	91.17	0.000	24	98.77	2.579	38	104.16	0.000	52	112.16	0.000
11	92.30	0.000	25	99.17	1.857	39	104.16	1.368	53	112.69	0.008
12	92.85	0.103	26	99.17	1.857	40	105.10	0.738	54	115.31	0.000
13	93.63	0.665	27	99.17	3.818	41	105.82	0.000	55	116.64	0.020
14	94.16	0.000	28	99.90	0.000	42	105.84	0.000	56	119.36	0.000

−11 −10 −9 −8 −7 −6 −5 −4 −3 −2 −1 0 +1 +2 +3 +4 +5 +6 +7 +8 +9 +10 +11

5-111

$J_{AA'}$	J_{AB}	$J_{AB'}$	$J_{BB'}$
4	4	-9	4
4	-9	4	4

The maximum summed intensity is 6.686.

LINE	FREQ	INTEN	LINE	FREQ	INTEN	LINE	FREQ	INTEN	LINE	FREQ	INTEN
1	75.51	0.000	15	93.15	0.394	29	100.21	0.000	43	107.55	0.000
2	81.21	0.023	16	93.23	0.000	30	100.48	4.849	44	108.29	0.087
3	81.96	0.000	17	93.41	0.000	31	100.66	1.908	45	108.66	0.000
4	82.77	0.002	18	93.59	0.000	32	100.66	1.908	46	109.42	0.353
5	85.59	0.000	19	93.59	0.720	33	100.96	2.257	47	110.17	0.000
6	85.90	0.000	20	94.34	0.000	34	101.41	0.000	48	110.98	0.035
7	86.34	0.092	21	96.26	0.000	35	101.41	3.280	49	113.66	0.092
8	86.34	0.092	22	98.59	0.000	36	103.72	0.000	50	113.66	0.092
9	89.02	0.035	23	98.59	3.280	37	105.66	0.000	51	114.10	0.000
10	89.83	0.000	24	99.04	2.257	38	106.41	0.000	52	114.41	0.000
11	90.58	0.353	25	99.34	1.908	39	106.41	0.720	53	117.23	0.002
12	91.34	0.000	26	99.34	1.908	40	106.59	0.000	54	118.04	0.000
13	91.71	0.087	27	99.52	4.849	41	106.77	0.000	55	118.79	0.023
14	92.45	0.000	28	99.79	0.000	42	106.85	0.394	56	124.49	0.000

−11 −10 −9 −8 −7 −6 −5 −4 −3 −2 −1 0 +1 +2 +3 +4 +5 +6 +7 +8 +9 +10 +11

5-112

$J_{AA'}$	J_{AB}	$J_{AB'}$	$J_{BB'}$
6	6	-1	6
6	-1	6	6

The maximum summed intensity is 7.571.

LINE	FREQ	INTEN	LINE	FREQ	INTEN	LINE	FREQ	INTEN	LINE	FREQ	INTEN
1	80.08	0.001	15	94.41	0.000	29	101.11	1.759	43	106.41	0.000
2	84.28	0.000	16	94.59	0.000	30	101.11	1.759	44	106.41	0.720
3	85.37	0.000	17	94.75	0.000	31	101.21	3.940	45	106.50	0.000
4	86.59	0.000	18	95.55	1.150	32	101.41	0.000	46	108.11	0.241
5	86.89	0.	19	96.03	0.000	33	101.41	3.280	47	108.11	0.241
6	87.89	0.092	20	96.11	0.	34	101.93	0.000	48	109.02	0.003
7	88.85	0.000	21	96.64	1.309	35	102.73	1.474	49	110.54	0.031
8	89.46	0.031	22	97.27	1.474	36	103.36	1.309	50	111.15	0.000
9	90.98	0.003	23	98.07	0.000	37	103.89	0.	51	112.11	0.092
10	91.89	0.241	24	98.59	0.000	38	103.97	0.000	52	113.11	0.000
11	91.89	0.241	25	98.59	3.280	39	104.45	1.150	53	113.41	0.000
12	93.50	0.000	26	98.79	3.940	40	105.25	0.000	54	114.63	0.000
13	93.59	0.000	27	98.89	1.759	41	105.41	0.000	55	115.72	0.000
14	93.59	0.720	28	98.89	1.759	42	105.59	0.000	56	119.92	0.001

−11 −10 −9 −8 −7 −6 −5 −4 −3 −2 −1 0 +1 +2 +3 +4 +5 +6 +7 +8 +9 +10 +11

5-113

$J_{AA'}$	J_{AB}	$J_{AB'}$	$J_{BB'}$
6	6	-2	6
6	-2	6	6

The maximum summed intensity is 5.484.

LINE	FREQ	INTEN	LINE	FREQ	INTEN	LINE	FREQ	INTEN	LINE	FREQ	INTEN
1	79.92	0.002	15	94.39	0.891	29	101.00	1.800	43	105.61	0.891
2	83.69	0.000	16	94.53	0.000	30	101.00	1.800	44	106.31	0.000
3	84.53	0.000	17	94.94	0.000	31	101.61	0.000	45	106.39	0.000
4	86.39	0.000	18	95.06	0.000	32	101.61	3.109	46	108.91	0.000
5	87.00	0.000	19	95.29	1.071	33	101.70	3.122	47	109.00	0.200
6	87.13	0.076	20	97.00	0.000	34	102.11	0.000	48	109.00	0.200
7	87.89	0.000	21	97.50	1.942	35	102.34	1.743	49	109.55	0.043
8	90.45	0.043	22	97.66	1.743	36	102.50	1.942	50	112.11	0.000
9	91.00	0.200	23	97.89	0.000	37	103.00	0.000	51	112.87	0.076
10	91.00	0.200	24	98.30	3.122	38	104.71	1.071	52	113.00	0.000
11	91.09	0.000	25	98.39	0.000	39	104.94	0.000	53	113.61	0.000
12	93.61	0.000	26	98.39	3.109	40	105.06	0.000	54	115.47	0.000
13	93.69	0.000	27	99.00	1.800	41	105.47	0.000	55	116.31	0.000
14	94.39	0.000	28	99.00	1.800	42	105.61	0.000	56	120.08	0.002

-11 -10 -9 -8 -7 -6 -5 -4 -3 -2 -1 0 +1 +2 +3 +4 +5 +6 +7 +8 +9 +10 +11

5-114

$J_{AA'}$	J_{AB}	$J_{AB'}$	$J_{BB'}$
6	6	-4	6
6	-4	6	6

The maximum summed intensity is 3.607.

LINE	FREQ	INTEN	LINE	FREQ	INTEN	LINE	FREQ	INTEN	LINE	FREQ	INTEN
1	79.43	0.005	15	94.43	0.000	29	100.83	1.857	43	106.70	0.000
2	81.64	0.000	16	95.11	0.928	30	100.83	1.857	44	106.98	0.000
3	82.77	0.000	17	95.32	0.000	31	101.17	0.000	45	107.84	0.000
4	85.76	0.053	18	95.84	0.000	32	101.44	3.048	46	108.01	0.073
5	85.84	0.000	19	95.84	1.368	33	101.69	2.365	47	109.69	0.022
6	86.44	0.000	20	96.63	1.507	34	101.89	0.000	48	110.83	0.143
7	87.17	0.000	21	97.84	0.000	35	102.16	0.000	49	110.83	0.143
8	89.17	0.143	22	97.84	2.632	36	102.16	2.632	50	112.83	0.000
9	89.17	0.143	23	98.11	0.000	37	103.37	1.507	51	113.56	0.000
10	90.31	0.022	24	98.31	2.365	38	104.16	0.000	52	114.16	0.000
11	91.99	0.073	25	98.56	3.048	39	104.16	1.368	53	114.24	0.053
12	92.16	0.000	26	98.83	0.000	40	104.68	0.000	54	117.23	0.000
13	93.02	0.000	27	99.17	1.857	41	104.89	0.928	55	118.36	0.000
14	93.30	0.000	28	99.17	1.857	42	105.57	0.000	56	120.57	0.005

-11 -10 -9 -8 -7 -6 -5 -4 -3 -2 -1 0 +1 +2 +3 +4 +5 +6 +7 +8 +9 +10 +11

5-115

$J_{AA'}$	J_{AB}	$J_{AB'}$	$J_{BB'}$
6	6	-6	6
6	-6	6	6

The maximum summed intensity is 5.230

LINE	FREQ	INTEN	LINE	FREQ	INTEN	LINE	FREQ	INTEN	LINE	FREQ	INTEN
1	78.65	0.009	15	94.35	0.000	29	100.71	1.894	43	107.19	0.098
2	78.71	0.000	16	94.41	0.747	30	100.71	1.894	44	107.88	0.000
3	80.94	0.000	17	95.04	0.809	31	100.71	0.000	45	108.52	0.000
4	84.65	0.036	18	95.10	0.000	32	101.04	3.145	46	109.00	0.000
5	85.00	0.000	19	97.00	0.000	33	101.19	3.131	47	111.59	0.023
6	85.33	0.000	20	97.00	0.000	34	101.25	0.000	48	112.71	0.106
7	87.29	0.106	21	97.00	2.000	35	103.00	0.000	49	112.71	0.106
8	87.29	0.106	22	97.00	2.000	36	103.00	0.000	50	112.71	0.000
9	87.29	0.000	23	98.75	0.000	37	103.00	2.000	51	114.67	0.000
10	88.41	0.023	24	98.81	3.131	38	103.00	2.000	52	115.00	0.000
11	91.00	0.000	25	98.96	3.145	39	104.90	0.000	53	115.35	0.036
12	91.48	0.000	26	99.29	1.894	40	104.96	0.809	54	119.06	0.000
13	92.12	0.000	27	99.29	1.894	41	105.59	0.747	55	121.29	0.000
14	92.81	0.098	28	99.29	0.000	42	105.65	0.000	56	121.35	0.009

5-116

$J_{AA'}$	J_{AB}	$J_{AB'}$	$J_{BB'}$
6	6	-9	6
6	-9	6	6

The maximum summed intensity is 8.153.

LINE	FREQ	INTEN	LINE	FREQ	INTEN	LINE	FREQ	INTEN	LINE	FREQ	INTEN
1	73.58	0.000	15	92.59	0.101	29	100.43	0.000	43	108.99	0.364
2	76.85	0.014	16	93.87	0.000	30	100.58	1.928	44	110.03	0.000
3	78.12	0.000	17	94.13	0.547	31	100.58	1.928	45	110.15	0.000
4	83.15	0.000	18	94.28	0.000	32	100.70	4.321	46	110.26	0.000
5	83.41	0.000	19	95.15	0.000	33	100.84	2.627	47	112.58	0.000
6	83.55	0.019	20	95.15	1.106	34	101.85	0.000	48	115.58	0.072
7	84.31	0.008	21	96.42	0.000	35	101.85	2.894	49	115.58	0.072
8	84.42	0.072	22	98.15	0.000	36	103.58	0.000	50	115.69	0.008
9	84.42	0.072	23	98.15	2.894	37	104.85	0.000	51	116.45	0.019
10	87.42	0.000	24	99.16	2.627	38	104.85	1.106	52	116.59	0.000
11	89.74	0.000	25	99.30	4.321	39	105.72	0.000	53	116.85	0.000
12	89.85	0.000	26	99.42	1.928	40	105.87	0.547	54	121.88	0.000
13	89.97	0.000	27	99.42	1.928	41	106.13	0.000	55	123.15	0.014
14	91.01	0.364	28	99.57	0.000	42	107.41	0.101	56	126.42	0.000

5-117

$J_{AA'}$	J_{AB}	$J_{AB'}$	$J_{BB'}$
9	9	-1	9
9	-1	9	9

The maximum summed intensity is 6.824.

LINE	FREQ	INTEN	LINE	FREQ	INTEN	LINE	FREQ	INTEN	LINE	FREQ	INTEN
1	71.67	0.000	15	91.20	0.000	29	100.63	5.027	43	109.00	0.000
2	79.53	0.000	16	91.50	0.000	30	100.83	1.857	44	109.00	0.000
3	79.84	0.000	17	92.83	0.000	31	100.83	1.857	45	109.00	0.400
4	81.00	0.000	18	93.28	0.000	32	101.00	0.000	46	110.63	0.016
5	81.17	0.000	19	94.81	0.546	33	101.00	3.600	47	110.83	0.143
6	81.67	0.038	20	95.06	0.000	34	102.98	0.000	48	110.83	0.143
7	85.36	0.000	21	95.19	0.988	35	103.11	1.359	49	113.11	0.026
8	86.89	0.026	22	96.89	1.359	36	104.81	0.988	50	114.64	0.000
9	89.17	0.143	23	97.02	0.000	37	104.94	0.000	51	118.33	0.038
10	89.17	0.143	24	99.00	0.000	38	105.19	0.546	52	118.83	0.000
11	89.37	0.016	25	99.00	3.600	39	106.72	0.000	53	119.00	0.000
12	91.00	0.000	26	99.17	1.857	40	107.17	0.000	54	120.16	0.000
13	91.00	0.000	27	99.17	1.857	41	108.50	0.000	55	120.47	0.000
14	91.00	0.400	28	99.37	5.027	42	108.80	0.000	56	128.33	0.000

5-118

$J_{AA'}$	J_{AB}	$J_{AB'}$	$J_{BB'}$
9	9	-2	9
9	-2	9	9

The maximum summed intensity is 8.181.

LINE	FREQ	INTEN	LINE	FREQ	INTEN	LINE	FREQ	INTEN	LINE	FREQ	INTEN
1	71.58	0.001	15	91.89	0.000	29	100.76	1.878	43	108.19	0.000
2	78.92	0.000	16	91.89	0.481	30	100.76	1.878	44	108.55	0.000
3	79.28	0.000	17	92.06	0.000	31	100.84	4.608	45	109.89	0.000
4	80.80	0.033	18	93.76	0.	32	101.11	0.000	46	110.06	0.007
5	80.89	0.000	19	94.70	0.898	33	101.11	3.519	47	111.76	0.122
6	81.24	0.000	20	95.41	0.000	34	102.72	1.543	48	111.76	0.122
7	84.04	0.000	21	96.08	0.874	35	103.43	0.000	49	111.94	0.036
8	88.06	0.036	22	96.57	0.000	36	103.92	0.874	50	115.96	0.000
9	88.24	0.122	23	97.28	1.543	37	104.59	0.000	51	118.76	0.000
10	88.24	0.122	24	98.89	3.519	38	105.30	0.898	52	119.11	0.000
11	89.94	0.007	25	98.89	0.000	39	106.24	0.	53	119.20	0.033
12	90.11	0.000	26	99.16	4.608	40	107.94	0.000	54	120.72	0.000
13	91.45	0.000	27	99.24	1.878	41	108.11	0.481	55	121.08	0.000
14	91.81	0.000	28	99.24	1.878	42	108.11	0.000	56	128.42	0.001

5-119

$J_{AA'}$	J_{AB}	$J_{AB'}$	$J_{BB'}$
9	9	-4	9
9	-4	9	9

The maximum summed intensity is 5.276.

LINE	FREQ	INTEN	LINE	FREQ	INTEN	LINE	FREQ	INTEN	LINE	FREQ	INTEN
1	71.31	0.001	15	92.49	0.000	29	100.66	1.908	43	108.62	0.000
2	77.06	0.000	16	93.59	0.000	30	100.66	1.908	44	109.62	0.008
3	78.13	0.000	17	93.59	0.720	31	101.41	0.000	45	109.90	0.062
4	79.12	0.026	18	94.03	0.754	32	101.41	3.280	46	110.17	0.000
5	80.59	0.000	19	95.66	0.000	33	101.81	2.812	47	111.59	0.000
6	81.34	0.000	20	95.85	0.000	34	101.84	2.405	48	113.66	0.092
7	81.78	0.000	21	96.09	0.000	35	102.09	1.931	49	113.66	0.092
8	86.34	0.092	22	97.91	1.931	36	103.91	0.000	50	118.22	0.000
9	86.34	0.092	23	98.16	2.405	37	104.15	0.000	51	118.66	0.000
10	88.41	0.000	24	98.19	2.812	38	104.34	0.000	52	119.41	0.000
11	89.83	0.000	25	98.59	0.000	39	105.97	0.754	53	120.88	0.026
12	90.10	0.062	26	98.59	3.280	40	106.41	0.000	54	121.87	0.000
13	90.38	0.008	27	99.34	1.908	41	106.41	0.720	55	122.94	0.000
14	91.38	0.000	28	99.34	1.908	42	107.55	0.000	56	128.69	0.001

−11 −10 −9 −8 −7 −6 −5 −4 −3 −2 −1 0 +1 +2 +3 +4 +5 +6 +7 +8 +9 +10 +11

5-120

$J_{AA'}$	J_{AB}	$J_{AB'}$	$J_{BB'}$
9	9	-6	9
9	-6	9	9

The maximum summed intensity is 4.041.

LINE	FREQ	INTEN	LINE	FREQ	INTEN	LINE	FREQ	INTEN	LINE	FREQ	INTEN
1	70.89	0.003	15	91.81	0.000	29	100.58	1.928	43	108.32	0.093
2	75.16	0.000	16	94.19	0.650	30	100.58	1.928	44	108.68	0.000
3	75.65	0.000	17	95.15	0.000	31	100.90	3.728	45	110.62	0.050
4	77.60	0.021	18	95.15	1.106	32	101.61	2.385	46	112.11	0.000
5	80.15	0.000	19	95.96	0.000	33	101.85	0.000	47	113.15	0.000
6	80.47	0.000	20	96.09	1.071	34	101.85	2.894	48	115.58	0.072
7	81.42	0.000	21	96.62	0.000	35	102.42	0.000	49	115.58	0.072
8	84.42	0.072	22	97.58	0.000	36	103.38	0.000	50	118.58	0.000
9	84.42	0.072	23	98.15	0.000	37	103.91	1.071	51	119.53	0.000
10	86.85	0.000	24	98.15	2.894	38	104.04	0.000	52	119.85	0.000
11	87.89	0.000	25	98.39	2.385	39	104.85	0.000	53	122.40	0.021
12	89.38	0.050	26	99.10	3.728	40	104.85	1.106	54	124.35	0.000
13	91.32	0.000	27	99.42	1.928	41	105.81	0.650	55	124.84	0.000
14	91.68	0.093	28	99.42	1.928	42	108.19	0.000	56	129.11	0.003

−11 −10 −9 −8 −7 −6 −5 −4 −3 −2 −1 0 +1 +2 +3 +4 +5 +6 +7 +8 +9 +10 +11

5-121

$J_{AA'}$	J_{AB}	$J_{AB'}$	$J_{BB'}$
9	9	-9	9
9	-9	9	9

The maximum summed intensity is 6.767

LINE	FREQ	INTEN	LINE	FREQ	INTEN	LINE	FREQ	INTEN	LINE	FREQ	INTEN
1	69.77	0.005	15	92.13	0.386	29	100.49	1.949	43	108.74	0.000
2	70.64	0.000	16	92.93	0.123	30	100.49	1.949	44	110.39	0.000
3	72.28	0.000	17	94.58	0.629	31	100.49	0.000	45	113.87	0.032
4	75.77	0.013	18	95.45	0.000	32	100.58	3.486	46	114.42	0.000
5	79.00	0.000	19	97.00	0.000	33	101.07	3.326	47	115.00	0.000
6	79.09	0.000	20	97.00	0.000	34	101.94	0.000	48	118.49	0.051
7	81.51	0.051	21	97.00	2.000	35	103.00	0.000	49	118.49	0.051
8	81.51	0.051	22	97.00	2.000	36	103.00	0.000	50	118.49	0.000
9	81.51	0.000	23	98.06	0.000	37	103.00	2.000	51	120.91	0.000
10	85.00	0.000	24	98.93	3.326	38	103.00	2.000	52	121.00	0.000
11	85.58	0.000	25	99.42	3.486	39	104.55	0.	53	124.23	0.013
12	86.13	0.032	26	99.51	1.949	40	105.42	0.629	54	127.72	0.000
13	89.61	0.000	27	99.51	1.949	41	107.07	0.123	55	129.36	0.000
14	91.26	0.000	28	99.51	0.000	42	107.87	0.386	56	130.23	0.005

5-122

$J_{AA'}$	J_{AB}	$J_{AB'}$	$J_{BB'}$
12	12	-1	12
12	-1	12	12

The maximum summed intensity is 7.210.

LINE	FREQ	INTEN	LINE	FREQ	INTEN	LINE	FREQ	INTEN	LINE	FREQ	INTEN
1	62.99	0.000	15	88.41	0.000	29	100.39	5.497	43	111.76	0.244
2	74.09	0.000	16	88.50	0.000	30	100.66	1.908	44	111.76	0.000
3	74.19	0.	17	89.66	0.000	31	100.66	1.908	45	112.24	0.000
4	75.24	0.000	18	90.41	0.	32	100.76	0.000	46	112.92	0.019
5	75.34	0.	19	92.39	0.236	33	100.76	3.756	47	113.66	0.092
6	75.52	0.021	20	95.08	0.916	34	103.30	1.289	48	113.66	0.092
7	82.19	0.000	21	95.28	0.000	35	103.50	0.000	49	115.83	0.022
8	84.17	0.022	22	96.50	0.000	36	104.72	0.	50	117.81	0.000
9	86.34	0.092	23	96.70	1.289	37	104.92	0.916	51	124.48	0.021
10	86.34	0.092	24	99.24	0.000	38	107.61	0.236	52	124.66	0.
11	87.08	0.019	25	99.24	3.756	39	109.59	0.000	53	124.76	0.000
12	87.76	0.000	26	99.34	1.908	40	110.34	0.000	54	125.81	0.000
13	88.24	0.000	27	99.34	1.908	41	111.50	0.000	55	125.91	0.000
14	88.24	0.244	28	99.61	5.497	42	111.59	0.000	56	137.01	0.000

5-123

$J_{AA'}$	J_{AB}	$J_{AB'}$	$J_{BB'}$
12	12	-2	12
12	-2	12	12

The maximum summed intensity is 7.888.

LINE	FREQ	INTEN	LINE	FREQ	INTEN	LINE	FREQ	INTEN	LINE	FREQ	INTEN
1	62.93	0.000	15	89.17	0.000	29	100.47	5.346	43	110.88	0.000
2	73.15	0.000	16	89.17	0.285	30	100.62	1.919	44	111.62	0.000
3	74.08	0.000	17	89.31	0.000	31	100.62	1.919	45	112.13	0.017
4	74.59	0.019	18	90.62	0.000	32	100.83	0.000	46	113.17	0.000
5	75.17	0.000	19	93.84	0.340	33	100.83	3.715	47	114.57	0.029
6	75.38	0.	20	94.50	0.810	34	102.91	1.439	48	114.62	0.081
7	80.71	0.000	21	95.64	0.000	35	104.06	0.000	49	114.62	0.081
8	85.38	0.081	22	95.94	0.000	36	104.36	0.000	50	119.29	0.000
9	85.38	0.081	23	97.09	1.439	37	105.50	0.810	51	124.62	0.
10	85.43	0.029	24	99.17	0.000	38	106.16	0.340	52	124.83	0.000
11	86.83	0.000	25	99.17	3.715	39	109.38	0.000	53	125.41	0.019
12	87.87	0.017	26	99.38	1.919	40	110.69	0.000	54	125.92	0.000
13	88.38	0.000	27	99.38	1.919	41	110.83	0.000	55	126.85	0.
14	89.12	0.000	28	99.53	5.346	42	110.83	0.285	56	137.07	0.000

−11 −10 −9 −8 −7 −6 −5 −4 −3 −2 −1 0 +1 +2 +3 +4 +5 +6 +7 +8 +9 +10 +11

5-124

$J_{AA'}$	J_{AB}	$J_{AB'}$	$J_{BB'}$
12	12	-4	12
12	-4	12	12

The maximum summed intensity is 6.583.

LINE	FREQ	INTEN	LINE	FREQ	INTEN	LINE	FREQ	INTEN	LINE	FREQ	INTEN
1	62.78	0.000	15	90.72	0.000	29	100.54	1.936	43	110.82	0.003
2	71.24	0.000	16	91.00	0.000	30	100.54	1.936	44	111.68	0.000
3	72.78	0.016	17	91.00	0.400	31	100.82	4.594	45	112.29	0.049
4	73.63	0.000	18	92.54	0.000	32	101.00	0.000	46	113.25	0.000
5	75.00	0.000	19	93.32	0.652	33	101.00	3.600	47	115.00	0.000
6	75.46	0.000	20	94.86	0.000	34	102.29	1.729	48	116.54	0.064
7	77.77	0.000	21	96.17	0.000	35	103.32	0.957	49	116.54	0.064
8	83.46	0.064	22	96.68	0.957	36	103.83	0.000	50	122.23	0.000
9	83.46	0.064	23	97.71	1.729	37	105.14	0.000	51	124.54	0.000
10	85.00	0.000	24	99.00	0.000	38	106.68	0.652	52	125.00	0.000
11	86.75	0.000	25	99.00	3.600	39	107.46	0.000	53	126.37	0.000
12	87.71	0.049	26	99.18	4.594	40	109.00	0.000	54	127.22	0.016
13	88.32	0.000	27	99.46	1.936	41	109.00	0.400	55	128.76	0.000
14	89.18	0.003	28	99.46	1.936	42	109.28	0.000	56	137.22	0.000

−11 −10 −9 −8 −7 −6 −5 −4 −3 −2 −1 0 +1 +2 +3 +4 +5 +6 +7 +8 +9 +10 +11

5-125

$J_{AA'}$	J_{AB}	$J_{AB'}$	$J_{BB'}$
12	12	-6	12
12	-6	12	12

The maximum summed intensity is 6.134.

LINE	FREQ	INTEN	LINE	FREQ	INTEN	LINE	FREQ	INTEN	LINE	FREQ	INTEN
1	62.55	0.001	15	91.20	0.000	29	100.49	1.949	43	110.32	0.076
2	69.31	0.000	16	92.76	0.000	30	100.49	1.949	44	110.53	0.027
3	71.04	0.013	17	92.76	0.527	31	101.24	0.000	45	111.72	0.000
4	72.23	0.000	18	92.76	0.586	32	101.24	3.073	46	115.41	0.000
5	74.76	0.000	19	94.49	0.000	33	101.24	3.414	47	116.76	0.000
6	75.51	0.000	20	94.49	0.000	34	101.84	2.018	48	118.49	0.051
7	75.51	0.000	21	96.43	0.000	35	102.04	2.265	49	118.49	0.051
8	81.51	0.051	22	97.96	2.265	36	103.57	0.000	50	124.49	0.000
9	81.51	0.051	23	98.16	2.018	37	105.51	0.000	51	124.49	0.000
10	83.24	0.000	24	98.76	3.073	38	105.51	0.000	52	125.24	0.000
11	84.59	0.000	25	98.76	0.000	39	107.24	0.527	53	127.77	0.000
12	88.28	0.000	26	98.76	3.414	40	107.24	0.000	54	128.96	0.013
13	89.47	0.027	27	99.51	1.949	41	107.24	0.586	55	130.69	0.000
14	89.68	0.076	28	99.51	1.949	42	108.80	0.000	56	137.45	0.001

−11 −10 −9 −8 −7 −6 −5 −4 −3 −2 −1 0 +1 +2 +3 +4 +5 +6 +7 +8 +9 +10 +11

5-126

$J_{AA'}$	J_{AB}	$J_{AB'}$	$J_{BB'}$
12	12	-9	12
12	-9	12	12

The maximum summed intensity is 8.188.

LINE	FREQ	INTEN	LINE	FREQ	INTEN	LINE	FREQ	INTEN	LINE	FREQ	INTEN
1	61.96	0.002	15	91.94	0.122	29	100.40	4.314	43	110.52	0.000
2	66.39	0.000	16	93.69	0.461	30	100.42	1.962	44	111.76	0.000
3	67.64	0.000	17	93.92	0.456	31	100.42	1.962	45	112.79	0.069
4	68.67	0.010	18	95.15	0.000	32	101.35	2.566	46	118.21	0.000
5	74.13	0.000	19	95.15	1.106	33	101.85	0.000	47	119.15	0.000
6	74.15	0.000	20	95.97	0.000	34	101.85	2.894	48	121.42	0.038
7	75.58	0.000	21	96.37	0.000	35	102.58	0.000	49	121.42	0.038
8	78.58	0.038	22	97.42	0.000	36	103.63	0.000	50	124.42	0.000
9	78.58	0.038	23	98.15	0.000	37	104.03	0.000	51	125.85	0.000
10	80.85	0.000	24	98.15	2.894	38	104.85	0.000	52	125.87	0.000
11	81.79	0.000	25	98.65	2.566	39	104.85	1.106	53	131.33	0.010
12	87.21	0.069	26	99.58	1.962	40	106.08	0.456	54	132.36	0.000
13	88.24	0.000	27	99.58	1.962	41	106.31	0.461	55	133.61	0.000
14	89.48	0.000	28	99.60	4.314	42	108.06	0.122	56	138.04	0.002

−11 −10 −9 −8 −7 −6 −5 −4 −3 −2 −1 0 +1 +2 +3 +4 +5 +6 +7 +8 +9 +10 +11

5-127

$J_{AA'}$	J_{AB}	$J_{AB'}$	$J_{BB'}$
12	12	-12	12
12	-12	12	12

The maximum summed intensity is 7.018

LINE	FREQ	INTEN	LINE	FREQ	INTEN	LINE	FREQ	INTEN	LINE	FREQ	INTEN
1	60.83	0.003	15	89.55	0.217	29	100.31	3.637	43	111.80	0.000
2	62.18	0.000	16	93.03	0.143	30	100.37	1.970	44	113.08	0.000
3	63.46	0.000	17	94.31	0.529	31	100.37	1.970	45	116.45	0.032
4	66.83	0.006	18	95.66	0.000	32	100.37	0.000	46	120.40	0.000
5	72.94	0.000	19	97.00	0.000	33	100.97	3.433	47	121.00	0.000
6	73.00	0.000	20	97.00	0.000	34	102.32	0.000	48	124.37	0.030
7	75.63	0.030	21	97.00	2.000	35	103.00	0.000	49	124.37	0.000
8	75.63	0.000	22	97.00	2.000	36	103.00	0.000	50	124.37	0.030
9	75.63	0.030	23	97.68	0.000	37	103.00	2.000	51	127.00	0.000
10	79.00	0.000	24	99.03	3.433	38	103.00	2.000	52	127.06	0.000
11	79.60	0.000	25	99.63	1.970	39	104.34	0.000	53	133.17	0.006
12	83.55	0.032	26	99.63	1.970	40	105.69	0.529	54	136.54	0.000
13	86.92	0.000	27	99.63	0.000	41	106.97	0.143	55	137.82	0.000
14	88.20	0.000	28	99.69	3.637	42	110.45	0.217	56	139.17	0.003

5-128

$J_{AA'}$	J_{AB}	$J_{AB'}$	$J_{BB'}$
1	-1	1	-1
1	1	-1	-1
-1	-1	1	1
-1	1	-1	1

The maximum summed intensity is 6.134

LINE	FREQ	INTEN	LINE	FREQ	INTEN	LINE	FREQ	INTEN	LINE	FREQ	INTEN
1	89.71	0.000	15	96.83	1.838	29	100.82	0.684	43	103.21	0.000
2	90.83	0.000	16	96.83	1.838	30	101.26	0.000	44	103.65	1.316
3	90.83	0.000	17	96.85	0.000	31	101.59	0.000	45	103.93	0.000
4	91.60	0.000	18	97.00	2.000	32	101.59	0.000	46	103.97	0.739
5	94.46	0.143	19	97.00	2.000	33	102.03	1.422	47	103.97	0.739
6	94.90	0.000	20	97.29	1.857	34	102.03	1.422	48	104.12	0.000
7	95.59	0.000	21	97.76	0.000	35	102.05	0.000	49	104.41	0.000
8	95.59	0.000	22	97.95	0.000	36	102.24	0.000	50	104.41	0.000
9	95.88	0.000	23	97.97	1.422	37	102.71	1.857	51	105.10	0.000
10	96.03	0.739	24	97.97	1.422	38	103.00	2.000	52	105.54	0.143
11	96.03	0.739	25	98.41	0.000	39	103.00	2.000	53	108.40	0.000
12	96.07	0.000	26	98.41	0.000	40	103.15	0.000	54	109.17	0.000
13	96.35	1.316	27	98.74	0.000	41	103.17	1.838	55	109.17	0.000
14	96.79	0.000	28	99.18	0.684	42	103.17	1.838	56	110.29	0.000

5-129

$J_{AA'}$	J_{AB}	$J_{AB'}$	$J_{BB'}$
1	-2	1	-2
1	1	-2	-2
-2	-2	1	1
-2	1	-2	1

The maximum summed intensity is 4.540.

LINE	FREQ	INTEN	LINE	FREQ	INTEN	LINE	FREQ	INTEN	LINE	FREQ	INTEN
1	88.91	0.000	15	96.46	1.671	29	100.00	1.000	43	103.97	1.361
2	89.95	0.001	16	96.48	0.000	30	100.42	0.000	44	104.10	0.928
3	91.12	0.001	17	96.65	0.000	31	100.73	0.000	45	104.22	0.000
4	91.37	0.000	18	96.88	0.	32	101.12	0.	46	104.24	1.000
5	93.14	0.106	19	97.20	2.035	33	101.15	1.381	47	104.66	0.000
6	93.69	0.000	20	97.38	1.894	34	101.42	0.000	48	104.94	0.389
7	94.34	0.000	21	97.46	2.329	35	101.77	0.000	49	105.66	0.000
8	95.06	0.389	22	98.02	1.903	36	101.98	1.903	50	105.74	0.000
9	95.34	0.000	23	98.40	0.000	37	102.54	2.329	51	106.14	0.000
10	95.61	0.000	24	98.58	0.000	38	102.62	1.894	52	106.86	0.106
11	95.76	1.000	25	98.85	1.381	39	102.80	2.035	53	108.46	0.000
12	95.90	0.928	26	99.44	0.000	40	103.18	0.000	54	108.88	0.001
13	96.03	1.361	27	99.58	0.000	41	103.54	1.671	55	110.05	0.001
14	96.26	0.000	28	100.00	1.000	42	103.68	0.000	56	111.25	0.000

−11 −10 −9 −8 −7 −6 −5 −4 −3 −2 −1 0 +1 +2 +3 +4 +5 +6 +7 +8 +9 +10 +11

5-130

$J_{AA'}$	J_{AB}	$J_{AB'}$	$J_{BB'}$
1	-4	1	-4
1	1	-4	-4
-4	-4	1	1
-4	1	-4	1

The maximum summed intensity is 5.763.

LINE	FREQ	INTEN	LINE	FREQ	INTEN	LINE	FREQ	INTEN	LINE	FREQ	INTEN
1	87.03	0.000	15	95.23	0.858	29	100.06	1.585	43	104.85	1.106
2	87.22	0.002	16	95.54	0.000	30	100.37	0.000	44	105.39	0.000
3	89.52	0.000	17	95.87	0.000	31	100.64	0.000	45	105.46	0.000
4	90.42	0.064	18	96.96	0.000	32	100.99	1.555	46	106.08	0.661
5	91.04	0.000	19	97.49	1.936	33	101.32	0.000	47	106.09	0.445
6	91.22	0.002	20	97.93	2.596	34	101.68	0.000	48	106.77	0.187
7	91.61	0.000	21	98.06	2.109	35	101.85	2.894	49	107.95	0.000
8	93.23	0.187	22	98.15	2.894	36	101.89	0.000	50	108.39	0.000
9	93.91	0.445	23	98.32	0.000	37	101.94	2.109	51	108.78	0.002
10	93.92	0.661	24	98.68	0.000	38	102.07	2.596	52	109.04	0.000
11	94.45	0.	25	99.01	1.555	39	102.51	1.936	53	109.48	0.
12	94.61	0.000	26	99.12	0.000	40	103.13	0.000	54	109.58	0.064
13	94.62	0.000	27	99.55	0.000	41	104.38	0.000	55	112.78	0.002
14	95.15	1.106	28	99.94	1.585	42	104.77	0.858	56	113.97	0.000

−11 −10 −9 −8 −7 −6 −5 −4 −3 −2 −1 0 +1 +2 +3 +4 +5 +6 +7 +8 +9 +10 +11

5-131

$J_{AA'}$	J_{AB}	$J_{AB'}$	$J_{BB'}$
1	-6	1	-6
1	1	-6	-6
-6	-6	1	1
-6	1	-6	1

The maximum summed intensity is 8.445.

LINE	FREQ	INTEN	LINE	FREQ	INTEN	LINE	FREQ	INTEN	LINE	FREQ	INTEN
1	83.59	0.001	15	94.38	0.699	29	100.62	1.685	43	106.35	0.000
2	84.80	0.000	16	94.44	0.000	30	100.68	0.000	44	106.41	0.720
3	86.46	0.000	17	94.64	0.000	31	101.41	3.280	45	107.75	0.000
4	87.67	0.042	18	96.46	0.000	32	101.41	3.440	46	108.43	0.128
5	88.41	0.000	19	97.57	1.958	33	101.41	1.800	47	108.49	0.200
6	88.65	0.000	20	97.62	0.000	34	101.46	0.000	48	108.60	0.336
7	90.78	0.000	21	97.81	1.711	35	101.51	0.000	49	109.22	0.000
8	91.40	0.336	22	98.54	0.000	36	102.19	1.711	50	109.40	0.000
9	91.46	0.000	23	98.54	0.000	37	102.43	1.958	51	111.35	0.000
10	91.51	0.200	24	98.59	1.800	38	102.62	0.000	52	111.35	0.000
11	91.57	0.128	25	98.59	3.440	39	103.17	0.000	53	112.33	0.042
12	93.53	0.000	26	98.59	3.280	40	103.54	0.000	54	112.38	0.000
13	93.59	0.720	27	99.38	1.685	41	104.28	0.	55	116.41	0.001
14	93.65	0.000	28	99.57	0.000	42	105.62	0.699	56	117.39	0.000

5-132

$J_{AA'}$	J_{AB}	$J_{AB'}$	$J_{BB'}$
1	-9	1	-9
1	1	-9	-9
-9	-9	1	1
-9	1	-9	1

The maximum summed intensity is 6.716.

LINE	FREQ	INTEN	LINE	FREQ	INTEN	LINE	FREQ	INTEN	LINE	FREQ	INTEN
1	77.37	0.000	15	92.48	0.000	29	100.41	0.000	43	108.07	0.000
2	80.82	0.000	16	92.70	0.000	30	100.75	4.712	44	109.00	0.400
3	80.99	0.000	17	93.21	0.510	31	100.92	1.729	45	110.75	0.007
4	83.49	0.026	18	93.93	0.000	32	101.00	3.600	46	110.92	0.088
5	83.93	0.000	19	96.79	0.799	33	101.69	1.919	47	111.18	0.000
6	84.77	0.000	20	97.39	0.000	34	101.93	0.000	48	111.35	0.000
7	86.61	0.	21	97.64	1.974	35	102.36	1.974	49	112.46	0.081
8	87.37	0.154	22	98.07	0.000	36	103.21	0.799	50	112.63	0.154
9	87.54	0.081	23	98.31	1.919	37	103.47	0.000	51	115.14	0.000
10	89.08	0.088	24	98.57	0.000	38	103.64	0.000	52	116.07	0.000
11	89.25	0.007	25	99.00	3.600	39	104.19	0.000	53	116.51	0.026
12	91.00	0.400	26	99.08	1.729	40	104.36	0.000	54	117.43	0.000
13	91.76	0.000	27	99.25	4.712	41	106.07	0.000	55	122.63	0.000
14	91.93	0.000	28	99.68	0.000	42	106.79	0.510	56	123.06	0.000

5-133

$J_{AA'}$	J_{AB}	$J_{AB'}$	$J_{BB'}$
2	-1	2	-1
2	2	-1	-1
-1	-1	2	2
-1	2	-1	2

The maximum summed intensity is 4.540.

LINE	FREQ	INTEN	LINE	FREQ	INTEN	LINE	FREQ	INTEN	LINE	FREQ	INTEN
1	88.75	0.000	15	96.32	0.000	29	100.00	1.000	43	103.74	0.000
2	89.95	0.001	16	96.46	1.671	30	100.42	0.000	44	103.97	1.361
3	91.12	0.001	17	96.82	0.000	31	100.56	0.000	45	104.10	0.928
4	91.54	0.000	18	97.20	2.035	32	101.15	1.381	46	104.24	1.000
5	93.14	0.106	19	97.38	1.894	33	101.42	0.000	47	104.39	0.000
6	93.86	0.000	20	97.46	2.329	34	101.60	0.000	48	104.66	0.000
7	94.26	0.000	21	98.02	1.903	35	101.98	1.903	49	104.94	0.389
8	94.34	0.000	22	98.23	0.000	36	102.54	2.329	50	105.66	0.000
9	95.06	0.389	23	98.58	0.000	37	102.62	1.894	51	106.31	0.000
10	95.34	0.000	24	98.85	1.381	38	102.80	2.035	52	106.86	0.106
11	95.76	1.000	25	98.88	0.	39	103.12	0.	53	108.63	0.000
12	95.78	0.000	26	99.27	0.000	40	103.35	0.000	54	108.88	0.001
13	95.90	0.928	27	99.58	0.000	41	103.52	0.000	55	110.05	0.001
14	96.03	1.361	28	100.00	1.000	42	103.54	1.671	56	111.09	0.000

-11 -10 -9 -8 -7 -6 -5 -4 -3 -2 -1 0 +1 +2 +3 +4 +5 +6 +7 +8 +9 +10 +11

5-134

$J_{AA'}$	J_{AB}	$J_{AB'}$	$J_{BB'}$
2	-2	2	-2
2	2	-2	-2
-2	-2	2	2
-2	2	-2	2

The maximum summed intensity is 4.005

LINE	FREQ	INTEN	LINE	FREQ	INTEN	LINE	FREQ	INTEN	LINE	FREQ	INTEN
1	87.92	0.000	15	96.31	1.418	29	100.17	0.000	43	104.03	0.000
2	90.31	0.004	16	96.31	1.418	30	100.17	0.000	44	104.46	0.000
3	90.31	0.004	17	96.41	0.000	31	100.44	0.000	45	104.79	0.582
4	91.07	0.000	18	97.00	2.000	32	100.59	1.316	46	104.79	0.582
5	91.79	0.081	19	97.00	2.000	33	101.21	1.996	47	105.06	0.684
6	92.82	0.000	20	97.44	1.919	34	101.21	1.996	48	105.39	0.000
7	94.17	0.000	21	97.76	0.000	35	101.31	0.000	49	105.83	0.000
8	94.17	0.000	22	98.69	0.000	36	102.24	0.000	50	105.83	0.000
9	94.61	0.000	23	98.79	1.996	37	102.56	1.919	51	107.18	0.000
10	94.94	0.684	24	98.79	1.996	38	103.00	2.000	52	108.21	0.081
11	95.21	0.582	25	99.41	1.316	39	103.00	2.000	53	108.93	0.000
12	95.21	0.582	26	99.56	0.000	40	103.59	0.000	54	109.69	0.004
13	95.54	0.000	27	99.83	0.000	41	103.69	1.418	55	109.69	0.004
14	95.97	0.000	28	99.83	0.000	42	103.69	1.418	56	112.08	0.000

-11 -10 -9 -8 -7 -6 -5 -4 -3 -2 -1 0 +1 +2 +3 +4 +5 +6 +7 +8 +9 +10 +11

5-135

$J_{AA'}$	J_{AB}	$J_{AB'}$	$J_{BB'}$
2	-4	2	-4
2	2	-4	-4
-4	-4	2	2
-4	2	-4	2

The maximum summed intensity is 4.125.

LINE	FREQ	INTEN	LINE	FREQ	INTEN	LINE	FREQ	INTEN	LINE	FREQ	INTEN
1	86.09	0.000	15	95.00	0.000	29	100.08	0.000	43	105.17	0.657
2	87.65	0.005	16	95.29	0.	30	100.13	2.065	44	106.01	0.000
3	88.82	0.000	17	95.32	0.000	31	100.97	0.	45	106.02	0.631
4	89.05	0.051	18	95.84	1.368	32	101.00	0.000	46	106.19	0.284
5	90.28	0.000	19	96.96	1.628	33	101.15	2.715	47	106.40	0.000
6	90.64	0.013	20	97.53	1.949	34	101.24	1.707	48	107.24	0.293
7	91.60	0.000	21	97.84	2.632	35	101.48	0.000	49	108.40	0.000
8	92.76	0.293	22	97.92	0.000	36	102.08	0.000	50	108.71	0.000
9	93.60	0.000	23	98.76	1.707	37	102.16	2.632	51	108.74	0.000
10	93.81	0.284	24	98.85	2.715	38	102.47	1.949	52	109.36	0.013
11	93.98	0.631	25	99.51	0.000	39	103.04	1.628	53	110.20	0.000
12	94.82	0.000	26	99.87	2.065	40	103.70	0.000	54	110.95	0.051
13	94.83	0.657	27	99.92	0.000	41	104.16	1.368	55	112.35	0.005
14	94.97	0.000	28	100.0[illegible]	0.000	42	104.20	0.000	56	114.89	0.000

5-136

$J_{AA'}$	J_{AB}	$J_{AB'}$	$J_{BB'}$
2	-6	2	-6
2	2	-6	-6
-6	-6	2	2
-6	2	-6	2

The maximum summed intensity is 4.739.

LINE	FREQ	INTEN	LINE	FREQ	INTEN	LINE	FREQ	INTEN	LINE	FREQ	INTEN
1	84.06	0.000	15	93.94	0.000	29	100.18	0.000	43	106.04	0.563
2	84.08	0.003	16	93.96	0.563	30	100.31	0.000	44	107.26	0.000
3	85.57	0.000	17	94.39	0.891	31	100.39	1.999	45	107.61	0.183
4	86.28	0.035	18	95.94	0.000	32	101.17	2.829	46	108.56	0.000
5	87.51	0.000	19	95.95	0.000	33	101.53	1.857	47	108.70	0.315
6	88.74	0.000	20	97.59	1.965	34	101.61	3.109	48	109.48	0.014
7	90.22	0.143	21	97.73	2.094	35	102.12	0.000	49	109.78	0.143
8	90.52	0.014	22	98.39	3.109	36	102.25	0.000	50	110.06	0.000
9	91.30	0.315	23	98.47	1.857	37	102.27	2.094	51	111.26	0.000
10	91.88	0.000	24	98.83	2.829	38	102.41	1.965	52	112.00	0.000
11	92.39	0.183	25	99.61	1.999	39	103.63	0.000	53	112.06	0.000
12	92.74	0.000	26	99.95	0.000	40	103.75	0.000	54	113.72	0.035
13	93.81	0.000	27	100.05	0.000	41	104.05	0.000	55	115.92	0.003
14	93.88	0.000	28	100.12	0.000	42	105.61	0.891	56	118.37	0.000

5-137

$J_{AA'}$	J_{AB}	$J_{AB'}$	$J_{BB'}$
2	-9	2	-9
2	2	-9	-9
-9	-9	2	2
-9	2	-9	2

The maximum summed intensity is 6.321.

LINE	FREQ	INTEN	LINE	FREQ	INTEN	LINE	FREQ	INTEN	LINE	FREQ	INTEN
1	77.93	0.001	15	92.08	0.000	29	100.41	0.000	43	108.11	0.481
2	79.99	0.000	16	92.14	0.000	30	100.71	1.908	44	108.89	0.000
3	80.55	0.000	17	92.43	0.426	31	100.80	0.000	45	109.93	0.117
4	82.10	0.022	18	93.33	0.000	32	101.11	3.519	46	110.44	0.001
5	83.42	0.000	19	96.88	0.000	33	101.22	3.522	47	111.94	0.000
6	84.11	0.000	20	97.65	1.978	34	101.65	1.878	48	112.50	0.000
7	86.18	0.064	21	98.26	1.936	35	101.74	1.936	49	112.85	0.146
8	86.96	0.000	22	98.35	1.878	36	102.35	1.978	50	113.82	0.064
9	87.15	0.146	23	98.78	3.522	37	103.29	0.000	51	115.37	0.000
10	89.56	0.001	24	98.89	3.519	38	103.67	0.000	52	115.89	0.000
11	90.07	0.117	25	99.04	0.000	39	103.84	0.000	53	117.12	0.000
12	91.11	0.000	26	99.29	1.908	40	104.22	0.000	54	117.90	0.022
13	91.70	0.000	27	99.67	0.000	41	106.67	0.000	55	122.07	0.001
14	91.89	0.481	28	100.33	0.000	42	107.57	0.426	56	124.09	0.

−11 −10 −9 −8 −7 −6 −5 −4 −3 −2 −1 0 +1 +2 +3 +4 +5 +6 +7 +8 +9 +10 +11

5-138

$J_{AA'}$	J_{AB}	$J_{AB'}$	$J_{BB'}$
4	-1	4	-1
4	4	-1	-1
-1	-1	4	4
-1	4	-1	4

The maximum summed intensity is 5.763.

LINE	FREQ	INTEN	LINE	FREQ	INTEN	LINE	FREQ	INTEN	LINE	FREQ	INTEN
1	86.03	0.000	15	95.23	0.858	29	100.06	1.585	43	104.85	1.106
2	87.22	0.002	16	95.62	0.000	30	100.45	0.000	44	105.38	0.000
3	90.42	0.064	17	96.87	0.000	31	100.88	0.000	45	105.39	0.000
4	90.52	0.000	18	97.49	1.936	32	100.99	1.555	46	105.55	0.
5	90.96	0.000	19	97.93	2.596	33	101.32	0.000	47	106.08	0.661
6	91.22	0.002	20	98.06	2.109	34	101.68	0.000	48	106.09	0.445
7	91.61	0.000	21	98.11	0.000	35	101.85	2.894	49	106.77	0.187
8	92.05	0.000	22	98.15	2.894	36	101.94	2.109	50	108.39	0.000
9	93.23	0.187	23	98.32	0.000	37	102.07	2.596	51	108.78	0.002
10	93.91	0.445	24	98.68	0.000	38	102.51	1.936	52	108.96	0.000
11	93.92	0.661	25	99.01	1.555	39	103.04	0.000	53	109.58	0.064
12	94.54	0.000	26	99.36	0.000	40	104.13	0.000	54	110.48	0.000
13	94.61	0.000	27	99.63	0.000	41	104.46	0.000	55	112.78	0.002
14	95.15	1.106	28	99.94	1.585	42	104.77	0.858	56	112.97	0.000

−11 −10 −9 −8 −7 −6 −5 −4 −3 −2 −1 0 +1 +2 +3 +4 +5 +6 +7 +8 +9 +10 +11

5-139

$J_{AA'}$	J_{AB}	$J_{AB'}$	$J_{BB'}$
4	-2	4	-2
4	4	-2	-2
-2	-2	4	4
-2	4	-2	4

The maximum summed intensity is 4.124.

LINE	FREQ	INTEN	LINE	FREQ	INTEN	LINE	FREQ	INTEN	LINE	FREQ	INTEN
1	85.11	0.000	15	95.80	0.000	29	99.99	0.000	43	105.03	0.000
2	87.65	0.005	16	95.84	1.368	30	100.08	0.000	44	105.17	0.657
3	89.05	0.051	17	96.30	0.000	31	100.13	2.065	45	105.18	0.000
4	89.80	0.000	18	96.96	1.628	32	100.49	0.000	46	106.02	0.631
5	90.64	0.013	19	97.53	1.949	33	101.15	2.715	47	106.19	0.284
6	91.26	0.000	20	97.84	2.632	34	101.24	1.707	48	106.40	0.000
7	91.29	0.000	21	97.92	0.000	35	102.08	0.000	49	107.24	0.293
8	91.60	0.000	22	98.52	0.000	36	102.16	2.632	50	108.40	0.000
9	92.76	0.293	23	98.76	1.707	37	102.47	1.949	51	109.36	0.013
10	93.60	0.000	24	98.85	2.715	38	103.04	1.628	52	109.72	0.000
11	93.81	0.284	25	99.00	0.000	39	104.16	1.368	53	110.95	0.051
12	93.98	0.631	26	99.03	0.000	40	104.68	0.000	54	111.18	0.000
13	93.99	0.000	27	99.87	2.065	41	104.71	0.000	55	112.35	0.005
14	94.83	0.657	28	99.92	0.000	42	105.00	0.000	56	113.91	0.000

5-140

$J_{AA'}$	J_{AB}	$J_{AB'}$	$J_{BB'}$
4	-4	4	-4
4	4	-4	-4
-4	-4	4	4
-4	4	-4	4

The maximum summed intensity is 5.606

LINE	FREQ	INTEN	LINE	FREQ	INTEN	LINE	FREQ	INTEN	LINE	FREQ	INTEN
1	83.19	0.000	15	94.26	0.587	29	100.26	2.980	43	105.74	0.413
2	86.28	0.035	16	94.68	0.000	30	100.26	2.980	44	105.74	0.413
3	87.13	0.000	17	95.38	0.000	31	100.68	0.000	45	105.74	0.587
4	88.26	0.020	18	95.88	0.000	32	101.38	0.000	46	106.87	0.000
5	88.26	0.020	19	97.00	2.000	33	101.53	1.857	47	108.06	0.000
6	89.19	0.000	20	97.00	2.000	34	102.41	1.965	48	108.66	0.000
7	90.22	0.143	21	97.34	0.000	35	102.66	0.000	49	108.66	0.000
8	91.34	0.000	22	97.34	0.000	36	102.66	0.000	50	109.78	0.143
9	91.34	0.000	23	97.59	1.965	37	103.00	2.000	51	110.81	0.000
10	91.94	0.000	24	98.47	1.857	38	103.00	2.000	52	111.74	0.020
11	93.13	0.000	25	98.62	0.000	39	104.12	0.000	53	111.74	0.020
12	94.26	0.413	26	99.32	0.000	40	104.62	0.000	54	112.87	0.000
13	94.26	0.587	27	99.74	2.980	41	105.32	0.000	55	113.72	0.035
14	94.26	0.413	28	99.74	2.980	42	105.74	0.587	56	116.81	0.000

5-141

$J_{AA'}$	J_{AB}	$J_{AB'}$	$J_{BB'}$
4	-6	4	-6
4	4	-6	-6
-6	-6	4	4
-6	4	-6	4

The maximum summed intensity is 6.194.

LINE	FREQ	INTEN	LINE	FREQ	INTEN	LINE	FREQ	INTEN	LINE	FREQ	INTEN
1	81.21	0.000	15	93.50	0.293	29	100.17	2.650	43	106.08	0.398
2	83.49	0.026	16	93.92	0.398	30	100.24	3.758	44	106.50	0.293
3	83.67	0.000	17	94.44	0.000	31	101.51	0.000	45	108.78	0.278
4	84.90	0.010	18	94.81	0.571	32	101.69	1.919	46	109.23	0.000
5	86.64	0.000	19	95.09	0.000	33	102.16	2.632	47	109.31	0.000
6	87.54	0.081	20	95.84	1.368	34	102.36	1.974	48	111.23	0.000
7	88.48	0.041	21	97.09	0.000	35	102.91	0.000	49	111.43	0.000
8	88.77	0.000	22	97.64	1.974	36	103.05	0.000	50	111.52	0.041
9	90.77	0.000	23	97.84	2.632	37	103.39	0.000	51	111.77	0.000
10	91.22	0.278	24	98.31	1.919	38	103.97	0.000	52	112.46	0.081
11	92.28	0.000	25	98.54	0.000	39	104.16	1.368	53	114.74	0.000
12	92.57	0.000	26	99.76	3.758	40	104.91	0.000	54	115.10	0.010
13	92.61	0.000	27	99.83	2.650	41	105.19	0.571	55	116.51	0.026
14	92.90	0.000	28	100.08	0.000	42	105.51	0.000	56	120.38	0.000

5-142

$J_{AA'}$	J_{AB}	$J_{AB'}$	$J_{BB'}$
4	-9	4	-9
4	4	-9	-9
-9	-9	4	4
-9	4	-9	4

The maximum summed intensity is 4.816.

LINE	FREQ	INTEN	LINE	FREQ	INTEN	LINE	FREQ	INTEN	LINE	FREQ	INTEN
1	77.97	0.000	15	92.21	0.000	29	100.46	2.253	43	107.79	0.000
2	78.15	0.000	16	92.42	0.276	30	101.17	0.000	44	108.27	0.186
3	78.95	0.003	17	92.74	0.000	31	101.41	3.280	45	110.60	0.000
4	79.30	0.017	18	93.49	0.000	32	101.81	1.958	46	111.74	0.059
5	82.31	0.000	19	93.59	0.720	33	102.32	1.983	47	113.24	0.132
6	83.43	0.042	20	96.07	0.666	34	102.38	0.000	48	113.38	0.000
7	84.40	0.000	21	97.21	0.000	35	102.79	0.000	49	113.56	0.000
8	86.76	0.132	22	97.68	1.983	36	102.96	0.000	50	115.60	0.000
9	87.62	0.000	23	98.19	1.958	37	103.13	0.000	51	116.51	0.000
10	88.26	0.059	24	98.59	3.280	38	103.93	0.666	52	116.97	0.042
11	89.40	0.000	25	98.79	0.000	39	105.34	0.000	53	117.72	0.000
12	90.36	0.000	26	99.54	2.253	40	105.51	0.000	54	120.70	0.017
13	90.75	0.000	27	99.77	4.426	41	106.41	0.720	55	121.05	0.003
14	91.73	0.186	28	100.23	4.426	42	107.58	0.276	56	126.16	0.000

5-143

$J_{AA'}$	J_{AB}	$J_{AB'}$	$J_{BB'}$
6	-1	6	-1
6	6	-1	-1
-1	-1	6	6
-1	6	-1	6

The maximum summed intensity is 8.494.

LINE	FREQ	INTEN	LINE	FREQ	INTEN	LINE	FREQ	INTEN	LINE	FREQ	INTEN
1	82.61	0.000	15	94.38	0.699	29	100.43	0.000	43	106.35	0.000
2	83.59	0.001	16	95.72	0.000	30	100.62	1.685	44	106.41	0.720
3	87.62	0.000	17	96.46	0.000	31	101.41	3.280	45	106.47	0.000
4	87.67	0.042	18	96.83	0.000	32	101.41	3.440	46	108.43	0.128
5	88.65	0.000	19	97.38	0.000	33	101.41	1.800	47	108.49	0.200
6	88.65	0.000	20	97.57	1.958	34	101.46	0.000	48	108.54	0.000
7	90.60	0.000	21	97.81	1.711	35	101.46	0.000	49	108.60	0.336
8	90.78	0.000	22	98.49	0.000	36	102.19	1.711	50	109.22	0.000
9	91.40	0.336	23	98.54	0.000	37	102.38	0.000	51	111.35	0.000
10	91.51	0.200	24	98.59	1.800	38	102.43	1.958	52	111.59	0.000
11	91.57	0.128	25	98.59	3.440	39	103.54	0.000	53	112.33	0.042
12	92.25	0.000	26	98.59	3.280	40	105.36	0.000	54	113.54	0.000
13	93.59	0.720	27	99.32	0.000	41	105.56	0.000	55	115.20	0.000
14	93.65	0.000	28	99.38	1.685	42	105.62	0.699	56	116.41	0.001

5-144

$J_{AA'}$	J_{AB}	$J_{AB'}$	$J_{BB'}$
6	-2	6	-2
6	6	-2	-2
-2	-2	6	6
-2	6	-2	6

The maximum summed intensity is 4.739.

LINE	FREQ	INTEN	LINE	FREQ	INTEN	LINE	FREQ	INTEN	LINE	FREQ	INTEN
1	81.63	0.000	15	94.39	0.891	29	99.88	0.000	43	106.12	0.000
2	84.08	0.003	16	95.95	0.000	30	99.95	0.000	44	106.19	0.000
3	86.28	0.035	17	96.25	0.000	31	100.05	0.000	45	107.26	0.000
4	87.94	0.000	18	96.37	0.000	32	100.39	1.999	46	107.61	0.183
5	88.00	0.000	19	97.59	1.965	33	101.17	2.829	47	108.12	0.000
6	88.74	0.000	20	97.73	2.094	34	101.53	1.857	48	108.70	0.315
7	89.94	0.000	21	97.75	0.000	35	101.61	3.109	49	109.48	0.014
8	90.22	0.143	22	97.88	0.000	36	102.27	2.094	50	109.78	0.143
9	90.52	0.014	23	98.39	3.109	37	102.41	1.965	51	111.26	0.000
10	91.30	0.315	24	98.47	1.857	38	104.05	0.000	52	112.49	0.000
11	91.44	0.000	25	98.83	2.829	39	104.06	0.000	53	113.72	0.035
12	92.39	0.183	26	99.61	1.999	40	105.61	0.891	54	114.43	0.000
13	92.74	0.000	27	99.69	0.000	41	106.04	0.563	55	115.92	0.003
14	93.96	0.563	28	99.82	0.000	42	106.06	0.000	56	115.94	0.000

5-145

$J_{AA'}$	J_{AB}	$J_{AB'}$	$J_{BB'}$
6	-4	6	-4
6	6	-4	-4
-4	-4	6	6
-4	6	-4	6

The maximum summed intensity is 6.144

LINE	FREQ	INTEN	LINE	FREQ	INTEN	LINE	FREQ	INTEN	LINE	FREQ	INTEN
1	79.62	0.000	15	94.49	0.000	29	99.92	0.000	43	107.10	0.000
2	83.49	0.026	16	94.81	0.571	30	100.17	2.650	44	107.39	0.000
3	84.90	0.010	17	95.09	0.000	31	100.24	3.758	45	107.43	0.000
4	85.26	0.000	18	95.84	1.368	32	101.46	0.000	46	107.72	0.000
5	87.54	0.081	19	96.03	0.000	33	101.69	1.919	47	108.78	0.278
6	88.23	0.000	20	96.61	0.000	34	102.16	2.632	48	109.23	0.000
7	88.48	0.041	21	96.95	0.000	35	102.36	1.974	49	111.23	0.000
8	88.57	0.000	22	97.09	0.000	36	102.91	0.000	50	111.52	0.041
9	88.77	0.000	23	97.64	1.974	37	104.16	1.368	51	112.46	0.081
10	90.69	0.000	24	97.84	2.632	38	104.91	0.000	52	113.35	0.000
11	90.77	0.000	25	98.31	1.919	39	105.19	0.571	53	115.10	0.010
12	91.22	0.278	26	98.49	0.000	40	105.56	0.000	54	116.33	0.000
13	93.50	0.293	27	99.76	3.758	41	106.08	0.398	55	116.51	0.026
14	93.92	0.398	28	99.83	2.650	42	106.50	0.293	56	118.79	0.000

−11 −10 −9 −8 −7 −6 −5 −4 −3 −2 −1 0 +1 +2 +3 +4 +5 +6 +7 +8 +9 +10 +11

5-146

$J_{AA'}$	J_{AB}	$J_{AB'}$	$J_{BB'}$
6	-6	6	-6
6	6	-6	-6
-6	-6	6	6
-6	6	-6	6

The maximum summed intensity is 9.602

LINE	FREQ	INTEN	LINE	FREQ	INTEN	LINE	FREQ	INTEN	LINE	FREQ	INTEN
1	77.59	0.000	15	93.29	0.000	29	100.11	3.390	43	107.71	0.000
2	80.70	0.019	16	93.89	0.342	30	100.11	3.390	44	108.59	0.243
3	81.70	0.000	17	93.89	0.342	31	100.77	0.000	45	108.59	0.243
4	84.81	0.051	18	94.51	0.000	32	101.78	1.949	46	109.81	0.000
5	85.41	0.025	19	94.51	0.000	33	102.33	1.981	47	110.82	0.000
6	85.41	0.025	20	95.12	0.000	34	103.00	2.000	48	111.49	0.000
7	86.08	0.000	21	96.40	0.000	35	103.00	2.000	49	111.49	0.000
8	88.51	0.000	22	97.00	2.000	36	103.60	0.000	50	113.92	0.000
9	88.51	0.000	23	97.00	2.000	37	104.88	0.000	51	114.59	0.025
10	89.18	0.000	24	97.67	1.981	38	105.49	0.000	52	114.59	0.025
11	90.19	0.000	25	98.22	1.949	39	105.49	0.000	53	115.19	0.051
12	91.41	0.243	26	99.23	0.000	40	106.11	0.342	54	118.30	0.000
13	91.41	0.243	27	99.89	3.390	41	106.11	0.342	55	119.30	0.019
14	92.29	0.000	28	99.89	3.390	42	106.71	0.000	56	122.41	0.000

−11 −10 −9 −8 −7 −6 −5 −4 −3 −2 −1 0 +1 +2 +3 +4 +5 +6 +7 +8 +9 +10 +11

5-147

$J_{AA'}$	J_{AB}	$J_{AB'}$	$J_{BB'}$
6	-9	6	-9
6	6	-9	-9
-9	-9	6	6
-9	6	-9	6

The maximum summed intensity is 6.905.

LINE	FREQ	INTEN	LINE	FREQ	INTEN	LINE	FREQ	INTEN	LINE	FREQ	INTEN
1	74.50	0.000	15	91.25	0.000	29	100.31	0.000	43	107.96	0.000
2	75.92	0.000	16	92.26	0.203	30	100.35	2.675	44	108.75	0.000
3	76.49	0.014	17	92.94	0.261	31	101.85	2.894	45	112.46	0.000
4	79.81	0.007	18	93.20	0.264	32	101.86	1.970	46	113.48	0.117
5	80.65	0.030	19	93.41	0.000	33	102.30	1.986	47	113.69	0.000
6	82.15	0.000	20	94.25	0.000	34	102.43	0.000	48	114.45	0.049
7	84.54	0.000	21	95.15	1.106	35	103.85	0.000	49	115.11	0.000
8	85.55	0.049	22	96.20	0.000	36	104.85	1.106	50	115.46	0.000
9	86.52	0.117	23	97.70	1.986	37	105.75	0.000	51	115.90	0.000
10	87.54	0.000	24	98.14	1.970	38	105.75	0.000	52	119.35	0.030
11	88.25	0.000	25	98.15	2.894	39	106.54	0.000	53	120.19	0.007
12	89.05	0.000	26	99.65	2.675	40	106.80	0.264	54	121.34	0.000
13	89.30	0.000	27	99.91	4.424	41	107.06	0.261	55	123.51	0.014
14	90.10	0.000	28	100.09	4.424	42	107.74	0.203	56	128.24	0.000

−11 −10 −9 −8 −7 −6 −5 −4 −3 −2 −1 0 +1 +2 +3 +4 +5 +6 +7 +8 +9 +10 +11

5-148

$J_{AA'}$	J_{AB}	$J_{AB'}$	$J_{BB'}$
9	-1	9	-1
9	9	-1	-1
-1	-1	9	9
-1	9	-1	9

The maximum summed intensity is 6.716.

LINE	FREQ	INTEN	LINE	FREQ	INTEN	LINE	FREQ	INTEN	LINE	FREQ	INTEN
1	76.94	0.000	15	93.21	0.510	29	100.32	0.000	43	108.07	0.000
2	77.37	0.000	16	93.93	0.000	30	100.75	4.712	44	108.24	0.000
3	82.57	0.000	17	95.64	0.000	31	100.92	1.729	45	109.00	0.400
4	83.49	0.026	18	95.81	0.000	32	101.00	3.600	46	110.75	0.007
5	83.93	0.000	19	96.36	0.000	33	101.43	0.000	47	110.92	0.088
6	84.86	0.000	20	96.53	0.000	34	101.69	1.919	48	112.46	0.081
7	87.37	0.154	21	96.79	0.799	35	101.93	0.000	49	112.63	0.154
8	87.54	0.081	22	97.64	1.974	36	102.36	1.974	50	113.39	0.
9	88.65	0.000	23	98.07	0.000	37	102.61	0.000	51	115.23	0.000
10	88.82	0.000	24	98.31	1.919	38	103.21	0.799	52	116.07	0.000
11	89.08	0.088	25	99.00	3.600	39	106.07	0.000	53	116.51	0.026
12	89.25	0.007	26	99.08	1.729	40	106.79	0.510	54	119.01	0.
13	91.00	0.400	27	99.25	4.712	41	107.30	0.000	55	119.18	0.000
14	91.93	0.000	28	99.59	0.000	42	107.52	0.000	56	122.63	0.000

−11 −10 −9 −8 −7 −6 −5 −4 −3 −2 −1 0 +1 +2 +3 +4 +5 +6 +7 +8 +9 +10 +11

5-149

$J_{AA'}$	J_{AB}	$J_{AB'}$	$J_{BB'}$
9	-2	9	-2
9	9	-2	-2
-2	-2	9	9
-2	9	-2	9

The maximum summed intensity is 6.231.

LINE	FREQ	INTEN	LINE	FREQ	INTEN	LINE	FREQ	INTEN	LINE	FREQ	INTEN
1	75.91	0.000	15	92.43	0.426	29	99.67	0.000	43	108.11	0.481
2	77.93	0.001	16	93.33	0.000	30	100.33	0.000	44	108.30	0.000
3	82.10	0.022	17	95.78	0.000	31	100.71	1.908	45	108.89	0.000
4	82.88	0.000	18	96.16	0.000	32	100.96	0.	46	109.93	0.117
5	84.11	0.000	19	96.33	0.000	33	101.11	3.519	47	110.44	0.001
6	84.63	0.000	20	96.71	0.000	34	101.22	3.522	48	112.85	0.146
7	86.18	0.064	21	97.65	1.978	35	101.65	1.878	49	113.04	0.000
8	87.15	0.146	22	98.26	1.936	36	101.74	1.936	50	113.82	0.064
9	87.50	0.000	23	98.35	1.878	37	102.35	1.978	51	115.89	0.000
10	88.06	0.000	24	98.78	3.522	38	103.12	0.000	52	116.58	0.000
11	89.56	0.001	25	98.89	3.519	39	106.67	0.000	53	117.90	0.022
12	90.07	0.117	26	99.20	0.000	40	107.57	0.426	54	119.45	0.000
13	91.11	0.000	27	99.29	1.908	41	107.86	0.000	55	120.01	0.000
14	91.89	0.481	28	99.59	0.000	42	107.92	0.000	56	122.07	0.001

−11 −10 −9 −8 −7 −6 −5 −4 −3 −2 −1 0 +1 +2 +3 +4 +5 +6 +7 +8 +9 +10 +11

5-150

$J_{AA'}$	J_{AB}	$J_{AB'}$	$J_{BB'}$
9	-4	9	-4
9	9	-4	-4
-4	-4	9	9
-4	9	-4	9

The maximum summed intensity is 4.816.

LINE	FREQ	INTEN	LINE	FREQ	INTEN	LINE	FREQ	INTEN	LINE	FREQ	INTEN
1	73.84	0.000	15	92.42	0.276	29	99.77	4.426	43	108.27	0.186
2	78.95	0.003	16	93.59	0.720	30	100.23	4.426	44	109.25	0.000
3	79.30	0.017	17	94.49	0.000	31	100.46	2.253	45	109.64	0.000
4	82.28	0.000	18	94.66	0.000	32	101.21	0.000	46	110.60	0.000
5	83.43	0.042	19	96.07	0.666	33	101.41	3.280	47	111.74	0.059
6	83.49	0.000	20	96.87	0.000	34	101.81	1.958	48	112.38	0.000
7	84.40	0.000	21	97.04	0.000	35	102.32	1.983	49	113.24	0.132
8	86.44	0.000	22	97.21	0.000	36	102.79	0.000	50	115.60	0.000
9	86.62	0.000	23	97.62	0.000	37	103.93	0.666	51	116.57	0.042
10	86.76	0.132	24	97.68	1.983	38	106.41	0.720	52	117.69	0.000
11	88.26	0.059	25	98.19	1.958	39	106.51	0.000	53	120.70	0.017
12	89.40	0.000	26	98.59	3.280	40	107.26	0.000	54	121.05	0.003
13	91.73	0.186	27	98.83	0.000	41	107.58	0.276	55	121.85	0.000
14	92.21	0.000	28	99.54	2.253	42	107.79	0.000	56	122.03	0.000

−11 −10 −9 −8 −7 −6 −5 −4 −3 −2 −1 0 +1 +2 +3 +4 +5 +6 +7 +8 +9 +10 +11

5-151

$J_{AA'}$	J_{AB}	$J_{AB'}$	$J_{BB'}$
9	-6	9	-6
9	9	-6	-6
-6	-6	9	9
-6	9	-6	9

The maximum summed intensity is 6.905.

LINE	FREQ	INTEN	LINE	FREQ	INTEN	LINE	FREQ	INTEN	LINE	FREQ	INTEN
1	71.76	0.000	15	92.26	0.203	29	99.91	4.424	43	109.90	0.000
2	76.49	0.014	16	92.94	0.261	30	100.09	4.424	44	110.70	0.000
3	78.66	0.000	17	93.20	0.264	31	100.35	2.675	45	110.95	0.000
4	79.81	0.007	18	93.46	0.000	32	101.85	2.894	46	111.75	0.000
5	80.65	0.030	19	94.25	0.000	33	101.86	1.970	47	112.46	0.000
6	84.10	0.000	20	94.25	0.000	34	102.30	1.986	48	113.48	0.117
7	84.54	0.000	21	95.15	1.106	35	103.80	0.000	49	114.45	0.049
8	84.89	0.000	22	96.15	0.000	36	104.85	1.106	50	115.46	0.000
9	85.55	0.049	23	97.57	0.000	37	105.75	0.000	51	117.85	0.000
10	86.31	0.000	24	97.70	1.986	38	106.59	0.000	52	119.35	0.030
11	86.52	0.117	25	98.14	1.970	39	106.80	0.264	53	120.19	0.007
12	87.54	0.000	26	98.15	2.894	40	107.06	0.261	54	123.51	0.014
13	91.25	0.000	27	99.65	2.675	41	107.74	0.203	55	124.08	0.000
14	92.04	0.000	28	99.69	0.000	42	108.75	0.000	56	125.50	0.000

-11 -10 -9 -8 -7 -6 -5 -4 -3 -2 -1 0 +1 +2 +3 +4 +5 +6 +7 +8 +9 +10 +11

5-152

$J_{AA'}$	J_{AB}	$J_{AB'}$	$J_{BB'}$
9	-9	9	-9
9	9	-9	-9
-9	-9	9	9
-9	9	-9	9

The maximum summed intensity is 7.172

LINE	FREQ	INTEN	LINE	FREQ	INTEN	LINE	FREQ	INTEN	LINE	FREQ	INTEN
1	68.63	0.000	15	89.18	0.000	29	100.30	3.586	43	111.70	0.000
2	72.27	0.010	16	90.27	0.000	30	100.30	3.586	44	113.37	0.091
3	72.81	0.000	17	90.27	0.000	31	101.37	0.000	45	113.37	0.091
4	76.46	0.019	18	92.48	0.000	32	101.91	1.981	46	114.11	0.000
5	80.63	0.020	19	93.70	0.303	33	102.27	1.990	47	115.00	0.000
6	80.63	0.020	20	93.70	0.303	34	103.00	2.000	48	115.73	0.000
7	81.70	0.000	21	94.44	0.000	35	103.00	2.000	49	115.73	0.000
8	84.27	0.000	22	97.00	2.000	36	105.56	0.000	50	118.30	0.000
9	84.27	0.000	23	97.00	2.000	37	106.30	0.303	51	119.37	0.020
10	85.00	0.	24	97.73	1.990	38	106.30	0.303	52	119.37	0.020
11	85.89	0.000	25	98.09	1.981	39	107.52	0.000	53	123.54	0.019
12	86.63	0.091	26	98.63	0.000	40	109.73	0.000	54	127.19	0.000
13	86.63	0.091	27	99.70	3.586	41	109.73	0.000	55	127.73	0.010
14	88.30	0.000	28	99.70	3.586	42	110.82	0.000	56	131.37	0.000

-11 -10 -9 -8 -7 -6 -5 -4 -3 -2 -1 0 +1 +2 +3 +4 +5 +6 +7 +8 +9 +10 +11

5-153

$J_{AA'}$	J_{AB}	$J_{AB'}$	$J_{BB'}$
12	-12	12	-1
12	12	-2	-1
-1	-1	12	12
-1	12	-1	12

The maximum summed intensity is 5.298

LINE	FREQ	INTEN	LINE	FREQ	INTEN	LINE	FREQ	INTEN	LINE	FREQ	INTEN
1	70.75	0.000	15	91.57	0.000	29	100.44	5.375	43	109.96	0.000
2	71.01	0.000	16	92.22	0.385	30	100.51	0.000	44	110.10	0.000
3	77.49	0.	17	94.03	0.000	31	100.70	0.000	45	111.76	0.244
4	79.04	0.000	18	94.36	0.000	32	100.76	3.756	46	112.97	0.014
5	79.30	0.017	19	95.17	0.000	33	100.98	1.758	47	113.51	0.065
6	80.41	0.000	20	95.25	0.315	34	101.81	1.958	48	116.57	0.042
7	83.28	0.087	21	95.51	0.000	35	102.32	1.983	49	116.72	0.087
8	83.43	0.042	22	97.43	0.000	36	102.57	0.000	50	118.38	0.000
9	85.60	0.000	23	97.68	1.983	37	103.62	0.000	51	118.53	0.000
10	86.49	0.065	24	98.19	1.958	38	104.75	0.315	52	120.70	0.017
11	86.75	0.000	25	99.02	1.758	39	107.78	0.385	53	120.96	0.000
12	87.03	0.014	26	99.24	3.756	40	108.43	0.000	54	123.72	0.000
13	88.24	0.244	27	99.56	5.375	41	109.12	0.000	55	124.87	0.000
14	90.04	0.000	28	100.36	0.000	42	109.77	0.000	56	129.25	0.000

5-154

$J_{AA'}$	J_{AB}	$J_{AB'}$	$J_{BB'}$
12	-2	12	-22
12	12	-2	-2
-2	-2	12	12
-2	12	-2	12

The maximum summed intensity is 7.657.

LINE	FREQ	INTEN	LINE	FREQ	INTEN	LINE	FREQ	INTEN	LINE	FREQ	INTEN
1	69.96	0.000	15	90.93	0.000	29	100.05	0.000	43	110.58	0.000
2	71.34	0.000	16	91.16	0.323	30	100.62	4.914	44	110.73	0.000
3	77.79	0.000	17	93.57	0.000	31	100.80	1.873	45	110.83	0.285
4	77.89	0.015	18	94.37	0.000	32	100.83	3.715	46	112.28	0.005
5	79.27	0.000	19	95.80	0.000	33	100.93	0.000	47	112.46	0.082
6	80.49	0.000	20	96.61	0.000	34	101.84	1.965	48	117.00	0.084
7	82.04	0.035	21	97.18	0.718	35	101.94	0.000	49	117.96	0.035
8	83.00	0.084	22	97.69	1.985	36	102.21	0.000	50	118.06	0.000
9	83.93	0.000	23	98.16	1.965	37	102.31	1.985	51	120.22	0.000
10	86.16	0.000	24	99.07	0.000	38	102.82	0.718	52	120.73	0.000
11	87.54	0.082	25	99.17	3.715	39	108.84	0.323	53	122.11	0.015
12	87.72	0.005	26	99.20	1.873	40	109.07	0.000	54	123.66	0.000
13	89.17	0.285	27	99.25	0.000	41	109.69	0.000	55	125.90	0.000
14	89.27	0.000	28	99.38	4.914	42	109.77	0.000	56	128.66	0.000

5-155

$J_{AA'}$	J_{AB}	$J_{AB'}$	$J_{BB'}$
12	-4	12	-4
12	12	-4	-4
-4	-4	12	12
-4	12	-4	12

The maximum summed intensity is 4.771.

LINE	FREQ	INTEN	LINE	FREQ	INTEN	LINE	FREQ	INTEN	LINE	FREQ	INTEN
1	67.86	0.000	15	90.34	0.202	29	99.66	4.334	43	110.57	0.122
2	72.46	0.001	16	91.00	0.400	30	100.34	4.334	44	111.00	0.000
3	75.08	0.012	17	92.13	0.000	31	100.57	2.075	45	112.03	0.000
4	78.40	0.	18	95.06	0.000	32	100.78	0.000	46	112.31	0.000
5	79.12	0.000	19	95.07	0.000	33	101.00	3.600	47	112.45	0.047
6	79.25	0.026	20	97.55	1.143	34	101.88	1.974	48	117.43	0.000
7	79.69	0.000	21	97.69	0.000	35	102.29	1.988	49	117.54	0.077
8	81.91	0.000	22	97.71	1.988	36	102.31	0.000	50	120.31	0.000
9	82.46	0.077	23	97.84	0.000	37	102.45	1.143	51	120.75	0.026
10	84.83	0.000	24	97.99	0.000	38	105.60	0.000	52	122.26	0.000
11	87.55	0.047	25	98.12	1.974	39	109.00	0.400	53	124.92	0.012
12	87.69	0.000	26	98.57	0.000	40	109.10	0.000	54	125.05	0.000
13	89.43	0.122	27	99.00	3.600	41	109.66	0.202	55	127.54	0.001
14	89.69	0.000	28	99.45	2.075	42	110.31	0.000	56	127.97	0.000

5-156

$J_{AA'}$	J_{AB}	$J_{AB'}$	$J_{BB'}$
12	-6	12	-6
12	12	-6	-6
-6	-6	12	12
-6	12	-6	12

The maximum summed intensity is 8.597.

LINE	FREQ	INTEN	LINE	FREQ	INTEN	LINE	FREQ	INTEN	LINE	FREQ	INTEN
1	65.76	0.000	15	91.07	0.175	29	99.93	5.041	43	111.49	0.000
2	72.27	0.010	16	91.44	0.161	30	100.07	5.041	44	112.51	0.000
3	73.52	0.002	17	92.31	0.000	31	100.45	2.292	45	113.31	0.000
4	75.57	0.000	18	92.76	0.586	32	101.24	3.414	46	113.97	0.000
5	76.46	0.019	19	93.63	0.196	33	101.91	1.981	47	114.86	0.062
6	79.00	0.000	20	94.51	0.000	34	102.27	1.990	48	116.82	0.000
7	80.03	0.000	21	95.18	0.000	35	103.50	0.000	49	118.00	0.071
8	81.87	0.000	22	95.76	0.000	36	105.49	0.000	50	119.97	0.000
9	82.00	0.071	23	97.20	0.000	37	106.37	0.196	51	122.31	0.000
10	83.31	0.000	24	97.73	1.990	38	107.24	0.586	52	123.54	0.019
11	85.14	0.062	25	98.09	1.981	39	108.42	0.000	53	126.48	0.002
12	86.03	0.000	26	98.62	0.000	40	108.56	0.161	54	127.73	0.010
13	88.51	0.000	27	98.76	3.414	41	108.93	0.175	55	128.62	0.000
14	90.87	0.000	28	99.55	2.292	42	109.00	0.000	56	130.06	0.000

5-157

$J_{AA'}$	J_{AB}	$J_{AB'}$	$J_{BB'}$
12	-9	12	-9
12	12	-9	-9
-9	-9	12	12
-9	12	-9	12

The maximum summed intensity is 6.617.

LINE	FREQ	INTEN	LINE	FREQ	INTEN	LINE	FREQ	INTEN	LINE	FREQ	INTEN
1	62.59	0.000	15	88.01	0.000	29	100.26	4.555	43	114.10	0.000
2	68.05	0.008	16	89.33	0.000	30	100.32	0.000	44	114.87	0.000
3	69.67	0.000	17	90.00	0.000	31	100.38	2.795	45	115.14	0.000
4	72.25	0.014	18	90.10	0.000	32	101.85	2.894	46	115.90	0.000
5	74.84	0.006	19	92.91	0.267	33	101.95	1.986	47	116.70	0.000
6	79.90	0.000	20	93.03	0.216	34	102.25	1.992	48	118.45	0.060
7	80.30	0.000	21	95.15	1.106	35	104.85	1.106	49	119.28	0.035
8	80.66	0.000	22	95.48	0.000	36	106.97	0.216	50	119.70	0.000
9	80.72	0.035	23	96.80	0.000	37	107.09	0.267	51	122.22	0.000
10	81.55	0.060	24	97.75	1.992	38	107.40	0.000	52	125.16	0.006
11	81.98	0.000	25	98.05	1.986	39	107.79	0.000	53	127.75	0.014
12	83.30	0.000	26	98.15	2.894	40	110.00	0.000	54	131.95	0.008
13	87.00	0.000	27	99.62	2.795	41	112.57	0.067	55	133.21	0.000
14	87.43	0.067	28	99.74	4.555	42	113.00	0.000	56	134.53	0.000

−11 −10 −9 −8 −7 −6 −5 −4 −3 −2 −1 0 +1 +2 +3 +4 +5 +6 +7 +8 +9 +10 +11

5-158

$J_{AA'}$	J_{AB}	$J_{AB'}$	$J_{BB'}$
12	-12	12	-12
12	12	-12	-12
-12	-12	12	12
-12	12	-12	12

The maximum summed intensity is 7.096

LINE	FREQ	INTEN	LINE	FREQ	INTEN	LINE	FREQ	INTEN	LINE	FREQ	INTEN
1	59.42	0.000	15	85.00	0.000	29	100.37	3.652	43	115.84	0.000
2	63.63	0.000	16	86.03	0.000	30	100.37	3.652	44	118.37	0.045
3	63.82	0.006	17	86.03	0.000	31	101.97	1.990	45	118.37	0.045
4	68.03	0.010	18	88.37	0.000	32	102.16	0.000	46	118.37	0.000
5	75.63	0.014	19	93.63	0.288	33	102.24	1.994	47	119.21	0.000
6	75.63	0.014	20	93.63	0.288	34	103.00	2.000	48	119.97	0.000
7	77.42	0.000	21	93.63	0.000	35	103.00	2.000	49	119.97	0.000
8	80.03	0.000	22	97.00	2.000	36	106.37	0.288	50	122.58	0.000
9	80.03	0.000	23	97.00	2.000	37	106.37	0.000	51	124.37	0.014
10	80.79	0.000	24	97.76	1.994	38	106.37	0.288	52	124.37	0.014
11	81.63	0.045	25	97.84	0.000	39	111.63	0.000	53	131.97	0.010
12	81.63	0.000	26	98.03	1.990	40	113.97	0.000	54	136.18	0.006
13	81.63	0.045	27	99.63	3.652	41	113.97	0.000	55	136.37	0.
14	84.16	0.000	28	99.63	3.652	42	115.00	0.000	56	140.58	0.000

−11 −10 −9 −8 −7 −6 −5 −4 −3 −2 −1 0 +1 +2 +3 +4 +5 +6 +7 +8 +9 +10 +11

5-159

$J_{AA'}$	J_{AB}	$J_{AB'}$	$J_{BB'}$
1	1	2	4
1	2	1	4
4	2	1	1
4	1	2	1

The maximum summed intensity is 4.330.

LINE	FREQ	INTEN	LINE	FREQ	INTEN	LINE	FREQ	INTEN	LINE	FREQ	INTEN
1	87.99	0.	15	96.53	1.551	29	100.00	0.200	43	103.96	0.000
2	88.73	0.000	16	96.76	1.760	30	100.00	0.200	44	104.27	0.000
3	91.66	0.003	17	96.84	1.800	31	100.73	0.000	45	104.57	1.203
4	91.70	0.006	18	97.05	0.000	32	100.80	0.000	46	104.85	1.106
5	92.56	0.000	19	97.05	1.978	33	100.89	0.000	47	105.90	0.000
6	93.00	0.000	20	97.56	0.000	34	101.59	0.140	48	106.11	0.022
7	93.09	0.000	21	97.58	0.000	35	101.63	3.338	49	106.97	0.000
8	93.89	0.022	22	97.92	0.000	36	101.85	2.894	50	107.44	0.000
9	94.42	0.000	23	98.15	2.894	37	102.15	0.000	51	108.30	0.006
10	95.15	1.106	24	98.37	3.338	38	102.44	0.000	52	108.34	0.003
11	95.43	1.203	25	98.41	0.140	39	102.95	1.978	53	108.53	0.
12	95.73	0.000	26	99.14	0.000	40	103.16	1.800	54	109.06	0.000
13	95.98	0.000	27	99.27	0.000	41	103.24	1.760	55	109.95	0.000
14	96.16	0.000	28	99.47	0.000	42	103.47	1.551	56	111.27	0.000

−11 −10 −9 −8 −7 −6 −5 −4 −3 −2 −1 0 +1 +2 +3 +4 +5 +6 +7 +8 +9 +10 +11

5-160

$J_{AA'}$	J_{AB}	$J_{AB'}$	$J_{BB'}$
1	1	2	6
1	2	1	6
6	2	1	1
6	1	2	1

The maximum summed intensity is 4.450.

LINE	FREQ	INTEN	LINE	FREQ	INTEN	LINE	FREQ	INTEN	LINE	FREQ	INTEN
1	86.00	0.000	15	96.08	0.000	29	99.10	0.000	43	104.07	0.000
2	88.52	0.000	16	96.51	1.550	30	99.48	0.000	44	104.30	0.000
3	89.93	0.002	17	96.64	0.415	31	101.63	3.342	45	104.77	0.911
4	90.60	0.000	18	96.74	1.555	32	101.84	0.445	46	104.85	1.106
5	91.11	0.000	19	96.78	1.777	33	101.85	2.894	47	107.77	0.000
6	91.67	0.003	20	97.03	1.994	34	102.16	0.000	48	108.07	0.006
7	91.93	0.006	21	97.04	0.000	35	102.40	0.000	49	108.33	0.003
8	94.29	0.000	22	97.30	0.000	36	102.66	0.000	50	108.74	0.000
9	94.67	0.000	23	97.49	0.000	37	102.70	0.000	51	109.19	0.000
10	95.15	1.106	24	97.60	0.000	38	102.97	1.994	52	109.40	0.000
11	95.23	0.911	25	97.70	0.000	39	103.22	1.777	53	110.07	0.002
12	95.70	0.000	26	98.15	2.894	40	103.26	1.555	54	110.15	0.000
13	95.71	0.000	27	98.16	0.445	41	103.36	0.415	55	110.52	0.
14	96.07	0.000	28	98.37	3.342	42	103.49	1.550	56	111.48	0.000

−11 −10 −9 −8 −7 −6 −5 −4 −3 −2 −1 0 +1 +2 +3 +4 +5 +6 +7 +8 +9 +10 +11

5-161

$J_{AA'}$	J_{AB}	$J_{AB'}$	$J_{BB'}$
1	1	2	9
1	2	1	9
9	2	1	1
9	1	2	1

The maximum summed intensity is 4.184.

LINE	FREQ	INTEN	LINE	FREQ	INTEN	LINE	FREQ	INTEN	LINE	FREQ	INTEN
1	83.00	0.000	15	95.63	0.000	29	98.47	0.000	43	105.15	0.057
2	86.46	0.000	16	95.68	0.000	30	99.48	0.000	44	105.68	0.000
3	87.61	0.000	17	95.71	1.271	31	101.62	3.345	45	105.97	0.000
4	88.13	0.	18	95.93	0.000	32	101.85	2.894	46	106.83	0.044
5	88.95	0.001	19	96.24	0.000	33	102.16	0.000	47	108.33	0.003
6	89.00	0.001	20	96.50	1.548	34	102.39	0.000	48	108.86	0.000
7	91.67	0.003	21	96.79	1.788	35	102.91	1.943	49	109.66	0.000
8	92.38	0.000	22	97.01	1.999	36	102.99	1.999	50	111.00	0.001
9	93.17	0.044	23	97.04	0.000	37	103.21	1.788	51	111.05	0.001
10	93.70	0.000	24	97.09	1.943	38	103.50	1.548	52	111.10	0.000
11	94.32	0.000	25	97.61	0.000	39	103.74	0.000	53	112.20	0.000
12	94.62	0.000	26	98.15	2.894	40	104.29	1.271	54	112.39	0.000
13	94.85	0.057	27	98.17	0.000	41	104.32	0.000	55	113.52	0.000
14	95.15	1.106	28	98.38	3.345	42	104.85	1.106	56	113.54	0.000

−11 −10 −9 −8 −7 −6 −5 −4 −3 −2 −1 0 +1 +2 +3 +4 +5 +6 +7 +8 +9 +10 +11

5-162

$J_{AA'}$	J_{AB}	$J_{AB'}$	$J_{BB'}$
1	1	2	12
1	2	1	12
12	2	1	1
12	1	2	1

The maximum summed intensity is 4.462.

LINE	FREQ	INTEN	LINE	FREQ	INTEN	LINE	FREQ	INTEN	LINE	FREQ	INTEN
1	80.01	0.000	15	95.15	1.106	29	99.49	0.000	43	108.07	0.006
2	83.55	0.000	16	95.63	1.305	30	101.32	0.000	44	108.33	0.003
3	84.62	0.000	17	95.67	0.000	31	101.62	3.348	45	108.67	0.000
4	85.14	0.000	18	95.95	0.000	32	101.85	2.894	46	108.90	0.000
5	85.96	0.001	19	96.22	0.000	33	102.17	0.000	47	108.93	0.000
6	88.92	0.001	20	96.49	1.546	34	102.38	0.000	48	109.74	0.006
7	89.45	0.000	21	96.80	1.793	35	102.97	1.994	49	109.74	0.000
8	90.26	0.006	22	97.01	1.999	36	102.99	1.999	50	111.08	0.001
9	90.86	0.000	23	97.03	1.994	37	103.20	1.793	51	114.03	0.000
10	91.33	0.000	24	97.04	0.000	38	103.51	1.546	52	114.04	0.001
11	91.67	0.003	25	97.62	0.000	39	103.80	0.000	53	115.11	0.000
12	91.93	0.006	26	98.08	0.000	40	104.33	0.000	54	115.38	0.000
13	92.71	0.000	27	98.15	2.894	41	104.37	1.305	55	116.45	0.000
14	94.55	0.000	28	98.38	3.348	42	104.85	1.106	56	116.51	0.000

−11 −10 −9 −8 −7 −6 −5 −4 −3 −2 −1 0 +1 +2 +3 +4 +5 +6 +7 +8 +9 +10 +11

5-163

$J_{AA'}$	J_{AB}	$J_{AB'}$	$J_{BB'}$
1	1	2	15
1	2	1	15
15	2	1	1
15	1	2	1

The maximum summed intensity is 4.529.

LINE	FREQ	INTEN	LINE	FREQ	INTEN	LINE	FREQ	INTEN	LINE	FREQ	INTEN
1	77.01	0.000	15	95.15	1.106	29	99.49	0.000	43	108.33	0.003
2	80.58	0.000	16	95.60	1.306	30	101.62	3.349	44	108.94	0.000
3	81.63	0.000	17	95.66	0.000	31	101.85	2.894	45	109.76	0.000
4	82.14	0.000	18	95.96	0.000	32	102.17	0.000	46	111.05	0.001
5	82.97	0.000	19	96.22	0.000	33	102.37	0.000	47	111.11	0.001
6	86.47	0.000	20	96.49	1.544	34	102.99	1.999	48	111.66	0.000
7	87.29	0.002	21	96.80	1.795	35	102.99	2.000	49	111.87	0.000
8	87.90	0.000	22	97.01	2.000	36	103.20	1.795	50	112.71	0.002
9	88.34	0.000	23	97.01	1.999	37	103.51	1.544	51	117.01	0.000
10	88.89	0.001	24	97.04	0.000	38	103.81	0.000	52	117.03	0.000
11	88.95	0.001	25	97.63	0.000	39	104.28	0.000	53	118.08	0.000
12	89.74	0.000	26	98.05	0.000	40	104.34	0.000	54	118.37	0.000
13	91.67	0.003	27	98.15	2.894	41	104.40	1.306	55	119.42	0.000
14	94.53	0.000	28	98.38	3.349	42	104.85	1.106	56	119.51	0.

5-164

$J_{AA'}$	J_{AB}	$J_{AB'}$	$J_{BB'}$
1	1	2	18
1	2	1	18
18	2	1	1
18	1	2	1

The maximum summed intensity is4.556.

LINE	FREQ	INTEN	LINE	FREQ	INTEN	LINE	FREQ	INTEN	LINE	FREQ	INTEN
1	74.01	0.000	15	95.15	1.106	29	99.49	0.000	43	108.33	0.003
2	77.59	0.000	16	95.59	1.305	30	101.62	3.351	44	108.95	0.000
3	78.63	0.000	17	95.66	0.000	31	101.85	2.894	45	109.77	0.000
4	79.15	0.000	18	95.97	0.000	32	102.17	0.000	46	111.12	0.001
5	79.97	0.000	19	96.21	0.000	33	102.37	0.000	47	114.04	0.001
6	83.48	0.000	20	96.49	1.543	34	102.99	1.999	48	114.66	0.000
7	84.30	0.001	21	96.81	1.797	35	103.00	2.000	49	114.86	0.000
8	84.93	0.000	22	97.00	2.000	36	103.19	1.797	50	115.70	0.001
9	85.34	0.000	23	97.01	1.999	37	103.51	1.543	51	120.00	0.000
10	85.96	0.001	24	97.04	0.000	38	103.82	0.000	52	120.03	0.000
11	86.75	0.000	25	97.63	0.000	39	104.34	0.000	53	121.06	0.000
12	88.88	0.001	26	98.04	0.000	40	104.41	1.305	54	121.37	0.000
13	91.67	0.003	27	98.15	2.894	41	104.85	1.106	55	122.41	0.000
14	94.52	0.000	28	98.38	3.351	42	107.26	0.000	56	122.51	0.

5-165

$J_{AA'}$	J_{AB}	$J_{AB'}$	$J_{BB'}$
1	1	4	2
1	4	1	2
2	4	1	1
2	1	4	1

The maximum summed intensity is 4.491.

LINE	FREQ	INTEN	LINE	FREQ	INTEN	LINE	FREQ	INTEN	LINE	FREQ	INTEN
1	86.30	0.000	15	95.92	1.067	29	100.19	0.	43	104.49	0.000
2	88.79	0.000	16	96.01	0.000	30	100.54	0.814	44	104.50	0.783
3	89.72	0.	17	96.18	0.000	31	100.82	0.000	45	104.60	0.000
4	91.12	0.009	18	96.27	0.979	32	101.05	0.000	46	105.39	0.336
5	92.73	0.115	19	97.33	0.000	33	101.07	4.187	47	105.67	0.000
6	93.01	0.000	20	97.77	1.664	34	101.33	1.217	48	105.89	0.829
7	93.08	0.	21	98.05	0.000	35	101.41	3.280	49	106.41	0.720
8	93.59	0.720	22	98.59	3.280	36	102.13	0.000	50	106.99	0.000
9	94.11	0.829	23	98.67	1.217	37	102.23	1.664	51	107.27	0.115
10	94.51	0.000	24	98.76	0.000	38	103.56	0.000	52	107.81	0.000
11	94.61	0.336	25	98.92	0.	39	103.73	0.979	53	108.88	0.009
12	94.62	0.	26	98.93	4.187	40	103.82	0.000	54	109.39	0.000
13	95.22	0.000	27	99.18	0.000	41	103.99	0.000	55	112.10	0.000
14	95.50	0.783	28	99.46	0.814	42	104.08	1.067	56	113.70	0.000

5-166

$J_{AA'}$	J_{AB}	$J_{AB'}$	$J_{BB'}$
1	1	6	2
1	6	1	2
2	6	1	1
2	1	6	1

The maximum summed intensity is 5.710.

LINE	FREQ	INTEN	LINE	FREQ	INTEN	LINE	FREQ	INTEN	LINE	FREQ	INTEN
1	83.27	0.000	15	94.34	0.000	29	100.56	0.000	43	105.80	0.000
2	85.85	0.000	16	94.63	0.586	30	100.61	1.334	44	106.09	0.445
3	88.85	0.000	17	96.15	0.593	31	100.70	0.000	45	106.31	0.
4	90.04	0.014	18	96.44	0.000	32	100.74	4.778	46	106.80	0.000
5	91.34	0.000	19	97.45	0.000	33	100.99	1.555	47	106.85	0.270
6	91.39	0.147	20	98.20	0.000	34	101.04	0.000	48	107.51	0.547
7	91.46	0.	21	98.25	1.730	35	101.11	3.519	49	108.11	0.481
8	91.89	0.481	22	98.54	0.000	36	101.75	1.730	50	108.61	0.147
9	92.49	0.547	23	98.73	0.000	37	102.04	0.000	51	108.66	0.000
10	92.92	0.000	24	98.89	3.519	38	103.32	0.000	52	109.30	0.000
11	93.15	0.270	25	99.01	1.555	39	103.56	0.000	53	109.96	0.014
12	93.44	0.000	26	99.26	4.778	40	103.85	0.593	54	110.39	0.000
13	93.91	0.445	27	99.39	1.334	41	105.37	0.586	55	114.92	0.000
14	93.97	0.000	28	99.44	0.000	42	105.66	0.000	56	116.73	0.000

5-167

$J_{AA'}$	J_{AB}	$J_{AB'}$	$J_{BB'}$
1	1	9	2
1	9	1	2
2	9	1	1
2	1	9	1

The maximum summed intensity is 7.339.

LINE	FREQ	INTEN	LINE	FREQ	INTEN	LINE	FREQ	INTEN	LINE	FREQ	INTEN
1	78.17	0.000	15	91.64	0.000	29	100.30	0.000	43	108.36	0.000
2	80.79	0.000	16	92.23	0.262	30	100.48	5.284	44	108.75	0.224
3	86.87	0.000	17	96.11	0.312	31	100.58	1.691	45	109.07	0.000
4	87.86	0.016	18	96.70	0.000	32	100.69	1.776	46	109.18	0.000
5	88.64	0.000	19	97.50	0.000	33	100.83	3.715	47	109.35	0.172
6	88.78	0.	20	98.22	0.	34	100.97	0.000	48	110.16	0.316
7	88.92	0.119	21	98.44	0.000	35	101.18	0.	49	110.83	0.285
8	89.17	0.285	22	98.72	1.828	36	101.28	1.828	50	111.08	0.119
9	89.84	0.316	23	98.72	0.000	37	101.88	0.000	51	111.36	0.000
10	90.22	0.000	24	99.17	3.715	38	103.09	0.000	52	111.82	0.000
11	90.65	0.172	25	99.31	1.776	39	103.30	0.000	53	112.14	0.016
12	91.25	0.000	26	99.42	1.691	40	103.89	0.312	54	112.53	0.000
13	91.25	0.224	27	99.52	5.284	41	107.77	0.262	55	119.81	0.000
14	91.53	0.000	28	99.70	0.000	42	108.15	0.000	56	121.83	0.000

−11 −10 −9 −8 −7 −6 −5 −4 −3 −2 −1 0 +1 +2 +3 +4 +5 +6 +7 +8 +9 +10 +11

5-168

$J_{AA'}$	J_{AB}	$J_{AB'}$	$J_{BB'}$
1	1	12	2
1	12	1	2
2	12	1	1
2	1	12	1

The maximum summed intensity is 8.014.

LINE	FREQ	INTEN	LINE	FREQ	INTEN	LINE	FREQ	INTEN	LINE	FREQ	INTEN
1	72.72	0.000	15	88.82	0.000	29	100.14	0.000	43	111.18	0.000
2	75.34	0.	16	89.58	0.139	30	100.34	5.544	44	111.56	0.131
3	84.48	0.000	17	96.11	0.188	31	100.51	1.830	45	111.66	0.000
4	85.34	0.014	18	96.86	0.000	32	100.52	1.869	46	112.04	0.111
5	85.82	0.000	19	97.52	0.000	33	100.66	3.816	47	112.10	0.000
6	85.96	0.	20	98.04	0.	34	100.90	0.000	48	112.96	0.200
7	86.20	0.085	21	98.63	0.000	35	101.00	1.889	49	113.66	0.184
8	86.34	0.184	22	98.72	0.000	36	101.48	0.000	50	113.80	0.085
9	87.04	0.200	23	99.00	1.889	37	101.75	0.000	51	114.18	0.000
10	87.42	0.000	24	99.34	3.816	38	102.96	0.000	52	114.52	0.000
11	87.96	0.111	25	99.48	1.869	39	103.14	0.000	53	114.66	0.014
12	88.44	0.131	26	99.49	1.830	40	103.89	0.188	54	115.04	0.000
13	88.72	0.000	27	99.66	5.544	41	110.42	0.139	55	125.14	0.000
14	88.81	0.000	28	99.86	0.000	42	110.81	0.000	56	127.28	0.000

−11 −10 −9 −8 −7 −6 −5 −4 −3 −2 −1 0 +1 +2 +3 +4 +5 +6 +7 +8 +9 +10 +11

5-169

$J_{AA'}$	J_{AB}	$J_{AB'}$	$J_{BB'}$
1	1	15	2
1	15	1	2
2	15	1	1
2	1	15	1

The maximum summed intensity is 8.903.

LINE	FREQ	INTEN	LINE	FREQ	INTEN	LINE	FREQ	INTEN	LINE	FREQ	INTEN
1	67.08	0.000	15	86.01	0.000	29	100.03	0.000	43	114.06	0.000
2	69.69	0.000	16	86.79	0.084	30	100.26	5.687	44	114.42	0.000
3	81.87	0.000	17	96.12	0.124	31	100.42	1.915	45	114.45	0.085
4	82.65	0.012	18	96.97	0.000	32	100.45	1.895	46	114.84	0.076
5	82.94	0.000	19	97.52	0.000	33	100.54	3.873	47	115.05	0.000
6	83.07	0.	20	97.93	0.000	34	100.81	1.924	48	115.83	0.137
7	83.36	0.061	21	98.73	0.000	35	100.84	0.000	49	116.54	0.127
8	83.46	0.127	22	98.77	0.000	36	101.66	0.000	50	116.64	0.061
9	84.17	0.137	23	99.19	1.924	37	101.67	0.000	51	117.06	0.000
10	84.56	0.000	24	99.46	3.873	38	102.87	0.000	52	117.33	0.000
11	85.16	0.076	25	99.55	1.895	39	103.03	0.000	53	117.35	0.012
12	85.55	0.085	26	99.58	1.915	40	103.88	0.124	54	117.74	0.000
13	85.94	0.000	27	99.74	5.687	41	113.21	0.084	55	130.70	0.000
14	85.97	0.000	28	99.97	0.000	42	113.59	0.000	56	132.92	0.000

5-170

$J_{AA'}$	J_{AB}	$J_{AB'}$	$J_{BB'}$
1	1	18	2
1	18	1	2
2	18	1	1
2	1	18	1

The maximum summed intensity is 9.566.

LINE	FREQ	INTEN	LINE	FREQ	INTEN	LINE	FREQ	INTEN	LINE	FREQ	INTEN
1	61.33	0.000	15	83.21	0.000	29	100.05	0.000	43	116.98	0.000
2	63.94	0.000	16	83.94	0.055	30	100.21	5.774	44	117.26	0.000
3	79.13	0.000	17	96.13	0.088	31	100.35	1.941	45	117.37	0.059
4	79.86	0.010	18	97.05	0.000	32	100.40	1.929	46	117.71	0.055
5	80.02	0.000	19	97.52	0.000	33	100.46	3.907	47	118.01	0.000
6	80.14	0.	20	97.86	0.	34	100.68	1.945	48	118.74	0.099
7	80.47	0.045	21	98.73	0.000	35	100.80	0.000	49	119.46	0.093
8	80.54	0.093	22	98.87	0.000	36	101.60	0.000	50	119.53	0.045
9	81.26	0.099	23	99.32	1.945	37	101.81	0.000	51	119.98	0.000
10	81.66	0.000	24	99.54	3.907	38	102.81	0.000	52	120.14	0.010
11	82.29	0.055	25	99.60	1.929	39	102.95	0.000	53	120.19	0.
12	82.63	0.059	26	99.65	1.941	40	103.87	0.088	54	120.53	0.000
13	83.02	0.000	27	99.79	5.774	41	116.06	0.055	55	136.40	0.000
14	83.08	0.000	28	99.95	0.000	42	116.45	0.000	56	138.67	0.000

5-171

$J_{AA'}$	J_{AB}	$J_{AB'}$	$J_{BB'}$
1	2	4	1
1	4	2	1

The maximum summed intensity is 4.592.

LINE	FREQ	INTEN	LINE	FREQ	INTEN	LINE	FREQ	INTEN	LINE	FREQ	INTEN
1	85.57	0.001	15	95.84	0.684	29	100.82	4.658	43	104.24	0.000
2	87.65	0.000	16	95.84	0.684	30	100.84	0.000	44	104.24	0.000
3	90.69	0.017	17	96.10	0.947	31	101.24	3.414	45	104.59	0.594
4	90.77	0.000	18	96.18	0.000	32	101.63	0.000	46	104.69	0.000
5	92.76	0.586	19	97.10	0.000	33	101.71	0.755	47	105.95	0.866
6	92.84	0.000	20	97.49	0.000	34	102.16	1.316	48	106.03	0.000
7	93.22	0.162	21	97.76	0.000	35	102.16	1.316	49	106.24	0.000
8	93.76	0.000	22	97.84	1.316	36	102.24	0.000	50	106.78	0.162
9	93.97	0.000	23	97.84	1.316	37	102.51	0.000	51	107.16	0.000
10	94.05	0.866	24	98.29	0.755	38	102.90	0.000	52	107.24	0.586
11	95.31	0.000	25	98.37	0.000	39	103.82	0.000	53	109.23	0.000
12	95.41	0.594	26	98.76	3.414	40	103.90	0.947	54	109.31	0.017
13	95.76	0.000	27	99.16	0.000	41	104.16	0.684	55	112.35	0.000
14	95.76	0.000	28	99.18	4.658	42	104.16	0.684	56	114.43	0.001

5-172

$J_{AA'}$	J_{AB}	$J_{AB'}$	$J_{BB'}$
1	2	4	2
1	4	2	2
2	4	2	1
2	2	4	1

The maximum summed intensity is 4.788.

LINE	FREQ	INTEN	LINE	FREQ	INTEN	LINE	FREQ	INTEN	LINE	FREQ	INTEN
1	85.54	0.001	15	95.55	0.000	29	100.82	4.666	43	104.62	0.000
2	88.59	0.000	16	96.14	0.000	30	100.86	0.000	44	104.76	0.324
3	89.80	0.000	17	96.19	1.083	31	100.94	0.000	45	104.83	0.671
4	90.69	0.018	18	96.35	1.215	32	100.99	0.500	46	105.08	0.000
5	92.50	0.076	19	97.08	0.000	33	101.24	3.414	47	105.40	0.000
6	92.76	0.586	20	97.48	1.676	34	101.57	0.917	48	105.98	0.853
7	92.81	0.000	21	98.12	0.000	35	101.62	0.000	49	106.86	0.000
8	93.14	0.000	22	98.19	0.000	36	102.52	1.676	50	107.24	0.586
9	93.97	0.000	23	98.22	0.000	37	102.73	0.000	51	107.50	0.076
10	94.02	0.853	24	98.38	0.000	38	103.60	0.000	52	108.14	0.000
11	95.17	0.671	25	98.43	0.917	39	103.65	1.215	53	109.26	0.000
12	95.24	0.324	26	98.76	3.414	40	103.81	1.083	54	109.31	0.018
13	95.38	0.000	27	99.01	0.500	41	103.86	0.000	55	112.36	0.000
14	95.45	0.000	28	99.18	4.666	42	103.87	0.000	56	114.46	0.001

5-173

$J_{AA'}$	J_{AB}	$J_{AB'}$	$J_{BB'}$
1	2	4	4
1	4	2	4
4	4	2	1
4	2	4	1

The maximum summed intensity is 4.879.

LINE	FREQ	INTEN	LINE	FREQ	INTEN	LINE	FREQ	INTEN	LINE	FREQ	INTEN
1	85.45	0.001	15	95.75	0.000	29	100.00	0.615	43	104.94	0.000
2	87.83	0.	16	96.30	0.000	30	100.00	0.615	44	105.04	0.716
3	90.39	0.000	17	96.39	1.385	31	100.06	0.000	45	105.76	0.000
4	90.70	0.018	18	96.45	0.000	32	100.70	0.309	46	106.07	0.812
5	90.81	0.021	19	96.56	1.446	33	100.82	4.676	47	106.41	0.067
6	91.45	0.000	20	97.05	0.000	34	100.89	0.000	48	107.06	0.000
7	92.70	0.000	21	97.19	1.933	35	101.24	3.414	49	107.24	0.586
8	92.76	0.586	22	97.84	0.000	36	102.81	1.933	50	108.55	0.000
9	93.59	0.067	23	98.76	3.414	37	102.91	0.000	51	109.19	0.021
10	93.69	0.000	24	99.18	4.676	38	103.20	0.000	52	109.30	0.018
11	93.93	0.812	25	99.30	0.309	39	103.44	1.446	53	109.36	0.000
12	93.99	0.000	26	99.36	0.000	40	103.50	0.000	54	110.11	0.000
13	94.96	0.716	27	99.89	0.000	41	103.55	0.000	55	112.42	0.000
14	95.06	0.000	28	99.94	0.000	42	103.61	1.385	56	114.55	0.001

−11 −10 −9 −8 −7 −6 −5 −4 −3 −2 −1 0 +1 +2 +3 +4 +5 +6 +7 +8 +9 +10 +11

5-174

$J_{AA'}$	J_{AB}	$J_{AB'}$	$J_{BB'}$
1	2	6	1
1	6	2	1

The maximum summed intensity is 5.088.

LINE	FREQ	INTEN	LINE	FREQ	INTEN	LINE	FREQ	INTEN	LINE	FREQ	INTEN
1	82.68	0.001	15	94.68	0.446	29	100.58	5.110	43	105.61	0.445
2	85.07	0.000	16	95.07	0.000	30	101.00	3.600	44	105.61	0.445
3	89.42	0.021	17	95.32	0.316	31	101.02	0.000	45	106.00	0.000
4	89.81	0.000	18	96.00	0.000	32	101.39	0.000	46	106.19	0.000
5	91.00	0.400	19	97.02	0.000	33	101.42	1.322	47	107.32	0.610
6	91.39	0.000	20	97.72	0.000	34	101.61	1.555	48	107.72	0.000
7	91.42	0.174	21	98.00	0.000	35	101.61	1.555	49	108.00	0.000
8	92.00	0.000	22	98.39	1.555	36	102.00	0.000	50	108.58	0.174
9	92.28	0.000	23	98.39	1.555	37	102.28	0.000	51	108.61	0.000
10	92.68	0.610	24	98.58	1.322	38	102.98	0.000	52	109.00	0.400
11	93.81	0.000	25	98.61	0.000	39	104.00	0.000	53	110.19	0.000
12	94.00	0.000	26	98.98	0.000	40	104.68	0.316	54	110.58	0.021
13	94.39	0.445	27	99.00	3.600	41	104.93	0.000	55	114.93	0.000
14	94.39	0.445	28	99.42	5.110	42	105.32	0.446	56	117.32	0.001

−11 −10 −9 −8 −7 −6 −5 −4 −3 −2 −1 0 +1 +2 +3 +4 +5 +6 +7 +8 +9 +10 +11

5-175

$J_{AA'}$	J_{AB}	$J_{AB'}$	$J_{BB'}$
1	2	6	2
1	6	2	2
2	6	2	1
2	2	6	1

The maximum summed intensity is 5.564.

LINE	FREQ	INTEN	LINE	FREQ	INTEN	LINE	FREQ	INTEN	LINE	FREQ	INTEN
1	82.60	0.000	15	94.74	0.583	29	100.58	5.125	43	105.26	0.583
2	85.89	0.000	16	94.83	0.345	30	100.70	0.000	44	105.56	0.000
3	88.89	0.000	17	95.17	0.618	31	101.00	1.169	45	106.09	0.308
4	89.42	0.021	18	95.56	0.000	32	101.00	3.600	46	106.53	0.000
5	91.00	0.130	19	96.95	0.000	33	101.14	1.417	47	106.87	0.000
6	91.00	0.400	20	97.70	0.000	34	101.44	0.000	48	107.40	0.592
7	91.30	0.000	21	98.03	1.692	35	101.47	0.000	49	108.56	0.000
8	91.44	0.000	22	98.12	0.000	36	101.97	1.692	50	109.00	0.130
9	92.30	0.000	23	98.47	0.000	37	102.70	0.000	51	109.00	0.400
10	92.60	0.592	24	98.56	0.000	38	103.88	0.000	52	109.53	0.000
11	93.91	0.308	25	98.86	1.417	39	104.44	0.000	53	110.28	0.000
12	94.30	0.000	26	99.00	1.169	40	104.53	0.000	54	110.58	0.021
13	94.44	0.000	27	99.00	3.600	41	104.83	0.618	55	114.94	0.000
14	94.64	0.000	28	99.42	5.125	42	105.17	0.345	56	117.40	0.000

5-176

$J_{AA'}$	J_{AB}	$J_{AB'}$	$J_{BB'}$
1	2	6	6
1	6	2	6
6	6	2	1
6	2	6	1

The maximum summed intensity is 5.001.

LINE	FREQ	INTEN	LINE	FREQ	INTEN	LINE	FREQ	INTEN	LINE	FREQ	INTEN
1	82.06	0.000	15	94.70	0.000	29	100.23	0.000	43	105.30	0.000
2	85.08	0.000	16	94.74	0.583	30	100.57	5.156	44	106.21	0.414
3	88.30	0.000	17	95.02	0.000	31	101.00	3.600	45	107.00	0.000
4	88.50	0.000	18	95.30	0.000	32	101.14	1.417	46	107.94	0.466
5	88.58	0.030	19	96.21	1.185	33	101.42	0.726	47	108.77	0.000
6	89.43	0.023	20	96.79	0.000	34	101.65	0.000	48	109.00	0.400
7	90.44	0.000	21	97.06	0.000	35	101.70	0.000	49	109.05	0.053
8	90.95	0.053	22	97.35	1.947	36	102.65	1.947	50	110.57	0.023
9	91.00	0.400	23	98.30	0.000	37	103.56	0.000	51	111.13	0.000
10	91.86	0.000	24	98.58	0.726	38	103.59	0.000	52	111.42	0.030
11	92.06	0.466	25	98.86	1.417	39	103.79	1.185	53	111.70	0.000
12	92.62	0.000	26	99.00	3.600	40	104.35	0.000	54	113.35	0.000
13	93.79	0.414	27	99.15	0.000	41	104.70	0.000	55	115.29	0.000
14	94.56	0.000	28	99.43	5.156	42	105.26	0.583	56	117.94	0.000

5-177

$J_{AA'}$	J_{AB}	$J_{AB'}$	$J_{BB'}$
1	2	9	1
1	9	2	1

The maximum summed intensity is 5.222.

LINE	FREQ	INTEN	LINE	FREQ	INTEN	LINE	FREQ	INTEN	LINE	FREQ	INTEN
1	77.71	0.000	15	92.14	0.198	29	100.39	0.000	43	108.11	0.241
2	80.36	0.000	16	92.80	0.000	30	100.39	5.470	44	108.11	0.241
3	87.08	0.019	17	95.33	0.168	31	100.76	3.756	45	108.76	0.000
4	87.73	0.000	18	96.24	0.000	32	101.04	1.664	46	108.83	0.000
5	88.24	0.244	19	96.95	0.000	33	101.11	1.759	47	109.76	0.363
6	88.51	0.118	20	97.98	0.000	34	101.11	1.759	48	110.42	0.000
7	88.89	0.000	21	98.11	0.000	35	101.76	0.000	49	110.76	0.000
8	89.24	0.000	22	98.24	0.000	36	101.89	0.000	50	111.11	0.000
9	89.58	0.000	23	98.89	1.759	37	102.02	0.000	51	111.49	0.118
10	90.24	0.363	24	98.89	1.759	38	103.05	0.000	52	111.76	0.244
11	91.17	0.000	25	98.96	1.664	39	103.76	0.000	53	112.27	0.000
12	91.24	0.000	26	99.24	3.756	40	104.67	0.168	54	112.92	0.019
13	91.89	0.241	27	99.61	5.470	41	107.20	0.000	55	119.64	0.000
14	91.89	0.241	28	99.61	0.000	42	107.86	0.198	56	122.29	0.000

5-178

$J_{AA'}$	J_{AB}	$J_{AB'}$	$J_{BB'}$
1	2	9	2
1	9	2	2
2	9	2	1
2	2	9	1

The maximum summed intensity is 6.885.

LINE	FREQ	INTEN	LINE	FREQ	INTEN	LINE	FREQ	INTEN	LINE	FREQ	INTEN
1	77.57	0.000	15	92.60	0.000	29	100.37	0.000	43	107.84	0.277
2	81.03	0.000	16	92.79	0.255	30	100.39	5.486	44	108.30	0.000
3	86.90	0.000	17	94.68	0.162	31	100.76	3.756	45	108.49	0.200
4	87.08	0.020	18	95.77	0.000	32	100.77	1.723	46	108.89	0.
5	88.24	0.244	19	96.80	0.000	33	100.83	1.621	47	109.72	0.000
6	88.30	0.108	20	97.30	0.000	34	101.23	0.000	48	109.90	0.348
7	88.70	0.000	21	98.15	0.000	35	101.41	1.800	49	111.30	0.000
8	88.70	0.000	22	98.59	1.800	36	102.05	0.000	50	111.70	0.108
9	89.64	0.000	23	98.77	0.000	37	102.50	0.000	51	111.76	0.244
10	90.10	0.348	24	98.99	0.000	38	103.85	0.000	52	111.95	0.000
11	91.51	0.200	25	99.17	1.621	39	104.23	0.000	53	112.45	0.000
12	91.70	0.000	26	99.23	1.723	40	105.32	0.162	54	112.92	0.020
13	91.76	0.000	27	99.24	3.756	41	106.75	0.000	55	119.61	0.000
14	92.16	0.277	28	99.61	5.486	42	107.21	0.255	56	122.43	0.000

5-179

$J_{AA'}$	J_{AB}	$J_{AB'}$	$J_{BB'}$
1	2	9	9
1	9	2	9
9	9	2	1
9	2	9	1

The maximum summed intensity is 5.434.

LINE	FREQ	INTEN	LINE	FREQ	INTEN	LINE	FREQ	INTEN	LINE	FREQ	INTEN
1	75.96	0.000	15	93.14	0.000	29	100.37	5.529	43	107.99	0.000
2	80.54	0.000	16	93.38	0.000	30	100.66	0.000	44	108.15	0.194
3	83.42	0.000	17	93.42	0.000	31	100.76	3.756	45	108.96	0.160
4	83.59	0.000	18	94.05	0.000	32	101.68	1.840	46	110.80	0.000
5	85.76	0.032	19	95.15	0.000	33	101.71	1.103	47	111.51	0.207
6	85.86	0.000	20	95.62	0.912	34	102.51	1.968	48	111.76	0.244
7	86.86	0.032	21	95.95	0.000	35	102.67	0.000	49	112.90	0.022
8	87.10	0.022	22	96.19	0.000	36	104.05	0.000	50	113.14	0.032
9	88.24	0.244	23	97.49	1.968	37	104.38	0.912	51	114.24	0.032
10	88.49	0.207	24	98.29	1.103	38	104.71	0.000	52	115.27	0.000
11	89.06	0.000	25	98.32	1.840	39	104.94	0.000	53	116.58	0.000
12	90.87	0.000	26	99.24	3.756	40	105.95	0.000	54	118.33	0.000
13	91.04	0.160	27	99.47	0.000	41	106.58	0.000	55	120.60	0.000
14	91.85	0.194	28	99.63	5.529	42	106.75	0.000	56	124.04	0.000

5-180

$J_{AA'}$	J_{AB}	$J_{AB'}$	$J_{BB'}$
1	2	12	1
1	12	2	1

The maximum summed intensity is 5.434.

LINE	FREQ	INTEN	LINE	FREQ	INTEN	LINE	FREQ	INTEN	LINE	FREQ	INTEN
1	72.33	0.000	15	89.42	0.109	29	100.02	0.000	43	110.83	0.143
2	75.11	0.000	16	90.21	0.000	30	100.29	5.653	44	110.83	0.143
3	84.48	0.016	17	95.35	0.105	31	100.62	3.838	45	111.62	0.000
4	85.26	0.000	18	96.38	0.000	32	100.80	1.808	46	111.65	0.000
5	85.38	0.162	19	96.92	0.000	33	100.83	1.857	47	112.44	0.229
6	85.57	0.080	20	97.83	0.	34	100.83	1.857	48	113.23	0.000
7	86.17	0.	21	98.13	0.000	35	101.62	0.000	49	113.62	0.000
8	86.38	0.000	22	98.38	0.000	36	101.87	0.000	50	113.83	0.
9	86.77	0.000	23	99.17	1.857	37	102.17	0.	51	114.43	0.080
10	87.56	0.229	24	99.17	1.857	38	103.08	0.000	52	114.62	0.162
11	88.35	0.000	25	99.20	1.808	39	103.62	0.000	53	114.74	0.000
12	88.38	0.000	26	99.38	3.838	40	104.65	0.105	54	115.52	0.016
13	89.17	0.143	27	99.71	5.653	41	109.79	0.000	55	124.89	0.000
14	89.17	0.143	28	99.98	0.000	42	110.58	0.109	56	127.67	0.000

5-181

$J_{AA'}$	J_{AB}	$J_{AB'}$	$J_{BB'}$
1	2	12	2
1	12	2	2
2	12	2	1
2	2	12	1

The maximum summed intensity is 7.371.

LINE	FREQ	INTEN	LINE	FREQ	INTEN	LINE	FREQ	INTEN	LINE	FREQ	INTEN
1	72.15	0.000	15	90.12	0.132	29	100.15	0.000	43	110.62	0.155
2	75.68	0.000	16	90.13	0.000	30	100.29	5.667	44	111.13	0.128
3	84.48	0.016	17	94.65	0.094	31	100.57	1.845	45	111.14	0.000
4	84.49	0.000	18	95.91	0.000	32	100.62	3.838	46	111.54	0.000
5	85.38	0.162	19	96.70	0.000	33	100.67	1.794	47	112.61	0.219
6	85.44	0.077	20	97.09	0.000	34	101.08	1.872	48	112.63	0.000
7	85.86	0.000	21	98.18	0.000	35	101.09	0.000	49	114.14	0.000
8	85.91	0.000	22	98.91	0.000	36	102.33	0.000	50	114.56	0.077
9	86.86	0.000	23	98.92	1.872	37	102.40	0.000	51	114.60	0.000
10	87.39	0.219	24	99.33	1.794	38	103.81	0.000	52	114.62	0.162
11	88.86	0.000	25	99.34	0.000	39	104.09	0.000	53	114.99	0.000
12	88.87	0.128	26	99.38	3.838	40	105.35	0.094	54	115.52	0.016
13	88.97	0.000	27	99.43	1.845	41	109.36	0.000	55	124.83	0.000
14	89.38	0.155	28	99.71	5.667	42	109.88	0.132	56	127.85	0.000

5-182

$J_{AA'}$	J_{AB}	$J_{AB'}$	$J_{BB'}$
1	2	12	12
1	12	2	12
12	12	2	1
12	2	12	1

The maximum summed intensity is 5.713.

LINE	FREQ	INTEN	LINE	FREQ	INTEN	LINE	FREQ	INTEN	LINE	FREQ	INTEN
1	69.36	0.000	15	91.45	0.000	29	100.27	5.708	43	109.51	0.000
2	75.75	0.000	16	91.62	0.000	30	100.62	3.838	44	110.19	0.100
3	77.89	0.	17	92.09	0.000	31	101.67	1.314	45	112.65	0.000
4	78.45	0.000	18	92.93	0.000	32	101.84	1.933	46	113.02	0.067
5	80.91	0.000	19	93.32	0.000	33	102.43	1.979	47	114.62	0.162
6	82.71	0.021	20	93.68	0.000	34	102.80	0.000	48	115.41	0.111
7	83.10	0.030	21	94.96	0.719	35	103.64	0.000	49	115.50	0.018
8	84.50	0.018	22	95.48	0.000	36	105.04	0.719	50	116.90	0.030
9	84.59	0.111	23	97.57	1.979	37	105.94	0.000	51	117.29	0.021
10	85.38	0.162	24	98.16	1.933	38	106.32	0.000	52	119.97	0.000
11	86.22	0.000	25	98.33	1.314	39	106.66	0.000	53	121.55	0.000
12	86.98	0.067	26	98.33	0.000	40	106.68	0.000	54	123.36	0.000
13	89.07	0.	27	99.38	3.838	41	108.55	0.000	55	126.38	0.000
14	89.81	0.100	28	99.73	5.708	42	108.79	0.000	56	130.64	0.000

5-183

$J_{AA'}$	J_{AB}	$J_{AB'}$	$J_{BB'}$
1	2	15	1
1	15	2	1

The maximum summed intensity is 8.376.

LINE	FREQ	INTEN	LINE	FREQ	INTEN	LINE	FREQ	INTEN	LINE	FREQ	INTEN
1	66.73	0.000	15	86.60	0.068	29	100.21	0.000	43	113.66	0.092
2	69.59	0.	16	87.46	0.000	30	100.23	5.757	44	113.66	0.092
3	81.74	0.012	17	95.37	0.072	31	100.51	3.886	45	114.51	0.000
4	82.49	0.114	18	96.49	0.000	32	100.64	1.879	46	114.53	0.000
5	82.60	0.000	19	96.92	0.000	33	100.66	1.908	47	115.24	0.154
6	82.62	0.057	20	97.66	0.	34	100.66	1.908	48	116.10	0.000
7	83.34	0.	21	98.22	0.000	35	101.51	0.000	49	116.51	0.000
8	83.49	0.000	22	98.49	0.000	36	101.78	0.000	50	116.66	0.
9	83.90	0.000	23	99.34	1.908	37	102.34	0.	51	117.38	0.057
10	84.76	0.154	24	99.34	1.908	38	103.08	0.000	52	117.40	0.000
11	85.47	0.000	25	99.36	1.879	39	103.51	0.000	53	117.51	0.114
12	85.49	0.000	26	99.49	3.886	40	104.63	0.072	54	118.26	0.012
13	86.34	0.092	27	99.77	5.757	41	112.54	0.000	55	130.41	0.000
14	86.34	0.092	28	99.79	0.000	42	113.40	0.068	56	133.27	0.000

```
-11  -10  -9  -8  -7  -6  -5  -4  -3  -2  -1  0  +1  +2  +3  +4  +5  +6  +7  +8  +9  +10  +11
```

5-184

$J_{AA'}$	J_{AB}	$J_{AB'}$	$J_{BB'}$
1	2	15	2
1	15	2	2
2	15	2	1
2	2	15	1

The maximum summed intensity is 7.867.

LINE	FREQ	INTEN	LINE	FREQ	INTEN	LINE	FREQ	INTEN	LINE	FREQ	INTEN
1	66.54	0.000	15	87.32	0.079	29	100.01	0.000	43	113.48	0.097
2	70.09	0.	16	87.45	0.000	30	100.23	5.769	44	113.90	0.086
3	81.75	0.013	17	94.65	0.062	31	100.44	1.903	45	114.03	0.000
4	81.88	0.000	18	96.01	0.000	32	100.51	3.886	46	114.34	0.000
5	82.49	0.114	19	96.64	0.000	33	100.56	1.873	47	115.44	0.148
6	82.53	0.056	20	96.96	0.000	34	100.86	1.914	48	115.57	0.000
7	82.97	0.000	21	98.20	0.000	35	100.99	0.000	49	117.03	0.000
8	83.04	0.	22	99.01	0.000	36	102.22	0.000	50	117.38	0.000
9	84.01	0.000	23	99.14	1.914	37	102.62	0.000	51	117.47	0.056
10	84.56	0.148	24	99.44	1.873	38	103.78	0.000	52	117.51	0.114
11	85.97	0.000	25	99.49	3.886	39	103.99	0.000	53	117.70	0.000
12	86.08	0.000	26	99.56	1.903	40	105.35	0.062	54	118.25	0.013
13	86.10	0.086	27	99.57	0.000	41	112.13	0.000	55	130.33	0.
14	86.52	0.097	28	99.77	5.769	42	112.68	0.079	56	133.46	0.000

```
-11  -10  -9  -8  -7  -6  -5  -4  -3  -2  -1  0  +1  +2  +3  +4  +5  +6  +7  +8  +9  +10  +11
```

5-185

$J_{AA'}$	J_{AB}	$J_{AB'}$	$J_{BB'}$
1	2	15	15
1	15	2	15
15	15	2	1
15	2	15	1

The maximum summed intensity is 6.007.

LINE	FREQ	INTEN	LINE	FREQ	INTEN	LINE	FREQ	INTEN	LINE	FREQ	INTEN
1	62.56	0.000	15	89.43	0.000	29	100.21	5.803	43	112.26	0.056
2	70.85	0.000	16	89.81	0.000	30	100.51	3.886	44	112.39	0.000
3	71.94	0.000	17	90.63	0.000	31	101.54	1.458	45	114.48	0.000
4	73.43	0.000	18	91.13	0.	32	101.92	1.964	46	117.18	0.036
5	75.87	0.000	19	91.46	0.000	33	102.37	1.985	47	117.51	0.114
6	78.52	0.015	20	92.54	0.000	34	104.57	0.000	48	118.24	0.014
7	80.43	0.027	21	94.23	0.573	35	105.08	0.000	49	119.41	0.068
8	80.59	0.068	22	94.70	0.000	36	105.77	0.573	50	119.57	0.027
9	81.76	0.014	23	97.13	0.000	37	107.17	0.000	51	121.48	0.015
10	82.49	0.114	24	97.63	1.985	38	107.46	0.000	52	124.86	0.000
11	82.82	0.036	25	98.08	1.964	39	108.50	0.000	53	126.57	0.000
12	83.32	0.000	26	98.46	1.458	40	108.54	0.000	54	128.43	0.000
13	87.21	0.000	27	99.49	3.886	41	109.59	0.000	55	132.35	0.000
14	87.74	0.056	28	99.79	5.803	42	110.57	0.000	56	137.44	0.000

5-186

$J_{AA'}$	J_{AB}	$J_{AB'}$	$J_{BB'}$
1	2	18	1
1	18	2	1

The maximum summed intensity is 9.297.

LINE	FREQ	INTEN	LINE	FREQ	INTEN	LINE	FREQ	INTEN	LINE	FREQ	INTEN
1	61.01	0.000	15	83.74	0.046	29	100.19	5.821	43	116.54	0.064
2	63.91	0.000	16	84.63	0.000	30	100.36	0.000	44	116.54	0.064
3	78.93	0.010	17	95.38	0.053	31	100.44	3.916	45	117.44	0.000
4	79.56	0.084	18	96.56	0.000	32	100.54	1.918	46	117.45	0.000
5	79.65	0.042	19	96.91	0.000	33	100.54	1.936	47	118.11	0.110
6	79.83	0.000	20	97.54	0.000	34	100.54	1.936	48	119.00	0.000
7	80.46	0.	21	98.28	0.000	35	101.44	0.000	49	119.44	0.000
8	80.56	0.000	22	98.56	0.000	36	101.72	0.000	50	119.54	0.000
9	81.00	0.000	23	99.46	1.936	37	102.46	0.000	51	120.17	0.000
10	81.89	0.110	24	99.46	1.936	38	103.09	0.000	52	120.35	0.042
11	82.55	0.000	25	99.46	1.918	39	103.44	0.000	53	120.44	0.084
12	82.56	0.000	26	99.56	3.916	40	104.62	0.053	54	121.07	0.010
13	83.46	0.064	27	99.64	0.000	41	115.37	0.000	55	136.09	0.000
14	83.46	0.064	28	99.81	5.821	42	116.26	0.046	56	138.99	0.000

5-187

$J_{AA'}$	J_{AB}	$J_{AB'}$	$J_{BB'}$
1	2	18	2
1	18	2	2
2	18	2	1
2	2	18	1

The maximum summed intensity is8.686.

LINE	FREQ	INTEN	LINE	FREQ	INTEN	LINE	FREQ	INTEN	LINE	FREQ	INTEN
1	60.80	0.000	15	84.47	0.052	29	99.92	0.000	43	116.40	0.066
2	64.36	0.	16	84.67	0.000	30	100.19	5.830	44	116.75	0.061
3	78.93	0.010	17	94.65	0.044	31	100.37	1.934	45	116.96	0.000
4	79.14	0.000	18	96.08	0.000	32	100.44	3.916	46	117.20	0.000
5	79.56	0.084	19	96.61	0.000	33	100.48	1.915	47	118.32	0.106
6	79.60	0.042	20	96.88	0.000	34	100.72	1.939	48	118.52	0.000
7	80.04	0.000	21	98.21	0.000	35	100.92	0.000	49	119.96	0.000
8	80.12	0.000	22	99.08	0.000	36	102.14	0.000	50	120.23	0.000
9	81.13	0.000	23	99.28	1.939	37	102.77	0.000	51	120.40	0.042
10	81.68	0.106	24	99.52	1.915	38	103.74	0.000	52	120.44	0.084
11	83.04	0.000	25	99.56	3.916	39	103.92	0.000	53	120.51	0.000
12	83.16	0.000	26	99.63	1.934	40	105.35	0.044	54	121.07	0.010
13	83.25	0.061	27	99.73	0.000	41	114.97	0.000	55	135.99	0.000
14	83.60	0.066	28	99.81	5.830	42	115.53	0.052	56	139.20	0.000

5-188

$J_{AA'}$	J_{AB}	$J_{AB'}$	$J_{BB'}$
1	2	18	18
1	18	2	18
18	18	2	1
18	2	18	1

The maximum summed intensity is 6.458.

LINE	FREQ	INTEN	LINE	FREQ	INTEN	LINE	FREQ	INTEN	LINE	FREQ	INTEN
1	55.66	0.000	15	87.39	0.000	29	100.17	5.859	43	114.31	0.033
2	65.88	0.000	16	87.95	0.000	30	100.44	3.916	44	115.33	0.000
3	65.89	0.000	17	88.33	0.000	31	101.40	1.566	45	116.35	0.000
4	68.39	0.000	18	89.27	0.000	32	101.96	1.977	46	120.44	0.084
5	70.79	0.	19	90.21	0.	33	102.34	1.989	47	121.05	0.011
6	74.32	0.011	20	91.73	0.000	34	105.49	0.	48	121.38	0.023
7	76.54	0.046	21	93.43	0.461	35	106.57	0.461	49	122.28	0.024
8	77.72	0.024	22	93.90	0.000	36	107.37	0.000	50	123.46	0.046
9	78.62	0.023	23	95.92	0.000	37	108.27	0.000	51	125.68	0.011
10	78.95	0.011	24	97.66	1.989	38	108.38	0.000	52	129.82	0.000
11	79.56	0.084	25	98.04	1.977	39	110.39	0.000	53	131.61	0.000
12	80.36	0.000	26	98.60	1.566	40	110.40	0.000	54	133.51	0.000
13	85.31	0.000	27	99.56	3.916	41	110.73	0.000	55	138.41	0.000
14	85.69	0.033	28	99.83	5.859	42	112.61	0.000	56	144.34	0.000

5-189

$J_{AA'}$	J_{AB}	$J_{AB'}$	$J_{BB'}$
2	1	2	4
2	2	1	4
4	2	1	2
4	1	2	2

The maximum summed intensity is 4.222.

LINE	FREQ	INTEN	LINE	FREQ	INTEN	LINE	FREQ	INTEN	LINE	FREQ	INTEN
1	87.99	0.000	15	96.52	1.551	29	100.47	0.000	43	104.63	1.128
2	88.67	0.000	16	96.77	1.770	30	100.76	0.000	44	104.85	1.106
3	90.77	0.003	17	96.82	1.759	31	100.81	0.000	45	104.93	0.000
4	91.67	0.003	18	97.08	0.000	32	100.94	0.241	46	105.15	0.057
5	92.53	0.000	19	97.09	1.943	33	100.95	0.000	47	105.24	0.000
6	92.96	0.000	20	97.48	0.205	34	101.16	0.000	48	105.92	0.000
7	93.10	0.000	21	97.56	0.000	35	101.47	0.000	49	106.90	0.000
8	93.44	0.000	22	98.15	2.894	36	101.63	3.340	50	107.47	0.000
9	94.76	0.000	23	98.37	3.340	37	101.85	2.894	51	108.33	0.003
10	94.85	0.057	24	98.53	0.000	38	102.52	0.205	52	108.53	0.000
11	95.07	0.000	25	98.84	0.000	39	102.91	1.943	53	109.01	0.000
12	95.15	1.106	26	99.06	0.241	40	103.18	1.759	54	109.23	0.003
13	95.37	1.128	27	99.19	0.000	41	103.23	1.770	55	110.04	0.000
14	96.05	0.000	28	99.24	0.000	42	103.48	1.551	56	111.33	0.000

−11 −10 −9 −8 −7 −6 −5 −4 −3 −2 −1 0 +1 +2 +3 +4 +5 +6 +7 +8 +9 +10 +11

5-190

$J_{AA'}$	J_{AB}	$J_{AB'}$	$J_{BB'}$
2	1	2	6
2	2	1	6
6	2	1	2
6	1	2	2

The maximum summed intensity is 4.203.

LINE	FREQ	INTEN	LINE	FREQ	INTEN	LINE	FREQ	INTEN	LINE	FREQ	INTEN
1	86.00	0.000	15	96.04	0.892	29	99.50	0.000	43	104.85	1.106
2	88.12	0.000	16	96.05	0.000	30	100.48	0.000	44	104.98	0.000
3	89.34	0.002	17	96.51	1.549	31	100.94	0.241	45	105.18	0.429
4	90.58	0.000	18	96.59	0.000	32	101.16	0.000	46	105.29	0.000
5	91.11	0.000	19	96.79	1.782	33	101.42	0.000	47	107.09	0.011
6	91.67	0.003	20	96.82	1.759	34	101.62	3.343	48	107.86	0.000
7	92.91	0.011	21	97.04	1.989	35	101.85	2.894	49	108.33	0.003
8	93.38	0.000	22	97.29	0.000	36	102.71	0.000	50	108.33	0.000
9	94.35	0.000	23	97.81	0.000	37	102.74	0.000	51	109.42	0.000
10	94.71	0.000	24	98.15	2.894	38	102.96	1.989	52	109.55	0.000
11	94.82	0.429	25	98.28	0.000	39	103.18	1.759	53	110.10	0.000
12	95.15	1.106	26	98.38	3.343	40	103.21	1.782	54	110.52	0.000
13	95.57	0.000	27	98.58	0.000	41	103.49	1.549	55	110.66	0.002
14	95.62	0.000	28	99.06	0.241	42	103.96	0.892	56	111.88	0.000

−11 −10 −9 −8 −7 −6 −5 −4 −3 −2 −1 0 +1 +2 +3 +4 +5 +6 +7 +8 +9 +10 +11

5-191

$J_{AA'}$	J_{AB}	$J_{AB'}$	$J_{BB'}$
2	1	2	9
2	2	1	9
9	2	1	2
9	1	2	2

The maximum summed intensity is 4.183.

LINE	FREQ	INTEN	LINE	FREQ	INTEN	LINE	FREQ	INTEN	LINE	FREQ	INTEN
1	83.00	0.000	15	95.15	1.106	29	99.12	0.000	43	105.32	0.000
2	85.51	0.000	16	95.67	1.294	30	100.48	0.000	44	105.68	0.000
3	87.61	0.000	17	95.67	0.000	31	101.17	0.000	45	106.06	0.000
4	88.13	0.000	18	95.76	0.200	32	101.39	0.000	46	107.79	0.019
5	88.96	0.001	19	96.04	0.000	33	101.62	3.346	47	108.33	0.003
6	89.95	0.002	20	96.50	1.547	34	101.85	2.894	48	108.71	0.000
7	91.67	0.003	21	96.80	1.790	35	102.83	1.800	49	109.77	0.000
8	92.21	0.019	22	97.02	1.998	36	102.98	1.998	50	110.05	0.002
9	92.29	0.000	23	97.10	0.000	37	103.20	1.790	51	111.04	0.001
10	93.65	0.000	24	97.17	1.800	38	103.50	1.547	52	111.18	0.000
11	93.71	0.000	25	98.15	2.894	39	104.24	0.200	53	112.16	0.000
12	94.32	0.000	26	98.38	3.346	40	104.33	1.294	54	112.39	0.000
13	94.68	0.000	27	98.52	0.000	41	104.64	0.000	55	113.52	0.000
14	95.07	0.000	28	98.61	0.000	42	104.85	1.106	56	114.49	0.000

5-192

$J_{AA'}$	J_{AB}	$J_{AB'}$	$J_{BB'}$
2	1	2	12
2	2	1	12
12	2	1	2
12	1	2	2

The maximum summed intensity is 4.429.

LINE	FREQ	INTEN	LINE	FREQ	INTEN	LINE	FREQ	INTEN	LINE	FREQ	INTEN
1	80.01	0.000	15	94.67	0.000	29	100.48	0.000	43	107.09	0.011
2	82.56	0.000	16	94.98	0.000	30	101.17	0.000	44	108.33	0.003
3	84.62	0.000	17	95.15	1.106	31	101.32	0.000	45	108.67	0.000
4	85.14	0.000	18	95.62	1.306	32	101.38	0.000	46	108.75	0.000
5	86.96	0.001	19	96.04	0.000	33	101.62	3.348	47	108.91	0.000
6	88.91	0.001	20	96.49	1.545	34	101.85	2.894	48	109.91	0.000
7	89.27	0.003	21	96.80	1.794	35	102.96	1.989	49	110.73	0.003
8	89.44	0.000	22	97.01	1.999	36	102.99	1.999	50	111.09	0.001
9	90.86	0.000	23	97.04	1.989	37	103.20	1.794	51	113.04	0.001
10	91.33	0.000	24	97.20	0.000	38	103.51	1.545	52	114.04	0.000
11	91.67	0.003	25	98.15	2.894	39	104.38	1.306	53	115.10	0.000
12	92.72	0.000	26	98.38	3.348	40	104.78	0.000	54	115.38	0.000
13	92.91	0.011	27	98.62	0.000	41	104.85	1.106	55	116.52	0.000
14	93.56	0.000	28	99.07	0.000	42	105.33	0.000	56	117.44	0.000

5-193

$J_{AA'}$	J_{AB}	$J_{AB'}$	$J_{BB'}$
2	1	2	15
2	2	1	15
15	2	1	2
15	1	2	2

The maximum summed intensity is 4.529.

LINE	FREQ	INTEN	LINE	FREQ	INTEN	LINE	FREQ	INTEN	LINE	FREQ	INTEN
1	77.01	0.000	15	94.67	0.000	29	100.49	0.000	43	108.33	0.003
2	79.59	0.000	16	94.98	0.000	30	101.17	0.000	44	108.77	0.000
3	81.63	0.000	17	95.15	1.106	31	101.37	0.000	45	109.94	0.000
4	82.14	0.000	18	95.60	1.306	32	101.62	3.350	46	110.05	0.002
5	83.97	0.000	19	96.04	0.000	33	101.85	2.894	47	111.11	0.001
6	86.29	0.001	20	96.49	1.544	34	102.98	1.998	48	111.67	0.000
7	86.46	0.000	21	96.80	1.796	35	102.99	2.000	49	111.88	0.000
8	87.90	0.000	22	97.01	2.000	36	103.20	1.796	50	113.71	0.001
9	88.33	0.000	23	97.02	1.998	37	103.51	1.544	51	116.03	0.000
10	88.89	0.001	24	97.21	0.000	38	104.28	0.000	52	117.01	0.000
11	89.74	0.000	25	98.15	2.894	39	104.40	1.306	53	118.07	0.000
12	89.95	0.002	26	98.38	3.350	40	104.81	0.000	54	118.37	0.000
13	91.67	0.003	27	98.63	0.000	41	104.85	1.106	55	119.51	0.000
14	93.54	0.000	28	99.05	0.000	42	105.33	0.000	56	120.41	0.000

5-194

$J_{AA'}$	J_{AB}	$J_{AB'}$	$J_{BB'}$
2	1	2	18
2	2	1	18
18	2	1	2
18	1	2	2

The maximum summed intensity is 4.560.

LINE	FREQ	INTEN	LINE	FREQ	INTEN	LINE	FREQ	INTEN	LINE	FREQ	INTEN
1	74.01	0.000	15	94.66	0.000	29	100.49	0.000	43	108.33	0.003
2	76.60	0.000	16	94.98	0.000	30	101.17	0.000	44	108.78	0.000
3	78.63	0.000	17	95.15	1.106	31	101.37	0.000	45	109.95	0.000
4	79.15	0.000	18	95.59	1.305	32	101.62	3.351	46	111.12	0.001
5	80.97	0.000	19	96.04	0.000	33	101.85	2.894	47	113.04	0.001
6	83.31	0.000	20	96.49	1.543	34	102.99	1.999	48	114.66	0.000
7	83.48	0.000	21	96.81	1.798	35	103.00	2.000	49	114.86	0.000
8	84.93	0.000	22	97.00	2.000	36	103.19	1.798	50	116.69	0.000
9	85.34	0.000	23	97.01	1.999	37	103.51	1.543	51	119.03	0.000
10	86.75	0.000	24	97.21	0.000	38	104.41	1.305	52	120.00	0.000
11	86.96	0.001	25	98.15	2.894	39	104.81	0.000	53	121.06	0.000
12	88.88	0.001	26	98.38	3.351	40	104.85	1.106	54	121.37	0.000
13	91.67	0.003	27	98.63	0.000	41	105.34	0.000	55	122.51	0.000
14	93.52	0.000	28	99.04	0.000	42	107.26	0.000	56	123.40	0.000

5-195

$J_{AA'}$	J_{AB}	$J_{AB'}$	$J_{BB'}$
2	1	4	2
2	4	1	2

The maximum summed intensity is 4.216.

LINE	FREQ	INTEN	LINE	FREQ	INTEN	LINE	FREQ	INTEN	LINE	FREQ	INTEN
1	86.21	0.000	15	95.59	0.000	29	100.17	0.701	43	104.53	0.000
2	88.76	0.000	16	96.09	1.003	30	100.41	0.000	44	104.85	0.553
3	89.68	0.000	17	96.10	1.220	31	101.06	4.209	45	104.85	0.553
4	91.13	0.010	18	96.39	0.000	32	101.15	0.	46	105.35	0.000
5	92.02	0.068	19	96.59	0.000	33	101.28	0.000	47	105.43	0.000
6	92.15	0.	20	98.15	1.447	34	101.36	0.000	48	105.98	0.789
7	92.59	0.000	21	98.15	1.447	35	101.41	3.280	49	106.41	0.720
8	93.59	0.720	22	98.59	3.280	36	101.85	1.447	50	107.41	0.000
9	94.02	0.789	23	98.64	0.000	37	101.85	1.447	51	107.85	0.
10	94.57	0.000	24	98.72	0.000	38	103.41	0.000	52	107.98	0.068
11	94.65	0.000	25	98.85	0.	39	103.61	0.000	53	108.87	0.010
12	95.15	0.553	26	98.94	4.209	40	103.90	1.220	54	110.32	0.000
13	95.15	0.553	27	99.59	0.000	41	103.91	1.003	55	111.24	0.000
14	95.47	0.000	28	99.83	0.701	42	104.41	0.000	56	113.79	0.000

5-196

$J_{AA'}$	J_{AB}	$J_{AB'}$	$J_{BB'}$
2	1	4	4
2	4	1	4
4	4	1	2
4	1	4	2

The maximum summed intensity is 4.127.

LINE	FREQ	INTEN	LINE	FREQ	INTEN	LINE	FREQ	INTEN	LINE	FREQ	INTEN
1	85.92	0.000	15	95.70	0.945	29	100.27	0.000	43	105.10	0.000
2	87.77	0.000	16	95.87	1.014	30	100.70	1.055	44	105.27	0.000
3	90.32	0.000	17	96.32	0.000	31	100.90	0.000	45	105.46	0.000
4	90.55	0.027	18	96.32	1.397	32	101.05	4.239	46	106.07	0.188
5	91.14	0.010	19	97.00	0.000	33	101.23	0.	47	106.27	0.663
6	91.29	0.000	20	97.29	0.000	34	101.41	3.280	48	106.41	0.720
7	92.00	0.000	21	97.53	1.812	35	101.50	0.000	49	106.82	0.000
8	92.96	0.000	22	98.27	0.000	36	101.64	0.650	50	108.71	0.000
9	93.59	0.720	23	98.36	0.650	37	102.47	1.812	51	108.86	0.010
10	93.73	0.663	24	98.59	3.280	38	102.71	0.000	52	109.45	0.027
11	93.93	0.188	25	98.95	4.239	39	102.91	0.	53	109.77	0.000
12	94.90	0.000	26	99.10	0.000	40	103.68	1.397	54	110.46	0.000
13	94.95	0.000	27	99.30	1.055	41	104.13	1.014	55	111.45	0.000
14	95.32	0.000	28	99.95	0.000	42	104.30	0.945	56	114.08	0.000

5-197

$J_{AA'}$	J_{AB}	$J_{AB'}$	$J_{BB'}$
2	1	6	2
2	6	1	2

The maximum summed intensity is 4.692.

LINE	FREQ	INTEN	LINE	FREQ	INTEN	LINE	FREQ	INTEN	LINE	FREQ	INTEN
1	83.12	0.000	15	94.89	0.000	29	100.11	0.000	43	106.29	0.000
2	85.83	0.000	16	95.01	0.720	30	100.15	1.231	44	106.36	0.000
3	88.75	0.000	17	95.77	0.594	31	100.73	4.813	45	106.36	0.000
4	90.05	0.015	18	95.89	0.000	32	101.11	3.519	46	106.41	0.360
5	90.59	0.	19	96.56	0.000	33	101.41	1.640	47	106.41	0.360
6	90.89	0.000	20	98.41	0.000	34	101.41	1.640	48	107.66	0.514
7	90.93	0.111	21	98.48	0.000	35	101.45	0.000	49	108.11	0.481
8	91.89	0.481	22	98.55	0.000	36	101.52	0.000	50	109.07	0.111
9	92.34	0.514	23	98.59	1.640	37	101.59	0.000	51	109.11	0.000
10	93.59	0.360	24	98.59	1.640	38	103.44	0.000	52	109.41	0.000
11	93.59	0.360	25	98.89	3.519	39	104.11	0.000	53	109.95	0.015
12	93.64	0.000	26	99.27	4.813	40	104.23	0.594	54	111.25	0.000
13	93.64	0.000	27	99.85	1.231	41	104.99	0.720	55	114.17	0.000
14	93.71	0.000	28	99.89	0.000	42	105.11	0.000	56	116.88	0.000

5-198

$J_{AA'}$	J_{AB}	$J_{AB'}$	$J_{BB'}$
2	1	6	6
2	6	1	6
6	6	1	2
6	1	6	2

The maximum summed intensity is 5.387.

LINE	FREQ	INTEN	LINE	FREQ	INTEN	LINE	FREQ	INTEN	LINE	FREQ	INTEN
1	82.15	0.000	15	94.73	0.000	29	100.51	1.493	43	105.89	0.507
2	85.10	0.000	16	94.89	0.599	30	100.70	4.885	44	106.19	0.000
3	88.07	0.000	17	95.19	0.000	31	100.81	0.000	45	106.62	0.000
4	88.19	0.000	18	95.89	1.134	32	101.11	3.519	46	108.11	0.481
5	88.81	0.034	19	96.19	0.000	33	101.91	0.000	47	108.17	0.000
6	89.81	0.	20	96.28	0.000	34	101.97	0.995	48	108.63	0.334
7	90.08	0.018	21	96.99	0.000	35	102.09	0.000	49	108.79	0.092
8	90.91	0.000	22	97.41	0.000	36	102.39	1.908	50	109.92	0.018
9	91.21	0.092	23	97.61	1.908	37	102.59	0.000	51	111.19	0.034
10	91.37	0.334	24	98.03	0.995	38	103.65	0.000	52	111.81	0.000
11	91.89	0.481	25	98.89	3.519	39	103.81	0.000	53	112.01	0.
12	93.45	0.000	26	99.30	4.885	40	104.11	1.134	54	113.09	0.000
13	94.11	0.507	27	99.49	1.493	41	105.11	0.599	55	114.83	0.000
14	94.59	0.000	28	100.12	0.000	42	105.41	0.000	56	117.85	0.000

5-199

$J_{AA'}$	J_{AB}	$J_{AB'}$	$J_{BB'}$
2	1	9	2
2	9	1	2

The maximum summed intensity is 6.102.

LINE	FREQ	INTEN	LINE	FREQ	INTEN	LINE	FREQ	INTEN	LINE	FREQ	INTEN
1	77.97	0.000	15	92.17	0.000	29	100.17	0.000	43	108.39	0.000
2	80.81	0.000	16	92.78	0.321	30	100.34	1.649	44	108.49	0.000
3	86.70	0.000	17	95.55	0.288	31	100.47	5.320	45	109.00	0.200
4	87.87	0.017	18	96.17	0.000	32	100.83	3.715	46	109.00	0.200
5	88.00	0.	19	96.70	0.000	33	101.00	1.800	47	109.19	0.000
6	88.17	0.000	20	98.00	0.000	34	101.00	1.800	48	110.36	0.298
7	88.68	0.107	21	98.39	0.000	35	101.51	0.000	49	110.83	0.285
8	89.17	0.285	22	98.49	0.000	36	101.61	0.000	50	111.32	0.107
9	89.64	0.298	23	99.00	1.800	37	102.00	0.000	51	111.83	0.000
10	90.81	0.000	24	99.00	1.800	38	103.30	0.000	52	112.00	0.000
11	91.00	0.200	25	99.17	3.715	39	103.83	0.000	53	112.13	0.017
12	91.00	0.200	26	99.53	5.320	40	104.45	0.288	54	113.30	0.000
13	91.51	0.000	27	99.66	1.649	41	107.22	0.321	55	119.19	0.000
14	91.61	0.000	28	99.83	0.000	42	107.83	0.000	56	122.03	0.000

5-200

$J_{AA'}$	J_{AB}	$J_{AB'}$	$J_{BB'}$
2	1	9	9
2	9	1	9
9	9	1	2
9	1	9	2

The maximum summed intensity is 5.231.

LINE	FREQ	INTEN	LINE	FREQ	INTEN	LINE	FREQ	INTEN	LINE	FREQ	INTEN
1	75.79	0.000	15	93.53	0.	29	100.43	5.410	43	107.73	0.000
2	80.60	0.000	16	93.66	0.000	30	100.83	3.715	44	108.45	0.000
3	83.09	0.	17	93.98	0.000	31	101.28	1.828	45	109.35	0.172
4	83.35	0.000	18	94.35	0.000	32	101.72	0.000	46	109.94	0.000
5	85.47	0.	19	94.67	0.000	33	101.98	1.245	47	110.83	0.285
6	86.36	0.036	20	95.02	0.000	34	102.32	1.955	48	112.10	0.021
7	87.05	0.045	21	95.25	0.867	35	102.87	0.000	49	112.54	0.152
8	87.46	0.152	22	95.87	0.000	36	103.22	0.000	50	112.95	0.045
9	87.90	0.021	23	97.68	1.955	37	104.75	0.867	51	113.64	0.036
10	87.95	0.000	24	98.02	1.245	38	104.98	0.000	52	115.80	0.000
11	89.17	0.285	25	98.72	1.828	39	105.24	0.000	53	116.65	0.000
12	90.65	0.172	26	99.17	3.715	40	105.65	0.000	54	118.13	0.
13	91.16	0.000	27	99.57	5.410	41	106.02	0.000	55	120.51	0.000
14	93.09	0.269	28	100.39	0.000	42	106.91	0.269	56	124.21	0.000

5-201

$J_{AA'}$	J_{AB}	$J_{AB'}$	$J_{BB'}$
2	1	12	2
2	12	1	2

The maximum summed intensity is 7.143.

LINE	FREQ	INTEN	LINE	FREQ	INTEN	LINE	FREQ	INTEN	LINE	FREQ	INTEN
1	72.50	0.000	15	89.34	0.000	29	100.33	5.573	43	110.90	0.000
2	75.39	0.	16	90.21	0.164	30	100.34	0.000	44	111.05	0.000
3	84.24	0.000	17	95.48	0.162	31	100.37	1.815	45	111.76	0.122
4	85.24	0.	18	96.34	0.000	32	100.66	3.816	46	111.76	0.122
5	85.34	0.000	19	96.77	0.000	33	100.76	1.878	47	112.08	0.000
6	85.35	0.015	20	97.76	0.	34	100.76	1.878	48	113.19	0.190
7	86.06	0.081	21	98.37	0.000	35	101.48	0.000	49	113.66	0.184
8	86.34	0.184	22	98.52	0.000	36	101.63	0.000	50	113.94	0.081
9	86.81	0.190	23	99.24	1.878	37	102.24	0.	51	114.65	0.015
10	87.92	0.000	24	99.24	1.878	38	103.23	0.000	52	114.66	0.000
11	88.24	0.122	25	99.34	3.816	39	103.66	0.000	53	114.76	0.
12	88.24	0.122	26	99.63	1.815	40	104.52	0.162	54	115.76	0.000
13	88.95	0.000	27	99.66	0.000	41	109.79	0.164	55	124.61	0.
14	89.10	0.000	28	99.67	5.573	42	110.66	0.000	56	127.50	0.000

5-202

$J_{AA'}$	J_{AB}	$J_{AB'}$	$J_{BB'}$
2	1	12	12
2	12	1	12
12	12	1	2
12	1	12	2

The maximum summed intensity is 5.722.

LINE	FREQ	INTEN	LINE	FREQ	INTEN	LINE	FREQ	INTEN	LINE	FREQ	INTEN
1	69.10	0.000	15	92.17	0.000	29	100.30	5.651	43	108.90	0.131
2	75.83	0.000	16	92.27	0.000	30	100.66	3.816	44	111.11	0.000
3	77.41	0.	17	92.35	0.	31	101.58	1.925	45	111.69	0.000
4	78.41	0.000	18	92.41	0.000	32	101.82	1.397	46	113.29	0.075
5	80.65	0.000	19	92.73	0.000	33	102.28	1.974	47	113.66	0.184
6	82.86	0.026	20	93.27	0.000	34	103.79	0.000	48	114.62	0.019
7	83.42	0.086	21	94.58	0.683	35	103.87	0.000	49	116.14	0.033
8	83.86	0.033	22	95.25	0.000	36	104.45	0.000	50	116.58	0.086
9	85.03	0.000	23	97.72	1.974	37	105.42	0.683	51	117.14	0.026
10	85.38	0.019	24	98.18	1.397	38	106.73	0.000	52	120.31	0.000
11	86.34	0.184	25	98.42	1.925	39	107.03	0.000	53	121.59	0.000
12	86.71	0.075	26	99.34	3.816	40	107.27	0.000	54	123.21	0.000
13	89.11	0.000	27	99.41	0.000	41	107.59	0.000	55	126.45	0.000
14	91.10	0.131	28	99.70	5.651	42	108.61	0.000	56	130.90	0.000

5-203

$J_{AA'}$	J_{AB}	$J_{AB'}$	$J_{BB'}$
2	1	15	2
2	15	1	2

The maximum summed intensity is 8.144.

LINE	FREQ	INTEN	LINE	FREQ	INTEN	LINE	FREQ	INTEN	LINE	FREQ	INTEN
1	66.85	0.000	15	86.46	0.000	29	100.26	5.710	43	113.61	0.000
2	69.77	0.000	16	87.46	0.096	30	100.36	1.888	44	113.80	0.000
3	81.58	0.000	17	95.45	0.103	31	100.46	0.000	45	114.62	0.081
4	82.38	0.	18	96.46	0.000	32	100.54	3.873	46	114.62	0.081
5	82.46	0.000	19	96.82	0.000	33	100.62	1.919	47	114.99	0.000
6	82.66	0.013	20	97.62	0.	34	100.62	1.919	48	116.07	0.131
7	83.27	0.059	21	98.38	0.000	35	101.43	0.000	49	116.54	0.127
8	83.46	0.127	22	98.57	0.000	36	101.62	0.000	50	116.73	0.059
9	83.93	0.131	23	99.38	1.919	37	102.38	0.	51	117.34	0.013
10	85.01	0.000	24	99.38	1.919	38	103.18	0.000	52	117.54	0.000
11	85.38	0.081	25	99.46	3.873	39	103.54	0.000	53	117.62	0.000
12	85.38	0.081	26	99.54	0.000	40	104.55	0.103	54	118.42	0.000
13	86.20	0.000	27	99.64	1.888	41	112.54	0.096	55	130.23	0.000
14	86.39	0.000	28	99.74	5.710	42	113.54	0.000	56	133.15	0.000

−11 −10 −9 −8 −7 −6 −5 −4 −3 −2 −1 0 +1 +2 +3 +4 +5 +6 +7 +8 +9 +10 +11

5-204

$J_{AA'}$	J_{AB}	$J_{AB'}$	$J_{BB'}$
2	1	15	15
2	15	1	15
15	15	1	2
15	1	15	2

The maximum summed intensity is 5.741.

LINE	FREQ	INTEN	LINE	FREQ	INTEN	LINE	FREQ	INTEN	LINE	FREQ	INTEN
1	62.26	0.000	15	89.88	0.000	29	100.23	5.773	43	110.93	0.070
2	70.93	0.000	16	90.40	0.000	30	100.54	3.873	44	113.48	0.000
3	71.47	0.000	17	90.49	0.000	31	101.64	1.511	45	113.94	0.000
4	73.40	0.000	18	90.49	0.000	32	101.73	1.960	46	116.54	0.127
5	75.67	0.000	19	91.33	0.000	33	102.25	1.982	47	117.32	0.015
6	78.65	0.018	20	92.51	0.000	34	104.70	0.000	48	117.38	0.040
7	79.34	0.055	21	93.85	0.546	35	105.69	0.000	49	118.73	0.030
8	81.27	0.030	22	94.53	0.000	36	106.14	0.000	50	120.66	0.055
9	82.09	0.000	23	97.75	1.982	37	106.15	0.546	51	121.35	0.018
10	82.62	0.040	24	98.27	1.960	38	107.49	0.000	52	125.10	0.000
11	82.68	0.015	25	98.28	0.000	39	108.90	0.000	53	126.60	0.000
12	83.46	0.127	26	98.36	1.511	40	109.45	0.000	54	128.30	0.000
13	87.13	0.000	27	99.46	3.873	41	109.51	0.000	55	132.50	0.000
14	89.07	0.070	28	99.77	5.773	42	109.60	0.000	56	137.74	0.000

−11 −10 −9 −8 −7 −6 −5 −4 −3 −2 −1 0 +1 +2 +3 +4 +5 +6 +7 +8 +9 +10 +11

5-205

$J_{AA'}$	J_{AB}	$J_{AB'}$	$J_{BB'}$
2	1	18	2
2	18	1	2

The maximum summed intensity is 9.597.

LINE	FREQ	INTEN	LINE	FREQ	INTEN	LINE	FREQ	INTEN	LINE	FREQ	INTEN
1	61.09	0.000	15	83.58	0.000	29	100.21	5.792	43	116.46	0.000
2	64.04	0.000	16	84.64	0.062	30	100.34	1.926	44	116.64	0.000
3	78.82	0.000	17	95.44	0.071	31	100.46	3.907	45	117.51	0.057
4	79.49	0.	18	96.54	0.000	32	100.51	1.943	46	117.51	0.057
5	79.54	0.000	19	96.84	0.000	33	100.51	1.943	47	117.93	0.000
6	79.87	0.010	20	97.51	0.	34	100.54	0.000	48	118.98	0.095
7	80.41	0.045	21	98.39	0.000	35	101.39	0.000	49	119.46	0.093
8	80.54	0.093	22	98.61	0.000	36	101.61	0.000	50	119.59	0.045
9	81.02	0.095	23	99.46	0.000	37	102.49	0.	51	120.13	0.010
10	82.07	0.000	24	99.49	1.943	38	103.16	0.000	52	120.46	0.000
11	82.49	0.057	25	99.49	1.943	39	103.46	0.000	53	120.51	0.
12	82.49	0.057	26	99.54	3.907	40	104.56	0.071	54	121.18	0.000
13	83.36	0.000	27	99.66	1.926	41	115.36	0.062	55	135.96	0.000
14	83.54	0.000	28	99.79	5.792	42	116.42	0.000	56	138.91	0.000

5-206

$J_{AA'}$	J_{AB}	$J_{AB'}$	$J_{BB'}$
2	1	18	18
2	18	1	18
18	18	1	2
18	1	18	2

The maximum summed intensity is6.327.

LINE	FREQ	INTEN	LINE	FREQ	INTEN	LINE	FREQ	INTEN	LINE	FREQ	INTEN
1	55.33	0.000	15	87.53	0.000	29	100.18	5.841	43	112.98	0.040
2	65.43	0.000	16	88.29	0.000	30	100.46	3.907	44	115.33	0.000
3	65.95	0.000	17	88.36	0.000	31	101.47	1.602	45	116.85	0.000
4	68.36	0.000	18	88.71	0.000	32	101.81	1.975	46	119.46	0.093
5	70.64	0.000	19	90.36	0.000	33	102.23	1.988	47	120.11	0.012
6	74.43	0.012	20	91.71	0.000	34	105.60	0.000	48	121.39	0.026
7	75.26	0.039	21	93.05	0.440	35	106.92	0.000	49	121.53	0.025
8	78.47	0.025	22	93.75	0.000	36	106.95	0.440	50	124.74	0.039
9	78.61	0.026	23	97.12	0.000	37	108.29	0.000	51	125.57	0.012
10	79.11	0.000	24	97.77	1.988	38	108.43	0.000	52	130.01	0.000
11	79.89	0.012	25	98.19	1.975	39	110.29	0.000	53	131.64	0.000
12	80.54	0.093	26	98.53	1.602	40	110.80	0.000	54	133.40	0.000
13	85.16	0.000	27	99.54	3.907	41	111.64	0.000	55	138.61	0.000
14	87.02	0.040	28	99.82	5.841	42	111.71	0.000	56	144.67	0.000

5-207

$J_{AA'}$	J_{AB}	$J_{AB'}$	$J_{BB'}$
2	2	4	6
2	4	2	6
6	4	2	2
6	2	4	2

The maximum summed intensity is 5.343.

LINE	FREQ	INTEN	LINE	FREQ	INTEN	LINE	FREQ	INTEN	LINE	FREQ	INTEN
1	85.09	0.000	15	94.84	0.723	29	100.81	4.685	43	105.16	0.723
2	85.85	0.000	16	95.11	0.000	30	100.82	0.684	44	106.01	0.000
3	88.28	0.006	17	96.04	0.000	31	101.24	3.414	45	106.42	0.629
4	89.52	0.000	18	96.35	1.316	32	101.56	0.000	46	107.24	0.586
5	90.70	0.018	19	96.67	1.545	33	101.67	0.000	47	107.34	0.035
6	91.59	0.000	20	96.77	0.394	34	101.90	0.000	48	107.64	0.000
7	91.82	0.000	21	97.14	1.965	35	101.99	0.000	49	108.58	0.000
8	91.92	0.000	22	97.52	0.000	36	102.01	0.000	50	109.30	0.018
9	92.66	0.035	23	97.94	0.000	37	102.48	0.000	51	110.47	0.000
10	92.76	0.586	24	98.01	0.000	38	102.86	1.965	52	110.48	0.000
11	93.58	0.629	25	98.38	0.000	39	103.23	0.394	53	111.72	0.006
12	93.99	0.000	26	98.76	3.414	40	103.33	1.545	54	111.76	0.000
13	94.41	0.000	27	99.18	0.684	41	103.65	1.316	55	112.10	0.000
14	94.75	0.000	28	99.19	4.685	42	104.50	0.000	56	114.91	0.000

−11 −10 −9 −8 −7 −6 −5 −4 −3 −2 −1 0 +1 +2 +3 +4 +5 +6 +7 +8 +9 +10 +11

5-208

$J_{AA'}$	J_{AB}	$J_{AB'}$	$J_{BB'}$
2	2	4	9
2	4	2	9
9	4	2	2
9	2	4	2

The maximum summed intensity is 4.682.

LINE	FREQ	INTEN	LINE	FREQ	INTEN	LINE	FREQ	INTEN	LINE	FREQ	INTEN
1	82.87	0.000	15	94.79	0.721	29	99.91	0.000	43	105.66	0.000
2	83.77	0.000	16	95.10	0.000	30	100.81	4.690	44	106.10	0.000
3	86.62	0.000	17	95.14	0.804	31	101.24	3.414	45	107.24	0.586
4	86.65	0.004	18	95.24	0.324	32	101.92	0.000	46	107.74	0.186
5	88.89	0.000	19	95.28	0.000	33	102.04	0.000	47	109.30	0.019
6	89.78	0.008	20	96.02	0.000	34	102.38	0.000	48	109.44	0.000
7	90.38	0.000	21	96.72	1.578	35	102.52	1.676	49	110.18	0.000
8	90.70	0.019	22	97.03	0.000	36	102.94	1.992	50	110.22	0.008
9	92.26	0.186	23	97.06	1.992	37	103.28	1.578	51	111.67	0.000
10	92.40	0.000	24	97.48	1.676	38	103.42	0.000	52	113.06	0.000
11	92.62	0.000	25	97.51	0.000	39	104.76	0.324	53	113.35	0.004
12	92.76	0.586	26	97.62	0.000	40	104.86	0.804	54	113.38	0.000
13	93.90	0.000	27	98.76	3.414	41	104.90	0.000	55	115.08	0.000
14	94.63	0.000	28	99.19	4.690	42	105.21	0.721	56	116.23	0.000

−11 −10 −9 −8 −7 −6 −5 −4 −3 −2 −1 0 +1 +2 +3 +4 +5 +6 +7 +8 +9 +10 +11

5-209

$J_{AA'}$	J_{AB}	$J_{AB'}$	$J_{BB'}$
2	2	4	12
12	4	2	12
12	4	2	2
12	2	4	2

The maximum summed intensity is 4.689.

LINE	FREQ	INTEN	LINE	FREQ	INTEN	LINE	FREQ	INTEN	LINE	FREQ	INTEN
1	79.89	0.000	15	93.86	0.000	29	99.65	0.000	43	107.34	0.035
2	81.28	0.000	16	94.52	0.000	30	100.81	4.693	44	107.86	0.000
3	83.66	0.000	17	94.66	0.942	31	101.24	3.414	45	108.25	0.000
4	85.93	0.000	18	94.76	0.000	32	101.94	0.000	46	109.29	0.019
5	86.17	0.003	19	94.77	0.719	33	102.05	0.000	47	109.82	0.000
6	86.84	0.003	20	95.18	0.000	34	102.34	0.000	48	110.24	0.032
7	87.76	0.000	21	96.01	0.000	35	102.86	1.965	49	110.65	0.000
8	89.76	0.032	22	96.75	1.593	36	102.96	1.997	50	113.16	0.003
9	90.28	0.000	23	97.04	1.997	37	103.25	1.593	51	113.83	0.003
10	90.71	0.019	24	97.14	1.965	38	103.78	0.000	52	114.29	0.000
11	92.14	0.000	25	97.66	0.000	39	105.23	0.719	53	115.54	0.000
12	92.24	0.000	26	98.76	3.414	40	105.34	0.942	54	116.34	0.000
13	92.66	0.035	27	99.19	4.693	41	106.14	0.000	55	118.06	0.000
14	92.76	0.586	28	99.42	0.000	42	107.24	0.586	56	118.72	0.000

−11 −10 −9 −8 −7 −6 −5 −4 −3 −2 −1 0 +1 +2 +3 +4 +5 +6 +7 +8 +9 +10 +11

5-210

$J_{AA'}$	J_{AB}	$J_{AB'}$	$J_{BB'}$
2	2	4	15
2	4	2	15
15	4	2	2
15	2	4	2

The maximum summed intensity is 4.694.

LINE	FREQ	INTEN	LINE	FREQ	INTEN	LINE	FREQ	INTEN	LINE	FREQ	INTEN
1	76.90	0.000	15	92.76	0.586	29	100.81	4.695	43	109.29	0.019
2	78.44	0.000	16	93.83	0.000	30	101.24	3.414	44	109.91	0.000
3	80.68	0.000	17	94.51	0.956	31	101.95	0.000	45	110.22	0.008
4	82.95	0.000	18	94.75	0.717	32	102.06	0.000	46	110.78	0.000
5	83.87	0.001	19	94.83	0.000	33	102.32	0.000	47	110.83	0.000
6	84.86	0.000	20	95.13	0.000	34	102.41	0.000	48	111.14	0.000
7	86.02	0.002	21	96.00	0.000	35	102.94	1.992	49	113.07	0.009
8	86.93	0.009	22	96.76	1.602	36	102.98	1.999	50	113.98	0.002
9	87.55	0.000	23	97.02	1.999	37	103.24	1.602	51	116.13	0.001
10	89.17	0.000	24	97.06	1.992	38	103.86	0.000	52	117.19	0.000
11	89.78	0.008	25	97.68	0.000	39	105.25	0.717	53	118.37	0.000
12	90.71	0.019	26	98.76	3.414	40	105.49	0.956	54	119.32	0.000
13	91.68	0.000	27	99.19	4.695	41	106.17	0.000	55	121.05	0.
14	92.14	0.000	28	99.26	0.000	42	107.24	0.586	56	121.56	0.000

−11 −10 −9 −8 −7 −6 −5 −4 −3 −2 −1 0 +1 +2 +3 +4 +5 +6 +7 +8 +9 +10 +11

5-211

$J_{AA'}$	J_{AB}	$J_{AB'}$	$J_{BB'}$
2	2	4	18
2	4	2	18
18	4	2	2
18	2	4	2

The maximum summed intensity is 4.697.

LINE	FREQ	INTEN	LINE	FREQ	INTEN	LINE	FREQ	INTEN	LINE	FREQ	INTEN
1	73.90	0.000	15	92.76	0.586	29	100.81	4.697	43	109.29	0.019
2	75.52	0.000	16	93.82	0.000	30	101.24	3.414	44	109.95	0.000
3	77.70	0.000	17	94.44	0.956	31	101.95	0.000	45	110.85	0.000
4	79.97	0.000	18	94.74	0.715	32	102.06	0.000	46	113.16	0.003
5	80.89	0.001	19	94.86	0.000	33	102.30	0.000	47	113.82	0.000
6	81.90	0.000	20	95.10	0.000	34	102.96	1.997	48	114.04	0.002
7	84.01	0.003	21	96.00	0.000	35	102.98	1.999	49	114.08	0.000
8	84.67	0.000	22	96.77	1.608	36	103.23	1.608	50	115.99	0.003
9	85.96	0.002	23	97.02	1.999	37	103.89	0.000	51	119.11	0.001
10	86.18	0.000	24	97.04	1.997	38	105.26	0.715	52	120.15	0.000
11	86.84	0.003	25	97.70	0.000	39	105.30	0.000	53	121.28	0.000
12	88.75	0.000	26	98.76	3.414	40	105.56	0.956	54	122.30	0.000
13	90.71	0.019	27	99.19	0.000	41	106.18	0.000	55	124.05	0.000
14	92.10	0.000	28	99.19	4.697	42	107.24	0.586	56	124.48	0.000

5-212

$J_{AA'}$	J_{AB}	$J_{AB'}$	$J_{BB'}$
2	2	6	4
2	6	2	4
4	6	2	2
4	2	6	2

The maximum summed intensity is 6.171.

LINE	FREQ	INTEN	LINE	FREQ	INTEN	LINE	FREQ	INTEN	LINE	FREQ	INTEN
1	82.24	0.000	15	94.42	0.000	29	100.08	0.000	43	105.74	0.000
2	86.96	0.000	16	94.94	0.684	30	100.24	0.000	44	105.76	0.000
3	87.41	0.000	17	95.76	0.000	31	100.57	5.151	45	106.06	0.406
4	89.25	0.043	18	95.83	0.	32	100.59	1.316	46	106.71	0.200
5	89.43	0.023	19	95.90	0.000	33	100.75	0.783	47	107.22	0.000
6	89.76	0.000	20	96.06	1.087	34	101.00	3.600	48	107.76	0.507
7	90.17	0.	21	97.76	1.800	35	102.24	1.800	49	109.00	0.400
8	91.00	0.400	22	98.28	0.000	36	102.53	0.000	50	110.24	0.000
9	92.24	0.507	23	99.00	3.600	37	102.53	0.000	51	110.57	0.023
10	93.07	0.000	24	99.11	0.000	38	103.94	1.087	52	110.75	0.043
11	93.29	0.200	25	99.25	0.783	39	104.24	0.000	53	111.40	0.000
12	93.59	0.000	26	99.41	1.316	40	104.77	0.000	54	111.47	0.000
13	93.94	0.406	27	99.43	5.151	41	105.06	0.684	55	114.23	0.000
14	94.24	0.000	28	99.76	0.000	42	105.29	0.000	56	117.76	0.000

5-213

$J_{AA'}$	J_{AB}	$J_{AB'}$	$J_{BB'}$
2	2	9	4
2	9	2	4
4	9	2	2
4	2	9	2

The maximum summed intensity is 7.213.

LINE	FREQ	INTEN	LINE	FREQ	INTEN	LINE	FREQ	INTEN	LINE	FREQ	INTEN
1	77.04	0.000	15	93.09	0.000	29	100.05	1.417	43	106.91	0.000
2	82.28	0.000	16	93.10	0.171	30	100.38	0.000	44	107.67	0.301
3	85.04	0.000	17	94.37	0.511	31	100.38	5.513	45	108.38	0.000
4	87.09	0.021	18	94.38	0.000	32	100.39	1.699	46	108.63	0.000
5	87.09	0.000	19	95.53	0.000	33	100.71	0.000	47	108.96	0.160
6	87.42	0.071	20	95.67	0.000	34	100.76	3.756	48	110.43	0.295
7	87.47	0.	21	98.00	0.000	35	101.68	1.840	49	111.76	0.244
8	88.24	0.244	22	98.32	1.840	36	102.95	0.000	50	112.58	0.071
9	89.57	0.295	23	98.34	0.000	37	103.18	0.000	51	112.91	0.000
10	90.34	0.000	24	99.24	3.756	38	105.61	0.000	52	112.91	0.021
11	91.04	0.160	25	99.61	1.699	39	105.62	0.000	53	113.67	0.000
12	92.32	0.000	26	99.62	5.513	40	105.63	0.511	54	113.82	0.000
13	92.33	0.301	27	99.62	0.000	41	106.40	0.000	55	119.01	0.000
14	92.65	0.000	28	99.95	1.417	42	106.90	0.171	56	122.96	0.000

5-214

$J_{AA'}$	J_{AB}	$J_{AB'}$	$J_{BB'}$
2	2	12	4
2	12	2	4
4	12	2	2
4	2	12	2

The maximum summed intensity is 8.785.

LINE	FREQ	INTEN	LINE	FREQ	INTEN	LINE	FREQ	INTEN	LINE	FREQ	INTEN
1	71.54	0.000	15	90.29	0.000	29	100.19	1.716	43	109.71	0.000
2	76.77	0.000	16	92.01	0.239	30	100.28	5.690	44	110.48	0.162
3	82.70	0.000	17	92.76	0.083	31	100.29	1.838	45	110.83	0.000
4	84.29	0.000	18	94.48	0.000	32	100.48	0.000	46	111.44	0.000
5	84.49	0.017	19	95.39	0.	33	100.62	3.838	47	111.50	0.112
6	84.61	0.	20	95.51	0.000	34	100.96	0.000	48	113.23	0.189
7	84.96	0.065	21	97.99	0.000	35	101.30	1.888	49	114.62	0.162
8	85.38	0.162	22	98.02	0.000	36	103.03	0.000	50	115.04	0.065
9	86.77	0.189	23	98.70	1.888	37	103.60	0.	51	115.51	0.017
10	87.54	0.000	24	99.38	3.838	38	105.51	0.000	52	115.71	0.000
11	88.50	0.112	25	99.52	0.000	39	105.52	0.000	53	116.28	0.000
12	89.52	0.162	26	99.71	1.838	40	107.24	0.083	54	116.40	0.000
13	90.19	0.000	27	99.72	5.690	41	107.99	0.239	55	124.25	0.000
14	90.22	0.000	28	99.81	1.716	42	108.76	0.000	56	128.46	0.000

5-215

$J_{AA'}$	J_{AB}	$J_{AB'}$	$J_{BB'}$
2	2	15	4
2	15	2	4
4	15	2	2
4	2	15	2

The maximum summed intensity is 9.462.

LINE	FREQ	INTEN	LINE	FREQ	INTEN	LINE	FREQ	INTEN	LINE	FREQ	INTEN
1	65.88	0.000	15	87.74	0.000	29	100.22	5.787	43	112.59	0.000
2	71.09	0.000	16	89.36	0.129	30	100.22	1.900	44	113.38	0.100
3	80.14	0.000	17	92.62	0.048	31	100.26	1.841	45	113.39	0.000
4	81.41	0.000	18	94.56	0.000	32	100.51	3.886	46	114.21	0.079
5	81.70	0.000	19	95.30	0.000	33	100.56	0.000	47	114.48	0.000
6	81.75	0.013	20	95.40	0.000	34	101.05	0.000	48	116.10	0.130
7	82.23	0.051	21	97.83	0.000	35	101.06	1.921	49	117.51	0.114
8	82.49	0.114	22	98.12	0.000	36	103.00	0.000	50	117.77	0.051
9	83.90	0.130	23	98.94	1.921	37	103.87	0.000	51	118.25	0.013
10	84.69	0.000	24	99.44	0.000	38	105.43	0.000	52	118.59	0.000
11	85.79	0.079	25	99.49	3.886	39	105.44	0.000	53	119.03	0.000
12	86.62	0.100	26	99.74	1.841	40	107.38	0.048	54	119.13	0.000
13	87.41	0.000	27	99.78	1.900	41	110.64	0.129	55	129.74	0.000
14	87.45	0.000	28	99.78	5.787	42	111.43	0.000	56	134.12	0.000

5-216

$J_{AA'}$	J_{AB}	$J_{AB'}$	$J_{BB'}$
2	2	18	4
2	18	2	4
4	18	2	2
4	2	18	2

The maximum summed intensity is 10.042.

LINE	FREQ	INTEN	LINE	FREQ	INTEN	LINE	FREQ	INTEN	LINE	FREQ	INTEN
1	60.12	0.000	15	85.07	0.000	29	100.18	5.845	43	115.50	0.000
2	65.31	0.	16	86.57	0.078	30	100.18	1.933	44	116.11	0.000
3	77.44	0.000	17	92.55	0.031	31	100.27	1.901	45	116.31	0.067
4	78.50	0.000	18	94.62	0.000	32	100.44	3.916	46	117.01	0.057
5	78.75	0.	19	95.25	0.	33	100.62	0.000	47	117.50	0.000
6	78.94	0.011	20	95.32	0.000	34	100.88	1.943	48	119.00	0.095
7	79.39	0.040	21	97.74	0.000	35	101.08	0.000	49	120.44	0.084
8	79.56	0.084	22	98.22	0.000	36	102.95	0.000	50	120.61	0.040
9	81.00	0.095	23	99.12	1.943	37	104.06	0.000	51	121.06	0.011
10	81.80	0.000	24	99.38	0.000	38	105.37	0.000	52	121.50	0.000
11	82.99	0.057	25	99.56	3.916	39	105.38	0.000	53	121.87	0.000
12	83.69	0.067	26	99.73	1.901	40	107.45	0.031	54	121.94	0.
13	84.50	0.000	27	99.82	1.933	41	113.43	0.078	55	135.39	0.000
14	84.59	0.000	28	99.82	5.845	42	114.24	0.000	56	139.88	0.000

5-217

$J_{AA'}$	J_{AB}	$J_{AB'}$	$J_{BB'}$
2	4	6	2
2	6	4	2

The maximum summed intensity is 5.476.

LINE	FREQ	INTEN	LINE	FREQ	INTEN	LINE	FREQ	INTEN	LINE	FREQ	INTEN
1	80.76	0.001	15	95.17	0.000	29	100.40	5.465	43	105.07	0.000
2	85.43	0.000	16	95.84	0.684	30	100.75	0.000	44	105.57	0.000
3	87.94	0.025	17	95.84	0.684	31	100.83	3.715	45	106.83	0.000
4	88.60	0.000	18	96.16	0.000	32	101.42	0.669	46	107.58	0.608
5	89.17	0.285	19	96.43	0.000	33	102.16	1.316	47	108.24	0.186
6	89.76	0.063	20	96.58	0.983	34	102.16	1.316	48	108.25	0.000
7	89.84	0.000	21	97.17	0.000	35	102.75	0.000	49	108.83	0.000
8	91.17	0.000	22	97.25	0.000	36	102.83	0.000	50	110.16	0.000
9	91.75	0.000	23	97.84	1.316	37	103.42	0.983	51	110.24	0.063
10	91.76	0.186	24	97.84	1.316	38	103.57	0.000	52	110.83	0.285
11	92.42	0.608	25	98.58	0.669	39	103.84	0.000	53	111.40	0.000
12	93.17	0.000	26	99.17	3.715	40	104.16	0.684	54	112.06	0.025
13	94.43	0.000	27	99.25	0.000	41	104.16	0.684	55	114.57	0.000
14	94.93	0.000	28	99.60	5.465	42	104.83	0.000	56	119.24	0.001

−11 −10 −9 −8 −7 −6 −5 −4 −3 −2 −1 0 +1 +2 +3 +4 +5 +6 +7 +8 +9 +10 +11

5-218

$J_{AA'}$	J_{AB}	$J_{AB'}$	$J_{BB'}$
2	4	6	4
2	6	4	4
4	6	4	2
4	4	6	2

The maximum summed intensity is 5.542.

LINE	FREQ	INTEN	LINE	FREQ	INTEN	LINE	FREQ	INTEN	LINE	FREQ	INTEN
1	80.70	0.001	15	94.75	0.000	29	99.82	0.277	43	106.35	0.000
2	86.64	0.000	16	94.89	0.000	30	100.18	0.277	44	107.00	0.000
3	87.29	0.000	17	95.63	0.000	31	100.40	5.466	45	107.13	0.000
4	87.94	0.025	18	95.75	0.000	32	100.82	0.684	46	107.42	0.000
5	88.16	0.015	19	96.35	1.316	33	100.83	3.715	47	107.64	0.593
6	89.17	0.285	20	96.92	1.390	34	101.42	0.000	48	108.58	0.233
7	89.75	0.000	21	97.29	1.857	35	102.48	0.000	49	110.25	0.000
8	89.76	0.000	22	98.01	0.000	36	102.71	1.857	50	110.83	0.285
9	91.42	0.233	23	98.58	0.000	37	103.08	1.390	51	111.47	0.000
10	91.77	0.000	24	98.89	0.000	38	103.65	1.316	52	111.84	0.015
11	92.36	0.593	25	99.17	3.715	39	103.88	0.000	53	112.06	0.025
12	92.58	0.000	26	99.18	0.684	40	103.88	0.000	54	112.12	0.000
13	94.24	0.000	27	99.23	0.000	41	104.25	0.000	55	114.59	0.000
14	94.46	0.143	28	99.60	5.466	42	105.54	0.143	56	119.30	0.001

−11 −10 −9 −8 −7 −6 −5 −4 −3 −2 −1 0 +1 +2 +3 +4 +5 +6 +7 +8 +9 +10 +11

5-219

$J_{AA'}$	J_{AB}	$J_{AB'}$	$J_{BB'}$
2	4	6	6
2	6	4	6
6	6	4	2
6	4	6	2

The maximum summed intensity is 5.481.

LINE	FREQ	INTEN	LINE	FREQ	INTEN	LINE	FREQ	INTEN	LINE	FREQ	INTEN
1	80.60	0.001	15	93.76	0.000	29	99.72	0.000	43	107.34	0.035
2	84.67	0.000	16	94.78	0.000	30	100.40	5.467	44	107.59	0.000
3	86.37	0.006	17	94.87	0.000	31	100.41	0.000	45	107.74	0.565
4	87.93	0.000	18	95.93	0.000	32	100.82	0.684	46	108.69	0.242
5	87.94	0.025	19	96.35	1.316	33	100.83	3.715	47	108.82	0.000
6	89.02	0.000	20	97.03	1.500	34	101.97	0.195	48	108.90	0.000
7	89.17	0.285	21	97.14	1.965	35	102.55	0.000	49	110.83	0.285
8	89.59	0.000	22	97.61	0.000	36	102.86	1.965	50	111.65	0.000
9	91.31	0.242	23	98.03	0.195	37	102.97	1.500	51	112.06	0.025
10	91.85	0.000	24	98.70	0.000	38	103.65	1.316	52	112.07	0.000
11	92.26	0.565	25	99.17	3.715	39	103.90	0.000	53	113.63	0.006
12	92.41	0.000	26	99.18	0.684	40	103.96	0.000	54	114.10	0.
13	92.41	0.000	27	99.59	0.000	41	104.07	0.000	55	114.67	0.000
14	92.66	0.035	28	99.60	5.467	42	104.47	0.000	56	119.40	0.001

5-220

$J_{AA'}$	J_{AB}	$J_{AB'}$	$J_{BB'}$
2	4	9	2
2	9	4	2

The maximum summed intensity is 5.719.

LINE	FREQ	INTEN	LINE	FREQ	INTEN	LINE	FREQ	INTEN	LINE	FREQ	INTEN
1	75.96	0.000	15	93.59	0.360	29	100.09	0.000	43	106.66	0.000
2	81.21	0.	16	93.59	0.360	30	100.29	5.671	44	107.66	0.000
3	85.39	0.020	17	94.41	0.310	31	100.66	3.816	45	107.70	0.000
4	86.34	0.184	18	94.46	0.000	32	101.16	1.470	46	108.72	0.063
5	86.65	0.000	19	95.41	0.000	33	101.41	1.640	47	109.73	0.384
6	86.84	0.082	20	95.66	0.000	34	101.41	1.640	48	110.98	0.000
7	87.59	0.000	21	96.53	0.000	35	102.66	0.000	49	111.66	0.000
8	88.34	0.000	22	97.34	0.000	36	103.47	0.000	50	112.41	0.
9	89.02	0.000	23	98.59	1.640	37	104.34	0.000	51	113.16	0.082
10	90.27	0.384	24	98.59	1.640	38	104.59	0.000	52	113.35	0.000
11	91.28	0.063	25	98.84	1.470	39	105.54	0.000	53	113.66	0.184
12	92.10	0.000	26	99.34	3.816	40	105.59	0.310	54	114.61	0.020
13	92.34	0.000	27	99.71	5.671	41	106.41	0.360	55	118.79	0.000
14	93.34	0.000	28	99.91	0.000	42	106.41	0.360	56	124.04	0.000

5-221

$J_{AA'}$	J_{AB}	$J_{AB'}$	$J_{BB'}$
2	4	9	4
2	9	4	4
4	9	4	2
4	4	6	2

The maximum summed intensity is 6.609.

LINE	FREQ	INTEN	LINE	FREQ	INTEN	LINE	FREQ	INTEN	LINE	FREQ	INTEN
1	75.76	0.000	15	93.15	0.000	29	99.71	5.673	43	107.41	0.193
2	82.72	0.000	16	93.70	0.000	30	100.29	5.673	44	107.47	0.000
3	84.84	0.000	17	94.11	0.507	31	100.47	1.194	45	108.41	0.000
4	85.40	0.020	18	94.27	0.000	32	100.51	1.493	46	109.36	0.000
5	86.15	0.055	19	94.96	0.000	33	100.66	3.816	47	109.84	0.088
6	86.34	0.184	20	95.52	0.608	34	101.47	0.000	48	109.92	0.361
7	87.15	0.000	21	97.12	0.000	35	102.02	1.807	49	112.85	0.000
8	87.30	0.	22	97.98	1.807	36	103.52	0.000	50	113.65	0.000
9	89.12	0.	23	98.53	0.000	37	104.39	0.000	51	113.66	0.184
10	90.08	0.361	24	98.97	0.000	38	104.48	0.608	52	113.85	0.055
11	90.16	0.088	25	99.34	3.816	39	104.78	0.000	53	114.22	0.000
12	92.53	0.000	26	99.49	1.493	40	105.89	0.507	54	114.60	0.020
13	92.59	0.193	27	99.51	0.000	41	106.85	0.000	55	118.79	0.000
14	93.11	0.000	28	99.53	1.194	42	107.24	0.000	56	124.24	0.000

−11 −10 −9 −8 −7 −6 −5 −4 −3 −2 −1 0 +1 +2 +3 +4 +5 +6 +7 +8 +9 +10 +11

5-222

$J_{AA'}$	J_{AB}	$J_{AB'}$	$J_{BB'}$
2	4	9	9
2	9	4	9
9	9	4	2
9	4	9	2

The maximum summed intensity is 5.711.

LINE	FREQ	INTEN	LINE	FREQ	INTEN	LINE	FREQ	INTEN	LINE	FREQ	INTEN
1	74.93	0.000	15	91.64	0.000	29	99.71	5.676	43	108.36	0.000
2	80.09	0.000	16	93.15	0.270	30	100.29	5.676	44	110.39	0.000
3	83.04	0.000	17	93.34	0.000	31	100.66	3.816	45	110.75	0.267
4	83.23	0.013	18	94.02	0.000	32	101.75	1.730	46	111.08	0.000
5	85.04	0.000	19	94.04	0.000	33	102.45	0.627	47	111.08	0.127
6	85.40	0.021	20	96.76	1.269	34	102.64	0.000	48	111.27	0.032
7	85.45	0.000	21	97.15	0.000	35	102.66	1.968	49	113.66	0.184
8	86.34	0.184	22	97.34	1.968	36	103.24	1.269	50	114.60	0.021
9	88.73	0.032	23	97.36	0.000	37	104.13	0.000	51	115.49	0.000
10	88.92	0.127	24	97.55	0.627	38	105.04	0.000	52	116.77	0.013
11	89.25	0.267	25	98.25	1.730	39	105.38	0.000	53	116.96	0.000
12	90.14	0.000	26	98.44	0.000	40	105.45	0.000	54	118.96	0.
13	90.55	0.000	27	99.03	0.000	41	105.96	0.000	55	119.38	0.000
14	91.46	0.000	28	99.34	3.816	42	106.85	0.270	56	125.07	0.000

−11 −10 −9 −8 −7 −6 −5 −4 −3 −2 −1 0 +1 +2 +3 +4 +5 +6 +7 +8 +9 +10 +11

5-223

$J_{AA'}$	J_{AB}	$J_{AB'}$	$J_{BB'}$
2	4	12	2
2	12	4	2

The maximum summed intensity is 5.800.

LINE	FREQ	INTEN	LINE	FREQ	INTEN	LINE	FREQ	INTEN	LINE	FREQ	INTEN
1	70.66	0.000	15	91.13	0.033	29	100.22	5.778	43	109.00	0.200
2	76.20	0.000	16	91.78	0.146	30	100.54	3.873	44	109.00	0.200
3	82.69	0.016	17	93.32	0.000	31	100.65	0.000	45	110.54	0.000
4	83.46	0.127	18	93.46	0.000	32	100.89	1.720	46	110.65	0.000
5	83.81	0.061	19	94.23	0.000	33	101.00	1.800	47	112.25	0.246
6	84.23	0.000	20	95.00	0.	34	101.00	1.800	48	113.80	0.000
7	85.00	0.	21	96.68	0.000	35	102.54	0.000	49	114.54	0.000
8	85.46	0.000	22	97.46	0.000	36	103.32	0.000	50	115.00	0.
9	86.20	0.000	23	99.00	1.800	37	105.00	0.	51	115.77	0.000
10	87.75	0.246	24	99.00	1.800	38	105.77	0.000	52	116.19	0.061
11	89.35	0.000	25	99.11	1.720	39	106.54	0.000	53	116.54	0.127
12	89.46	0.000	26	99.35	0.000	40	106.68	0.000	54	117.31	0.016
13	91.00	0.200	27	99.46	3.873	41	108.22	0.146	55	123.80	0.000
14	91.00	0.200	28	99.78	5.778	42	108.87	0.033	56	129.34	0.000

−11 −10 −9 −8 −7 −6 −5 −4 −3 −2 −1 0 +1 +2 +3 +4 +5 +6 +7 +8 +9 +10 +11

5-224

$J_{AA'}$	J_{AB}	$J_{AB'}$	$J_{BB'}$
2	4	12	4
2	12	4	4
4	12	4	2
4	4	12	2

The maximum summed intensity is 7.323.

LINE	FREQ	INTEN	LINE	FREQ	INTEN	LINE	FREQ	INTEN	LINE	FREQ	INTEN
1	70.38	0.000	15	91.40	0.241	29	99.78	5.780	43	109.67	0.000
2	77.45	0.000	16	92.58	0.000	30	100.22	5.780	44	109.78	0.143
3	82.58	0.000	17	93.03	0.000	31	100.35	1.759	45	110.23	0.039
4	82.69	0.016	18	93.14	0.249	32	100.54	1.634	46	110.66	0.000
5	83.46	0.054	19	93.47	0.000	33	100.54	3.873	47	112.42	0.000
6	83.46	0.127	20	93.89	0.000	34	101.42	0.000	48	112.53	0.229
7	84.33	0.000	21	96.84	0.000	35	101.53	1.857	49	115.67	0.000
8	84.53	0.000	22	98.47	1.857	36	104.35	0.000	50	116.24	0.000
9	86.39	0.000	23	98.58	0.000	37	105.34	0.000	51	116.54	0.054
10	87.47	0.229	24	99.34	0.000	38	105.78	0.000	52	116.54	0.127
11	89.77	0.039	25	99.46	1.634	39	106.86	0.249	53	116.66	0.000
12	90.22	0.143	26	99.46	3.873	40	107.29	0.000	54	117.31	0.016
13	90.33	0.000	27	99.47	0.000	41	107.42	0.000	55	123.74	0.000
14	90.53	0.000	28	99.65	1.759	42	108.60	0.241	56	129.62	0.000

−11 −10 −9 −8 −7 −6 −5 −4 −3 −2 −1 0 +1 +2 +3 +4 +5 +6 +7 +8 +9 +10 +11

5-225

$J_{AA'}$	J_{AB}	$J_{AB'}$	$J_{BB'}$
2	4	12	12
2	12	4	12
12	12	4	2
12	4	12	2

The maximum summed intensity is 5.839.

LINE	FREQ	INTEN	LINE	FREQ	INTEN	LINE	FREQ	INTEN	LINE	FREQ	INTEN
1	68.47	0.000	15	89.47	0.000	29	100.22	5.785	43	110.88	0.092
2	75.29	0.000	16	90.86	0.000	30	100.54	3.873	44	111.29	0.000
3	78.05	0.000	17	91.61	0.000	31	100.55	0.000	45	112.86	0.000
4	79.54	0.000	18	92.05	0.000	32	101.93	1.908	46	113.40	0.073
5	80.53	0.000	19	93.18	0.000	33	102.38	0.921	47	114.44	0.137
6	80.54	0.015	20	94.98	0.000	34	102.54	1.978	48	115.35	0.022
7	82.69	0.016	21	95.14	0.000	35	103.69	1.054	49	116.54	0.127
8	83.46	0.127	22	96.31	1.054	36	104.86	0.000	50	117.31	0.016
9	84.65	0.022	23	97.46	1.978	37	106.06	0.000	51	119.46	0.015
10	85.56	0.137	24	97.62	0.921	38	106.61	0.000	52	120.24	0.000
11	86.60	0.073	25	97.67	0.000	39	106.80	0.000	53	121.95	0.000
12	88.49	0.000	26	98.07	1.908	40	107.04	0.000	54	123.94	0.000
13	88.91	0.	27	99.46	3.873	41	107.95	0.000	55	124.93	0.000
14	89.12	0.092	28	99.78	5.785	42	109.14	0.000	56	131.53	0.000

−11 −10 −9 −8 −7 −6 −5 −4 −3 −2 −1 0 +1 +2 +3 +4 +5 +6 +7 +8 +9 +10 +11

5-226

$J_{AA'}$	J_{AB}	$J_{AB'}$	$J_{BB'}$
2	4	15	2
2	15	4	2

The maximum summed intensity is 6.322.

LINE	FREQ	INTEN	LINE	FREQ	INTEN	LINE	FREQ	INTEN	LINE	FREQ	INTEN
1	65.11	0.000	15	89.00	0.085	29	100.18	5.840	43	111.76	0.122
2	70.81	0.	16	90.70	0.000	30	100.46	3.907	44	111.76	0.122
3	79.89	0.012	17	91.07	0.021	31	100.71	1.831	45	113.46	0.000
4	80.54	0.093	18	93.54	0.000	32	100.76	1.878	46	113.52	0.000
5	80.79	0.046	19	94.12	0.000	33	100.76	1.878	47	114.97	0.165
6	81.59	0.000	20	94.76	0.	34	100.99	0.000	48	116.66	0.000
7	82.24	0.	21	96.77	0.000	35	102.46	0.000	49	117.46	0.000
8	82.54	0.000	22	97.54	0.000	36	103.23	0.000	50	117.76	0.
9	83.34	0.000	23	99.01	0.000	37	105.24	0.	51	118.41	0.000
10	85.03	0.165	24	99.24	1.878	38	105.88	0.000	52	119.21	0.046
11	86.48	0.000	25	99.24	1.878	39	106.46	0.000	53	119.46	0.093
12	86.54	0.000	26	99.29	1.831	40	108.93	0.021	54	120.11	0.012
13	88.24	0.122	27	99.54	3.907	41	109.30	0.000	55	129.19	0.000
14	88.24	0.122	28	99.82	5.840	42	111.00	0.085	56	134.89	0.000

−11 −10 −9 −8 −7 −6 −5 −4 −3 −2 −1 0 +1 +2 +3 +4 +5 +6 +7 +8 +9 +10 +11

5-227

$J_{AA'}$	J_{AB}	$J_{AB'}$	$J_{BB'}$
2	4	15	4
2	15	4	4
4	15	4	2
4	4	15	2

The maximum summed intensity is 8.085.

LINE	FREQ	INTEN	LINE	FREQ	INTEN	LINE	FREQ	INTEN	LINE	FREQ	INTEN
1	64.77	0.000	15	89.62	0.022	29	99.82	5.842	43	111.44	0.136
2	71.88	0.000	16	90.45	0.127	30	100.18	5.842	44	112.39	0.099
3	79.89	0.012	17	90.62	0.000	31	100.26	1.864	45	112.55	0.000
4	80.05	0.000	18	92.63	0.000	32	100.46	3.907	46	113.26	0.000
5	80.54	0.093	19	93.35	0.000	33	100.50	1.799	47	115.30	0.154
6	80.58	0.043	20	93.66	0.000	34	101.21	1.901	48	115.47	0.000
7	81.45	0.000	21	96.73	0.000	35	101.37	0.000	49	118.55	0.000
8	81.65	0.000	22	98.63	0.000	36	104.22	0.000	50	119.00	0.000
9	83.59	0.000	23	98.79	1.901	37	105.70	0.000	51	119.30	0.000
10	84.70	0.154	24	99.39	0.000	38	107.29	0.000	52	119.42	0.043
11	87.45	0.000	25	99.50	1.799	39	107.37	0.000	53	119.46	0.093
12	87.61	0.099	26	99.54	3.907	40	108.44	0.000	54	120.11	0.012
13	87.69	0.000	27	99.66	0.000	41	109.55	0.127	55	129.07	0.000
14	88.56	0.136	28	99.74	1.864	42	110.38	0.022	56	135.23	0.000

−11 −10 −9 −8 −7 −6 −5 −4 −3 −2 −1 0 +1 +2 +3 +4 +5 +6 +7 +8 +9 +10 +11

5-228

$J_{AA'}$	J_{AB}	$J_{AB'}$	$J_{BB'}$
2	4	15	15
2	15	4	15
15	15	4	-2
15	4	15	2

The maximum summed intensity is 6.306.

LINE	FREQ	INTEN	LINE	FREQ	INTEN	LINE	FREQ	INTEN	LINE	FREQ	INTEN
1	61.72	0.000	15	88.52	0.000	29	100.18	5.847	43	112.12	0.000
2	70.38	0.000	16	89.87	0.000	30	100.46	3.907	44	114.59	0.000
3	73.02	0.000	17	90.02	0.000	31	102.00	1.955	45	115.03	0.045
4	73.66	0.000	18	90.05	0.000	32	102.15	1.136	46	115.68	0.044
5	75.48	0.000	19	92.34	0.000	33	102.46	1.984	47	118.35	0.081
6	77.93	0.016	20	92.63	0.000	34	102.91	0.000	48	119.46	0.093
7	79.90	0.013	21	92.95	0.000	35	104.25	0.864	49	119.49	0.016
8	80.51	0.016	22	95.75	0.864	36	107.02	0.	50	120.10	0.013
9	80.54	0.093	23	96.27	0.	37	107.05	0.000	51	122.07	0.016
10	81.65	0.081	24	97.54	1.984	38	108.19	0.000	52	125.16	0.000
11	84.32	0.044	25	97.85	1.136	39	108.84	0.000	53	126.98	0.000
12	84.97	0.045	26	98.00	1.955	40	109.31	0.000	54	128.98	0.
13	86.24	0.000	27	99.54	3.907	41	109.95	0.000	55	130.79	0.000
14	86.70	0.000	28	99.82	5.847	42	109.98	0.000	56	138.28	0.000

−11 −10 −9 −8 −7 −6 −5 −4 −3 −2 −1 0 +1 +2 +3 +4 +5 +6 +7 +8 +9 +10 +11

5-229

$J_{AA'}$	J_{AB}	$J_{AB'}$	$J_{BB'}$
2	4	18	2
2	18	4	2

The maximum summed intensity is 7.123.

LINE	FREQ	INTEN	LINE	FREQ	INTEN	LINE	FREQ	INTEN	LINE	FREQ	INTEN
1	59.42	0.000	15	86.16	0.055	29	100.15	5.880	43	114.62	0.081
2	65.20	0.000	16	87.94	0.000	30	100.40	3.930	44	114.62	0.081
3	77.04	0.010	17	91.04	0.015	31	100.58	1.889	45	116.40	0.000
4	77.60	0.070	18	93.60	0.000	32	100.62	1.919	46	116.43	0.000
5	77.78	0.035	19	94.06	0.000	33	100.62	1.919	47	117.78	0.117
6	78.83	0.000	20	94.62	0.000	34	101.20	0.000	48	119.56	0.000
7	79.38	0.	21	96.82	0.000	35	102.40	0.000	49	120.40	0.000
8	79.60	0.000	22	97.60	0.000	36	103.18	0.000	50	120.62	0.000
9	80.44	0.000	23	98.80	0.000	37	105.38	0.000	51	121.17	0.000
10	82.22	0.117	24	99.38	1.919	38	105.94	0.000	52	122.22	0.035
11	83.57	0.000	25	99.38	1.919	39	106.40	0.000	53	122.40	0.070
12	83.60	0.000	26	99.42	1.889	40	108.96	0.015	54	122.96	0.010
13	85.38	0.081	27	99.60	3.930	41	112.06	0.000	55	134.80	0.000
14	85.38	0.081	28	99.85	5.880	42	113.84	0.055	56	140.58	0.000

```
     X          X
    XX          XX
    XX  X    X  XX
    XXXXXX XXXXXX
    XXXXXX XXXXXX
    XXXXXXXXXXXXX
    XXXXXXXXXXXXX
    XXXXXXXXXXXXX
    XXXXXXXXXXXXX
   XXXXXXXXXXXXXXX
   XXXXXXXXXXXXXXX
   XXXXXXXXXXXXXXX
   XXXXXXXXXXXXXXX
   XXXXXXXXXXXXXXX
   XXXXXXXXXXXXXXX
   XXXXXXXXXXXXXXX
   XXXXXXXXXXXXXXX
   XXXXXXXXXXXXXXX
   XXXXXXXXXXXXXXX
  XXXXXXXXXXXXXXXXX
  XXXXXXXXXXXXXXXXX
  XXXXXXXXXXXXXXXXX
  XXXXXXXXXXXXXXXXX
  XXXXXXXXXXXXXXXXX
 XXXXXXXXXXXXXXXXXXX
```

−11 −10 −9 −8 −7 −6 −5 −4 −3 −2 −1 0 +1 +2 +3 +4 +5 +6 +7 +8 +9 +10 +11

5-230

$J_{AA'}$	J_{AB}	$J_{AB'}$	$J_{BB'}$
2	4	18	4
2	18	4	4
4	18	4	2
4	4	18	2

The maximum summed intensity is 8.967.

LINE	FREQ	INTEN	LINE	FREQ	INTEN	LINE	FREQ	INTEN	LINE	FREQ	INTEN
1	59.04	0.000	15	87.64	0.076	29	99.89	0.000	43	114.35	0.087
2	66.16	0.	16	87.98	0.000	30	100.15	5.882	44	115.13	0.070
3	77.04	0.010	17	89.55	0.014	31	100.21	1.913	45	115.47	0.000
4	77.38	0.000	18	92.67	0.000	32	100.40	3.930	46	116.02	0.000
5	77.60	0.070	19	93.28	0.000	33	100.44	1.875	47	118.15	0.110
6	77.64	0.034	20	93.51	0.000	34	100.99	1.930	48	118.49	0.000
7	78.53	0.000	21	96.68	0.000	35	101.33	0.000	49	121.47	0.000
8	78.72	0.	22	98.67	0.000	36	104.11	0.000	50	121.84	0.000
9	80.73	0.000	23	99.01	1.930	37	105.94	0.000	51	122.06	0.000
10	81.85	0.110	24	99.32	0.000	38	107.28	0.000	52	122.36	0.034
11	84.53	0.000	25	99.56	1.875	39	107.33	0.000	53	122.40	0.070
12	84.76	0.000	26	99.60	3.930	40	110.45	0.014	54	122.96	0.010
13	84.87	0.070	27	99.79	1.913	41	111.24	0.000	55	134.62	0.000
14	85.65	0.087	28	99.85	5.882	42	112.36	0.076	56	140.96	0.000

```
             X   X
             X   X
            XX   XX
           XXX XXX
           XXX XXX
          XXXX XXXX
          XXXX XXXX
          XXXXXXXXX
          XXXXXXXXX
          XXXXXXXXX
          XXXXXXXXX
          XXXXXXXXX
         XXXXXXXXXXX
         XXXXXXXXXXX
         XXXXXXXXXXX
         XXXXXXXXXXX
         XXXXXXXXXXX
         XXXXXXXXXXX
         XXXXXXXXXXX
        XXXXXXXXXXXXX
  X     XXXXXXXXXXXXX     X
 XXX    XXXXXXXXXXXXX    XXX
 XXX    XXXXXXXXXXXXX    XXX
 XXXXXXXXXXXXXXXXXXXXXXXXXXX
XXXXXXXXXXXXXXXXXXXXXXXXXXXXX
```

−11 −10 −9 −8 −7 −6 −5 −4 −3 −2 −1 0 +1 +2 +3 +4 +5 +6 +7 +8 +9 +10 +11

5-231

$J_{AA'}$	J_{AB}	$J_{AB'}$	$J_{BB'}$
2	4	18	18
2	18	4	18
18	18	4	2
18	4	18	2

The maximum summed intensity is 6.715.

LINE	FREQ	INTEN	LINE	FREQ	INTEN	LINE	FREQ	INTEN	LINE	FREQ	INTEN
1	54.84	0.000	15	87.60	0.000	29	100.15	5.886	43	112.95	0.000
2	65.41	0.000	16	87.97	0.000	30	100.40	3.930	44	116.34	0.000
3	67.64	0.000	17	88.09	0.000	31	101.90	1.307	45	117.90	0.028
4	67.97	0.000	18	89.23	0.000	32	102.03	1.973	46	119.23	0.027
5	70.40	0.000	19	90.27	0.000	33	102.41	1.988	47	122.35	0.053
6	75.29	0.016	20	90.77	0.000	34	104.91	0.701	48	122.40	0.070
7	76.33	0.012	21	91.49	0.000	35	105.30	0.000	49	122.95	0.010
8	77.05	0.010	22	94.90	0.000	36	107.96	0.	50	123.67	0.012
9	77.60	0.070	23	95.09	0.701	37	109.23	0.000	51	124.71	0.016
10	77.65	0.053	24	97.59	1.988	38	109.53	0.000	52	130.15	0.000
11	80.77	0.027	25	97.97	1.973	39	110.72	0.000	53	132.03	0.000
12	82.10	0.028	26	98.10	1.307	40	110.77	0.000	54	134.04	0.
13	83.46	0.000	27	99.60	3.930	41	112.03	0.000	55	136.79	0.000
14	84.85	0.000	28	99.85	5.886	42	112.11	0.000	56	145.16	0.000

5-232

$J_{AA'}$	J_{AB}	$J_{AB'}$	$J_{BB'}$
4	1	2	4
4	2	1	4

The maximum summed intensity is 4.203.

LINE	FREQ	INTEN	LINE	FREQ	INTEN	LINE	FREQ	INTEN	LINE	FREQ	INTEN
1	87.98	0.000	15	96.46	0.836	29	100.15	0.000	43	103.96	0.892
2	88.12	0.000	16	96.46	0.836	30	100.27	0.	44	104.85	1.106
3	89.34	0.002	17	96.51	1.549	31	100.82	0.000	45	105.18	0.429
4	91.46	0.	18	96.79	1.782	32	101.15	0.000	46	105.94	0.000
5	91.67	0.003	19	97.46	1.164	33	101.49	0.	47	106.35	0.000
6	92.15	0.000	20	97.46	1.164	34	101.62	3.343	48	106.85	0.000
7	92.43	0.000	21	97.54	0.	35	101.85	2.894	49	106.90	0.000
8	93.10	0.000	22	98.15	2.894	36	102.46	0.	50	107.57	0.000
9	93.15	0.000	23	98.38	3.343	37	102.54	1.164	51	107.85	0.000
10	93.65	0.000	24	98.51	0.000	38	102.54	1.164	52	108.33	0.003
11	94.06	0.000	25	98.85	0.000	39	103.21	1.782	53	108.54	0.
12	94.82	0.429	26	99.18	0.000	40	103.49	1.549	54	110.66	0.002
13	95.15	1.106	27	99.73	0.	41	103.54	0.836	55	111.88	0.000
14	96.04	0.892	28	99.85	0.000	42	103.54	0.836	56	112.02	0.000

5-233

$J_{AA'}$	J_{AB}	$J_{AB'}$	$J_{BB'}$
4	2	4	6
4	4	2	6
6	4	2	4
6	2	4	4

The maximum summed intensity is 5.352.

LINE	FREQ	INTEN	LINE	FREQ	INTEN	LINE	FREQ	INTEN	LINE	FREQ	INTEN
1	84.39	0.000	15	94.46	0.143	29	100.07	0.000	43	105.54	0.143
2	85.82	0.000	16	94.81	0.722	30	100.66	0.000	44	106.29	0.000
3	87.03	0.004	17	95.51	0.671	31	100.81	4.688	45	107.13	0.326
4	89.34	0.000	18	95.86	0.000	32	100.82	0.684	46	107.24	0.586
5	89.76	0.000	19	96.35	1.316	33	101.24	3.414	47	107.82	0.000
6	90.70	0.019	20	96.71	1.570	34	101.81	0.000	48	107.83	0.000
7	91.39	0.000	21	97.29	1.857	35	102.17	0.000	49	107.85	0.000
8	91.83	0.000	22	97.83	0.000	36	102.25	0.000	50	109.30	0.019
9	92.17	0.000	23	98.50	0.000	37	102.71	1.857	51	110.49	0.000
10	92.76	0.586	24	98.76	3.414	38	103.29	1.570	52	110.66	0.000
11	92.87	0.326	25	99.18	0.684	39	103.65	1.316	53	112.12	0.000
12	94.03	0.000	26	99.19	4.688	40	103.88	0.000	54	112.29	0.000
13	94.07	0.000	27	99.34	0.000	41	104.49	0.671	55	112.97	0.004
14	94.24	0.000	28	99.61	0.000	42	105.19	0.722	56	115.61	0.000

5-234

$J_{AA'}$	J_{AB}	$J_{AB'}$	$J_{BB'}$
4	2	4	9
4	4	2	9
9	4	2	4
9	2	4	4

The maximum summed intensity is 4.687.

LINE	FREQ	INTEN	LINE	FREQ	INTEN	LINE	FREQ	INTEN	LINE	FREQ	INTEN
1	82.17	0.000	15	94.04	0.000	29	100.07	0.000	43	106.64	0.000
2	82.86	0.000	16	94.75	0.923	30	100.44	0.000	44	107.24	0.586
3	86.27	0.003	17	94.78	0.719	31	100.81	4.692	45	108.05	0.000
4	86.56	0.000	18	95.05	0.000	32	101.24	3.414	46	108.28	0.020
5	88.89	0.000	19	95.89	0.000	33	101.49	0.000	47	108.58	0.000
6	89.38	0.000	20	96.19	1.083	34	101.57	0.917	48	109.29	0.019
7	90.66	0.055	21	96.74	1.589	35	102.90	1.980	49	109.34	0.055
8	90.71	0.019	22	97.10	1.980	36	103.26	1.589	50	110.43	0.000
9	91.62	0.000	23	97.40	0.000	37	103.81	1.083	51	112.67	0.000
10	91.72	0.020	24	98.13	0.000	38	103.91	0.000	52	112.67	0.000
11	91.80	0.000	25	98.43	0.917	39	104.40	0.000	53	113.44	0.000
12	91.95	0.000	26	98.76	3.414	40	104.95	0.000	54	113.73	0.003
13	92.76	0.586	27	99.19	4.692	41	105.22	0.719	55	115.09	0.000
14	94.04	0.000	28	99.56	0.000	42	105.25	0.923	56	117.83	0.000

5-235

$J_{AA'}$	J_{AB}	$J_{AB'}$	$J_{BB'}$
4	2	4	12
4	4	2	12
12	4	2	4
12	2	4	4

The maximum summed intensity is 4.693.

LINE	FREQ	INTEN	LINE	FREQ	INTEN	LINE	FREQ	INTEN	LINE	FREQ	INTEN
1	79.40	0.000	15	93.06	0.000	29	100.07	0.000	43	107.88	0.000
2	79.88	0.000	16	94.02	0.000	30	100.37	0.000	44	108.12	0.000
3	83.63	0.000	17	94.46	0.143	31	100.81	4.694	45	108.41	0.000
4	85.93	0.000	18	94.55	0.955	32	101.24	3.414	46	108.77	0.000
5	86.06	0.002	19	94.63	0.000	33	101.28	0.000	47	109.29	0.019
6	87.59	0.000	20	94.76	0.717	34	102.71	1.857	48	111.19	0.005
7	87.89	0.013	21	96.76	1.599	35	102.95	1.995	49	111.64	0.000
8	88.81	0.005	22	96.89	0.000	36	103.24	1.599	50	112.11	0.013
9	90.23	0.000	23	97.05	1.995	37	103.93	0.000	51	113.94	0.002
10	90.41	0.000	24	97.29	1.857	38	105.24	0.717	52	114.47	0.000
11	90.71	0.019	25	98.76	3.414	39	105.45	0.955	53	115.43	0.000
12	91.88	0.000	26	99.19	4.694	40	105.54	0.143	54	116.37	0.000
13	92.12	0.000	27	99.63	0.000	41	105.59	0.000	55	118.07	0.
14	92.76	0.586	28	99.72	0.000	42	107.24	0.586	56	120.60	0.000

−11 −10 −9 −8 −7 −6 −5 −4 −3 −2 −1 0 +1 +2 +3 +4 +5 +6 +7 +8 +9 +10 +11

5-236

$J_{AA'}$	J_{AB}	$J_{AB'}$	$J_{BB'}$
4	2	4	15
4	4	2	15
15	4	2	4
15	2	4	4

The maximum summed intensity is 4.696.

LINE	FREQ	INTEN	LINE	FREQ	INTEN	LINE	FREQ	INTEN	LINE	FREQ	INTEN
1	76.50	0.000	15	91.85	0.000	29	100.33	0.000	43	108.28	0.020
2	76.89	0.000	16	92.76	0.586	30	100.81	4.696	44	108.84	0.000
3	80.67	0.000	17	92.94	0.000	31	101.20	0.000	45	109.29	0.019
4	82.95	0.000	18	94.01	0.000	32	101.24	3.414	46	110.85	0.000
5	84.81	0.000	19	94.46	0.956	33	102.41	0.000	47	111.18	0.000
6	84.99	0.004	20	94.74	0.716	34	102.90	1.980	48	111.86	0.000
7	85.85	0.002	21	96.77	1.606	35	102.97	1.998	49	114.02	0.002
8	85.98	0.002	22	97.03	0.000	36	103.23	1.606	50	114.15	0.002
9	87.55	0.000	23	97.03	1.998	37	103.94	0.000	51	115.01	0.004
10	89.15	0.000	24	97.10	1.980	38	105.26	0.716	52	117.24	0.000
11	90.19	0.000	25	98.76	3.414	39	105.54	0.956	53	118.31	0.000
12	90.71	0.019	26	99.19	4.696	40	105.80	0.000	54	119.33	0.000
13	91.72	0.020	27	99.67	0.000	41	107.24	0.586	55	121.06	0.000
14	91.72	0.000	28	100.07	0.000	42	108.15	0.000	56	123.50	0.000

−11 −10 −9 −8 −7 −6 −5 −4 −3 −2 −1 0 +1 +2 +3 +4 +5 +6 +7 +8 +9 +10 +11

5-237

$J_{AA'}$	J_{AB}	$J_{AB'}$	$J_{BB'}$
4	2	4	18
4	4	2	18
18	4	2	4
18	2	4	4

The maximum summed intensity is 4.699.

LINE	FREQ	INTEN	LINE	FREQ	INTEN	LINE	FREQ	INTEN	LINE	FREQ	INTEN
1	73.56	0.000	15	91.83	0.000	29	100.31	0.000	43	108.88	0.000
2	73.90	0.000	16	92.76	0.586	30	100.81	4.698	44	109.29	0.019
3	77.69	0.000	17	92.92	0.000	31	101.15	0.000	45	111.19	0.005
4	79.97	0.000	18	94.00	0.000	32	101.24	3.414	46	111.93	0.000
5	81.88	0.000	19	94.42	0.955	33	102.95	1.995	47	113.83	0.000
6	82.04	0.002	20	94.74	0.715	34	102.98	1.999	48	114.07	0.002
7	82.88	0.001	21	96.78	1.610	35	103.22	1.610	49	114.10	0.000
8	84.68	0.000	22	97.02	1.999	36	103.95	0.000	50	117.12	0.001
9	85.93	0.002	23	97.05	0.000	37	105.26	0.715	51	117.96	0.002
10	86.17	0.000	24	97.05	1.995	38	105.30	0.000	52	120.17	0.000
11	88.78	0.000	25	98.76	3.414	39	105.58	0.955	53	121.25	0.
12	88.81	0.005	26	99.19	4.698	40	105.86	0.000	54	122.31	0.000
13	90.12	0.000	27	99.69	0.000	41	107.24	0.586	55	124.05	0.000
14	90.71	0.019	28	100.07	0.000	42	108.17	0.000	56	126.44	0.000

5-238

$J_{AA'}$	J_{AB}	$J_{AB'}$	$J_{BB'}$
4	2	6	4
4	6	2	4

The maximum summed intensity is 4.987.

LINE	FREQ	INTEN	LINE	FREQ	INTEN	LINE	FREQ	INTEN	LINE	FREQ	INTEN
1	81.84	0.000	15	94.39	0.445	29	100.53	0.000	43	105.96	0.000
2	86.83	0.000	16	94.39	0.445	30	100.56	5.160	44	106.28	0.000
3	87.23	0.000	17	94.44	0.000	31	100.93	0.000	45	106.33	0.418
4	87.92	0.022	18	95.61	0.000	32	101.00	0.000	46	106.68	0.000
5	88.39	0.	19	96.33	1.259	33	101.00	3.600	47	107.00	0.000
6	89.00	0.000	20	97.00	0.000	34	101.61	1.555	48	108.16	0.418
7	89.44	0.023	21	97.92	0.700	35	101.61	1.555	49	109.00	0.400
8	91.00	0.400	22	98.39	1.555	36	102.08	0.700	50	110.56	0.023
9	91.84	0.418	23	98.39	1.555	37	103.00	0.000	51	111.00	0.000
10	93.00	0.000	24	99.00	0.000	38	103.67	1.259	52	111.61	0.000
11	93.32	0.000	25	99.00	3.600	39	104.39	0.000	53	112.08	0.022
12	93.67	0.418	26	99.07	0.000	40	105.56	0.000	54	112.77	0.000
13	93.72	0.000	27	99.44	5.160	41	105.61	0.445	55	113.17	0.000
14	94.04	0.000	28	99.47	0.000	42	105.61	0.445	56	118.16	0.000

5-239

$J_{AA'}$	J_{AB}	$J_{AB'}$	$J_{BB'}$
4	2	6	6
4	6	2	6
6	6	2	4
6	2	6	4

The maximum summed intensity is 6.275.

LINE	FREQ	INTEN	LINE	FREQ	INTEN	LINE	FREQ	INTEN	LINE	FREQ	INTEN
1	81.21	0.000	15	93.89	0.000	29	100.56	5.166	43	106.49	0.421
2	84.97	0.000	16	93.91	0.000	30	100.59	1.316	44	106.71	0.200
3	86.72	0.013	17	94.03	0.000	31	100.69	0.000	45	107.73	0.000
4	87.76	0.000	18	94.94	0.684	32	100.96	0.000	46	107.75	0.000
5	88.17	0.000	19	96.49	1.356	33	101.00	3.600	47	107.76	0.000
6	88.38	0.000	20	96.72	0.720	34	102.24	0.000	48	108.79	0.301
7	89.44	0.023	21	97.76	0.000	35	102.24	0.000	49	109.00	0.400
8	91.00	0.400	22	97.76	0.000	36	102.24	1.800	50	110.56	0.023
9	91.21	0.301	23	97.76	1.800	37	103.28	0.720	51	112.24	0.000
10	92.01	0.000	24	98.81	0.000	38	103.51	1.356	52	113.27	0.000
11	92.24	0.000	25	99.00	3.600	39	104.32	0.000	53	113.28	0.013
12	93.29	0.200	26	99.41	1.316	40	104.53	0.	54	113.39	0.000
13	93.51	0.421	27	99.44	5.166	41	105.06	0.684	55	113.47	0.000
14	93.83	0.000	28	99.55	0.000	42	106.34	0.000	56	118.79	0.000

5-240

$J_{AA'}$	J_{AB}	$J_{AB'}$	$J_{BB'}$
4	2	9	4
4	9	2	4

The maximum summed intensity is 5.460.

LINE	FREQ	INTEN	LINE	FREQ	INTEN	LINE	FREQ	INTEN	LINE	FREQ	INTEN
1	76.57	0.000	15	92.76	0.000	29	100.37	5.523	43	107.64	0.184
2	82.23	0.000	16	93.24	0.000	30	100.76	3.756	44	107.71	0.000
3	84.75	0.000	17	93.97	0.000	31	100.84	1.249	45	108.11	0.241
4	85.89	0.	18	94.24	0.000	32	101.11	1.759	46	108.11	0.241
5	86.24	0.000	19	95.11	0.721	33	101.11	1.759	47	108.56	0.000
6	86.63	0.049	20	95.11	0.000	34	101.24	0.000	48	110.90	0.253
7	87.10	0.022	21	98.02	0.000	35	101.51	0.000	49	111.76	0.244
8	88.24	0.244	22	98.49	0.000	36	101.98	0.000	50	112.90	0.022
9	89.10	0.253	23	98.76	0.000	37	104.89	0.000	51	113.37	0.049
10	91.44	0.000	24	98.89	1.759	38	104.89	0.721	52	113.76	0.000
11	91.89	0.241	25	98.89	1.759	39	105.76	0.000	53	114.11	0.000
12	91.89	0.241	26	99.16	1.249	40	106.03	0.000	54	115.25	0.000
13	92.29	0.000	27	99.24	3.756	41	106.76	0.000	55	117.77	0.000
14	92.36	0.184	28	99.63	5.523	42	107.24	0.000	56	123.43	0.000

5-241

$J_{AA'}$	J_{AB}	$J_{AB'}$	$J_{BB'}$
4	2	9	9
4	9	2	4
9	9	2	4
9	2	9	4

The maximum summed intensity is 5.434.

LINE	FREQ	INTEN	LINE	FREQ	INTEN	LINE	FREQ	INTEN	LINE	FREQ	INTEN
1	74.75	0.000	15	91.54	0.000	29	100.59	0.000	43	108.46	0.000
2	80.35	0.000	16	92.16	0.277	30	100.76	3.756	44	108.64	0.202
3	82.93	0.000	17	93.39	0.000	31	100.77	1.723	45	109.29	0.000
4	83.98	0.	18	93.70	0.000	32	100.77	0.000	46	109.60	0.000
5	84.46	0.	19	95.46	0.000	33	102.22	1.927	47	110.82	0.073
6	84.47	0.018	20	95.93	0.000	34	102.40	0.000	48	111.76	0.244
7	87.10	0.022	21	96.11	1.122	35	103.00	0.961	49	112.72	0.139
8	87.28	0.139	22	96.25	0.000	36	103.89	1.122	50	112.90	0.022
9	88.24	0.244	23	97.00	0.961	37	104.07	0.000	51	115.53	0.018
10	89.18	0.073	24	97.78	1.927	38	104.54	0.000	52	116.67	0.000
11	89.36	0.000	25	99.23	1.723	39	105.48	0.000	53	117.07	0.000
12	91.05	0.000	26	99.24	3.756	40	105.97	0.000	54	118.52	0.000
13	91.36	0.202	27	99.63	5.536	41	107.66	0.000	55	119.01	0.000
14	91.54	0.000	28	100.37	5.536	42	107.84	0.277	56	125.25	0.000

−11 −10 −9 −8 −7 −6 −5 −4 −3 −2 −1 0 +1 +2 +3 +4 +5 +6 +7 +8 +9 +10 +11

5-242

$J_{AA'}$	J_{AB}	$J_{AB'}$	$J_{BB'}$
4	2	12	4
4	12	2	4

The maximum summed intensity is 7.208.

LINE	FREQ	INTEN	LINE	FREQ	INTEN	LINE	FREQ	INTEN	LINE	FREQ	INTEN
1	71.04	0.000	15	91.38	0.000	29	100.24	1.628	43	109.14	0.000
2	76.82	0.000	16	91.69	0.086	30	100.27	5.698	44	109.69	0.000
3	82.28	0.000	17	93.07	0.349	31	100.62	3.838	45	110.83	0.143
4	83.17	0.	18	93.38	0.000	32	100.83	1.857	46	110.83	0.143
5	83.38	0.000	19	93.94	0.000	33	100.83	1.857	47	111.51	0.000
6	84.49	0.017	20	94.83	0.	34	101.38	0.000	48	113.73	0.167
7	84.53	0.055	21	97.48	0.000	35	101.98	0.000	49	114.62	0.162
8	85.38	0.162	22	98.02	0.000	36	102.52	0.000	50	115.47	0.055
9	86.27	0.167	23	98.62	0.000	37	105.17	0.	51	115.51	0.017
10	88.49	0.000	24	99.17	1.857	38	106.06	0.000	52	116.62	0.000
11	89.17	0.143	25	99.17	1.857	39	106.62	0.000	53	116.83	0.
12	89.17	0.143	26	99.38	3.838	40	106.93	0.349	54	117.72	0.000
13	90.31	0.000	27	99.73	5.698	41	108.31	0.086	55	123.18	0.000
14	90.86	0.000	28	99.76	1.628	42	108.62	0.000	56	128.96	0.000

−11 −10 −9 −8 −7 −6 −5 −4 −3 −2 −1 0 +1 +2 +3 +4 +5 +6 +7 +8 +9 +10 +11

5-243

$J_{AA'}$	J_{AB}	$J_{AB'}$	$J_{BB'}$
4	2	12	12
4	12	2	12
12	12	2	4
12	2	12	4

The maximum summed intensity is 5.695.

LINE	FREQ	INTEN	LINE	FREQ	INTEN	LINE	FREQ	INTEN	LINE	FREQ	INTEN
1	68.01	0.000	15	90.10	0.000	29	100.27	5.711	43	110.78	0.000
2	75.52	0.000	16	90.79	0.000	30	100.62	3.838	44	110.86	0.107
3	77.98	0.000	17	92.64	0.000	31	101.30	1.888	45	110.87	0.000
4	78.53	0.000	18	92.72	0.000	32	102.20	1.962	46	111.50	0.112
5	79.90	0.000	19	93.21	0.000	33	102.65	1.134	47	114.62	0.162
6	82.12	0.020	20	93.66	0.000	34	102.83	0.000	48	115.01	0.038
7	83.24	0.080	21	93.98	0.000	35	103.85	0.000	49	115.50	0.018
8	84.50	0.018	22	95.63	0.929	36	104.37	0.929	50	116.76	0.080
9	84.99	0.038	23	97.35	1.134	37	106.02	0.000	51	117.88	0.020
10	85.38	0.162	24	97.80	1.962	38	106.40	0.	52	120.98	0.000
11	86.64	0.000	25	98.70	1.888	39	106.79	0.000	53	122.02	0.000
12	88.50	0.112	26	99.38	3.838	40	107.77	0.000	54	123.60	0.000
13	88.73	0.000	27	99.65	0.000	41	109.21	0.000	55	124.97	0.000
14	89.14	0.107	28	99.73	5.711	42	109.85	0.000	56	131.99	0.000

5-244

$J_{AA'}$	J_{AB}	$J_{AB'}$	$J_{BB'}$
4	2	15	4
4	15	2	4

The maximum summed intensity is 7.027.

LINE	FREQ	INTEN	LINE	FREQ	INTEN	LINE	FREQ	INTEN	LINE	FREQ	INTEN
1	65.36	0.000	15	88.49	0.000	29	100.01	1.803	43	111.56	0.000
2	71.22	0.000	16	90.59	0.180	30	100.22	5.793	44	112.17	0.000
3	79.61	0.000	17	91.39	0.046	31	100.51	3.886	45	113.66	0.092
4	80.34	0.	18	93.49	0.000	32	100.66	1.908	46	113.66	0.092
5	80.49	0.000	19	93.93	0.000	33	100.66	1.908	47	114.46	0.000
6	81.76	0.014	20	94.66	0.	34	101.49	0.000	48	116.61	0.118
7	81.98	0.047	21	97.24	0.000	35	102.15	0.000	49	117.51	0.114
8	82.49	0.114	22	97.85	0.000	36	102.76	0.000	50	118.02	0.047
9	83.39	0.118	23	98.51	0.000	37	105.34	0.	51	118.24	0.014
10	85.54	0.000	24	99.34	1.908	38	106.07	0.000	52	119.51	0.000
11	86.34	0.092	25	99.34	1.908	39	106.51	0.000	53	119.66	0.000
12	86.34	0.092	26	99.49	3.886	40	108.61	0.046	54	120.39	0.000
13	87.83	0.000	27	99.78	5.793	41	109.41	0.180	55	128.78	0.000
14	88.44	0.000	28	99.99	1.803	42	111.51	0.000	56	134.64	0.000

5-245

$J_{AA'}$	J_{AB}	$J_{AB'}$	$J_{BB'}$
4	2	15	15
4	15	2	15
15	15	2	4
15	2	15	4

The maximum summed intensity is 6.013.

LINE	FREQ	INTEN	LINE	FREQ	INTEN	LINE	FREQ	INTEN	LINE	FREQ	INTEN
1	61.15	0.000	15	88.96	0.000	29	100.21	5.805	43	112.40	0.000
2	70.58	0.000	16	90.00	0.000	30	100.51	3.886	44	112.52	0.000
3	72.70	0.	17	91.00	0.000	31	101.55	1.944	45	113.08	0.061
4	72.97	0.000	18	91.12	0.000	32	102.19	1.977	46	115.48	0.056
5	75.04	0.000	19	91.21	0.000	33	102.31	1.283	47	117.51	0.114
6	79.18	0.052	20	91.97	0.000	34	104.95	0.764	48	118.24	0.014
7	79.66	0.020	21	91.98	0.000	35	105.14	0.000	49	119.22	0.023
8	80.78	0.023	22	95.05	0.764	36	105.26	0.000	50	120.34	0.020
9	81.76	0.014	23	97.69	1.283	37	107.30	0.000	51	120.82	0.052
10	82.49	0.114	24	97.81	1.977	38	108.03	0.000	52	125.69	0.000
11	83.86	0.000	25	98.45	1.944	39	109.00	0.000	53	127.03	0.000
12	84.52	0.056	26	98.47	0.000	40	109.64	0.	54	128.70	0.000
13	86.63	0.000	27	99.49	3.886	41	110.00	0.000	55	131.04	0.000
14	86.92	0.061	28	99.79	5.805	42	111.76	0.000	56	138.85	0.000

−11 −10 −9 −8 −7 −6 −5 −4 −3 −2 −1 0 +1 +2 +3 +4 +5 +6 +7 +8 +9 +10 +11

5-246

$J_{AA'}$	J_{AB}	$J_{AB'}$	$J_{BB'}$
4	2	18	4
4	18	2	4

The maximum summed intensity is 8.160.

LINE	FREQ	INTEN	LINE	FREQ	INTEN	LINE	FREQ	INTEN	LINE	FREQ	INTEN
1	59.60	0.000	15	85.78	0.000	29	100.11	1.883	43	114.44	0.000
2	65.49	0.000	16	87.88	0.104	30	100.18	5.850	44	114.87	0.000
3	76.84	0.000	17	91.23	0.028	31	100.44	3.916	45	116.54	0.064
4	77.46	0.	18	93.56	0.000	32	100.54	1.936	46	116.54	0.064
5	77.56	0.000	19	93.93	0.000	33	100.54	1.936	47	117.42	0.000
6	78.94	0.011	20	94.54	0.	34	101.56	0.000	48	119.52	0.087
7	79.23	0.038	21	97.13	0.000	35	102.21	0.000	49	120.44	0.084
8	79.56	0.084	22	97.79	0.000	36	102.87	0.000	50	120.77	0.038
9	80.48	0.087	23	98.44	0.000	37	105.46	0.	51	121.06	0.011
10	82.58	0.000	24	99.46	1.936	38	106.07	0.000	52	122.44	0.000
11	83.46	0.064	25	99.46	1.936	39	106.44	0.000	53	122.54	0.
12	83.46	0.064	26	99.56	3.916	40	108.77	0.028	54	123.16	0.000
13	85.13	0.000	27	99.82	5.850	41	112.12	0.104	55	134.51	0.000
14	85.56	0.000	28	99.89	1.883	42	114.22	0.000	56	140.40	0.000

−11 −10 −9 −8 −7 −6 −5 −4 −3 −2 −1 0 +1 +2 +3 +4 +5 +6 +7 +8 +9 +10 +11

5-247

$J_{AA'}$	J_{AB}	$J_{AB'}$	$J_{BB'}$
4	2	18	18
4	18	2	18
18	18	2	4
18	2	18	4

The maximum summed intensity is 6.452.

LINE	FREQ	INTEN	LINE	FREQ	INTEN	LINE	FREQ	INTEN	LINE	FREQ	INTEN
1	54.22	0.000	15	87.94	0.000	29	100.17	5.860	43	114.25	0.000
2	65.58	0.000	16	88.64	0.000	30	100.44	3.916	44	115.13	0.000
3	66.71	0.000	17	88.81	0.000	31	101.69	1.968	45	115.26	0.037
4	67.93	0.000	18	89.19	0.000	32	102.01	1.412	46	119.57	0.032
5	70.06	0.000	19	89.61	0.000	33	102.18	1.984	47	120.44	0.084
6	75.10	0.037	20	89.93	0.000	34	105.62	0.624	48	121.05	0.011
7	76.56	0.016	21	91.20	0.000	35	106.63	0.000	49	122.89	0.019
8	77.11	0.019	22	94.38	0.624	36	107.50	0.000	50	123.44	0.016
9	78.95	0.011	23	97.24	0.000	37	108.19	0.000	51	124.90	0.037
10	79.56	0.084	24	97.82	1.984	38	110.07	0.000	52	130.56	0.000
11	80.43	0.032	25	97.99	1.412	39	110.81	0.000	53	132.07	0.000
12	81.01	0.000	26	98.31	1.968	40	111.19	0.000	54	133.81	0.000
13	84.60	0.000	27	99.56	3.916	41	111.54	0.000	55	137.15	0.000
14	84.74	0.037	28	99.83	5.860	42	112.67	0.000	56	145.78	0.000

5-248

$J_{AA'}$	J_{AB}	$J_{AB'}$	$J_{BB'}$
4	4	6	9
4	6	4	9
9	6	4	4
9	4	6	4

The maximum summed intensity is 5.480.

LINE	FREQ	INTEN	LINE	FREQ	INTEN	LINE	FREQ	INTEN	LINE	FREQ	INTEN
1	79.59	0.000	15	92.86	0.000	29	100.40	5.468	43	108.28	0.020
2	81.68	0.000	16	93.04	0.000	30	100.83	3.715	44	108.75	0.260
3	82.47	0.002	17	93.68	0.000	31	101.57	0.917	45	108.78	0.244
4	84.98	0.000	18	94.13	0.433	32	102.02	0.000	46	109.64	0.000
5	87.38	0.000	19	95.92	0.000	33	102.04	0.000	47	110.79	0.000
6	87.94	0.025	20	96.19	1.083	34	102.43	0.000	48	110.83	0.285
7	89.17	0.285	21	96.64	0.000	35	102.49	0.	49	111.61	0.000
8	89.62	0.000	22	97.10	1.980	36	102.88	1.567	50	112.06	0.025
9	90.36	0.000	23	97.12	1.567	37	102.90	1.980	51	113.67	0.000
10	90.80	0.000	24	97.98	0.000	38	103.36	0.000	52	113.85	0.000
11	90.86	0.000	25	98.43	0.917	39	103.81	1.083	53	115.02	0.000
12	91.22	0.244	26	99.17	3.715	40	104.67	0.000	54	117.09	0.000
13	91.25	0.260	27	99.60	5.468	41	105.87	0.433	55	117.53	0.002
14	91.72	0.020	28	99.61	0.	42	105.91	0.000	56	120.41	0.000

5-249

$J_{AA'}$	J_{AB}	$J_{AB'}$	$J_{BB'}$
4	4	6	12
4	6	4	12
12	6	4	4
12	4	6	4

The maximum summed intensity is 5.480.

LINE	FREQ	INTEN	LINE	FREQ	INTEN	LINE	FREQ	INTEN	LINE	FREQ	INTEN
1	77.50	0.000	15	92.75	0.000	29	100.40	5.468	43	108.80	0.245
2	78.70	0.000	16	92.84	0.000	30	100.83	3.715	44	109.71	0.000
3	81.58	0.002	17	93.24	0.628	31	101.59	0.000	45	110.83	0.285
4	82.05	0.000	18	93.71	0.000	32	101.95	0.000	46	110.83	0.053
5	85.59	0.000	19	93.99	0.000	33	102.04	0.000	47	111.19	0.005
6	87.90	0.000	20	94.46	0.143	34	102.71	1.857	48	111.66	0.000
7	87.94	0.025	21	96.82	0.000	35	102.86	1.579	49	112.06	0.025
8	88.41	0.000	22	97.05	1.995	36	102.95	1.995	50	112.82	0.000
9	88.81	0.005	23	97.14	1.579	37	103.61	0.000	51	115.65	0.000
10	89.17	0.053	24	97.29	1.857	38	105.54	0.143	52	115.74	0.000
11	89.17	0.285	25	97.52	0.000	39	105.93	0.000	53	117.95	0.000
12	89.92	0.000	26	98.05	0.000	40	106.29	0.000	54	118.42	0.002
13	90.29	0.000	27	99.17	3.715	41	106.44	0.000	55	120.07	0.
14	91.20	0.245	28	99.60	5.468	42	106.76	0.628	56	122.50	0.000

−11 −10 −9 −8 −7 −6 −5 −4 −3 −2 −1 0 +1 +2 +3 +4 +5 +6 +7 +8 +9 +10 +11

5-250

$J_{AA'}$	J_{AB}	$J_{AB'}$	$J_{BB'}$
4	4	6	15
4	6	4	15
15	6	4	4
15	4	6	4

The maximum summed intensity is 5.481.

LINE	FREQ	INTEN	LINE	FREQ	INTEN	LINE	FREQ	INTEN	LINE	FREQ	INTEN
1	74.78	0.000	15	91.18	0.244	29	100.40	5.469	43	109.26	0.000
2	75.71	0.000	16	91.72	0.020	30	100.83	3.715	44	109.74	0.000
3	79.08	0.000	17	92.80	0.000	31	101.33	0.000	45	110.83	0.285
4	81.32	0.002	18	92.83	0.000	32	101.92	0.000	46	111.91	0.000
5	82.81	0.000	19	92.98	0.661	33	102.05	0.000	47	112.06	0.025
6	84.93	0.000	20	93.95	0.000	34	102.84	1.586	48	113.04	0.000
7	85.85	0.002	21	94.80	0.000	35	102.90	1.980	49	113.56	0.013
8	86.44	0.013	22	97.03	1.998	36	102.97	1.998	50	114.15	0.002
9	87.42	0.000	23	97.10	1.980	37	103.82	0.000	51	118.42	0.000
10	87.94	0.025	24	97.16	1.586	38	105.94	0.000	52	118.45	0.000
11	88.19	0.000	25	98.08	0.000	39	107.02	0.661	53	118.68	0.002
12	89.17	0.285	26	99.17	3.715	40	108.28	0.020	54	120.92	0.000
13	90.26	0.000	27	99.34	0.000	41	108.82	0.244	55	123.06	0.000
14	90.74	0.000	28	99.60	5.469	42	109.21	0.000	56	125.22	0.000

−11 −10 −9 −8 −7 −6 −5 −4 −3 −2 −1 0 +1 +2 +3 +4 +5 +6 +7 +8 +9 +10 +11

5-251

$J_{AA'}$	J_{AB}	$J_{AB'}$	$J_{BB'}$
4	4	9	6
4	9	4	6
6	9	4	4
6	4	9	4

The maximum summed intensity is 6.101.

LINE	FREQ	INTEN	LINE	FREQ	INTEN	LINE	FREQ	INTEN	LINE	FREQ	INTEN
1	75.16	0.000	15	92.59	0.193	29	99.71	5.676	43	107.97	0.000
2	82.84	0.000	16	92.83	0.000	30	100.29	5.676	44	108.69	0.000
3	83.87	0.016	17	94.07	0.000	31	100.51	1.493	45	109.24	0.000
4	84.11	0.000	18	94.11	0.507	32	100.53	0.000	46	109.47	0.000
5	85.15	0.000	19	95.15	0.000	33	100.66	3.816	47	110.53	0.291
6	85.30	0.	20	96.63	1.188	34	101.81	0.685	48	110.95	0.123
7	85.40	0.021	21	97.98	1.807	35	102.02	1.807	49	113.66	0.184
8	86.34	0.184	22	98.01	0.000	36	103.37	1.188	50	114.60	0.021
9	89.05	0.123	23	98.19	0.685	37	103.51	0.000	51	114.85	0.000
10	89.47	0.291	24	99.23	0.000	38	104.41	0.000	52	115.65	0.000
11	90.52	0.000	25	99.25	0.000	39	104.85	0.000	53	116.13	0.016
12	90.53	0.000	26	99.34	3.816	40	105.89	0.507	54	116.22	0.000
13	91.70	0.000	27	99.47	0.000	41	106.78	0.000	55	117.40	0.000
14	92.27	0.000	28	99.49	1.493	42	107.41	0.193	56	124.84	0.000

5-252

$J_{AA'}$	J_{AB}	$J_{AB'}$	$J_{BB'}$
4	4	12	6
4	12	4	6
6	12	4	4
6	4	12	4

The maximum summed intensity is 7.076.

LINE	FREQ	INTEN	LINE	FREQ	INTEN	LINE	FREQ	INTEN	LINE	FREQ	INTEN
1	69.62	0.000	15	91.40	0.241	29	100.22	5.783	43	109.42	0.000
2	78.69	0.	16	91.47	0.000	30	100.30	0.000	44	109.78	0.143
3	80.58	0.000	17	91.89	0.000	31	100.35	1.759	45	109.83	0.000
4	82.29	0.032	18	92.33	0.000	32	100.54	3.873	46	111.18	0.
5	82.33	0.000	19	93.10	0.000	33	100.58	0.000	47	112.30	0.057
6	82.53	0.	20	95.21	0.631	34	100.63	1.293	48	113.30	0.187
7	82.69	0.016	21	96.77	0.000	35	101.53	1.857	49	116.54	0.127
8	83.46	0.127	22	98.47	1.857	36	104.41	0.000	50	117.31	0.016
9	86.70	0.187	23	98.51	0.000	37	104.79	0.631	51	117.67	0.000
10	87.63	0.000	24	99.37	1.293	38	105.72	0.000	52	117.71	0.032
11	87.70	0.057	25	99.42	0.000	39	107.34	0.	53	118.24	0.000
12	90.22	0.143	26	99.46	3.873	40	107.67	0.000	54	118.66	0.
13	90.58	0.000	27	99.65	1.759	41	108.60	0.241	55	122.50	0.000
14	91.36	0.000	28	99.78	5.783	42	109.29	0.000	56	130.38	0.000

5-253

$J_{AA'}$	J_{AB}	$J_{AB'}$	$J_{BB'}$
4	4	15	6
4	15	4	6
6	15	4	4
6	4	15	4

The maximum summed intensity is 9.437.

LINE	FREQ	INTEN	LINE	FREQ	INTEN	LINE	FREQ	INTEN	LINE	FREQ	INTEN
1	63.93	0.000	15	89.45	0.000	29	100.13	1.659	43	111.44	0.136
2	73.04	0.	16	90.63	0.000	30	100.18	5.845	44	111.89	0.000
3	78.06	0.000	17	91.14	0.000	31	100.26	1.864	45	112.39	0.099
4	79.45	0.000	18	91.35	0.000	32	100.46	3.907	46	112.91	0.027
5	79.65	0.000	19	91.66	0.000	33	100.63	0.000	47	114.31	0.000
6	79.89	0.013	20	92.98	0.292	34	100.76	0.000	48	116.15	0.129
7	79.95	0.035	21	96.20	0.000	35	101.21	1.901	49	119.46	0.093
8	80.54	0.093	22	98.29	0.000	36	104.75	0.000	50	120.05	0.035
9	83.85	0.129	23	98.79	1.901	37	107.02	0.292	51	120.11	0.013
10	84.74	0.	24	99.37	0.000	38	107.70	0.000	52	120.55	0.000
11	87.09	0.027	25	99.54	3.907	39	107.91	0.000	53	121.00	0.000
12	87.61	0.099	26	99.74	1.864	40	109.29	0.000	54	121.30	0.000
13	88.56	0.136	27	99.82	5.845	41	109.37	0.000	55	127.91	0.000
14	89.06	0.000	28	99.87	1.659	42	110.55	0.000	56	136.07	0.000

```
-11  -10  -9  -8  -7  -6  -5  -4  -3  -2  -1  0  +1  +2  +3  +4  +5  +6  +7  +8  +9  +10  +11
```

5-254

$J_{AA'}$	J_{AB}	$J_{AB'}$	$J_{BB'}$
4	6	9	4
4	9	6	4

The maximum summed intensity is 5.923.

LINE	FREQ	INTEN	LINE	FREQ	INTEN	LINE	FREQ	INTEN	LINE	FREQ	INTEN
1	73.87	0.001	15	92.58	0.000	29	100.02	0.531	43	108.15	0.000
2	82.59	0.000	16	94.42	0.000	30	100.23	5.759	44	108.96	0.000
3	83.61	0.018	17	95.15	0.553	31	100.58	3.857	45	109.97	0.381
4	83.86	0.017	18	95.15	0.553	32	100.71	0.000	46	110.58	0.000
5	84.33	0.000	19	95.45	0.000	33	101.85	1.447	47	110.70	0.000
6	84.42	0.143	20	97.12	1.214	34	101.85	1.447	48	113.28	0.080
7	85.15	0.000	21	97.42	0.000	35	102.16	0.000	49	113.58	0.000
8	86.42	0.000	22	97.84	0.000	36	102.58	0.000	50	114.85	0.000
9	86.72	0.080	23	98.15	1.447	37	102.88	1.214	51	115.58	0.143
10	89.30	0.000	24	98.15	1.447	38	104.55	0.000	52	115.67	0.000
11	89.42	0.000	25	99.29	0.000	39	104.85	0.553	53	116.14	0.017
12	90.03	0.381	26	99.42	3.857	40	104.85	0.553	54	116.39	0.018
13	91.04	0.000	27	99.76	5.759	41	105.58	0.000	55	117.41	0.000
14	91.85	0.000	28	99.98	0.531	42	107.42	0.000	56	126.13	0.001

```
-11  -10  -9  -8  -7  -6  -5  -4  -3  -2  -1  0  +1  +2  +3  +4  +5  +6  +7  +8  +9  +10  +11
```

5-255

$J_{AA'}$	J_{AB}	$J_{AB'}$	$J_{BB'}$
4	6	9	6
4	9	6	6
6	9	6	4
6	6	9	4

The maximum summed intensity is 5.613.

LINE	FREQ	INTEN	LINE	FREQ	INTEN	LINE	FREQ	INTEN	LINE	FREQ	INTEN
1	73.75	0.001	15	92.81	0.000	29	100.23	5.759	43	108.90	0.000
2	82.24	0.006	16	93.93	0.188	30	100.41	0.000	44	108.96	0.000
3	82.42	0.000	17	95.12	0.000	31	100.58	3.857	45	110.10	0.363
4	83.61	0.018	18	95.70	0.945	32	100.70	1.055	46	110.81	0.000
5	84.32	0.	19	96.18	0.000	33	101.27	0.000	47	111.27	0.000
6	84.42	0.143	20	97.05	0.000	34	101.61	0.296	48	113.53	0.091
7	85.00	0.000	21	97.37	1.466	35	102.05	0.000	49	114.88	0.000
8	85.12	0.000	22	97.53	1.812	36	102.47	1.812	50	115.58	0.143
9	86.47	0.091	23	97.81	0.000	37	102.63	1.466	51	115.81	0.000
10	88.73	0.000	24	98.39	0.296	38	104.30	0.945	52	116.39	0.018
11	89.32	0.000	25	98.73	0.000	39	104.72	0.000	53	116.77	0.000
12	89.90	0.363	26	99.30	1.055	40	104.88	0.000	54	117.45	0.000
13	90.00	0.000	27	99.42	3.857	41	106.07	0.188	55	117.76	0.006
14	90.96	0.000	28	99.77	5.759	42	108.23	0.000	56	126.25	0.001

5-256

$J_{AA'}$	J_{AB}	$J_{AB'}$	$J_{BB'}$
4	6	9	9
4	9	6	9
9	9	6	4
9	6	9	4

The maximum summed intensity is 5.614.

LINE	FREQ	INTEN	LINE	FREQ	INTEN	LINE	FREQ	INTEN	LINE	FREQ	INTEN
1	73.42	0.000	15	91.38	0.037	29	100.02	0.000	43	108.62	0.037
2	79.49	0.000	16	92.70	0.000	30	100.23	5.760	44	110.43	0.315
3	79.70	0.003	17	93.39	0.000	31	100.58	3.857	45	111.42	0.000
4	82.51	0.000	18	95.50	0.783	32	101.33	1.217	46	111.66	0.000
5	83.61	0.018	19	95.51	0.000	33	101.34	0.000	47	113.23	0.000
6	84.42	0.000	20	95.86	0.228	34	102.49	1.582	48	113.67	0.094
7	84.42	0.143	21	95.86	0.000	35	102.49	0.000	49	115.58	0.143
8	86.33	0.094	22	97.21	1.963	36	102.79	1.963	50	116.39	0.018
9	86.42	0.000	23	97.51	1.582	37	104.14	0.228	51	116.39	0.000
10	87.58	0.000	24	98.66	0.000	38	104.49	0.000	52	117.49	0.000
11	88.34	0.000	25	98.67	1.217	39	104.50	0.783	53	117.70	0.000
12	89.57	0.315	26	99.33	0.000	40	104.79	0.000	54	119.70	0.000
13	89.58	0.000	27	99.42	3.857	41	106.30	0.000	55	120.30	0.003
14	90.89	0.000	28	99.77	5.760	42	108.30	0.000	56	126.58	0.000

5-257

$J_{AA'}$	J_{AB}	$J_{AB'}$	$J_{BB'}$
4	6	12	4
4	12	6	4

The maximum summed intensity is 6.284.

LINE	FREQ	INTEN	LINE	FREQ	INTEN	LINE	FREQ	INTEN	LINE	FREQ	INTEN
1	68.64	0.000	15	91.24	0.000	29	100.19	5.831	43	109.24	0.000
2	77.89	0.000	16	91.51	0.000	30	100.49	1.392	44	109.43	0.000
3	80.84	0.014	17	92.76	0.293	31	100.49	3.897	45	110.49	0.000
4	81.51	0.037	18	92.76	0.293	32	100.76	0.000	46	112.38	0.246
5	81.51	0.103	19	94.95	0.000	33	101.24	1.707	47	113.63	0.000
6	82.08	0.000	20	95.32	0.450	34	101.24	1.707	48	114.29	0.029
7	82.76	0.000	21	96.56	0.000	35	102.49	0.000	49	116.49	0.000
8	83.51	0.000	22	97.51	0.000	36	103.44	0.000	50	117.24	0.000
9	85.71	0.029	23	98.76	1.707	37	104.68	0.450	51	117.92	0.000
10	86.37	0.000	24	98.76	1.707	38	105.05	0.000	52	118.49	0.037
11	87.62	0.246	25	99.24	0.000	39	107.24	0.293	53	118.49	0.103
12	89.51	0.000	26	99.51	1.392	40	107.24	0.293	54	119.16	0.014
13	90.57	0.000	27	99.51	3.897	41	108.49	0.000	55	122.11	0.000
14	90.76	0.000	28	99.81	5.831	42	108.76	0.000	56	131.36	0.000

−11 −10 −9 −8 −7 −6 −5 −4 −3 −2 −1 0 +1 +2 +3 +4 +5 +6 +7 +8 +9 +10 +11

5-258

$J_{AA'}$	J_{AB}	$J_{AB'}$	$J_{BB'}$
4	6	12	6
4	12	6	6
6	12	6	4
6	6	12	4

The maximum summed intensity is 7.210.

LINE	FREQ	INTEN	LINE	FREQ	INTEN	LINE	FREQ	INTEN	LINE	FREQ	INTEN
1	68.40	0.000	15	91.58	0.000	29	99.81	0.000	43	109.81	0.000
2	79.28	0.000	16	91.84	0.178	30	100.19	5.832	44	111.07	0.000
3	80.32	0.000	17	92.35	0.000	31	100.33	1.060	45	111.32	0.000
4	80.70	0.024	18	93.23	0.386	32	100.44	1.614	46	112.11	0.000
5	80.84	0.014	19	95.65	0.000	33	100.49	3.897	47	112.63	0.230
6	81.51	0.103	20	95.75	0.000	34	101.32	0.000	48	115.23	0.042
7	82.35	0.000	21	96.26	0.799	35	101.84	1.822	49	117.65	0.000
8	82.39	0.000	22	98.16	1.822	36	102.86	0.000	50	118.28	0.000
9	84.77	0.042	23	98.68	0.000	37	103.74	0.799	51	118.49	0.103
10	86.49	0.000	24	98.79	0.000	38	105.75	0.000	52	119.00	0.000
11	87.37	0.230	25	99.51	3.897	39	106.77	0.386	53	119.16	0.014
12	88.68	0.000	26	99.56	1.614	40	107.65	0.000	54	119.30	0.024
13	89.61	0.000	27	99.67	1.060	41	108.16	0.178	55	122.11	0.000
14	90.32	0.000	28	99.81	5.832	42	109.00	0.000	56	131.60	0.000

−11 −10 −9 −8 −7 −6 −5 −4 −3 −2 −1 0 +1 +2 +3 +4 +5 +6 +7 +8 +9 +10 +11

5-259

$J_{AA'}$	J_{AB}	$J_{AB'}$	$J_{BB'}$
4	6	12	12
4	12	6	12
12	12	6	4
12	6	12	4

The maximum summed intensity is 6.173.

LINE	FREQ	INTEN	LINE	FREQ	INTEN	LINE	FREQ	INTEN	LINE	FREQ	INTEN
1	67.14	0.000	15	89.94	0.000	29	99.81	5.832	43	112.49	0.000
2	74.71	0.000	16	91.22	0.000	30	100.19	5.832	44	112.62	0.028
3	77.05	0.005	17	91.37	0.000	31	100.49	3.897	45	113.08	0.000
4	77.51	0.000	18	91.84	0.178	32	101.84	1.822	46	113.89	0.156
5	79.84	0.000	19	93.51	0.000	33	102.62	1.972	47	114.51	0.000
6	80.84	0.014	20	96.02	0.486	34	102.65	1.447	48	116.32	0.060
7	81.46	0.000	21	96.49	0.000	35	103.51	0.000	49	118.49	0.103
8	81.51	0.103	22	97.35	1.447	36	103.98	0.486	50	119.16	0.014
9	83.68	0.060	23	97.38	1.972	37	104.33	0.000	51	120.84	0.000
10	86.11	0.156	24	97.70	0.000	38	106.45	0.000	52	122.49	0.000
11	86.16	0.000	25	97.85	0.000	39	106.49	0.000	53	122.95	0.005
12	87.38	0.028	26	98.00	0.000	40	107.76	0.000	54	122.99	0.000
13	87.51	0.000	27	98.16	1.822	41	108.16	0.178	55	124.62	0.
14	87.79	0.000	28	99.51	3.897	42	109.38	0.	56	132.86	0.000

5-260

$J_{AA'}$	J_{AB}	$J_{AB'}$	$J_{BB'}$
4	6	15	4
4	15	6	4

The maximum summed intensity is 6.641.

LINE	FREQ	INTEN	LINE	FREQ	INTEN	LINE	FREQ	INTEN	LINE	FREQ	INTEN
1	63.11	0.000	15	90.09	0.168	29	100.16	5.875	43	110.42	0.000
2	72.62	0.000	16	90.09	0.168	30	100.42	3.923	44	111.42	0.000
3	78.00	0.011	17	90.33	0.000	31	100.52	1.709	45	111.81	0.000
4	78.58	0.077	18	90.91	0.000	32	100.91	1.832	46	114.63	0.014
5	78.68	0.034	19	92.79	0.191	33	100.91	1.832	47	115.05	0.166
6	79.51	0.000	20	94.30	0.000	34	101.00	0.000	48	116.56	0.000
7	80.09	0.000	21	94.88	0.000	35	102.42	0.000	49	119.42	0.000
8	80.58	0.000	22	97.58	0.000	36	105.12	0.000	50	119.91	0.000
9	83.44	0.000	23	99.00	0.000	37	105.70	0.000	51	120.49	0.000
10	84.95	0.166	24	99.09	1.832	38	107.21	0.191	52	121.32	0.034
11	85.37	0.014	25	99.09	1.832	39	109.09	0.000	53	121.42	0.077
12	88.19	0.000	26	99.48	1.709	40	109.67	0.000	54	122.00	0.011
13	88.58	0.000	27	99.58	3.923	41	109.91	0.168	55	127.38	0.000
14	89.58	0.000	28	99.84	5.875	42	109.91	0.168	56	136.89	0.000

5-261

$J_{AA'}$	J_{AB}	$J_{AB'}$	$J_{BB'}$
4	6	15	6
4	15	6	6
6	15	6	4
6	6	15	4

The maximum summed intensity is 9.188.

LINE	FREQ	INTEN	LINE	FREQ	INTEN	LINE	FREQ	INTEN	LINE	FREQ	INTEN
1	62.80	0.000	15	89.42	0.000	29	99.87	1.584	43	111.15	0.000
2	73.79	0.000	16	89.47	0.000	30	100.13	1.584	44	111.31	0.000
3	77.90	0.000	17	89.94	0.000	31	100.16	5.876	45	111.81	0.000
4	78.00	0.011	18	90.47	0.196	32	100.31	1.804	46	115.26	0.000
5	78.29	0.029	19	93.99	0.000	33	100.42	3.923	47	115.36	0.155
6	78.58	0.077	20	94.09	0.327	34	101.31	0.000	48	115.93	0.018
7	79.47	0.000	21	95.07	0.000	35	101.41	1.874	49	120.53	0.000
8	79.58	0.000	22	98.59	1.874	36	104.92	0.000	50	121.00	0.000
9	83.64	0.000	23	98.69	0.000	37	105.91	0.327	51	121.42	0.077
10	84.07	0.018	24	99.14	0.000	38	106.03	0.000	52	121.52	0.000
11	84.64	0.155	25	99.58	3.923	39	109.48	0.000	53	121.71	0.029
12	88.69	0.000	26	99.69	1.804	40	109.53	0.196	54	122.00	0.011
13	89.29	0.000	27	99.77	0.000	41	110.53	0.000	55	127.30	0.000
14	89.37	0.126	28	99.84	5.876	42	110.63	0.126	56	137.20	0.000

5-262

$J_{AA'}$	J_{AB}	$J_{AB'}$	$J_{BB'}$
4	6	15	15
4	15	6	15
15	15	6	4
15	6	15	4

The maximum summed intensity is 6.552.

LINE	FREQ	INTEN	LINE	FREQ	INTEN	LINE	FREQ	INTEN	LINE	FREQ	INTEN
1	60.44	0.000	15	87.75	0.071	29	100.16	5.876	43	113.31	0.000
2	69.80	0.000	16	88.85	0.000	30	100.18	0.000	44	114.59	0.
3	72.47	0.000	17	89.04	0.000	31	100.42	3.923	45	115.43	0.000
4	74.61	0.007	18	89.88	0.000	32	101.96	1.929	46	116.72	0.020
5	74.85	0.000	19	91.47	0.000	33	102.51	1.980	47	117.72	0.089
6	75.71	0.000	20	94.31	0.000	34	102.96	1.284	48	118.88	0.040
7	78.00	0.011	21	95.35	0.000	35	103.55	0.692	49	121.42	0.077
8	78.58	0.077	22	96.39	0.000	36	105.69	0.000	50	122.00	0.011
9	81.12	0.040	23	96.45	0.692	37	106.68	0.000	51	125.39	0.007
10	82.28	0.089	24	97.04	1.284	38	108.08	0.000	52	125.73	0.000
11	83.28	0.020	25	97.49	1.980	39	108.53	0.000	53	127.53	0.000
12	85.15	0.000	26	98.04	1.929	40	109.53	0.000	54	128.76	0.000
13	86.00	0.000	27	99.58	3.923	41	110.38	0.000	55	129.62	0.000
14	86.69	0.000	28	99.84	5.876	42	112.25	0.071	56	139.56	0.000

5-263

$J_{AA'}$	J_{AB}	$J_{AB'}$	$J_{BB'}$
6	1	2	6
6	2	1	6

The maximum summed intensity is 4.178.

LINE	FREQ	INTEN	LINE	FREQ	INTEN	LINE	FREQ	INTEN	LINE	FREQ	INTEN
1	84.53	0.000	15	95.64	1.302	29	101.33	0.000	43	104.46	0.000
2	85.98	0.000	16	96.46	0.836	30	101.62	3.347	44	104.75	0.000
3	88.93	0.001	17	96.46	0.836	31	101.85	2.894	45	104.85	1.106
4	89.46	0.000	18	96.49	1.546	32	102.15	0.000	46	107.94	0.000
5	90.15	0.000	19	96.80	1.791	33	102.54	1.164	47	108.33	0.003
6	90.85	0.000	20	96.85	0.000	34	102.54	1.164	48	108.76	0.010
7	91.11	0.000	21	96.93	0.000	35	102.81	0.000	49	108.85	0.000
8	91.15	0.000	22	97.19	0.000	36	103.07	0.000	50	108.89	0.
9	91.24	0.010	23	97.46	1.164	37	103.15	0.000	51	109.15	0.000
10	91.67	0.003	24	97.46	1.164	38	103.20	1.791	52	109.85	0.000
11	92.06	0.000	25	97.85	0.000	39	103.51	1.546	53	110.54	0.000
12	95.15	1.106	26	98.15	2.894	40	103.54	0.836	54	111.07	0.001
13	95.25	0.000	27	98.38	3.347	41	103.54	0.836	55	114.02	0.000
14	95.54	0.000	28	98.67	0.000	42	104.36	1.302	56	115.47	0.000

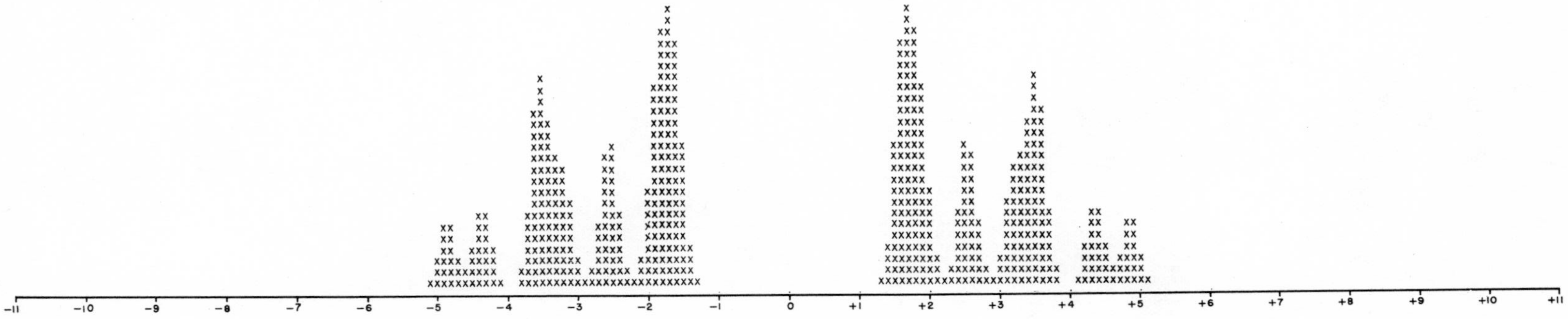

5-264

$J_{AA'}$	J_{AB}	$J_{AB'}$	$J_{BB'}$
6	2	4	6
6	4	2	6

The maximum summed intensity is 4.685.

LINE	FREQ	INTEN	LINE	FREQ	INTEN	LINE	FREQ	INTEN	LINE	FREQ	INTEN
1	83.02	0.000	15	94.78	0.720	29	100.18	0.000	43	105.84	0.000
2	85.79	0.000	16	94.90	0.883	30	100.76	0.000	44	106.50	0.000
3	86.42	0.003	17	95.84	0.684	31	100.81	4.691	45	107.24	0.586
4	87.84	0.000	18	95.84	0.684	32	101.24	3.414	46	107.89	0.000
5	88.76	0.000	19	96.42	0.000	33	101.86	0.000	47	108.19	0.000
6	90.10	0.000	20	96.73	1.584	34	102.16	1.316	48	108.50	0.100
7	90.70	0.019	21	97.24	0.	35	102.16	1.316	49	109.24	0.
8	90.76	0.000	22	97.84	1.316	36	102.76	0.	50	109.30	0.019
9	91.50	0.100	23	97.84	1.316	37	103.27	1.584	51	109.90	0.000
10	91.81	0.000	24	98.14	0.	38	103.58	0.	52	111.24	0.000
11	92.11	0.000	25	98.76	3.414	39	104.16	0.684	53	112.16	0.000
12	92.76	0.586	26	99.19	4.691	40	104.16	0.684	54	113.58	0.003
13	93.50	0.000	27	99.24	0.000	41	105.10	0.883	55	114.21	0.000
14	94.16	0.000	28	99.82	0.	42	105.22	0.720	56	116.98	0.000

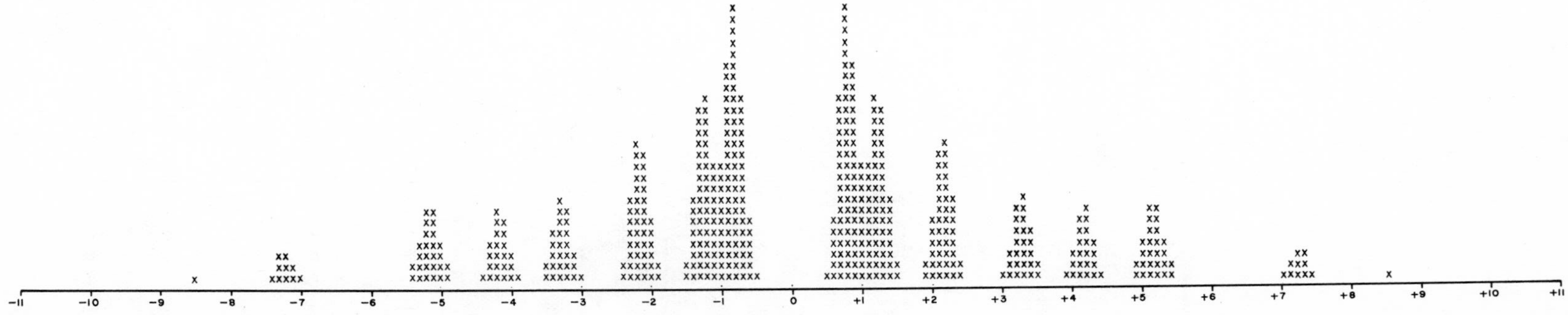

5-265

$J_{AA'}$	J_{AB}	$J_{AB'}$	$J_{BB'}$
6	4	6	9
6	6	4	9
9	6	4	6
9	4	6	6

The maximum summed intensity is 5.489.

LINE	FREQ	INTEN	LINE	FREQ	INTEN	LINE	FREQ	INTEN	LINE	FREQ	INTEN
1	78.32	0.000	15	93.29	0.000	29	100.08	0.000	43	107.89	0.000
2	81.66	0.000	16	93.42	0.592	30	100.13	0.000	44	108.80	0.245
3	81.76	0.002	17	93.45	0.000	31	100.30	0.000	45	109.52	0.000
4	84.87	0.000	18	93.59	0.067	32	100.40	5.468	46	110.02	0.092
5	85.70	0.000	19	96.39	1.385	33	100.83	3.715	47	110.83	0.285
6	87.94	0.025	20	96.53	0.000	34	102.73	0.000	48	111.53	0.000
7	88.47	0.000	21	96.89	0.000	35	102.81	1.933	49	111.93	0.000
8	89.17	0.285	22	97.14	1.576	36	102.86	1.576	50	112.06	0.025
9	89.30	0.000	23	97.19	1.933	37	103.47	0.000	51	112.96	0.000
10	89.84	0.000	24	99.17	3.715	38	103.61	1.385	52	115.13	0.000
11	89.98	0.092	25	99.60	5.468	39	103.74	0.000	53	115.53	0.000
12	90.86	0.000	26	99.87	0.000	40	106.34	0.000	54	117.11	0.000
13	90.88	0.000	27	100.00	0.615	41	106.41	0.067	55	118.24	0.002
14	91.20	0.245	28	100.00	0.615	42	106.58	0.592	56	121.68	0.000

−11 −10 −9 −8 −7 −6 −5 −4 −3 −2 −1 0 +1 +2 +3 +4 +5 +6 +7 +8 +9 +10 +11

5-266

$J_{AA'}$	J_{AB}	$J_{AB'}$	$J_{BB'}$
6	4	6	12
6	6	4	12
12	6	4	6
12	4	6	6

The maximum summed intensity is 5.481.

LINE	FREQ	INTEN	LINE	FREQ	INTEN	LINE	FREQ	INTEN	LINE	FREQ	INTEN
1	75.71	0.000	15	91.19	0.244	29	100.01	0.000	43	108.81	0.244
2	78.69	0.000	16	91.55	0.000	30	100.07	0.000	44	109.25	0.012
3	81.37	0.002	17	93.04	0.656	31	100.40	5.469	45	109.88	0.000
4	82.01	0.000	18	93.67	0.000	32	100.83	3.715	46	110.83	0.285
5	85.00	0.000	19	95.21	0.000	33	102.16	1.316	47	111.67	0.000
6	87.00	0.000	20	95.84	0.684	34	102.85	1.584	48	112.06	0.025
7	87.38	0.019	21	97.08	1.988	35	102.92	1.988	49	112.62	0.019
8	87.90	0.000	22	97.15	1.584	36	103.37	0.000	50	114.23	0.000
9	87.94	0.025	23	97.21	0.000	37	104.16	0.684	51	115.54	0.000
10	88.33	0.000	24	97.71	0.000	38	105.02	0.000	52	116.23	0.000
11	89.17	0.285	25	97.84	1.316	39	106.33	0.000	53	117.99	0.000
12	89.55	0.000	26	99.17	3.715	40	106.96	0.656	54	118.63	0.002
13	90.75	0.012	27	99.60	5.469	41	107.02	0.000	55	120.08	0.000
14	90.85	0.000	28	99.99	0.000	42	107.92	0.000	56	124.29	0.000

−11 −10 −9 −8 −7 −6 −5 −4 −3 −2 −1 0 +1 +2 +3 +4 +5 +6 +7 +8 +9 +10 +11

5-267

$J_{AA'}$	J_{AB}	$J_{AB'}$	$J_{BB'}$
6	4	6	15
6	6	4	12
15	6	4	6
15	4	6	6

The maximum summed intensity is 5.481.

LINE	FREQ	INTEN	LINE	FREQ	INTEN	LINE	FREQ	INTEN	LINE	FREQ	INTEN
1	72.86	0.000	15	90.83	0.000	29	100.06	0.000	43	109.31	0.000
2	75.70	0.000	16	91.00	0.000	30	100.06	0.000	44	110.00	0.000
3	79.06	0.000	17	91.18	0.244	31	100.40	5.469	45	110.83	0.285
4	81.24	0.002	18	92.90	0.665	32	100.83	3.715	46	111.72	0.000
5	82.70	0.000	19	93.59	0.067	33	102.81	1.933	47	112.06	0.025
6	84.52	0.006	20	94.87	0.000	34	102.84	1.589	48	112.18	0.004
7	84.93	0.000	21	95.76	0.000	35	102.96	1.996	49	114.93	0.000
8	86.30	0.000	22	97.04	1.996	36	103.24	0.000	50	115.48	0.006
9	87.39	0.000	23	97.16	1.589	37	105.70	0.000	51	118.37	0.000
10	87.82	0.004	24	97.19	1.933	38	106.41	0.067	52	118.53	0.000
11	87.94	0.025	25	99.17	3.715	39	107.10	0.665	53	118.76	0.002
12	88.28	0.000	26	99.37	0.000	40	107.93	0.000	54	120.94	0.000
13	89.17	0.285	27	99.60	5.469	41	108.82	0.244	55	123.07	0.000
14	90.72	0.000	28	99.94	0.000	42	109.28	0.000	56	127.14	0.000

5-268

$J_{AA'}$	J_{AB}	$J_{AB'}$	$J_{BB'}$
6	4	9	6
6	9	4	6

The maximum summed intensity is 5.710.

LINE	FREQ	INTEN	LINE	FREQ	INTEN	LINE	FREQ	INTEN	LINE	FREQ	INTEN
1	74.66	0.000	15	91.85	0.000	29	100.29	5.677	43	108.27	0.000
2	82.60	0.010	16	93.59	0.360	30	100.34	0.000	44	108.59	0.000
3	82.65	0.000	17	93.59	0.360	31	100.66	3.816	45	109.54	0.000
4	83.59	0.	18	94.12	0.000	32	101.34	0.000	46	110.66	0.000
5	83.92	0.000	19	96.34	0.000	33	101.41	1.640	47	111.02	0.241
6	84.34	0.000	20	96.86	1.331	34	101.41	1.640	48	111.18	0.129
7	85.40	0.021	21	96.91	0.592	35	101.93	0.000	49	113.66	0.184
8	86.34	0.184	22	98.07	0.000	36	103.09	0.592	50	114.60	0.021
9	88.82	0.129	23	98.59	1.640	37	103.14	1.331	51	115.66	0.000
10	88.98	0.241	24	98.59	1.640	38	103.66	0.000	52	116.08	0.000
11	89.34	0.000	25	98.66	0.000	39	105.88	0.000	53	116.41	0.
12	90.46	0.000	26	99.34	3.816	40	106.41	0.360	54	117.35	0.000
13	91.41	0.000	27	99.66	0.000	41	106.41	0.360	55	117.40	0.010
14	91.73	0.000	28	99.71	5.677	42	108.15	0.000	56	125.34	0.000

5-269

$J_{AA'}$	J_{AB}	$J_{AB'}$	$J_{BB'}$
6	4	9	9
6	9	4	9
9	9	4	6
9	4	9	6

The maximum summed intensity is 5.892.

LINE	FREQ	INTEN	LINE	FREQ	INTEN	LINE	FREQ	INTEN	LINE	FREQ	INTEN
1	73.54	0.000	15	91.57	0.000	29	100.00	1.471	43	108.85	0.000
2	79.91	0.000	16	91.94	0.134	30	100.28	5.678	44	109.57	0.000
3	80.91	0.006	17	92.66	0.000	31	100.37	0.000	45	111.37	0.133
4	82.43	0.000	18	94.17	0.529	32	100.66	3.816	46	111.74	0.000
5	83.08	0.000	19	95.23	0.566	33	101.86	0.000	47	112.03	0.000
6	85.28	0.000	20	96.74	0.000	34	102.23	1.866	48	112.14	0.153
7	85.40	0.021	21	97.06	1.445	35	102.57	0.000	49	113.66	0.184
8	86.34	0.184	22	97.43	0.000	36	102.94	1.445	50	114.60	0.021
9	87.86	0.153	23	97.77	1.866	37	103.26	0.000	51	116.95	0.000
10	88.26	0.000	24	98.49	0.000	38	104.77	0.566	52	117.57	0.000
11	88.63	0.133	25	99.28	0.000	39	105.83	0.529	53	117.86	0.000
12	88.92	0.000	26	99.34	3.816	40	106.20	0.000	54	119.09	0.006
13	90.20	0.000	27	99.72	5.678	41	106.66	0.000	55	119.15	0.000
14	91.11	0.000	28	100.00	1.471	42	108.06	0.134	56	126.46	0.000

5-270

$J_{AA'}$	J_{AB}	$J_{AB'}$	$J_{BB'}$
6	4	12	6
6	12	4	6

The maximum summed intensity is 5.835.

LINE	FREQ	INTEN	LINE	FREQ	INTEN	LINE	FREQ	INTEN	LINE	FREQ	INTEN
1	69.10	0.000	15	91.00	0.080	29	100.22	5.784	43	109.00	0.000
2	78.65	0.000	16	91.00	0.120	30	100.54	3.873	44	109.76	0.000
3	80.24	0.000	17	91.00	0.000	31	101.00	1.800	45	110.54	0.000
4	81.00	0.000	18	93.41	0.000	32	101.00	0.723	46	111.35	0.000
5	81.46	0.013	19	93.46	0.000	33	101.00	1.077	47	112.95	0.066
6	81.46	0.009	20	95.87	0.860	34	101.46	0.437	48	113.81	0.163
7	82.69	0.016	21	96.59	0.000	35	101.46	0.652	49	116.54	0.127
8	83.46	0.127	22	98.54	0.652	36	103.41	0.000	50	117.31	0.016
9	86.19	0.163	23	98.54	0.437	37	104.13	0.860	51	118.54	0.009
10	87.05	0.066	24	99.00	0.723	38	106.54	0.000	52	118.54	0.013
11	88.65	0.000	25	99.00	1.077	39	106.59	0.000	53	119.00	0.
12	89.46	0.000	26	99.00	1.800	40	109.00	0.120	54	119.76	0.000
13	90.24	0.000	27	99.46	3.873	41	109.00	0.080	55	121.35	0.000
14	91.00	0.200	28	99.78	5.784	42	109.00	0.200	56	130.90	0.000

5-271

$J_{AA'}$	J_{AB}	$J_{AB'}$	$J_{BB'}$
6	4	12	12
6	12	4	12
12	12	4	6
12	4	12	6

The maximum summed intensity is 5.845.

LINE	FREQ	INTEN	LINE	FREQ	INTEN	LINE	FREQ	INTEN	LINE	FREQ	INTEN
1	66.79	0.000	15	89.17	0.000	29	100.22	5.786	43	110.93	0.
2	75.03	0.000	16	89.45	0.000	30	100.28	0.000	44	112.21	0.057
3	77.46	0.000	17	91.00	0.200	31	100.54	3.873	45	112.54	0.000
4	78.74	0.008	18	92.28	0.000	32	101.00	1.800	46	113.76	0.000
5	79.00	0.	19	94.54	0.000	33	102.21	1.943	47	113.92	0.079
6	80.33	0.000	20	95.46	0.000	34	103.17	1.302	48	116.13	0.086
7	82.69	0.016	21	95.83	0.723	35	103.59	0.000	49	116.54	0.127
8	83.46	0.127	22	96.51	0.000	36	104.17	0.723	50	117.31	0.016
9	83.87	0.086	23	96.83	1.302	37	104.54	0.000	51	121.26	0.008
10	86.08	0.079	24	97.79	1.943	38	105.46	0.000	52	121.76	0.000
11	87.00	0.	25	99.00	1.800	39	107.62	0.000	53	122.54	0.000
12	87.46	0.000	26	99.46	3.873	40	108.46	0.000	54	122.88	0.000
13	87.79	0.057	27	99.62	0.000	41	109.00	0.200	55	124.21	0.
14	88.33	0.000	28	99.78	5.786	42	109.79	0.	56	133.21	0.000

−11 −10 −9 −8 −7 −6 −5 −4 −3 −2 −1 0 +1 +2 +3 +4 +5 +6 +7 +8 +9 +10 +11

5-272

$J_{AA'}$	J_{AB}	$J_{AB'}$	$J_{BB'}$
6	4	15	6
6	15	4	6

The maximum summed intensity is 6.327.

LINE	FREQ	INTEN	LINE	FREQ	INTEN	LINE	FREQ	INTEN	LINE	FREQ	INTEN
1	63.41	0.000	15	89.54	0.000	29	100.18	5.846	43	110.81	0.000
2	73.10	0.000	16	90.12	0.000	30	100.46	3.907	44	111.76	0.122
3	77.59	0.000	17	90.54	0.000	31	100.58	1.536	45	111.76	0.122
4	78.24	0.	18	90.76	0.000	32	100.76	1.878	46	113.93	0.032
5	78.54	0.000	19	91.70	0.000	33	100.76	1.878	47	114.37	0.000
6	79.49	0.030	20	94.00	0.429	34	101.54	0.000	48	116.67	0.116
7	79.90	0.013	21	95.77	0.000	35	101.72	0.000	49	119.46	0.093
8	80.54	0.093	22	98.28	0.000	36	104.23	0.000	50	120.10	0.013
9	83.33	0.116	23	98.46	0.000	37	106.00	0.429	51	120.51	0.030
10	85.63	0.000	24	99.24	1.878	38	108.30	0.000	52	121.46	0.000
11	86.07	0.032	25	99.24	1.878	39	109.24	0.000	53	121.76	0.000
12	88.24	0.122	26	99.42	1.536	40	109.46	0.000	54	122.41	0.
13	88.24	0.122	27	99.54	3.907	41	109.88	0.000	55	126.90	0.000
14	89.19	0.000	28	99.82	5.846	42	110.46	0.000	56	136.59	0.000

−11 −10 −9 −8 −7 −6 −5 −4 −3 −2 −1 0 +1 +2 +3 +4 +5 +6 +7 +8 +9 +10 +11

5-273

$J_{AA'}$	J_{AB}	$J_{AB'}$	$J_{BB'}$
6	4	15	15
6	15	4	15
15	15	4	6
15	4	15	6

The maximum summed intensity is 6.303.

LINE	FREQ	INTEN	LINE	FREQ	INTEN	LINE	FREQ	INTEN	LINE	FREQ	INTEN
1	59.91	0.000	15	86.65	0.000	29	100.18	5.848	43	112.81	0.087
2	70.06	0.000	16	87.19	0.087	30	100.46	3.907	44	113.36	0.000
3	72.43	0.000	17	88.66	0.000	31	101.41	1.913	45	114.94	0.000
4	74.30	0.000	18	91.23	0.000	32	102.19	1.968	46	116.41	0.032
5	74.67	0.	19	92.36	0.000	33	102.64	0.000	47	116.41	0.050
6	76.47	0.009	20	93.43	0.000	34	103.51	1.146	48	119.46	0.093
7	79.84	0.055	21	93.76	0.	35	103.60	0.879	49	120.10	0.013
8	79.90	0.013	22	96.40	0.879	36	105.25	0.000	50	120.16	0.055
9	80.54	0.093	23	96.49	1.146	37	106.57	0.000	51	123.53	0.009
10	83.59	0.050	24	97.81	1.968	38	107.64	0.000	52	126.34	0.000
11	83.59	0.032	25	98.35	0.000	39	109.75	0.000	53	127.57	0.000
12	85.70	0.000	26	98.59	1.913	40	110.33	0.000	54	128.93	0.000
13	86.08	0.000	27	99.54	3.907	41	110.70	0.000	55	129.30	0.000
14	86.64	0.000	28	99.82	5.848	42	112.37	0.000	56	140.09	0.000

−11 −10 −9 −8 −7 −6 −5 −4 −3 −2 −1 0 +1 +2 +3 +4 +5 +6 +7 +8 +9 +10 +11

5-274

$J_{AA'}$	J_{AB}	$J_{AB'}$	$J_{BB'}$
6	6	9	12
6	9	6	12
12	9	6	6
12	6	9	6

The maximum summed intensity is 5.616.

LINE	FREQ	INTEN	LINE	FREQ	INTEN	LINE	FREQ	INTEN	LINE	FREQ	INTEN
1	71.79	0.000	15	90.46	0.024	29	100.32	0.000	43	110.32	0.000
2	76.42	0.002	16	90.49	0.000	30	100.58	3.857	44	112.05	0.127
3	76.50	0.000	17	92.00	0.000	31	101.82	0.000	45	112.69	0.000
4	79.57	0.000	18	92.57	0.362	32	101.85	1.447	46	113.72	0.000
5	82.00	0.000	19	95.00	0.000	33	102.40	1.636	47	113.75	0.095
6	83.61	0.018	20	95.15	0.553	34	102.43	0.000	48	115.58	0.143
7	84.42	0.143	21	95.72	0.000	35	102.83	1.976	49	115.81	0.000
8	85.00	0.000	22	97.17	1.976	36	102.86	0.000	50	116.39	0.018
9	86.25	0.095	23	97.57	0.000	37	104.28	0.000	51	117.32	0.000
10	86.28	0.000	24	97.60	1.636	38	104.82	0.000	52	118.81	0.000
11	87.37	0.000	25	98.15	1.447	39	104.85	0.553	53	120.43	0.000
12	87.95	0.127	26	99.42	3.857	40	104.95	0.000	54	122.68	0.000
13	88.87	0.000	27	99.77	5.760	41	107.43	0.362	55	123.58	0.002
14	90.37	0.000	28	100.23	5.760	42	109.54	0.024	56	128.21	0.000

−11 −10 −9 −8 −7 −6 −5 −4 −3 −2 −1 0 +1 +2 +3 +4 +5 +6 +7 +8 +9 +10 +11

5-275

$J_{AA'}$	J_{AB}	$J_{AB'}$	$J_{BB'}$
6	6	9	15
6	9	6	15
15	9	6	6
15	6	9	6

The maximum summed intensity is 5.616.

LINE	FREQ	INTEN	LINE	FREQ	INTEN	LINE	FREQ	INTEN	LINE	FREQ	INTEN
1	69.70	0.000	15	88.84	0.000	29	100.23	5.760	43	112.39	0.008
2	73.54	0.	16	90.40	0.000	30	100.58	3.857	44	113.54	0.000
3	75.53	0.001	17	91.68	0.434	31	102.32	0.000	45	113.78	0.096
4	76.68	0.000	18	91.98	0.000	32	102.38	1.649	46	113.83	0.000
5	79.88	0.000	19	92.83	0.000	33	102.62	1.894	47	114.14	0.043
6	83.61	0.018	20	93.14	0.106	34	102.68	0.000	48	115.58	0.143
7	84.12	0.000	21	96.23	0.000	35	102.85	0.000	49	116.39	0.018
8	84.42	0.143	22	97.09	1.992	36	102.91	1.992	50	116.69	0.000
9	85.86	0.043	23	97.38	1.894	37	104.07	0.000	51	119.37	0.000
10	86.16	0.000	24	97.62	1.649	38	106.86	0.106	52	120.93	0.000
11	86.17	0.000	25	97.68	0.000	39	106.92	0.000	53	123.32	0.000
12	86.22	0.096	26	98.25	0.	40	107.17	0.000	54	124.47	0.001
13	87.55	0.000	27	99.42	3.857	41	108.32	0.434	55	125.65	0.
14	87.61	0.008	28	99.77	5.760	42	110.35	0.000	56	130.30	0.000

5-276

$J_{AA'}$	J_{AB}	$J_{AB'}$	$J_{BB'}$
6	6	12	9
6	12	6	9
9	12	6	6
9	6	12	6

The maximum summed intensity is 7.349.

LINE	FREQ	INTEN	LINE	FREQ	INTEN	LINE	FREQ	INTEN	LINE	FREQ	INTEN
1	67.42	0.000	15	91.24	0.132	29	100.00	1.600	43	110.74	0.000
2	77.42	0.000	16	91.31	0.000	30	100.00	1.600	44	111.09	0.000
3	77.68	0.006	17	93.29	0.400	31	100.19	5.832	45	113.60	0.171
4	79.66	0.000	18	93.84	0.000	32	100.49	3.897	46	113.63	0.000
5	80.15	0.	19	94.66	0.000	33	101.37	0.000	47	113.82	0.000
6	80.84	0.014	20	96.65	0.523	34	102.05	1.868	48	116.24	0.059
7	81.06	0.	21	97.27	1.394	35	102.73	1.394	49	118.49	0.103
8	81.51	0.103	22	97.39	0.000	36	103.35	0.523	50	119.16	0.014
9	83.76	0.059	23	97.95	1.868	37	104.10	0.000	51	120.34	0.000
10	86.37	0.000	24	98.02	0.000	38	104.66	0.000	52	120.53	0.000
11	86.40	0.171	25	98.63	0.000	39	105.34	0.000	53	121.00	0.
12	86.85	0.000	26	99.51	3.897	40	106.71	0.400	54	121.91	0.000
13	87.77	0.000	27	99.81	5.832	41	108.76	0.132	55	122.32	0.006
14	88.23	0.000	28	99.93	0.000	42	110.18	0.000	56	132.58	0.000

5-277

$J_{AA'}$	J_{AB}	$J_{AB'}$	$J_{BB'}$
6	6	15	9
6	15	6	9
9	15	6	6
9	6	15	6

The maximum summed intensity is 9.104.

LINE	FREQ	INTEN	LINE	FREQ	INTEN	LINE	FREQ	INTEN	LINE	FREQ	INTEN
1	61.72	0.000	15	88.89	0.106	29	100.00	1.800	43	111.64	0.000
2	75.06	0.000	16	90.24	0.000	30	100.00	1.800	44	113.50	0.
3	75.39	0.000	17	90.51	0.200	31	100.16	5.876	45	113.68	0.000
4	76.56	0.014	18	91.84	0.000	32	100.42	3.923	46	113.83	0.000
5	76.84	0.000	19	93.33	0.000	33	101.32	0.000	47	116.44	0.121
6	77.26	0.	20	95.56	0.000	34	101.60	1.033	48	118.11	0.033
7	78.00	0.011	21	96.27	0.912	35	101.62	1.894	49	121.42	0.077
8	78.58	0.077	22	98.38	1.894	36	103.73	0.912	50	122.00	0.011
9	81.89	0.033	23	98.40	1.033	37	105.05	0.000	51	123.16	0.000
10	83.56	0.121	24	98.66	0.000	38	106.06	0.000	52	123.32	0.000
11	84.88	0.000	25	98.68	0.000	39	108.16	0.000	53	123.44	0.014
12	86.32	0.000	26	99.58	3.923	40	109.49	0.200	54	124.36	0.000
13	86.74	0.000	27	99.72	0.000	41	111.11	0.106	55	126.23	0.000
14	87.79	0.000	28	99.84	5.876	42	111.38	0.000	56	138.28	0.000

5-278

$J_{AA'}$	J_{AB}	$J_{AB'}$	$J_{BB'}$
6	9	12	6
6	12	9	6

The maximum summed intensity is 6.539.

LINE	FREQ	INTEN	LINE	FREQ	INTEN	LINE	FREQ	INTEN	LINE	FREQ	INTEN
1	65.59	0.000	15	90.82	0.000	29	100.16	5.877	43	112.57	0.257
2	77.25	0.005	16	93.58	0.000	30	100.42	3.923	44	113.15	0.000
3	78.09	0.011	17	93.89	0.000	31	100.59	0.000	45	113.72	0.000
4	78.58	0.077	18	95.15	0.553	32	100.91	0.298	46	114.13	0.000
5	79.16	0.000	19	95.15	0.553	33	101.85	1.447	47	115.42	0.000
6	79.57	0.000	20	96.58	0.000	34	101.85	1.447	48	118.42	0.000
7	80.15	0.000	21	97.53	0.000	35	102.16	1.510	49	119.68	0.041
8	80.32	0.041	22	97.84	1.510	36	102.47	0.000	50	119.85	0.000
9	81.58	0.000	23	98.15	1.447	37	103.42	0.000	51	120.43	0.000
10	84.58	0.000	24	98.15	1.447	38	104.85	0.553	52	120.84	0.000
11	85.87	0.000	25	99.09	0.298	39	104.85	0.553	53	121.42	0.077
12	86.28	0.000	26	99.41	0.000	40	106.11	0.000	54	122.00	0.011
13	86.85	0.000	27	99.58	3.923	41	106.42	0.000	55	122.75	0.005
14	87.43	0.257	28	99.84	5.877	42	109.18	0.000	56	134.41	0.000

5-279

$J_{AA'}$	J_{AB}	$J_{AB'}$	$J_{BB'}$
6	9	12	9
6	12	9	9
9	12	9	6
9	9	12	6

The maximum summed intensity is 7.749.

LINE	FREQ	INTEN	LINE	FREQ	INTEN	LINE	FREQ	INTEN	LINE	FREQ	INTEN
1	65.43	0.000	15	90.88	0.000	29	100.00	1.000	43	111.74	0.000
2	74.59	0.001	16	93.14	0.106	30	100.16	5.877	44	112.73	0.244
3	76.68	0.000	17	94.46	0.000	31	100.42	3.923	45	113.26	0.000
4	78.00	0.011	18	95.13	0.000	32	100.69	0.000	46	116.30	0.000
5	78.58	0.077	19	95.76	1.000	33	101.30	0.000	47	116.45	0.000
6	79.46	0.000	20	96.43	0.139	34	101.99	1.683	48	119.85	0.044
7	79.88	0.000	21	96.45	0.000	35	102.25	0.000	49	120.54	0.000
8	80.15	0.044	22	96.68	0.000	36	102.62	1.894	50	120.70	0.000
9	81.72	0.000	23	97.38	1.894	37	103.57	0.139	51	120.90	0.000
10	83.70	0.000	24	98.01	1.683	38	104.24	1.000	52	121.42	0.077
11	84.12	0.000	25	98.70	0.000	39	105.54	0.000	53	122.00	0.011
12	85.97	0.000	26	99.58	3.923	40	106.17	0.000	54	122.74	0.000
13	86.17	0.000	27	99.84	5.877	41	106.86	0.106	55	125.41	0.001
14	87.27	0.244	28	100.00	1.000	42	111.41	0.000	56	134.57	0.000

5-280

$J_{AA'}$	J_{AB}	$J_{AB'}$	$J_{BB'}$
6	9	12	12
6	12	9	12
12	12	9	6
12	9	12	6

The maximum summed intensity is 6.538.

LINE	FREQ	INTEN	LINE	FREQ	INTEN	LINE	FREQ	INTEN	LINE	FREQ	INTEN
1	65.12	0.000	15	90.37	0.000	29	100.16	5.877	43	113.04	0.216
2	71.95	0.001	16	90.46	0.024	30	100.42	3.923	44	113.32	0.000
3	73.74	0.000	17	93.37	0.000	31	101.43	0.000	45	114.31	0.000
4	76.73	0.000	18	93.79	0.124	32	101.51	0.000	46	116.57	0.000
5	78.00	0.011	19	93.80	0.000	33	101.85	1.447	47	118.58	0.000
6	78.58	0.077	20	94.73	0.000	34	101.93	1.726	48	119.91	0.045
7	79.00	0.000	21	95.15	0.553	35	101.94	0.000	49	121.15	0.000
8	80.09	0.045	22	97.17	1.976	36	102.83	1.976	50	121.42	0.077
9	82.00	0.000	23	98.07	1.726	37	104.85	0.553	51	121.58	0.000
10	83.43	0.000	24	98.15	1.447	38	105.27	0.000	52	122.00	0.011
11	83.54	0.000	25	98.51	0.000	39	106.17	0.000	53	123.27	0.000
12	86.11	0.000	26	98.57	0.000	40	106.21	0.124	54	125.68	0.000
13	86.54	0.000	27	99.58	3.923	41	108.78	0.000	55	128.05	0.001
14	86.96	0.216	28	99.84	5.877	42	109.54	0.024	56	134.88	0.000

5-281

$J_{AA'}$	J_{AB}	$J_{AB'}$	$J_{BB'}$
6	9	15	6
6	15	9	6

The maximum summed intensity is 8.796.

LINE	FREQ	INTEN	LINE	FREQ	INTEN	LINE	FREQ	INTEN	LINE	FREQ	INTEN
1	60.28	0.000	15	89.48	0.000	29	100.09	1.208	43	113.76	0.000
2	74.40	0.000	16	90.63	0.000	30	100.13	5.906	44	114.26	0.000
3	75.13	0.009	17	92.76	0.293	31	100.37	3.940	45	114.98	0.177
4	75.36	0.018	18	92.76	0.293	32	101.24	1.707	46	115.37	0.000
5	75.63	0.060	19	92.88	0.000	33	101.24	1.707	47	117.11	0.000
6	77.25	0.000	20	96.51	0.665	34	101.37	0.000	48	121.24	0.017
7	77.76	0.000	21	96.63	0.000	35	102.03	0.000	49	121.37	0.000
8	78.63	0.000	22	97.97	0.000	36	103.37	0.000	50	122.24	0.000
9	78.76	0.017	23	98.63	0.000	37	103.49	0.665	51	122.75	0.000
10	82.89	0.000	24	98.76	1.707	38	107.12	0.000	52	124.37	0.060
11	84.63	0.000	25	98.76	1.707	39	107.24	0.293	53	124.64	0.018
12	85.02	0.177	26	99.63	3.940	40	107.24	0.293	54	124.87	0.009
13	85.74	0.000	27	99.87	5.906	41	109.37	0.000	55	125.60	0.000
14	86.24	0.000	28	99.91	1.208	42	110.52	0.000	56	139.72	0.000

−11 −10 −9 −8 −7 −6 −5 −4 −3 −2 −1 0 +1 +2 +3 +4 +5 +6 +7 +8 +9 +10 +11

5-282

$J_{AA'}$	J_{AB}	$J_{AB'}$	$J_{BB'}$
6	9	15	9
6	15	9	9
9	15	9	6
9	9	15	6

The maximum summed intensity is 10.094

LINE	FREQ	INTEN	LINE	FREQ	INTEN	LINE	FREQ	INTEN	LINE	FREQ	INTEN
1	59.94	0.000	15	90.18	0.000	29	100.00	1.600	43	114.09	0.000
2	73.67	0.007	16	91.24	0.132	30	100.13	5.906	44	114.78	0.000
3	74.59	0.000	17	91.78	0.000	31	100.37	3.940	45	115.32	0.163
4	75.13	0.009	18	93.29	0.400	32	101.00	0.000	46	116.52	0.000
5	75.63	0.060	19	94.29	0.000	33	101.05	0.000	47	116.65	0.000
6	76.46	0.	20	96.89	0.000	34	101.52	0.000	48	122.22	0.028
7	76.78	0.000	21	96.94	0.000	35	101.59	0.601	49	123.22	0.000
8	77.15	0.	22	97.48	1.286	36	102.05	1.868	50	123.36	0.000
9	77.78	0.028	23	97.95	1.868	37	102.52	1.286	51	124.37	0.060
10	83.17	0.000	24	98.41	0.601	38	106.71	0.400	52	124.87	0.009
11	83.48	0.000	25	98.48	0.000	39	107.76	0.000	53	124.91	0.000
12	83.85	0.	26	99.63	3.940	40	108.22	0.000	54	125.60	0.000
13	84.68	0.163	27	99.87	5.906	41	108.76	0.132	55	126.33	0.007
14	85.40	0.000	28	100.00	1.600	42	111.87	0.000	56	140.06	0.000

−11 −10 −9 −8 −7 −6 −5 −4 −3 −2 −1 0 +1 +2 +3 +4 +5 +6 +7 +8 +9 +10 +11

5-283

$J_{AA'}$	J_{AB}	$J_{AB'}$	$J_{BB'}$
6	9	15	15
6	15	9	15
15	15	9	6
15	9	15	6

The maximum summed intensity is 7.212.

LINE	FREQ	INTEN	LINE	FREQ	INTEN	LINE	FREQ	INTEN	LINE	FREQ	INTEN
1	58.76	0.000	15	86.51	0.021	29	99.87	5.906	43	114.42	0.000
2	68.92	0.000	16	88.89	0.000	30	100.13	5.906	44	115.83	0.000
3	69.37	0.001	17	91.24	0.132	31	100.37	3.940	45	116.51	0.117
4	71.72	0.000	18	91.79	0.000	32	102.00	1.661	46	117.46	0.000
5	74.15	0.000	19	92.72	0.000	33	102.05	1.868	47	119.65	0.000
6	75.13	0.009	20	94.11	0.273	34	102.67	1.979	48	122.74	0.033
7	75.63	0.060	21	95.60	0.000	35	103.48	0.000	49	124.37	0.060
8	77.26	0.033	22	96.46	0.000	36	103.54	0.000	50	124.87	0.009
9	78.27	0.000	23	96.77	0.000	37	105.89	0.273	51	126.36	0.000
10	80.85	0.000	24	97.33	1.979	38	107.28	0.000	52	126.45	0.000
11	82.54	0.000	25	97.95	1.868	39	107.95	0.000	53	128.28	0.000
12	83.49	0.117	26	98.00	1.661	40	108.76	0.132	54	130.58	0.000
13	84.98	0.000	27	99.63	3.940	41	110.30	0.000	55	130.63	0.001
14	85.07	0.000	28	99.68	0.000	42	113.49	0.021	56	141.24	0.000

5-284

$J_{AA'}$	J_{AB}	$J_{AB'}$	$J_{BB'}$
9	1	2	9
9	2	1	9

The maximum summed intensity is 4.156.

LINE	FREQ	INTEN	LINE	FREQ	INTEN	LINE	FREQ	INTEN	LINE	FREQ	INTEN
1	78.59	0.000	15	94.20	0.000	29	101.62	3.350	43	106.01	0.000
2	82.98	0.000	16	94.85	0.000	30	101.80	0.000	44	106.15	0.
3	85.30	0.001	17	95.15	1.106	31	101.85	2.894	45	107.46	0.000
4	86.46	0.000	18	95.59	1.305	32	102.54	1.164	46	108.33	0.003
5	87.15	0.000	19	95.72	0.000	33	102.54	1.164	47	110.93	0.000
6	87.90	0.000	20	96.46	0.836	34	103.20	1.797	48	111.11	0.001
7	88.12	0.000	21	96.46	0.836	35	103.51	1.544	49	111.85	0.000
8	88.15	0.000	22	96.49	1.544	36	103.54	0.836	50	111.88	0.000
9	88.89	0.001	23	96.80	1.797	37	103.54	0.836	51	112.10	0.000
10	89.07	0.000	24	97.46	1.164	38	104.28	0.000	52	112.85	0.
11	91.67	0.003	25	97.46	1.164	39	104.41	1.305	53	113.54	0.000
12	92.54	0.000	26	98.15	2.894	40	104.85	1.106	54	114.70	0.001
13	93.85	0.000	27	98.20	0.000	41	105.15	0.000	55	117.02	0.000
14	93.99	0.000	28	98.38	3.350	42	105.80	0.000	56	121.41	0.000

5-285

$J_{AA'}$	J_{AB}	$J_{AB'}$	$J_{BB'}$
9	2	4	9
9	4	2	9

The maximum summed intensity is 4.695.

LINE	FREQ	INTEN	LINE	FREQ	INTEN	LINE	FREQ	INTEN	LINE	FREQ	INTEN
1	77.48	0.000	15	94.24	0.000	29	100.81	4.696	43	106.12	0.000
2	82.79	0.000	16	94.48	0.957	30	101.24	3.414	44	107.24	0.586
3	84.84	0.000	17	94.75	0.716	31	102.16	1.316	45	108.84	0.000
4	85.76	0.000	18	95.17	0.000	32	102.16	1.316	46	109.29	0.019
5	85.96	0.006	19	95.84	0.684	33	102.40	0.	47	110.89	0.000
6	86.00	0.002	20	95.84	0.684	34	103.23	1.604	48	111.15	0.000
7	87.56	0.000	21	96.08	0.000	35	103.76	0.000	49	112.24	0.000
8	87.76	0.000	22	96.24	0.000	36	103.92	0.000	50	112.44	0.000
9	88.85	0.000	23	96.77	1.604	37	104.16	0.684	51	114.00	0.002
10	89.11	0.000	24	97.60	0.000	38	104.16	0.684	52	114.04	0.006
11	90.71	0.019	25	97.84	1.316	39	104.83	0.000	53	114.24	0.000
12	91.16	0.000	26	97.84	1.316	40	105.25	0.716	54	115.16	0.000
13	92.76	0.586	27	98.76	3.414	41	105.52	0.957	55	117.21	0.000
14	93.88	0.000	28	99.19	4.696	42	105.76	0.000	56	122.52	0.000

−11 −10 −9 −8 −7 −6 −5 −4 −3 −2 −1 0 +1 +2 +3 +4 +5 +6 +7 +8 +9 +10 +11

5-286

$J_{AA'}$	J_{AB}	$J_{AB'}$	$J_{BB'}$
9	4	6	9
9	6	4	9

The maximum summed intensity is 5.481.

LINE	FREQ	INTEN	LINE	FREQ	INTEN	LINE	FREQ	INTEN	LINE	FREQ	INTEN
1	75.71	0.000	15	93.04	0.656	29	100.40	5.469	43	108.81	0.244
2	81.37	0.002	16	93.04	0.000	30	100.63	0.	44	109.18	0.000
3	81.61	0.000	17	93.71	0.000	31	100.83	3.715	45	110.83	0.285
4	82.84	0.000	18	95.83	0.000	32	102.16	1.316	46	110.84	0.000
5	84.17	0.000	19	95.84	0.684	33	102.16	1.316	47	112.06	0.025
6	86.17	0.000	20	95.84	0.684	34	102.17	0.000	48	112.07	0.000
7	87.38	0.019	21	97.15	0.000	35	102.85	1.584	49	112.62	0.000
8	87.38	0.000	22	97.15	1.584	36	102.85	0.000	50	112.62	0.019
9	87.93	0.000	23	97.83	0.000	37	104.16	0.684	51	113.83	0.000
10	87.94	0.025	24	97.84	1.316	38	104.16	0.684	52	115.83	0.000
11	89.16	0.000	25	97.84	1.316	39	104.17	0.000	53	117.16	0.000
12	89.17	0.285	26	99.17	3.715	40	105.29	0.000	54	118.39	0.000
13	90.82	0.000	27	99.37	0.000	41	106.96	0.000	55	118.63	0.002
14	91.19	0.244	28	99.60	5.469	42	106.96	0.656	56	124.29	0.000

−11 −10 −9 −8 −7 −6 −5 −4 −3 −2 −1 0 +1 +2 +3 +4 +5 +6 +7 +8 +9 +10 +11

5-287	$J_{AA'}$	J_{AB}	$J_{AB'}$	$J_{BB'}$
	9	6	9	12
	9	9	6	12
	12	9	6	9
	12	6	9	9

The maximum summed intensity is 6.200.

LINE	FREQ	INTEN	LINE	FREQ	INTEN	LINE	FREQ	INTEN	LINE	FREQ	INTEN
1	69.70	0.000	15	90.46	0.000	29	100.00	1.000	43	110.64	0.000
2	75.53	0.001	16	91.68	0.434	30	100.23	5.760	44	113.26	0.000
3	76.44	0.000	17	91.98	0.000	31	100.30	0.000	45	113.78	0.096
4	79.30	0.000	18	93.14	0.106	32	100.58	3.857	46	114.14	0.043
5	79.88	0.000	19	95.46	0.000	33	101.15	0.000	47	115.58	0.143
6	83.54	0.000	20	95.76	1.000	34	102.38	1.649	48	116.39	0.018
7	83.61	0.018	21	96.23	0.000	35	102.62	1.894	49	116.46	0.000
8	84.12	0.000	22	97.38	1.894	36	102.68	0.000	50	116.46	0.000
9	84.42	0.143	23	97.62	1.649	37	104.24	1.000	51	116.69	0.000
10	85.86	0.043	24	99.42	3.857	38	104.54	0.000	52	120.70	0.000
11	85.93	0.000	25	99.70	0.000	39	106.86	0.106	53	120.93	0.000
12	86.16	0.000	26	99.77	5.760	40	106.92	0.000	54	122.74	0.
13	86.22	0.096	27	99.94	0.000	41	106.97	0.	55	124.47	0.001
14	90.40	0.000	28	100.00	1.000	42	108.32	0.434	56	130.30	0.000

−11 −10 −9 −8 −7 −6 −5 −4 −3 −2 −1 0 +1 +2 +3 +4 +5 +6 +7 +8 +9 +10 +11

5-288	$J_{AA'}$	J_{AB}	$J_{AB'}$	$J_{BB'}$
	9	6	9	15
	9	9	6	15
	15	9	6	9
	15	6	9	9

The maximum summed intensity is 5.617.

LINE	FREQ	INTEN	LINE	FREQ	INTEN	LINE	FREQ	INTEN	LINE	FREQ	INTEN
1	67.12	0.000	15	88.70	0.000	29	99.90	0.000	43	110.98	0.000
2	73.50	0.000	16	90.46	0.024	30	100.23	5.760	44	113.32	0.000
3	75.13	0.001	17	91.29	0.454	31	100.57	0.000	45	113.79	0.096
4	76.57	0.000	18	92.72	0.000	32	100.58	3.857	46	115.58	0.143
5	79.00	0.000	19	93.71	0.000	33	101.85	1.447	47	116.39	0.018
6	82.00	0.000	20	95.15	0.553	34	102.36	1.656	48	116.72	0.000
7	83.27	0.015	21	96.71	0.000	35	102.83	1.976	49	116.73	0.015
8	83.28	0.000	22	97.17	1.976	36	104.78	0.000	50	118.81	0.000
9	83.61	0.018	23	97.64	1.656	37	104.85	0.553	51	118.99	0.000
10	84.42	0.143	24	98.15	1.447	38	106.62	0.000	52	121.81	0.000
11	85.70	0.000	25	98.61	0.000	39	107.28	0.000	53	123.43	0.000
12	85.87	0.000	26	99.42	3.857	40	107.78	0.000	54	124.87	0.001
13	86.21	0.096	27	99.43	0.000	41	108.71	0.454	55	125.68	0.000
14	87.53	0.000	28	99.77	5.760	42	109.54	0.024	56	132.88	0.000

−11 −10 −9 −8 −7 −6 −5 −4 −3 −2 −1 0 +1 +2 +3 +4 +5 +6 +7 +8 +9 +10 +11

5-289

$J_{AA'}$	J_{AB}	$J_{AB'}$	$J_{BB'}$
9	6	12	9
9	12	6	9

The maximum summed intensity is 6.173.

LINE	FREQ	INTEN	LINE	FREQ	INTEN	LINE	FREQ	INTEN	LINE	FREQ	INTEN
1	66.44	0.000	15	90.12	0.000	29	100.19	5.832	43	110.83	0.000
2	75.87	0.003	16	92.76	0.293	30	100.49	3.897	44	113.76	0.000
3	77.08	0.	17	92.76	0.293	31	101.24	1.707	45	114.43	0.000
4	77.76	0.000	18	93.72	0.000	32	101.24	1.707	46	114.59	0.124
5	78.51	0.000	19	94.85	0.445	33	101.40	0.000	47	115.49	0.000
6	80.68	0.000	20	96.51	0.000	34	102.20	0.000	48	116.45	0.062
7	80.84	0.014	21	97.47	1.519	35	102.51	0.000	49	118.49	0.103
8	81.51	0.103	22	97.49	0.000	36	102.53	1.519	50	119.16	0.014
9	83.55	0.062	23	97.80	0.000	37	103.49	0.000	51	119.32	0.000
10	84.51	0.000	24	98.60	0.000	38	105.15	0.445	52	121.49	0.000
11	85.41	0.124	25	98.76	1.707	39	106.28	0.000	53	122.24	0.
12	85.57	0.000	26	98.76	1.707	40	107.24	0.293	54	122.92	0.000
13	86.24	0.000	27	99.51	3.897	41	107.24	0.293	55	124.13	0.003
14	89.17	0.000	28	99.81	5.832	42	109.88	0.000	56	133.56	0.000

5-290

$J_{AA'}$	J_{AB}	$J_{AB'}$	$J_{BB'}$
9	6	12	12
9	12	6	12
12	12	6	9
12	6	12	9

The maximum summed intensity is 7.434.

LINE	FREQ	INTEN	LINE	FREQ	INTEN	LINE	FREQ	INTEN	LINE	FREQ	INTEN
1	65.02	0.000	15	91.04	0.000	29	100.07	0.000	43	111.01	0.000
2	74.41	0.002	16	91.17	0.000	30	100.19	5.832	44	114.09	0.000
3	74.42	0.000	17	91.24	0.132	31	100.20	0.000	45	116.01	0.078
4	76.66	0.000	18	93.29	0.400	32	100.49	3.897	46	116.56	0.063
5	77.15	0.000	19	93.38	0.428	33	101.98	0.000	47	116.63	0.000
6	80.84	0.014	20	95.63	0.000	34	102.05	1.868	48	116.82	0.000
7	81.51	0.103	21	97.59	1.582	35	102.34	0.000	49	118.49	0.103
8	81.65	0.000	22	97.66	0.000	36	102.41	1.582	50	119.16	0.014
9	83.37	0.000	23	97.75	0.000	37	104.37	0.000	51	120.40	0.000
10	83.44	0.063	24	97.95	1.868	38	106.62	0.428	52	123.34	0.000
11	83.85	0.000	25	99.51	3.897	39	106.71	0.400	53	123.53	0.000
12	83.99	0.073	26	99.81	5.832	40	106.78	0.000	54	124.91	0.
13	85.23	0.000	27	100.00	1.600	41	108.76	0.132	55	125.59	0.002
14	88.36	0.000	28	100.00	1.600	42	109.59	0.000	56	134.98	0.000

5-291

$J_{AA'}$	J_{AB}	$J_{AB'}$	$J_{BB'}$
9	6	15	9
9	15	6	9

The maximum summed intensity is 6.553.

LINE	FREQ	INTEN	LINE	FREQ	INTEN	LINE	FREQ	INTEN	LINE	FREQ	INTEN
1	60.80	0.000	15	89.62	0.000	29	100.16	5.876	43	113.87	0.000
2	74.51	0.000	16	90.09	0.168	30	100.42	3.923	44	114.09	0.000
3	75.09	0.000	17	90.09	0.168	31	100.44	0.000	45	114.67	0.000
4	75.11	0.008	18	93.42	0.000	32	100.91	1.832	46	115.42	0.000
5	75.31	0.000	19	93.58	0.000	33	100.91	1.832	47	117.36	0.097
6	75.58	0.000	20	95.77	0.000	34	102.58	0.000	48	118.74	0.039
7	78.00	0.011	21	96.90	1.213	35	103.05	0.756	49	121.42	0.077
8	78.58	0.077	22	96.95	0.756	36	103.10	1.213	50	122.00	0.011
9	81.26	0.039	23	97.42	0.000	37	104.23	0.000	51	124.42	0.000
10	82.64	0.097	24	99.09	1.832	38	106.42	0.000	52	124.69	0.
11	84.58	0.000	25	99.09	1.832	39	106.58	0.000	53	124.89	0.008
12	85.33	0.000	26	99.56	0.000	40	109.91	0.168	54	124.91	0.
13	85.91	0.000	27	99.58	3.923	41	109.91	0.168	55	125.49	0.000
14	86.13	0.	28	99.84	5.876	42	110.38	0.000	56	139.20	0.000

−11 −10 −9 −8 −7 −6 −5 −4 −3 −2 −1 0 +1 +2 +3 +4 +5 +6 +7 +8 +9 +10 +11

5-292

$J_{AA'}$	J_{AB}	$J_{AB'}$	$J_{BB'}$
9	6	15	15
9	15	6	15
15	15	6	9
15	6	15	9

The maximum summed intensity is 6.550.

LINE	FREQ	INTEN	LINE	FREQ	INTEN	LINE	FREQ	INTEN	LINE	FREQ	INTEN
1	58.14	0.000	15	87.09	0.057	29	99.84	5.877	43	112.91	0.057
2	69.42	0.000	16	88.88	0.000	30	100.16	5.877	44	115.00	0.
3	71.67	0.000	17	90.09	0.168	31	100.42	3.923	45	117.51	0.000
4	72.33	0.003	18	90.75	0.000	32	100.91	1.832	46	118.58	0.000
5	73.00	0.000	19	93.51	0.000	33	102.09	1.943	47	119.30	0.043
6	76.56	0.000	20	94.17	0.515	34	102.54	1.499	48	120.02	0.052
7	78.00	0.011	21	95.67	0.000	35	103.88	0.000	49	121.42	0.077
8	78.58	0.077	22	97.25	0.000	36	104.33	0.000	50	122.00	0.011
9	79.98	0.052	23	97.46	1.499	37	105.83	0.515	51	126.44	0.000
10	80.70	0.043	24	97.91	1.943	38	106.49	0.000	52	127.58	0.000
11	82.00	0.000	25	99.09	1.832	39	108.12	0.000	53	127.67	0.003
12	82.49	0.000	26	99.12	0.000	40	109.91	0.168	54	128.33	0.000
13	84.42	0.000	27	99.58	3.923	41	111.44	0.000	55	130.00	0.000
14	85.56	0.	28	99.75	0.000	42	112.25	0.000	56	141.86	0.000

−11 −10 −9 −8 −7 −6 −5 −4 −3 −2 −1 0 +1 +2 +3 +4 +5 +6 +7 +8 +9 +10 +11

5-293

$J_{AA'}$	J_{AB}	$J_{AB'}$	$J_{BB'}$
9	9	12	15
9	12	9	15
15	12	9	9
15	9	12	9

The maximum summed intensity is 6.538.

LINE	FREQ	INTEN	LINE	FREQ	INTEN	LINE	FREQ	INTEN	LINE	FREQ	INTEN
1	63.10	0.000	15	89.44	0.000	29	100.42	3.923	43	115.06	0.076
2	68.02	0.001	16	89.86	0.237	30	101.47	0.000	44	115.25	0.000
3	70.74	0.000	17	90.46	0.024	31	101.85	1.447	45	116.32	0.000
4	73.73	0.000	18	90.85	0.000	32	101.89	1.752	46	119.57	0.000
5	76.00	0.000	19	92.44	0.000	33	102.27	0.000	47	119.95	0.045
6	78.00	0.011	20	95.15	0.553	34	102.83	1.976	48	120.17	0.000
7	78.58	0.077	21	95.57	0.000	35	102.88	0.000	49	121.42	0.077
8	79.00	0.000	22	97.17	1.976	36	103.22	0.000	50	121.58	0.000
9	80.05	0.045	23	97.73	0.000	37	104.43	0.000	51	122.00	0.011
10	80.43	0.000	24	98.11	1.752	38	104.47	0.000	52	124.58	0.000
11	83.11	0.000	25	98.15	1.447	39	104.85	0.553	53	126.27	0.000
12	84.52	0.000	26	99.58	3.923	40	107.80	0.000	54	128.68	0.000
13	84.94	0.076	27	99.84	5.877	41	109.54	0.024	55	131.98	0.001
14	87.52	0.000	28	100.16	5.877	42	110.14	0.237	56	136.90	0.000

5-294

$J_{AA'}$	J_{AB}	$J_{AB'}$	$J_{BB'}$
9	9	15	12
9	15	9	12
12	15	9	9
12	9	15	9

The maximum summed intensity is 10.098

LINE	FREQ	INTEN	LINE	FREQ	INTEN	LINE	FREQ	INTEN	LINE	FREQ	INTEN
1	58.76	0.000	15	88.89	0.000	29	100.00	1.600	43	113.16	0.000
2	69.37	0.001	16	91.24	0.132	30	100.13	5.906	44	116.51	0.117
3	71.59	0.000	17	93.29	0.400	31	100.37	3.940	45	117.09	0.000
4	73.78	0.000	18	94.11	0.273	32	101.48	0.000	46	119.52	0.000
5	74.15	0.	19	94.46	0.000	33	102.00	1.661	47	119.65	0.000
6	75.13	0.009	20	94.78	0.000	34	102.05	1.868	48	122.74	0.033
7	75.63	0.060	21	95.60	0.000	35	102.35	0.000	49	123.78	0.000
8	77.26	0.033	22	96.77	0.000	36	103.48	0.000	50	124.37	0.060
9	78.27	0.000	23	97.95	1.868	37	105.22	0.000	51	124.87	0.009
10	80.48	0.000	24	98.00	1.661	38	105.28	0.000	52	126.22	0.000
11	80.85	0.000	25	98.52	0.000	39	105.89	0.273	53	126.36	0.000
12	82.40	0.000	26	99.63	3.940	40	106.71	0.400	54	127.91	0.000
13	83.49	0.117	27	99.87	5.906	41	108.76	0.132	55	130.63	0.001
14	84.98	0.000	28	100.00	1.600	42	112.97	0.000	56	141.24	0.000

5-295

$J_{AA'}$	J_{AB}	$J_{AB'}$	$J_{BB'}$
9	12	15	9
9	15	12	9

The maximum summed intensity is 8.046.

LINE	FREQ	INTEN	LINE	FREQ	INTEN	LINE	FREQ	INTEN	LINE	FREQ	INTEN
1	57.01	0.000	15	88.07	0.000	29	100.12	5.926	43	115.34	0.179
2	68.59	0.001	16	93.44	0.000	30	100.15	0.000	44	116.81	0.000
3	72.22	0.007	17	93.67	0.000	31	100.33	3.952	45	119.15	0.000
4	72.67	0.048	18	94.78	0.000	32	101.62	1.772	46	119.59	0.000
5	73.70	0.000	19	95.15	0.553	33	101.85	1.447	47	121.33	0.000
6	73.96	0.026	20	95.15	0.553	34	101.85	1.447	48	123.52	0.000
7	74.15	0.000	21	96.25	0.090	35	103.33	0.000	49	124.33	0.000
8	75.67	0.000	22	96.67	0.000	36	103.75	0.090	50	125.85	0.000
9	76.48	0.000	23	98.15	1.447	37	104.85	0.553	51	126.04	0.026
10	78.67	0.000	24	98.15	1.447	38	104.85	0.553	52	126.30	0.000
11	80.41	0.000	25	98.38	1.772	39	105.22	0.000	53	127.33	0.048
12	80.85	0.000	26	99.67	3.952	40	106.33	0.000	54	127.78	0.007
13	83.19	0.000	27	99.85	0.000	41	106.56	0.000	55	131.41	0.001
14	84.66	0.179	28	99.88	5.926	42	111.93	0.000	56	142.99	0.000

−11 −10 −9 −8 −7 −6 −5 −4 −3 −2 −1 0 +1 +2 +3 +4 +5 +6 +7 +8 +9 +10 +11

5-296

$J_{AA'}$	J_{AB}	$J_{AB'}$	$J_{BB'}$
9	12	15	15
9	15	12	15
15	15	12	9
15	12	15	9

The maximum summed intensity is 8.046.

LINE	FREQ	INTEN	LINE	FREQ	INTEN	LINE	FREQ	INTEN	LINE	FREQ	INTEN
1	56.48	0.000	15	87.52	0.000	29	100.12	5.926	43	115.86	0.148
2	63.19	0.000	16	90.46	0.024	30	100.33	3.952	44	117.17	0.000
3	67.87	0.000	17	90.52	0.000	31	101.23	0.000	45	119.32	0.000
4	70.82	0.000	18	90.85	0.075	32	101.52	0.000	46	122.48	0.000
5	72.22	0.007	19	94.09	0.000	33	101.56	1.817	47	123.88	0.000
6	72.67	0.048	20	94.82	0.000	34	101.85	1.447	48	124.45	0.000
7	73.00	0.000	21	95.15	0.553	35	102.83	1.976	49	126.10	0.026
8	73.90	0.026	22	97.17	1.976	36	104.80	0.000	50	127.33	0.048
9	76.00	0.000	23	98.15	1.447	37	104.85	0.553	51	127.45	0.000
10	77.52	0.000	24	98.23	0.000	38	105.18	0.000	52	127.78	0.007
11	80.24	0.000	25	98.44	1.817	39	106.45	0.000	53	129.18	0.000
12	80.81	0.000	26	98.48	0.000	40	109.15	0.075	54	131.68	0.000
13	83.81	0.000	27	99.67	3.952	41	109.54	0.024	55	136.81	0.000
14	84.14	0.148	28	99.88	5.926	42	111.51	0.000	56	143.52	0.000

−11 −10 −9 −8 −7 −6 −5 −4 −3 −2 −1 0 +1 +2 +3 +4 +5 +6 +7 +8 +9 +10 +11

5-297

$J_{AA'}$	J_{AB}	$J_{AB'}$	$J_{BB'}$
12	1	2	12
12	2	1	12

The maximum summed intensity is 4.142.

LINE	FREQ	INTEN	LINE	FREQ	INTEN	LINE	FREQ	INTEN	LINE	FREQ	INTEN
1	72.61	0.000	15	91.67	0.003	29	101.19	0.000	43	108.80	0.000
2	79.32	0.000	16	91.85	0.000	30	101.62	3.352	44	109.00	0.000
3	79.98	0.000	17	92.73	0.000	31	101.85	2.894	45	109.15	0.
4	83.46	0.000	18	95.15	1.106	32	102.54	1.164	46	110.46	0.000
5	84.15	0.000	19	95.58	1.304	33	102.54	1.164	47	111.13	0.001
6	84.92	0.000	20	96.46	0.836	34	103.19	1.799	48	113.93	0.000
7	85.12	0.000	21	96.46	0.836	35	103.52	1.542	49	114.85	0.000
8	85.15	0.000	22	96.48	1.542	36	103.54	0.836	50	114.88	0.000
9	86.07	0.000	23	96.81	1.799	37	103.54	0.836	51	115.08	0.000
10	88.87	0.001	24	97.46	1.164	38	104.42	1.304	52	115.85	0.000
11	89.54	0.000	25	97.46	1.164	39	104.85	1.106	53	116.54	0.000
12	90.85	0.000	26	98.15	2.894	40	107.27	0.000	54	120.02	0.000
13	91.00	0.000	27	98.38	3.352	41	108.15	0.000	55	120.68	0.000
14	91.20	0.000	28	98.81	0.000	42	108.33	0.003	56	127.39	0.000

5-298

$J_{AA'}$	J_{AB}	$J_{AB'}$	$J_{BB'}$
12	2	4	12
12	4	2	12

The maximum summed intensity is 4.701.

LINE	FREQ	INTEN	LINE	FREQ	INTEN	LINE	FREQ	INTEN	LINE	FREQ	INTEN
1	71.58	0.000	15	92.19	0.000	29	100.81	4.698	43	108.76	0.000
2	79.79	0.000	16	92.76	0.586	30	101.01	0.	44	109.01	0.000
3	80.07	0.001	17	93.24	0.000	31	101.24	3.414	45	109.29	0.019
4	81.84	0.000	18	94.40	0.953	32	102.16	1.316	46	111.84	0.000
5	82.76	0.000	19	94.68	0.000	33	102.16	1.316	47	113.89	0.000
6	84.66	0.000	20	94.73	0.714	34	103.22	1.613	48	114.09	0.002
7	84.76	0.000	21	95.84	0.684	35	104.16	0.684	49	114.14	0.000
8	85.86	0.000	22	95.84	0.684	36	104.16	0.684	50	115.24	0.000
9	85.91	0.002	23	96.78	1.613	37	105.27	0.714	51	115.34	0.000
10	86.11	0.000	24	97.84	1.316	38	105.32	0.000	52	117.24	0.000
11	88.16	0.000	25	97.84	1.316	39	105.60	0.953	53	118.16	0.000
12	90.71	0.019	26	98.76	3.414	40	106.76	0.000	54	119.93	0.001
13	90.99	0.000	27	98.99	0.000	41	107.24	0.586	55	120.21	0.000
14	91.24	0.000	28	99.19	4.698	42	107.81	0.000	56	128.42	0.000

5-299

$J_{AA'}$	J_{AB}	$J_{AB'}$	$J_{BB'}$
12	4	6	12
12	6	4	12

The maximum summed intensity is 5.481.

LINE	FREQ	INTEN	LINE	FREQ	INTEN	LINE	FREQ	INTEN	LINE	FREQ	INTEN
1	69.94	0.000	15	91.17	0.244	29	100.40	5.469	43	109.07	0.000
2	78.61	0.000	16	92.83	0.072	30	100.83	3.715	44	110.83	0.285
3	79.84	0.000	17	92.83	0.593	31	102.16	1.316	45	112.06	0.025
4	81.17	0.000	18	94.16	0.000	32	102.16	1.175	46	112.16	0.000
5	81.17	0.002	19	94.83	0.000	33	102.16	0.142	47	113.84	0.000
6	81.60	0.002	20	95.84	0.684	34	102.83	1.592	48	115.07	0.000
7	83.17	0.000	21	95.84	0.610	35	104.16	0.074	49	115.39	0.000
8	84.61	0.000	22	95.84	0.074	36	104.16	0.610	50	116.83	0.000
9	84.93	0.000	23	97.17	1.592	37	104.16	0.684	51	118.40	0.002
10	86.16	0.000	24	97.84	1.175	38	105.17	0.000	52	118.83	0.000
11	87.84	0.000	25	97.84	0.142	39	105.84	0.000	53	118.83	0.002
12	87.94	0.025	26	97.84	1.316	40	107.17	0.593	54	120.16	0.000
13	89.17	0.285	27	99.17	3.715	41	107.17	0.072	55	121.39	0.000
14	90.93	0.000	28	99.60	5.469	42	108.83	0.244	56	130.06	0.000

5-300

$J_{AA'}$	J_{AB}	$J_{AB'}$	$J_{BB'}$
12	6	9	12
12	9	6	12

The maximum summed intensity is 5.617,

LINE	FREQ	INTEN	LINE	FREQ	INTEN	LINE	FREQ	INTEN	LINE	FREQ	INTEN
1	67.12	0.000	15	90.55	0.000	29	100.23	5.760	43	109.64	0.
2	75.13	0.001	16	91.29	0.454	30	100.58	3.857	44	113.79	0.096
3	76.33	0.000	17	91.85	0.000	31	101.44	0.000	45	115.58	0.143
4	77.15	0.000	18	94.58	0.000	32	101.85	1.447	46	116.15	0.000
5	78.42	0.000	19	95.15	0.553	33	101.85	1.447	47	116.16	0.000
6	81.42	0.000	20	95.15	0.553	34	102.36	1.656	48	116.39	0.018
7	83.04	0.000	21	97.07	0.000	35	102.42	0.000	49	116.73	0.015
8	83.27	0.015	22	97.58	0.000	36	102.93	0.000	50	116.96	0.000
9	83.61	0.018	23	97.64	1.656	37	104.85	0.553	51	118.58	0.000
10	83.84	0.000	24	98.15	1.447	38	104.85	0.553	52	121.58	0.
11	83.85	0.000	25	98.15	1.447	39	105.42	0.000	53	122.85	0.000
12	84.42	0.143	26	98.56	0.	40	108.15	0.000	54	123.67	0.000
13	86.21	0.096	27	99.42	3.857	41	108.71	0.454	55	124.87	0.001
14	90.36	0.000	28	99.77	5.760	42	109.45	0.000	56	132.88	0.000

5-301

$J_{AA'}$	J_{AB}	$J_{AB'}$	$J_{BB'}$
12	9	12	15
12	12	9	15
15	12	9	12
15	9	12	12

The maximum summed intensity is 7.751.

LINE	FREQ	INTEN	LINE	FREQ	INTEN	LINE	FREQ	INTEN	LINE	FREQ	INTEN
1	60.91	0.000	15	89.05	0.281	29	100.16	5.877	43	113.11	0.000
2	67.21	0.001	16	89.51	0.000	30	100.29	0.000	44	117.25	0.027
3	70.68	0.000	17	90.80	0.000	31	100.42	3.923	45	119.26	0.000
4	73.46	0.000	18	93.14	0.106	32	100.46	0.000	46	119.41	0.000
5	73.88	0.000	19	93.75	0.	33	101.88	1.758	47	119.96	0.045
6	77.70	0.000	20	95.30	0.000	34	102.34	0.000	48	121.42	0.077
7	78.00	0.011	21	95.76	1.000	35	102.62	1.894	49	122.00	0.011
8	78.12	0.	22	97.38	1.894	36	103.62	0.000	50	122.30	0.000
9	78.58	0.077	23	98.12	1.758	37	104.24	1.000	51	122.45	0.000
10	80.04	0.045	24	99.54	0.000	38	104.70	0.000	52	126.54	0.000
11	80.17	0.000	25	99.58	3.923	39	106.58	0.000	53	126.70	0.000
12	82.75	0.027	26	99.84	5.877	40	106.86	0.106	54	128.74	0.000
13	83.21	0.000	27	100.00	1.000	41	109.92	0.000	55	132.79	0.001
14	87.45	0.	28	100.00	1.000	42	110.95	0.281	56	139.09	0.000

5-302

$J_{AA'}$	J_{AB}	$J_{AB'}$	$J_{BB'}$
12	9	15	12
12	15	9	12

The maximum summed intensity is 10.101.

LINE	FREQ	INTEN	LINE	FREQ	INTEN	LINE	FREQ	INTEN	LINE	FREQ	INTEN
1	57.71	0.000	15	87.63	0.000	29	100.13	5.906	43	113.68	0.000
2	67.50	0.001	16	92.24	0.257	30	100.37	3.940	44	117.55	0.085
3	71.25	0.000	17	92.76	0.293	31	101.24	1.707	45	119.76	0.
4	71.76	0.	18	92.76	0.293	32	101.24	1.707	46	120.26	0.000
5	72.63	0.000	19	94.21	0.000	33	101.91	1.709	47	121.37	0.000
6	75.13	0.009	20	96.12	0.000	34	102.63	0.000	48	122.16	0.000
7	75.63	0.060	21	96.63	0.000	35	102.70	0.000	49	122.83	0.033
8	77.17	0.033	22	97.30	0.000	36	103.37	0.000	50	124.37	0.060
9	77.84	0.000	23	97.37	0.000	37	103.88	0.000	51	124.87	0.009
10	78.63	0.000	24	98.09	1.709	38	105.79	0.000	52	127.37	0.000
11	79.74	0.000	25	98.76	1.707	39	107.24	0.293	53	128.24	0.000
12	80.24	0.	26	98.76	1.707	40	107.24	0.293	54	128.75	0.000
13	82.45	0.085	27	99.63	3.940	41	107.76	0.257	55	132.50	0.001
14	86.32	0.000	28	99.87	5.906	42	112.37	0.000	56	142.29	0.000

5-303

$J_{AA'}$	J_{AB}	$J_{AB'}$	$J_{BB'}$
12	9	15	15
12	15	9	15
15	15	9	12
15	9	15	12

The maximum summed intensity is 10.101

LINE	FREQ	INTEN	LINE	FREQ	INTEN	LINE	FREQ	INTEN	LINE	FREQ	INTEN
1	56.23	0.000	15	88.55	0.000	29	100.00	1.600	43	113.51	0.000
2	66.03	0.001	16	90.77	0.262	30	100.13	5.906	44	119.03	0.054
3	68.59	0.000	17	91.24	0.132	31	100.37	3.940	45	120.09	0.000
4	70.78	0.000	18	91.60	0.000	32	101.86	1.735	46	122.52	0.000
5	71.15	0.000	19	93.29	0.400	33	102.05	1.868	47	122.65	0.000
6	75.13	0.009	20	95.26	0.000	34	102.22	0.000	48	122.88	0.033
7	75.63	0.060	21	95.52	0.000	35	102.42	0.000	49	123.30	0.000
8	77.12	0.033	22	97.78	0.000	36	102.69	0.000	50	124.37	0.060
9	77.48	0.000	23	97.95	1.868	37	104.48	0.000	51	124.87	0.009
10	77.85	0.000	24	98.14	1.735	38	106.35	0.000	52	129.22	0.000
11	78.75	0.000	25	99.63	3.940	39	106.71	0.400	53	129.36	0.000
12	79.40	0.000	26	99.64	0.000	40	108.76	0.132	54	130.91	0.000
13	80.97	0.054	27	99.87	5.906	41	109.23	0.262	55	133.97	0.001
14	85.46	0.000	28	100.00	1.600	42	112.49	0.000	56	143.77	0.000

−11 −10 −9 −8 −7 −6 −5 −4 −3 −2 −1 0 +1 +2 +3 +4 +5 +6 +7 +8 +9 +10 +11

5-304

$J_{AA'}$	J_{AB}	$J_{AB'}$	$J_{BB'}$
15	1	2	15
15	2	1	15

The maximum summed intensity is 4.134.

LINE	FREQ	INTEN	LINE	FREQ	INTEN	LINE	FREQ	INTEN	LINE	FREQ	INTEN
1	66.62	0.000	15	88.87	0.001	29	101.62	3.353	43	111.15	0.000
2	73.33	0.000	16	89.74	0.000	30	101.85	2.894	44	111.79	0.000
3	76.99	0.000	17	91.67	0.003	31	102.54	1.164	45	111.99	0.000
4	80.46	0.000	18	95.15	1.106	32	102.54	1.164	46	112.15	0.000
5	81.15	0.000	19	95.57	1.302	33	103.19	1.800	47	113.46	0.000
6	81.93	0.000	20	95.82	0.000	34	103.52	1.541	48	116.93	0.000
7	82.12	0.000	21	96.46	0.836	35	103.54	0.836	49	117.85	0.000
8	82.15	0.000	22	96.46	0.836	36	103.54	0.836	50	117.88	0.000
9	83.07	0.000	23	96.48	1.541	37	104.18	0.000	51	118.07	0.000
10	86.54	0.000	24	96.81	1.800	38	104.43	1.302	52	118.85	0.000
11	87.85	0.000	25	97.46	1.164	39	104.85	1.106	53	119.54	0.000
12	88.01	0.000	26	97.46	1.164	40	108.33	0.003	54	123.01	0.000
13	88.21	0.000	27	98.15	2.894	41	110.26	0.000	55	126.67	0.000
14	88.85	0.000	28	98.38	3.353	42	111.13	0.001	56	133.38	0.000

−11 −10 −9 −8 −7 −6 −5 −4 −3 −2 −1 0 +1 +2 +3 +4 +5 +6 +7 +8 +9 +10 +11

5-305

$J_{AA'}$	J_{AB}	$J_{AB'}$	$J_{BB'}$
15	2	4	15
15	4	2	15

The maximum summed intensity is 4.704.

LINE	FREQ	INTEN	LINE	FREQ	INTEN	LINE	FREQ	INTEN	LINE	FREQ	INTEN
1	65.63	0.000	15	90.24	0.000	29	100.81	4.700	43	110.80	0.
2	74.11	0.000	16	90.71	0.019	30	101.24	3.414	44	111.76	0.
3	76.79	0.000	17	91.72	0.000	31	101.95	0.	45	111.97	0.000
4	78.84	0.000	18	92.76	0.586	32	102.16	1.316	46	114.13	0.002
5	79.76	0.000	19	94.36	0.949	33	102.16	1.316	47	114.84	0.000
6	81.71	0.000	20	94.72	0.712	34	103.21	1.617	48	116.89	0.000
7	81.76	0.000	21	95.84	0.684	35	104.16	0.684	49	117.13	0.000
8	82.87	0.000	22	95.84	0.684	36	104.16	0.684	50	118.24	0.000
9	83.11	0.000	23	96.79	1.617	37	105.28	0.712	51	118.29	0.000
10	85.16	0.000	24	97.84	1.316	38	105.64	0.949	52	120.24	0.
11	85.87	0.002	25	97.84	1.316	39	107.24	0.586	53	121.16	0.000
12	88.03	0.000	26	98.05	0.000	40	108.28	0.	54	123.21	0.000
13	88.24	0.000	27	98.76	3.414	41	109.29	0.019	55	125.89	0.000
14	89.20	0.000	28	99.19	4.700	42	109.76	0.000	56	134.37	0.000

5-306

$J_{AA'}$	J_{AB}	$J_{AB'}$	$J_{BB'}$
15	4	6	15
15	6	4	15

The maximum summed intensity is 5.481.

LINE	FREQ	INTEN	LINE	FREQ	INTEN	LINE	FREQ	INTEN	LINE	FREQ	INTEN
1	64.01	0.000	15	89.83	0.000	29	100.40	5.469	43	110.83	0.285
2	75.61	0.000	16	91.16	0.244	30	100.83	3.715	44	111.99	0.000
3	75.67	0.001	17	91.17	0.000	31	101.23	0.000	45	112.06	0.025
4	76.84	0.000	18	91.83	0.000	32	102.16	1.316	46	115.15	0.
5	78.17	0.000	19	92.77	0.663	33	102.16	1.316	47	116.84	0.000
6	80.17	0.000	20	94.90	0.000	34	102.82	1.597	48	118.07	0.000
7	81.10	0.002	21	95.84	0.684	35	104.16	0.684	49	118.32	0.000
8	81.68	0.000	22	95.84	0.684	36	104.16	0.684	50	118.90	0.002
9	81.93	0.000	23	97.18	1.597	37	105.10	0.000	51	119.83	0.000
10	83.16	0.000	24	97.84	1.316	38	107.23	0.663	52	121.83	0.000
11	84.85	0.000	25	97.84	1.316	39	108.17	0.000	53	123.16	0.000
12	87.94	0.025	26	98.77	0.000	40	108.83	0.000	54	124.33	0.001
13	88.01	0.000	27	99.17	3.715	41	108.84	0.244	55	124.39	0.000
14	89.17	0.285	28	99.60	5.469	42	110.17	0.000	56	135.99	0.000

5-307

$J_{AA'}$	J_{AB}	$J_{AB'}$	$J_{BB'}$
15	6	9	15
15	9	6	15

The maximum summed intensity is 5.618.

LINE	FREQ	INTEN	LINE	FREQ	INTEN	LINE	FREQ	INTEN	LINE	FREQ	INTEN
1	61.45	0.000	15	87.89	0.000	29	100.23	5.760	43	112.62	0.000
2	73.33	0.000	16	90.97	0.457	30	100.58	3.857	44	113.81	0.096
3	74.15	0.000	17	91.58	0.000	31	101.25	0.000	45	115.58	0.143
4	74.81	0.001	18	94.09	0.	32	101.85	1.447	46	116.39	0.018
5	75.42	0.000	19	94.54	0.000	33	101.85	1.447	47	118.82	0.000
6	77.61	0.003	20	94.58	0.000	34	102.34	1.665	48	119.15	0.000
7	78.42	0.000	21	95.15	0.553	35	104.85	0.553	49	119.96	0.000
8	80.04	0.000	22	95.15	0.553	36	104.85	0.553	50	121.58	0.000
9	80.85	0.000	23	97.66	1.665	37	105.42	0.000	51	122.39	0.003
10	81.18	0.000	24	98.15	1.447	38	105.46	0.000	52	124.58	0.000
11	83.61	0.018	25	98.15	1.447	39	105.91	0.000	53	125.19	0.001
12	84.42	0.143	26	98.75	0.000	40	108.42	0.000	54	125.85	0.000
13	86.19	0.096	27	99.42	3.857	41	109.03	0.457	55	126.67	0.000
14	87.38	0.	28	99.77	5.760	42	112.11	0.000	56	138.55	0.000

5-308

$J_{AA'}$	J_{AB}	$J_{AB'}$	$J_{BB'}$
15	9	12	15
15	12	9	15

The maximum summed intensity is 6.538.

LINE	FREQ	INTEN	LINE	FREQ	INTEN	LINE	FREQ	INTEN	LINE	FREQ	INTEN
1	58.29	0.000	15	88.68	0.295	29	100.16	5.877	43	112.43	0.000
2	66.84	0.001	16	89.41	0.000	30	100.42	3.923	44	119.14	0.000
3	70.57	0.000	17	90.70	0.000	31	101.85	1.447	45	119.87	0.010
4	71.15	0.000	18	94.42	0.000	32	101.85	1.447	46	119.97	0.045
5	72.58	0.000	19	95.15	0.553	33	101.87	1.761	47	121.42	0.077
6	75.58	0.000	20	95.15	0.553	34	102.58	0.000	48	122.00	0.011
7	77.28	0.000	21	96.11	0.000	35	102.60	0.000	49	122.15	0.000
8	77.85	0.000	22	97.40	0.000	36	103.89	0.000	50	122.72	0.000
9	78.00	0.011	23	97.42	0.000	37	104.85	0.553	51	124.42	0.000
10	78.58	0.077	24	98.13	1.761	38	104.85	0.553	52	127.42	0.000
11	80.03	0.045	25	98.15	1.447	39	105.58	0.000	53	128.85	0.000
12	80.13	0.010	26	98.15	1.447	40	109.30	0.000	54	129.43	0.000
13	80.86	0.000	27	99.58	3.923	41	110.59	0.000	55	133.16	0.001
14	87.57	0.000	28	99.84	5.877	42	111.32	0.295	56	141.71	0.000

5-309

$J_{AA'}$	J_{AB}	$J_{AB'}$	$J_{BB'}$
18	1	2	18
18	2	1	18

The maximum summed intensity is 4.127.

LINE	FREQ	INTEN	LINE	FREQ	INTEN	LINE	FREQ	INTEN	LINE	FREQ	INTEN
1	60.62	0.000	15	86.74	0.000	29	101.62	3.354	43	114.15	0.000
2	67.33	0.000	16	88.86	0.001	30	101.85	2.894	44	114.79	0.000
3	73.99	0.000	17	91.67	0.003	31	102.54	1.164	45	114.98	0.000
4	77.46	0.000	18	92.82	0.000	32	102.54	1.164	46	115.15	0.000
5	78.15	0.000	19	95.15	1.106	33	103.19	1.801	47	116.46	0.000
6	78.94	0.000	20	95.57	1.301	34	103.52	1.540	48	119.93	0.000
7	79.13	0.000	21	96.46	0.836	35	103.54	0.836	49	120.85	0.000
8	79.15	0.000	22	96.46	0.836	36	103.54	0.836	50	120.87	0.000
9	80.07	0.000	23	96.48	1.540	37	104.43	1.301	51	121.06	0.000
10	83.54	0.000	24	96.81	1.801	38	104.85	1.106	52	121.85	0.000
11	84.85	0.000	25	97.46	1.164	39	107.18	0.000	53	122.54	0.000
12	85.02	0.000	26	97.46	1.164	40	108.33	0.003	54	126.01	0.000
13	85.21	0.000	27	98.15	2.894	41	111.14	0.001	55	132.67	0.000
14	85.85	0.000	28	98.38	3.354	42	113.26	0.	56	139.38	0.000

5-310

$J_{AA'}$	J_{AB}	$J_{AB'}$	$J_{BB'}$
18	2	4	18
18	4	2	18

The maximum summed intensity is 4.706.

LINE	FREQ	INTEN	LINE	FREQ	INTEN	LINE	FREQ	INTEN	LINE	FREQ	INTEN
1	59.66	0.000	15	87.24	0.000	29	100.80	4.701	43	113.80	0.
2	68.14	0.000	16	88.74	0.000	30	101.24	3.414	44	114.15	0.002
3	73.79	0.000	17	90.71	0.019	31	102.16	1.316	45	114.76	0.000
4	75.84	0.000	18	92.76	0.586	32	102.16	1.316	46	114.94	0.000
5	76.76	0.000	19	94.34	0.947	33	103.20	1.620	47	117.84	0.000
6	78.74	0.000	20	94.72	0.711	34	104.16	0.684	48	119.89	0.000
7	78.76	0.000	21	95.07	0.000	35	104.16	0.684	49	120.12	0.000
8	79.88	0.000	22	95.84	0.684	36	104.93	0.000	50	121.24	0.000
9	80.11	0.000	23	95.84	0.684	37	105.28	0.711	51	121.26	0.000
10	82.16	0.000	24	96.80	1.620	38	105.66	0.947	52	123.24	0.000
11	85.06	0.000	25	97.84	1.316	39	107.24	0.586	53	124.16	0.000
12	85.24	0.000	26	97.84	1.316	40	109.29	0.019	54	126.21	0.000
13	85.85	0.002	27	98.76	3.414	41	111.26	0.000	55	131.86	0.000
14	86.20	0.000	28	99.20	4.701	42	112.76	0.000	56	140.34	0.000

5-311

$J_{AA'}$	J_{AB}	$J_{AB'}$	$J_{BB'}$
2	-1	2	4
2	2	-1	4
4	2	-1	2
4	-1	2	2

The maximum summed intensity is 6.696.

LINE	FREQ	INTEN	LINE	FREQ	INTEN	LINE	FREQ	INTEN	LINE	FREQ	INTEN
1	87.02	0.000	15	96.46	1.671	29	100.53	0.000	43	104.24	0.000
2	88.86	0.005	16	96.61	1.661	30	100.70	1.055	44	104.30	0.945
3	91.25	0.000	17	97.31	2.097	31	100.82	0.000	45	105.05	0.564
4	91.99	0.024	18	97.33	2.203	32	100.85	0.000	46	105.85	0.000
5	92.16	0.000	19	97.41	0.000	33	100.92	0.000	47	106.07	0.188
6	92.37	0.000	20	97.46	2.329	34	101.76	0.000	48	106.21	0.000
7	92.41	0.000	21	97.53	1.812	35	101.84	0.000	49	106.24	0.000
8	93.93	0.188	22	97.70	0.000	36	101.93	1.446	50	107.77	0.000
9	94.00	0.000	23	98.07	1.446	37	102.47	1.812	51	107.84	0.000
10	94.95	0.564	24	98.16	0.000	38	102.54	2.329	52	108.01	0.024
11	95.53	0.000	25	98.24	0.000	39	102.67	2.203	53	108.75	0.000
12	95.56	0.000	26	99.00	0.000	40	102.69	2.097	54	109.37	0.000
13	95.70	0.945	27	99.23	0.000	41	103.39	1.661	55	111.14	0.005
14	95.76	0.000	28	99.30	1.055	42	103.54	1.671	56	111.21	0.000

−11 −10 −9 −8 −7 −6 −5 −4 −3 −2 −1 0 +1 +2 +3 +4 +5 +6 +7 +8 +9 +10 +11

5-312

$J_{AA'}$	J_{AB}	$J_{AB'}$	$J_{BB'}$
2	-1	2	6
2	2	-1	6
6	2	-1	2
6	-1	2	2

The maximum summed intensity is 8.110.

LINE	FREQ	INTEN	LINE	FREQ	INTEN	LINE	FREQ	INTEN	LINE	FREQ	INTEN
1	85.09	0.000	15	96.46	1.671	29	100.09	0.000	43	104.30	0.945
2	87.65	0.005	16	96.49	0.000	30	100.16	0.000	44	104.54	0.000
3	90.46	0.000	17	96.54	0.000	31	100.70	1.055	45	106.07	0.000
4	90.51	0.000	18	96.55	0.000	32	100.95	0.000	46	106.27	0.207
5	91.27	0.000	19	96.69	1.744	33	101.54	0.000	47	106.87	0.000
6	91.31	0.009	20	97.23	2.083	34	102.47	0.000	48	107.72	0.061
7	92.28	0.061	21	97.28	1.939	35	102.54	2.329	49	107.88	0.000
8	92.89	0.000	22	97.30	0.000	36	102.60	1.719	50	108.69	0.009
9	93.70	0.000	23	97.35	2.233	37	102.65	2.233	51	108.73	0.000
10	93.73	0.207	24	97.40	1.719	38	102.72	1.939	52	109.54	0.000
11	95.46	0.000	25	97.46	2.329	39	102.77	2.083	53	109.72	0.
12	95.53	0.000	26	98.46	0.000	40	103.31	1.744	54	110.53	0.000
13	95.70	0.945	27	99.28	0.000	41	103.46	0.000	55	111.49	0.000
14	96.43	0.000	28	99.30	1.055	42	103.54	1.671	56	112.35	0.005

−11 −10 −9 −8 −7 −6 −5 −4 −3 −2 −1 0 +1 +2 +3 +4 +5 +6 +7 +8 +9 +10 +11

5-313

$J_{AA'}$	J_{AB}	$J_{AB'}$	$J_{BB'}$
2	-1	2	9
2	2	-1	9
9	2	-1	2
9	-1	2	2

The maximum summed intensity is 5.238.

LINE	FREQ	INTEN	LINE	FREQ	INTEN	LINE	FREQ	INTEN	LINE	FREQ	INTEN
1	82.17	0.000	15	95.28	0.000	29	99.63	0.000	43	105.39	0.336
2	85.16	0.003	16	95.51	0.000	30	100.97	0.000	44	106.27	0.000
3	87.63	0.000	17	95.58	0.000	31	101.02	0.000	45	107.23	0.000
4	87.65	0.000	18	96.46	1.671	32	101.35	0.000	46	107.28	0.000
5	89.52	0.016	19	96.76	1.812	33	102.23	1.664	47	108.70	0.000
6	90.90	0.003	20	96.98	1.815	34	102.54	2.329	48	108.76	0.044
7	91.24	0.044	21	97.14	1.984	35	102.62	2.262	49	109.10	0.003
8	91.30	0.000	22	97.16	2.061	36	102.84	2.061	50	109.58	0.000
9	92.12	0.000	23	97.38	2.262	37	102.86	1.984	51	110.48	0.016
10	92.42	0.000	24	97.46	2.329	38	103.02	1.815	52	112.35	0.000
11	93.73	0.000	25	97.77	1.664	39	103.24	1.812	53	112.67	0.
12	93.89	0.000	26	97.86	0.000	40	103.54	1.671	54	112.74	0.000
13	94.61	0.336	27	98.65	0.000	41	104.12	0.000	55	112.97	0.000
14	95.27	0.000	28	99.33	0.000	42	104.73	0.000	56	114.84	0.003

5-314

$J_{AA'}$	J_{AB}	$J_{AB'}$	$J_{BB'}$
2	-1	2	12
2	2	-1	12
12	2	-1	2
12	-1	2	2

The maximum summed intensity is 5.868.

LINE	FREQ	INTEN	LINE	FREQ	INTEN	LINE	FREQ	INTEN	LINE	FREQ	INTEN
1	79.22	0.000	15	95.00	0.000	29	99.43	0.000	43	107.36	0.000
2	82.38	0.001	16	95.18	0.000	30	100.98	0.000	44	107.72	0.061
3	84.71	0.000	17	95.50	0.000	31	101.26	0.000	45	108.68	0.000
4	84.74	0.000	18	96.46	1.671	32	102.54	2.329	46	109.18	0.000
5	86.64	0.006	19	96.80	1.849	33	102.60	2.282	47	109.27	0.001
6	88.47	0.013	20	96.82	1.809	34	102.72	1.939	48	109.65	0.000
7	89.93	0.000	21	97.08	1.994	35	102.89	2.044	49	110.14	0.000
8	90.00	0.000	22	97.11	2.044	36	102.92	1.994	50	111.53	0.013
9	90.73	0.001	23	97.28	1.939	37	103.18	1.809	51	113.36	0.006
10	90.82	0.000	24	97.40	2.282	38	103.20	1.849	52	115.14	0.000
11	91.08	0.000	25	97.46	2.329	39	103.28	0.000	53	115.26	0.000
12	91.32	0.000	26	98.28	0.000	40	103.54	1.671	54	115.64	0.000
13	92.28	0.061	27	98.74	0.000	41	104.65	0.000	55	115.71	0.000
14	94.93	0.000	28	99.36	0.000	42	104.82	0.000	56	117.62	0.001

5-315

$J_{AA'}$	J_{AB}	$J_{AB'}$	$J_{BB'}$
2	-1	2	15
2	2	-1	15
15	2	-1	2
15	-1	2	2

The maximum summed intensity is 6.181.

LINE	FREQ	INTEN	LINE	FREQ	INTEN	LINE	FREQ	INTEN	LINE	FREQ	INTEN
1	76.25	0.000	15	94.86	0.000	29	99.38	0.000	43	107.42	0.000
2	79.51	0.001	16	95.13	0.000	30	100.99	0.000	44	108.67	0.000
3	81.76	0.000	17	95.49	0.000	31	101.21	0.000	45	109.35	0.001
4	81.79	0.000	18	96.46	1.671	32	102.54	2.329	46	110.32	0.000
5	83.71	0.002	19	96.74	1.794	33	102.59	2.296	47	110.48	0.016
6	85.59	0.005	20	96.83	1.872	34	102.86	1.984	48	112.13	0.000
7	87.19	0.000	21	97.05	1.998	35	102.91	2.031	49	112.43	0.000
8	87.24	0.000	22	97.09	2.031	36	102.95	1.998	50	114.41	0.005
9	87.87	0.000	23	97.14	1.984	37	103.17	1.872	51	116.29	0.002
10	88.19	0.000	24	97.41	2.296	38	103.26	1.794	52	117.94	0.000
11	89.52	0.016	25	97.46	2.329	39	103.54	1.671	53	118.21	0.000
12	90.65	0.001	26	98.39	0.000	40	104.82	0.000	54	118.57	0.000
13	91.33	0.000	27	98.79	0.000	41	104.87	0.000	55	118.62	0.000
14	94.81	0.000	28	99.33	0.000	42	106.00	0.000	56	120.49	0.001

−11 −10 −9 −8 −7 −6 −5 −4 −3 −2 −1 0 +1 +2 +3 +4 +5 +6 +7 +8 +9 +10 +11

5-316

$J_{AA'}$	J_{AB}	$J_{AB'}$	$J_{BB'}$
2	-1	2	18
2	2	-1	18
18	2	-1	2
18	-1	2	2

The maximum summed intensity is 6.337.

LINE	FREQ	INTEN	LINE	FREQ	INTEN	LINE	FREQ	INTEN	LINE	FREQ	INTEN
1	73.28	0.000	15	94.85	0.000	29	99.40	0.000	43	108.66	0.000
2	76.59	0.000	16	95.10	0.000	30	101.00	0.000	44	108.87	0.000
3	78.79	0.000	17	95.48	0.000	31	101.18	0.000	45	109.40	0.000
4	78.82	0.000	18	96.46	1.671	32	102.54	2.329	46	110.40	0.000
5	80.76	0.001	19	96.69	1.781	33	102.58	2.307	47	113.36	0.006
6	82.67	0.002	20	96.85	1.887	34	102.92	1.994	48	115.10	0.000
7	84.28	0.000	21	97.04	1.999	35	102.93	2.021	49	115.33	0.000
8	84.41	0.000	22	97.07	2.021	36	102.96	1.999	50	117.33	0.002
9	84.90	0.000	23	97.08	1.994	37	103.15	1.887	51	119.24	0.001
10	85.25	0.000	24	97.42	2.307	38	103.31	1.781	52	120.84	0.000
11	86.64	0.006	25	97.46	2.329	39	103.54	1.671	53	121.18	0.000
12	90.60	0.000	26	98.43	0.000	40	104.89	0.000	54	121.47	0.000
13	91.34	0.000	27	98.82	0.000	41	104.90	0.000	55	121.60	0.000
14	94.72	0.000	28	99.27	0.000	42	107.46	0.000	56	123.41	0.000

−11 −10 −9 −8 −7 −6 −5 −4 −3 −2 −1 0 +1 +2 +3 +4 +5 +6 +7 +8 +9 +10 +11

5-317

$J_{AA'}$	J_{AB}	$J_{AB'}$	$J_{BB'}$
2	-1	4	2
2	4	-1	2

The maximum summed intensity is 5.087.

LINE	FREQ	INTEN	LINE	FREQ	INTEN	LINE	FREQ	INTEN	LINE	FREQ	INTEN
1	86.97	0.002	15	96.15	0.000	29	100.41	0.	43	104.54	0.984
2	88.42	0.000	16	96.23	0.000	30	100.53	1.540	44	104.85	1.106
3	88.73	0.000	17	96.54	0.000	31	100.71	0.000	45	105.79	0.000
4	91.28	0.001	18	97.15	0.000	32	101.15	0.000	46	106.33	0.580
5	92.15	0.000	19	97.84	2.058	33	101.41	1.640	47	106.41	0.360
6	92.59	0.	20	97.98	0.000	34	101.41	1.640	48	106.41	0.360
7	92.76	0.133	21	97.98	2.701	35	101.85	2.894	49	107.10	0.000
8	92.90	0.000	22	98.15	2.894	36	102.02	2.701	50	107.24	0.133
9	93.59	0.360	23	98.59	1.640	37	102.02	0.000	51	107.41	0.
10	93.59	0.360	24	98.59	1.640	38	102.16	2.058	52	107.85	0.000
11	93.67	0.580	25	98.85	0.000	39	102.85	0.000	53	108.72	0.001
12	94.21	0.000	26	99.29	0.000	40	103.46	0.000	54	111.27	0.000
13	95.15	1.106	27	99.47	1.540	41	103.77	0.	55	111.58	0.
14	95.46	0.984	28	99.59	0.	42	103.85	0.000	56	113.03	0.002

-11 -10 -9 -8 -7 -6 -5 -4 -3 -2 -1 0 +1 +2 +3 +4 +5 +6 +7 +8 +9 +10 +11

5-318

$J_{AA'}$	J_{AB}	$J_{AB'}$	$J_{BB'}$
2	-1	4	4
2	4	-1	4
4	4	-1	2
4	-1	4	2

The maximum summed intensity is 6.583.

LINE	FREQ	INTEN	LINE	FREQ	INTEN	LINE	FREQ	INTEN	LINE	FREQ	INTEN
1	86.29	0.003	15	95.84	0.000	29	100.51	1.493	43	104.85	1.106
2	86.99	0.000	16	96.34	0.000	30	100.66	0.000	44	105.09	0.000
3	89.44	0.000	17	96.43	0.000	31	100.85	0.000	45	105.89	0.507
4	90.95	0.000	18	96.95	0.000	32	101.41	0.000	46	106.51	0.000
5	91.36	0.000	19	97.08	0.000	33	101.44	1.516	47	107.01	0.403
6	91.42	0.000	20	97.51	1.975	34	101.85	2.894	48	107.06	0.000
7	91.85	0.068	21	97.66	0.000	35	101.93	2.849	49	107.41	0.193
8	92.30	0.	22	97.98	1.807	36	102.02	1.807	50	108.15	0.068
9	92.59	0.193	23	98.07	2.849	37	102.34	0.000	51	108.64	0.000
10	92.99	0.403	24	98.15	2.894	38	102.49	1.975	52	109.05	0.000
11	94.11	0.507	25	98.56	1.516	39	102.64	0.000	53	109.22	0.000
12	95.01	0.000	26	98.70	0.000	40	103.05	0.000	54	111.49	0.000
13	95.15	1.106	27	99.49	1.493	41	103.66	0.000	55	112.08	0.000
14	95.78	1.186	28	99.78	0.000	42	104.22	1.186	56	113.71	0.003

-11 -10 -9 -8 -7 -6 -5 -4 -3 -2 -1 0 +1 +2 +3 +4 +5 +6 +7 +8 +9 +10 +11

5-319

$J_{AA'}$	J_{AB}	$J_{AB'}$	$J_{BB'}$
2	-1	6	2
2	6	-1	2

The maximum summed intensity is 6.293.

LINE	FREQ	INTEN	LINE	FREQ	INTEN	LINE	FREQ	INTEN	LINE	FREQ	INTEN
1	83.90	0.001	15	94.42	0.000	29	100.11	0.000	43	105.90	0.613
2	85.20	0.	16	94.59	0.000	30	100.27	1.727	44	106.41	0.720
3	88.01	0.000	17	97.23	0.000	31	100.62	0.000	45	106.79	0.000
4	90.59	0.000	18	97.57	0.000	32	101.11	1.759	46	108.08	0.158
5	90.71	0.000	19	97.59	0.000	33	101.11	1.759	47	108.11	0.241
6	90.89	0.000	20	98.09	1.847	34	101.41	3.280	48	108.11	0.241
7	91.40	0.000	21	98.41	0.000	35	101.48	3.274	49	108.29	0.379
8	91.71	0.379	22	98.52	3.274	36	101.59	0.000	50	108.60	0.000
9	91.89	0.241	23	98.59	3.280	37	101.91	1.847	51	109.11	0.000
10	91.89	0.241	24	98.89	1.759	38	102.41	0.000	52	109.29	0.000
11	91.92	0.158	25	98.89	1.759	39	102.43	0.000	53	109.41	0.000
12	93.21	0.000	26	99.38	0.000	40	102.77	0.000	54	111.99	0.000
13	93.59	0.720	27	99.73	1.727	41	105.41	0.000	55	114.80	0.000
14	94.10	0.613	28	99.89	0.000	42	105.58	0.000	56	116.10	0.001

5-320

$J_{AA'}$	J_{AB}	$J_{AB'}$	$J_{BB'}$
2	-1	6	6
2	6	-1	6
6	6	-1	2
6	-1	6	2

The maximum summed intensity is 6.118.

LINE	FREQ	INTEN	LINE	FREQ	INTEN	LINE	FREQ	INTEN	LINE	FREQ	INTEN
1	82.38	0.001	15	95.03	0.932	29	100.40	0.000	43	105.55	0.000
2	84.70	0.000	16	95.44	0.000	30	101.04	0.000	44	106.41	0.720
3	86.64	0.000	17	95.87	0.000	31	101.29	3.744	45	107.64	0.000
4	88.06	0.000	18	96.06	0.000	32	101.41	3.280	46	107.67	0.301
5	88.83	0.000	19	96.13	0.000	33	101.43	0.000	47	108.71	0.000
6	89.86	0.000	20	96.91	0.000	34	101.64	1.577	48	109.10	0.001
7	89.87	0.096	21	97.14	0.000	35	102.07	1.904	49	109.45	0.067
8	90.19	0.210	22	97.16	1.468	36	102.10	0.000	50	109.81	0.210
9	90.55	0.067	23	97.93	1.904	37	102.84	1.468	51	110.13	0.096
10	90.90	0.001	24	98.36	1.577	38	103.61	0.000	52	111.94	0.000
11	92.33	0.301	25	98.59	3.280	39	103.87	0.000	53	112.60	0.000
12	93.59	0.720	26	98.71	3.744	40	103.94	0.000	54	112.83	0.000
13	93.92	0.	27	99.61	1.699	41	104.13	0.000	55	115.82	0.000
14	94.82	0.000	28	100.39	1.699	42	104.97	0.932	56	117.62	0.001

5-321

$J_{AA'}$	J_{AB}	$J_{AB'}$	$J_{BB'}$
2	-1	9	2
2	9	-1	2

The maximum summed intensity is 9.708.

LINE	FREQ	INTEN	LINE	FREQ	INTEN	LINE	FREQ	INTEN	LINE	FREQ	INTEN
1	78.79	0.000	15	91.71	0.314	29	100.02	1.857	43	108.38	0.000
2	79.96	0.	16	92.00	0.000	30	100.17	0.000	44	108.85	0.000
3	86.23	0.000	17	97.19	0.000	31	100.54	0.000	45	109.00	0.400
4	88.00	0.000	18	97.89	0.000	32	100.83	1.857	46	110.02	0.137
5	88.17	0.000	19	98.00	0.000	33	100.83	1.857	47	110.83	0.143
6	88.79	0.229	20	98.00	0.000	34	100.94	4.047	48	110.83	0.143
7	88.88	0.000	21	98.29	1.415	35	101.00	3.600	49	110.94	0.000
8	89.06	0.000	22	99.00	3.600	36	101.71	1.415	50	111.12	0.000
9	89.17	0.143	23	99.06	4.047	37	102.00	0.000	51	111.21	0.229
10	89.17	0.143	24	99.17	1.857	38	102.00	0.000	52	111.83	0.000
11	89.98	0.137	25	99.17	1.857	39	102.11	0.000	53	112.00	0.000
12	91.00	0.400	26	99.46	0.000	40	102.81	0.000	54	113.77	0.000
13	91.15	0.000	27	99.83	0.000	41	108.00	0.000	55	120.04	0.000
14	91.62	0.	28	99.98	1.857	42	108.29	0.314	56	121.21	0.000

5-322

$J_{AA'}$	J_{AB}	$J_{AB'}$	$J_{BB'}$
2	-1	9	9
2	9	-1	9
9	9	-1	2
9	-1	9	2

The maximum summed intensity is 5.420.

LINE	FREQ	INTEN	LINE	FREQ	INTEN	LINE	FREQ	INTEN	LINE	FREQ	INTEN
1	75.99	0.000	15	93.40	0.000	29	101.00	3.600	43	106.60	0.000
2	80.61	0.000	16	93.83	0.000	30	101.08	1.872	44	109.00	0.400
3	81.46	0.	17	94.04	0.674	31	101.30	0.000	45	109.34	0.000
4	83.40	0.000	18	94.40	0.000	32	101.44	0.000	46	110.69	0.011
5	85.34	0.000	19	95.52	0.000	33	101.64	1.609	47	111.13	0.128
6	85.48	0.	20	95.60	0.000	34	101.74	0.000	48	111.49	0.000
7	85.70	0.046	21	95.96	0.661	35	102.10	1.954	49	111.64	0.061
8	85.99	0.106	22	97.01	0.000	36	103.88	0.000	50	114.01	0.106
9	88.36	0.061	23	97.90	1.954	37	104.04	0.661	51	114.30	0.046
10	88.87	0.128	24	98.36	1.609	38	104.40	0.000	52	116.22	0.000
11	89.31	0.011	25	98.92	1.872	39	105.31	0.000	53	116.60	0.000
12	91.00	0.400	26	99.00	3.600	40	105.60	0.000	54	117.70	0.000
13	91.51	0.000	27	99.31	4.878	41	105.96	0.674	55	121.71	0.000
14	92.94	0.	28	100.69	4.878	42	106.17	0.000	56	124.01	0.000

5-323

$J_{AA'}$	J_{AB}	$J_{AB'}$	$J_{BB'}$
2	-1	12	2
2	12	-1	2

The maximum summed intensity is 10.972

LINE	FREQ	INTEN	LINE	FREQ	INTEN	LINE	FREQ	INTEN	LINE	FREQ	INTEN
1	73.34	0.000	15	89.09	0.176	29	100.11	1.914	43	111.24	0.
2	74.45	0.000	16	89.24	0.000	30	100.34	0.000	44	111.31	0.000
3	83.94	0.000	17	96.99	0.000	31	100.51	0.000	45	111.76	0.244
4	85.24	0.000	18	97.76	0.000	32	100.63	4.619	46	112.42	0.101
5	85.34	0.	19	98.24	0.000	33	100.66	1.908	47	113.16	0.002
6	85.87	0.153	20	98.26	0.000	34	100.66	1.908	48	113.66	0.092
7	86.19	0.000	21	98.38	1.036	35	100.76	3.756	49	113.66	0.092
8	86.34	0.092	22	99.24	3.756	36	101.62	1.036	50	113.81	0.000
9	86.34	0.092	23	99.34	1.908	37	101.74	0.000	51	114.13	0.153
10	86.84	0.002	24	99.34	1.908	38	101.76	0.000	52	114.66	0.
11	87.58	0.101	25	99.37	4.619	39	102.24	0.000	53	114.76	0.000
12	88.24	0.244	26	99.49	0.000	40	103.01	0.000	54	116.06	0.000
13	88.69	0.000	27	99.66	0.000	41	110.76	0.000	55	125.55	0.000
14	88.76	0.000	28	99.89	1.914	42	110.91	0.176	56	126.66	0.000

−11 −10 −9 −8 −7 −6 −5 −4 −3 −2 −1 0 +1 +2 +3 +4 +5 +6 +7 +8 +9 +10 +11

5-324

$J_{AA'}$	J_{AB}	$J_{AB'}$	$J_{BB'}$
2	-1	12	12
2	12	-1	12
12	12	-1	2
12	-1	12	2

The maximum summed intensity is 5.413.

LINE	FREQ	INTEN	LINE	FREQ	INTEN	LINE	FREQ	INTEN	LINE	FREQ	INTEN
1	69.30	0.000	15	91.06	0.000	29	100.75	0.000	43	108.94	0.000
2	75.76	0.000	16	92.40	0.000	30	100.76	3.756	44	111.10	0.000
3	76.01	0.000	17	92.53	0.000	31	101.40	1.937	45	111.76	0.244
4	78.53	0.000	18	93.19	0.513	32	101.53	1.650	46	112.95	0.016
5	80.70	0.000	19	94.28	0.274	33	102.11	1.973	47	114.06	0.051
6	81.49	0.027	20	94.30	0.	34	102.19	0.000	48	114.35	0.000
7	81.83	0.065	21	94.94	0.000	35	102.76	0.000	49	115.00	0.063
8	82.15	0.000	22	96.62	0.000	36	105.06	0.000	50	118.17	0.065
9	85.00	0.063	23	97.89	1.973	37	105.72	0.274	51	118.51	0.027
10	85.94	0.051	24	98.47	1.650	38	106.00	0.	52	120.49	0.000
11	87.05	0.016	25	98.60	1.937	39	106.81	0.513	53	121.47	0.000
12	88.24	0.244	26	99.24	3.756	40	106.89	0.000	54	122.81	0.000
13	89.36	0.000	27	99.58	5.430	41	107.13	0.000	55	127.75	0.000
14	90.49	0.000	28	100.42	5.430	42	107.47	0.000	56	130.70	0.000

−11 −10 −9 −8 −7 −6 −5 −4 −3 −2 −1 0 +1 +2 +3 +4 +5 +6 +7 +8 +9 +10 +11

5-325

$J_{AA'}$	J_{AB}	$J_{AB'}$	$J_{BB'}$
2	-1	15	2
2	15	-1	2

The maximum summed intensity is 10.989.

LINE	FREQ	INTEN	LINE	FREQ	INTEN	LINE	FREQ	INTEN	LINE	FREQ	INTEN
1	67.71	0.000	15	86.34	0.108	29	100.17	1.942	43	113.99	0.000
2	68.78	0.000	16	86.38	0.000	30	100.46	0.000	44	114.13	0.000
3	81.38	0.000	17	96.90	0.000	31	100.46	5.006	45	114.62	0.162
4	82.38	0.000	18	97.62	0.000	32	100.50	0.000	46	115.06	0.073
5	82.46	0.	19	98.38	0.000	33	100.54	1.936	47	115.69	0.003
6	82.94	0.109	20	98.43	0.760	34	100.54	1.936	48	116.54	0.064
7	83.41	0.000	21	98.47	0.000	35	100.62	3.838	49	116.54	0.064
8	83.46	0.064	22	99.38	3.838	36	101.53	0.000	50	116.59	0.000
9	83.46	0.064	23	99.46	1.936	37	101.57	0.760	51	117.06	0.109
10	84.31	0.003	24	99.46	1.936	38	101.62	0.000	52	117.54	0.000
11	84.94	0.073	25	99.50	0.000	39	102.38	0.000	53	117.62	0.000
12	85.38	0.162	26	99.54	5.006	40	103.10	0.000	54	118.62	0.000
13	85.87	0.000	27	99.54	0.000	41	113.62	0.000	55	131.22	0.000
14	86.01	0.	28	99.83	1.942	42	113.66	0.108	56	132.29	0.000

−11 −10 −9 −8 −7 −6 −5 −4 −3 −2 −1 0 +1 +2 +3 +4 +5 +6 +7 +8 +9 +10 +11

5-326

$J_{AA'}$	J_{AB}	$J_{AB'}$	$J_{BB'}$
2	-1	15	15
2	15	-1	15
15	15	-1	2
15	-1	15	2

The maximum summed intensity is 5.837.

LINE	FREQ	INTEN	LINE	FREQ	INTEN	LINE	FREQ	INTEN	LINE	FREQ	INTEN
1	62.46	0.000	15	88.81	0.000	29	100.29	5.670	43	111.19	0.000
2	69.85	0.000	16	90.58	0.000	30	100.62	3.838	44	112.93	0.000
3	71.17	0.000	17	90.76	0.000	31	101.39	1.696	45	114.62	0.162
4	73.58	0.000	18	92.36	0.406	32	101.58	1.964	46	115.52	0.016
5	75.77	0.000	19	92.41	0.126	33	102.11	1.982	47	116.63	0.042
6	77.27	0.018	20	93.23	0.000	34	103.08	0.000	48	117.26	0.000
7	77.69	0.044	21	94.19	0.000	35	103.90	0.000	49	119.04	0.036
8	79.06	0.000	22	96.01	0.000	36	105.81	0.000	50	122.31	0.044
9	80.96	0.036	23	97.89	1.982	37	107.59	0.126	51	122.73	0.018
10	83.37	0.042	24	98.42	1.964	38	107.64	0.406	52	125.14	0.000
11	84.48	0.016	25	98.61	1.696	39	107.68	0.000	53	126.42	0.000
12	85.38	0.162	26	99.38	3.838	40	108.22	0.	54	127.92	0.000
13	87.31	0.000	27	99.71	5.670	41	109.00	0.000	55	133.84	0.000
14	88.09	0.000	28	99.79	0.000	42	109.42	0.000	56	137.54	0.000

−11 −10 −9 −8 −7 −6 −5 −4 −3 −2 −1 0 +1 +2 +3 +4 +5 +6 +7 +8 +9 +10 +11

5-327

$J_{AA'}$	J_{AB}	$J_{AB'}$	$J_{BB'}$
2	-1	18	2
2	18	-1	2

The maximum summed intensity is 11.441.

LINE	FREQ	INTEN	LINE	FREQ	INTEN	LINE	FREQ	INTEN	LINE	FREQ	INTEN
1	61.97	0.000	15	83.49	0.000	29	100.19	1.958	43	116.78	0.000
2	63.02	0.000	16	83.51	0.071	30	100.35	5.265	44	117.05	0.000
3	78.68	0.000	17	96.86	0.000	31	100.46	1.954	45	117.51	0.114
4	79.49	0.000	18	97.51	0.000	32	100.46	1.954	46	117.83	0.054
5	79.54	0.	19	98.46	0.568	33	100.49	0.000	47	118.38	0.004
6	80.00	0.081	20	98.49	0.000	34	100.51	3.886	48	119.43	0.000
7	80.54	0.046	21	98.60	0.000	35	100.54	0.	49	119.46	0.046
8	80.54	0.046	22	99.46	0.	36	101.40	0.000	50	119.46	0.046
9	80.57	0.000	23	99.49	3.886	37	101.51	0.000	51	120.00	0.081
10	81.62	0.004	24	99.51	0.000	38	101.54	0.568	52	120.46	0.
11	82.17	0.054	25	99.54	1.954	39	102.49	0.000	53	120.51	0.000
12	82.49	0.114	26	99.54	1.954	40	103.14	0.000	54	121.32	0.000
13	82.95	0.000	27	99.65	5.265	41	116.49	0.071	55	136.98	0.000
14	83.22	0.000	28	99.81	1.958	42	116.51	0.000	56	138.03	0.000

5-328

$J_{AA'}$	J_{AB}	$J_{AB'}$	$J_{BB'}$
2	-1	18	18
2	18	-1	18
18	18	-1	2
18	-1	18	2

The maximum summed intensity is 5.917.

LINE	FREQ	INTEN	LINE	FREQ	INTEN	LINE	FREQ	INTEN	LINE	FREQ	INTEN
1	55.55	0.000	15	86.59	0.000	29	100.22	5.787	43	113.41	0.000
2	63.83	0.000	16	88.57	0.000	30	100.51	3.886	44	114.81	0.000
3	66.23	0.000	17	88.99	0.000	31	101.26	1.740	45	117.51	0.114
4	68.57	0.000	18	90.46	0.065	32	101.68	1.977	46	118.25	0.013
5	70.76	0.000	19	91.51	0.329	33	102.11	1.987	47	119.29	0.034
6	73.05	0.013	20	92.24	0.000	34	103.97	0.000	48	120.21	0.000
7	73.58	0.032	21	93.41	0.000	35	105.06	0.000	49	123.16	0.023
8	75.99	0.000	22	95.30	0.000	36	106.59	0.000	50	126.42	0.032
9	76.84	0.023	23	97.89	1.987	37	108.49	0.329	51	126.95	0.013
10	80.71	0.034	24	98.32	1.977	38	108.50	0.000	52	129.97	0.000
11	81.75	0.013	25	98.74	1.740	39	109.54	0.065	53	131.43	0.000
12	82.49	0.114	26	98.74	0.000	40	110.46	0.000	54	133.03	0.
13	85.30	0.	27	99.49	3.886	41	110.90	0.000	55	139.97	0.000
14	85.74	0.000	28	99.78	5.787	42	111.43	0.000	56	144.45	0.000

5-329

$J_{AA'}$	J_{AB}	$J_{AB'}$	$J_{BB'}$
4	-1	1	1
4	1	-1	1
1	-1	1	4
1	1	-1	4

The maximum summed intensity is 7.331

LINE	FREQ	INTEN	LINE	FREQ	INTEN	LINE	FREQ	INTEN	LINE	FREQ	INTEN
1	89.61	0.000	15	96.81	1.807	29	100.42	0.000	43	103.61	1.385
2	90.31	0.003	16	96.91	1.923	30	100.70	0.000	44	103.69	1.085
3	90.91	0.000	17	97.00	2.000	31	101.30	0.000	45	103.70	0.000
4	91.20	0.000	18	97.00	2.000	32	101.60	1.107	46	103.90	0.000
5	92.40	0.019	19	97.19	2.054	33	102.11	0.000	47	103.98	0.000
6	92.70	0.000	20	97.19	1.933	34	102.30	0.000	48	104.30	0.000
7	92.89	0.000	21	97.70	0.000	35	102.38	0.000	49	105.99	0.000
8	93.21	0.000	22	98.08	0.000	36	102.51	0.000	50	106.41	0.067
9	93.29	0.000	23	98.40	1.107	37	102.81	1.933	51	107.30	0.000
10	93.59	0.067	24	98.70	0.000	38	102.81	2.054	52	107.30	0.000
11	95.51	0.000	25	99.11	0.000	39	103.00	2.000	53	107.60	0.019
12	96.30	0.000	26	100.00	0.615	40	103.00	2.000	54	109.09	0.000
13	96.31	1.085	27	100.00	0.615	41	103.09	1.923	55	109.69	0.003
14	96.39	1.385	28	100.30	0.000	42	103.19	1.807	56	113.20	0.000

5-330

$J_{AA'}$	J_{AB}	$J_{AB'}$	$J_{BB'}$
4	-1	1	2
4	1	-1	2
2	-1	1	4
2	1	-1	4

The maximum summed intensity is 7.423

LINE	FREQ	INTEN	LINE	FREQ	INTEN	LINE	FREQ	INTEN	LINE	FREQ	INTEN
1	88.68	0.000	15	96.84	1.845	29	100.76	0.	43	103.65	1.316
2	89.89	0.005	16	96.92	1.931	30	100.82	0.684	44	104.11	0.626
3	90.92	0.000	17	97.00	2.000	31	101.12	0.	45	104.37	0.000
4	91.76	0.000	18	97.00	2.000	32	101.41	0.000	46	104.59	0.000
5	91.87	0.009	19	97.16	2.056	33	101.41	0.000	47	104.96	0.
6	92.59	0.000	20	97.29	1.857	34	101.88	0.000	48	105.24	0.
7	92.88	0.	21	97.87	1.529	35	101.99	0.	49	105.54	0.143
8	93.15	0.000	22	98.59	0.000	36	102.13	1.529	50	106.35	0.000
9	93.74	0.000	23	98.59	0.000	37	102.71	1.857	51	107.29	0.000
10	94.46	0.143	24	99.04	0.000	38	102.84	2.056	52	107.41	0.000
11	94.60	0.000	25	99.07	0.000	39	103.00	2.000	53	108.13	0.009
12	95.41	0.000	26	99.18	0.684	40	103.00	2.000	54	109.08	0.000
13	95.89	0.626	27	99.90	0.	41	103.08	1.931	55	110.11	0.005
14	96.35	1.316	28	100.01	0.000	42	103.16	1.845	56	113.21	0.000

5-331

$J_{AA'}$	J_{AB}	$J_{AB'}$	$J_{BB'}$
4	-1	2	1
4	2	-1	1
1	-1	2	4
1	2	-1	4

The maximum summed intensity is 7.739

LINE	FREQ	INTEN	LINE	FREQ	INTEN	LINE	FREQ	INTEN	LINE	FREQ	INTEN
1	89.26	0.004	15	96.54	1.596	29	100.00	1.000	43	103.49	0.000
2	89.65	0.000	16	96.58	0.000	30	100.88	0.000	44	103.54	1.671
3	90.06	0.000	17	97.31	2.183	31	101.41	1.274	45	104.07	0.000
4	91.23	0.000	18	97.34	0.000	32	101.58	0.000	46	104.24	1.000
5	92.26	0.000	19	97.37	2.100	33	101.74	0.000	47	104.65	0.801
6	92.34	0.000	20	97.38	1.894	34	102.54	2.329	48	105.12	0.000
7	92.51	0.041	21	97.46	2.329	35	102.62	1.894	49	106.86	0.106
8	93.14	0.106	22	98.17	0.000	36	102.63	2.100	50	107.32	0.000
9	93.31	0.000	23	98.42	0.000	37	102.66	0.000	51	107.49	0.041
10	93.89	0.000	24	98.59	1.274	38	102.69	2.183	52	107.66	0.000
11	94.96	0.000	25	99.21	0.000	39	102.79	0.000	53	107.66	0.000
12	95.35	0.801	26	99.55	0.000	40	103.07	0.000	54	108.77	0.000
13	95.76	1.000	27	99.83	0.000	41	103.42	0.000	55	110.74	0.004
14	96.46	1.671	28	100.00	1.000	42	103.46	1.596	56	112.97	0.000

5-332

$J_{AA'}$	J_{AB}	$J_{AB'}$	$J_{BB'}$
4	-1	2	2
4	2	-1	2
2	-1	2	4
2	2	-1	4

The maximum summed intensity is 6.696

LINE	FREQ	INTEN	LINE	FREQ	INTEN	LINE	FREQ	INTEN	LINE	FREQ	INTEN
1	88.79	0.000	15	96.46	1.671	29	100.70	1.055	43	104.24	0.000
2	88.86	0.005	16	96.61	1.661	30	100.77	0.000	44	104.30	0.945
3	90.63	0.000	17	97.31	2.097	31	101.00	0.000	45	104.44	0.000
4	91.25	0.000	18	97.33	2.203	32	101.76	0.000	46	104.47	0.000
5	91.99	0.024	19	97.46	2.329	33	101.84	0.000	47	105.05	0.564
6	92.16	0.000	20	97.53	1.812	34	101.93	1.446	48	106.00	0.000
7	92.23	0.000	21	98.07	1.446	35	102.30	0.000	49	106.07	0.188
8	93.76	0.000	22	98.16	0.000	36	102.47	1.812	50	107.59	0.000
9	93.79	0.000	23	98.24	0.000	37	102.54	2.329	51	107.63	0.000
10	93.93	0.188	24	99.08	0.000	38	102.59	0.000	52	107.84	0.000
11	94.15	0.000	25	99.15	0.000	39	102.67	2.203	53	108.01	0.024
12	94.95	0.564	26	99.18	0.000	40	102.69	2.097	54	108.75	0.000
13	95.70	0.945	27	99.30	1.055	41	103.39	1.661	55	111.14	0.005
14	95.76	0.000	28	99.47	0.000	42	103.54	1.671	56	112.98	0.000

5-333

$J_{AA'}$	J_{AB}	$J_{AB'}$	$J_{BB'}$
4	-1	2	4
4	2	-1	4

The maximum summed intensity is 6.744.

LINE	FREQ	INTEN	LINE	FREQ	INTEN	LINE	FREQ	INTEN	LINE	FREQ	INTEN
1	86.96	0.000	15	96.46	1.671	29	100.54	0.000	43	104.85	0.553
2	87.65	0.005	16	96.69	1.744	30	100.92	0.000	44	104.85	0.553
3	91.27	0.000	17	97.23	2.083	31	101.15	0.	45	105.00	0.000
4	91.31	0.009	18	97.35	2.233	32	101.71	0.000	46	105.54	0.000
5	91.33	0.000	19	97.40	1.719	33	101.85	1.447	47	106.27	0.207
6	91.46	0.000	20	97.46	2.329	34	101.85	1.447	48	106.33	0.000
7	92.15	0.	21	97.54	0.000	35	101.96	0.000	49	107.62	0.000
8	92.38	0.000	22	98.04	0.000	36	102.46	0.000	50	107.85	0.
9	93.67	0.000	23	98.15	1.447	37	102.54	2.329	51	108.54	0.000
10	93.73	0.207	24	98.15	1.447	38	102.60	1.719	52	108.67	0.000
11	94.46	0.000	25	98.29	0.000	39	102.65	2.233	53	108.69	0.009
12	95.00	0.000	26	98.85	0.	40	102.77	2.083	54	108.73	0.000
13	95.15	0.553	27	99.08	0.000	41	103.31	1.744	55	112.35	0.005
14	95.15	0.553	28	99.46	0.000	42	103.54	1.671	56	113.04	0.000

5-334

$J_{AA'}$	J_{AB}	$J_{AB'}$	$J_{BB'}$
4	-1	4	2
4	4	-1	2
2	-1	4	4
2	4	-1	4

The maximum summed intensity is 6.583

LINE	FREQ	INTEN	LINE	FREQ	INTEN	LINE	FREQ	INTEN	LINE	FREQ	INTEN
1	86.29	0.003	15	95.78	1.186	29	100.22	0.000	43	104.22	1.186
2	87.92	0.000	16	96.34	0.000	30	100.51	1.493	44	104.85	1.106
3	88.51	0.000	17	96.95	0.000	31	101.30	0.	45	104.99	0.000
4	90.78	0.000	18	97.36	0.000	32	101.44	1.516	46	105.89	0.507
5	90.95	0.000	19	97.51	1.975	33	101.85	2.894	47	107.01	0.403
6	91.36	0.000	20	97.66	0.000	34	101.93	2.849	48	107.41	0.193
7	91.85	0.068	21	97.98	1.807	35	102.02	1.807	49	107.70	0.
8	92.59	0.193	22	98.07	2.849	36	102.34	0.000	50	108.15	0.068
9	92.94	0.000	23	98.15	2.894	37	102.49	1.975	51	108.58	0.000
10	92.99	0.403	24	98.56	1.516	38	102.92	0.000	52	108.64	0.000
11	93.49	0.000	25	98.59	0.000	39	103.05	0.000	53	109.05	0.000
12	94.11	0.507	26	99.15	0.000	40	103.57	0.000	54	110.56	0.000
13	94.91	0.000	27	99.34	0.000	41	103.66	0.000	55	113.01	0.000
14	95.15	1.106	28	99.49	1.493	42	104.16	0.000	56	113.71	0.003

5-335

$J_{AA'}$	J_{AB}	$J_{AB'}$	$J_{BB'}$
4	-1	6	4
4	6	-1	4

The maximum summed intensity is 7.266

LINE	FREQ	INTEN	LINE	FREQ	INTEN	LINE	FREQ	INTEN	LINE	FREQ	INTEN
1	82.38	0.001	15	95.03	0.932	29	100.46	0.000	43	105.11	0.
2	85.67	0.000	16	95.42	0.000	30	101.11	1.759	44	106.15	0.000
3	86.20	0.000	17	95.59	0.000	31	101.11	1.759	45	106.41	0.720
4	88.59	0.000	18	96.41	0.000	32	101.29	3.744	46	108.11	0.241
5	88.89	0.	19	96.59	0.000	33	101.41	3.280	47	108.11	0.241
6	90.19	0.210	20	96.93	0.000	34	101.64	1.577	48	109.10	0.001
7	90.32	0.000	21	97.16	1.468	35	101.89	0.000	49	109.45	0.067
8	90.55	0.067	22	98.11	0.000	36	102.84	1.468	50	109.68	0.000
9	90.90	0.001	23	98.36	1.577	37	103.07	0.000	51	109.81	0.210
10	91.89	0.241	24	98.59	3.280	38	103.41	0.000	52	111.11	0.000
11	91.89	0.241	25	98.71	3.744	39	103.59	0.000	53	111.41	0.000
12	93.59	0.720	26	98.89	1.759	40	104.41	0.000	54	113.80	0.000
13	93.85	0.000	27	98.89	1.759	41	104.58	0.000	55	114.33	0.000
14	94.89	0.000	28	99.54	0.000	42	104.97	0.932	56	117.62	0.001

5-336

$J_{AA'}$	J_{AB}	$J_{AB'}$	$J_{BB'}$
4	-2	2	2
4	2	-2	2
2	-2	2	4
2	2	-2	4

The maximum summed intensity is 4.039

LINE	FREQ	INTEN	LINE	FREQ	INTEN	LINE	FREQ	INTEN	LINE	FREQ	INTEN
1	87.82	0.000	15	96.41	1.493	29	100.17	0.000	43	103.76	0.000
2	88.59	0.011	16	96.65	1.725	30	100.59	1.316	44	104.36	0.000
3	90.12	0.000	17	97.00	2.000	31	101.47	0.000	45	104.88	0.000
4	90.65	0.001	18	97.00	2.000	32	101.53	2.108	46	105.06	0.684
5	91.76	0.000	19	97.59	2.223	33	102.24	0.000	47	105.41	0.397
6	92.47	0.041	20	97.76	1.800	34	102.24	1.800	48	105.83	0.000
7	92.53	0.000	21	97.76	0.000	35	102.24	0.000	49	106.71	0.200
8	93.29	0.200	22	97.76	0.000	36	102.41	2.223	50	107.53	0.041
9	93.48	0.000	23	98.47	2.108	37	102.58	0.000	51	108.07	0.000
10	93.58	0.000	24	98.71	0.000	38	102.94	0.000	52	108.24	0.000
11	93.99	0.000	25	99.06	0.000	39	103.00	2.000	53	108.24	0.000
12	94.59	0.397	26	99.12	0.000	40	103.00	2.000	54	109.35	0.001
13	94.94	0.684	27	99.23	0.000	41	103.35	1.725	55	111.41	0.011
14	96.24	0.000	28	99.41	1.316	42	103.59	1.493	56	113.82	0.000

5-337

$J_{AA'}$	J_{AB}	$J_{AB'}$	$J_{BB'}$
4	-2	2	4
4	2	-2	4

The maximum summed intensity is 4.115

LINE	FREQ	INTEN	LINE	FREQ	INTEN	LINE	FREQ	INTEN	LINE	FREQ	INTEN
1	86.09	0.000	15	96.53	1.614	29	100.39	0.	43	104.64	0.000
2	87.26	0.009	16	96.70	1.769	30	100.86	0.000	44	105.00	0.000
3	90.66	0.000	17	97.00	2.000	31	101.00	0.000	45	105.61	0.445
4	90.70	0.001	18	97.00	0.000	32	101.61	1.555	46	105.61	0.445
5	91.00	0.	19	97.00	2.000	33	101.61	1.555	47	106.69	0.000
6	91.93	0.000	20	97.43	0.000	34	102.03	2.223	48	106.74	0.162
7	91.97	0.017	21	97.47	2.204	35	102.13	0.000	49	107.61	0.
8	92.39	0.	22	97.87	0.000	36	102.53	2.204	50	108.03	0.017
9	93.26	0.162	23	97.97	2.223	37	102.57	0.000	51	108.07	0.000
10	93.31	0.000	24	98.39	1.555	38	103.00	0.000	52	109.00	0.000
11	94.39	0.445	25	98.39	1.555	39	103.00	2.000	53	109.30	0.001
12	94.39	0.445	26	99.00	0.000	40	103.00	2.000	54	109.34	0.000
13	95.00	0.000	27	99.14	0.000	41	103.30	1.769	55	112.74	0.009
14	95.36	0.000	28	99.61	0.	42	103.47	1.614	56	113.91	0.000

5-338

$J_{AA'}$	J_{AB}	$J_{AB'}$	$J_{BB'}$
4	-2	2	6
4	2	-2	6
6	-2	2	4
6	2	-2	4

The maximum summed intensity is 4.262

LINE	FREQ	INTEN	LINE	FREQ	INTEN	LINE	FREQ	INTEN	LINE	FREQ	INTEN
1	84.27	0.000	15	95.84	0.000	29	100.24	0.000	43	104.78	0.000
2	85.67	0.006	16	96.49	0.000	30	100.53	0.	44	105.06	0.684
3	89.76	0.	17	96.62	1.692	31	100.59	1.316	45	105.76	0.000
4	90.15	0.000	18	96.74	1.802	32	101.86	0.000	46	106.71	0.200
5	90.74	0.001	19	96.86	0.000	33	102.24	1.800	47	108.21	0.
6	90.84	0.000	20	97.00	2.000	34	102.31	2.241	48	108.31	0.008
7	91.67	0.067	21	97.00	2.000	35	102.52	0.000	49	108.33	0.067
8	91.69	0.008	22	97.38	2.184	36	102.55	0.000	50	108.43	0.000
9	92.17	0.	23	97.69	2.241	37	102.62	2.184	51	109.26	0.001
10	93.21	0.000	24	97.76	1.800	38	103.00	2.000	52	109.47	0.000
11	93.29	0.200	25	97.83	0.000	39	103.00	2.000	53	110.24	0.000
12	94.24	0.000	26	99.09	0.000	40	103.26	1.802	54	110.81	0.000
13	94.94	0.684	27	99.41	1.316	41	103.38	1.692	55	114.09	0.000
14	95.76	0.000	28	99.76	0.000	42	104.24	0.000	56	114.33	0.006

5-339

$J_{AA'}$	J_{AB}	$J_{AB'}$	$J_{BB'}$
4	-2	4	6
4	4	-2	6
6	4	-2	4
6	-2	4	4

The maximum summed intensity is 6.403.

LINE	FREQ	INTEN	LINE	FREQ	INTEN	LINE	FREQ	INTEN	LINE	FREQ	INTEN
1	83.80	0.005	15	95.43	0.000	29	100.44	1.614	43	105.00	0.000
2	84.36	0.000	16	95.57	0.000	30	101.00	0.000	44	105.43	0.000
3	88.36	0.000	17	95.84	1.368	31	101.32	0.000	45	106.77	0.386
4	88.68	0.000	18	95.96	0.000	32	101.84	1.822	46	107.04	0.000
5	89.17	0.000	19	96.01	1.344	33	102.16	2.632	47	108.16	0.178
6	90.13	0.105	20	97.52	2.301	34	102.22	0.000	48	108.60	0.031
7	90.39	0.000	21	97.61	0.000	35	102.27	1.916	49	108.80	0.003
8	91.20	0.003	22	97.67	2.295	36	102.33	2.295	50	109.43	0.000
9	91.40	0.031	23	97.73	1.916	37	102.48	2.301	51	109.87	0.105
10	91.84	0.178	24	97.84	2.632	38	103.04	0.000	52	111.00	0.000
11	93.23	0.386	25	98.16	1.822	39	103.17	0.000	53	111.32	0.000
12	94.36	0.000	26	98.68	0.000	40	103.99	1.344	54	113.04	0.000
13	95.00	0.000	27	99.17	0.000	41	104.16	1.368	55	114.25	0.000
14	95.00	0.000	28	99.56	1.614	42	105.00	0.000	56	116.20	0.005

5-340

$J_{AA'}$	J_{AB}	$J_{AB'}$	$J_{BB'}$
4	-2	6	6
4	6	-2	6
6	-2	6	4
6	6	-2	4

The maximum summed intensity is 5.970

LINE	FREQ	INTEN	LINE	FREQ	INTEN	LINE	FREQ	INTEN	LINE	FREQ	INTEN
1	81.21	0.003	15	94.88	0.000	29	100.35	1.759	43	105.61	0.891
2	83.96	0.000	16	94.99	0.000	30	101.34	0.000	44	105.91	0.000
3	85.34	0.	17	95.05	0.971	31	101.53	1.857	45	106.20	0.000
4	87.27	0.000	18	95.28	0.000	32	101.61	3.109	46	108.60	0.241
5	88.00	0.000	19	95.52	0.000	33	101.78	2.977	47	108.99	0.001
6	88.42	0.114	20	97.27	0.000	34	101.87	0.000	48	109.15	0.060
7	88.53	0.	21	97.47	0.000	35	101.94	1.804	49	109.78	0.143
8	90.22	0.143	22	97.74	2.070	36	102.26	2.070	50	110.81	0.000
9	90.85	0.060	23	98.06	1.804	37	102.73	0.000	51	111.58	0.114
10	91.01	0.001	24	98.22	2.977	38	103.93	0.	52	112.66	0.000
11	91.40	0.241	25	98.39	3.109	39	104.48	0.000	53	112.73	0.000
12	94.29	0.000	26	98.47	1.857	40	104.53	0.000	54	114.85	0.000
13	94.39	0.891	27	99.31	0.000	41	104.95	0.971	55	115.84	0.000
14	94.48	0.000	28	99.65	1.759	42	105.52	0.000	56	118.79	0.003

5-341

$J_{AA'}$	J_{AB}	$J_{AB'}$	$J_{BB'}$
4	-2	2	9
4	2	-2	9
9	-2	2	4
9	2	-2	4

The maximum summed intensity is 5.320

LINE	FREQ	INTEN	LINE	FREQ	INTEN	LINE	FREQ	INTEN	LINE	FREQ	INTEN
1	81.43	0.000	15	94.57	0.000	29	100.30	0.000	43	105.26	0.583
2	83.01	0.003	16	94.74	0.583	30	100.65	0.000	44	106.30	0.000
3	87.30	0.000	17	95.56	0.	31	101.14	1.417	45	106.70	0.000
4	87.35	0.000	18	96.70	1.766	32	101.63	0.000	46	108.53	0.004
5	89.01	0.021	19	96.78	1.837	33	102.53	2.212	47	108.86	0.000
6	90.45	0.000	20	97.00	2.000	34	102.65	1.947	48	109.05	0.053
7	90.78	0.001	21	97.00	2.000	35	102.70	2.156	49	109.22	0.001
8	90.95	0.053	22	97.30	2.156	36	103.00	2.000	50	110.66	0.000
9	91.44	0.	23	97.35	1.947	37	103.00	2.000	51	110.99	0.021
10	91.47	0.004	24	97.47	2.212	38	103.03	0.000	52	112.35	0.000
11	93.13	0.000	25	98.86	1.417	39	103.22	1.837	53	112.70	0.000
12	93.18	0.000	26	98.91	0.000	40	103.30	1.766	54	113.34	0.000
13	93.30	0.000	27	99.05	0.000	41	104.74	0.000	55	114.78	0.000
14	93.70	0.000	28	99.70	0.000	42	104.88	0.000	56	116.99	0.003

-11 -10 -9 -8 -7 -6 -5 -4 -3 -2 -1 0 +1 +2 +3 +4 +5 +6 +7 +8 +9 +10 +11

5-342

$J_{AA'}$	J_{AB}	$J_{AB'}$	$J_{BB'}$
4	-2	4	9
4	4	-2	9
9	4	-2	4
9	-2	4	4

The maximum summed intensity is 6.275.

LINE	FREQ	INTEN	LINE	FREQ	INTEN	LINE	FREQ	INTEN	LINE	FREQ	INTEN
1	81.50	0.004	15	94.21	0.000	29	100.57	0.000	43	105.76	0.000
2	81.67	0.000	16	94.24	0.000	30	100.86	1.653	44	106.95	0.347
3	86.43	0.000	17	95.54	0.000	31	101.24	0.000	45	107.24	0.000
4	86.59	0.000	18	95.84	1.368	32	102.16	2.632	46	108.72	0.002
5	87.83	0.045	19	96.19	1.463	33	102.36	1.930	47	109.02	0.000
6	88.12	0.000	20	97.29	1.858	34	102.40	2.403	48	109.04	0.016
7	89.46	0.000	21	97.49	2.210	35	102.51	2.210	49	110.17	0.070
8	89.83	0.070	22	97.58	0.000	36	102.57	0.000	50	110.19	0.000
9	90.96	0.016	23	97.60	2.403	37	102.71	1.858	51	112.17	0.045
10	91.28	0.002	24	97.64	1.930	38	103.67	0.000	52	113.57	0.000
11	92.76	0.000	25	97.84	2.632	39	103.81	1.463	53	113.76	0.000
12	93.05	0.347	26	99.12	0.000	40	104.11	0.000	54	115.10	0.000
13	93.11	0.000	27	99.14	1.653	41	104.16	1.368	55	115.10	0.000
14	94.20	0.000	28	99.43	0.000	42	105.64	0.000	56	118.50	0.004

-11 -10 -9 -8 -7 -6 -5 -4 -3 -2 -1 0 +1 +2 +3 +4 +5 +6 +7 +8 +9 +10 +11

5-343

$J_{AA'}$	J_{AB}	$J_{AB'}$	$J_{BB'}$
4	-2	4	12
4	4	-2	12
12	4	-2	4
12	-2	4	4

The maximum summed intensity is 4.363

LINE	FREQ	INTEN	LINE	FREQ	INTEN	LINE	FREQ	INTEN	LINE	FREQ	INTEN
1	78.88	0.000	15	93.84	0.000	29	100.16	0.000	43	106.16	0.000
2	78.96	0.002	16	94.11	0.000	30	101.38	0.000	44	108.16	0.178
3	83.84	0.000	17	94.16	0.000	31	101.84	1.822	45	108.67	0.001
4	83.86	0.000	18	95.84	1.368	32	102.16	2.632	46	109.32	0.010
5	85.29	0.021	19	96.31	1.543	33	102.26	0.000	47	109.84	0.000
6	86.96	0.000	20	97.01	1.803	34	102.34	2.474	48	110.34	0.000
7	87.38	0.028	21	97.36	2.147	35	102.62	1.972	49	111.69	0.000
8	87.84	0.000	22	97.38	1.972	36	102.64	2.147	50	112.62	0.028
9	90.16	0.000	23	97.66	2.474	37	102.99	1.803	51	114.71	0.021
10	90.54	0.000	24	97.84	2.632	38	103.69	1.543	52	116.16	0.000
11	90.68	0.010	25	98.16	1.822	39	104.16	1.368	53	116.62	0.000
12	91.33	0.001	26	98.68	0.000	40	105.01	0.000	54	116.67	0.000
13	91.84	0.178	27	99.09	0.000	41	105.36	0.000	55	117.49	0.000
14	93.29	0.000	28	99.84	0.000	42	105.77	0.000	56	121.04	0.002

5-344

$J_{AA'}$	J_{AB}	$J_{AB'}$	$J_{BB'}$
4	-2	4	15
4	4	-2	15
15	4	-2	4
15	-2	4	4

The maximum summed intensity is 5.734.

LINE	FREQ	INTEN	LINE	FREQ	INTEN	LINE	FREQ	INTEN	LINE	FREQ	INTEN
1	76.02	0.000	15	93.41	0.000	29	100.07	0.000	43	107.06	0.000
2	76.28	0.001	16	93.60	0.000	30	101.49	0.000	44	108.63	0.001
3	81.05	0.000	17	94.05	0.000	31	102.05	0.000	45	109.50	0.006
4	81.07	0.000	18	95.84	1.368	32	102.16	2.632	46	110.17	0.070
5	82.60	0.010	19	96.40	1.600	33	102.30	2.526	47	111.06	0.000
6	84.72	0.013	20	96.82	1.757	34	102.36	1.930	48	112.60	0.000
7	85.03	0.000	21	97.25	1.987	35	102.72	2.099	49	113.84	0.000
8	85.59	0.000	22	97.28	2.099	36	102.75	1.987	50	115.28	0.013
9	87.40	0.000	23	97.64	1.930	37	103.18	1.757	51	117.40	0.010
10	87.83	0.000	24	97.70	2.526	38	103.60	1.600	52	118.87	0.000
11	89.83	0.070	25	97.84	2.632	39	104.16	1.368	53	118.93	0.000
12	90.50	0.006	26	99.07	0.000	40	105.86	0.000	54	119.51	0.000
13	91.37	0.001	27	99.25	0.000	41	106.03	0.000	55	120.07	0.000
14	92.84	0.000	28	99.93	0.000	42	106.40	0.000	56	123.72	0.001

5-345

$J_{AA'}$	J_{AB}	$J_{AB'}$	$J_{BB'}$
4	-2	4	18
4	4	-2	18
18	4	-2	4
18	-2	4	4

The maximum summed intensity is 4.747.

LINE	FREQ	INTEN	LINE	FREQ	INTEN	LINE	FREQ	INTEN	LINE	FREQ	INTEN
1	73.13	0.000	15	93.00	0.000	29	100.22	0.000	43	108.59	0.000
2	73.50	0.001	16	93.45	0.000	30	101.56	0.000	44	109.53	0.000
3	78.19	0.000	17	94.01	0.000	31	101.89	0.000	45	109.63	0.005
4	78.22	0.000	18	95.84	1.368	32	102.16	2.632	46	111.43	0.000
5	79.83	0.006	19	96.46	1.641	33	102.27	2.565	47	112.62	0.028
6	81.94	0.006	20	96.69	1.720	34	102.62	1.972	48	115.45	0.000
7	82.67	0.000	21	97.18	1.994	35	102.79	2.062	49	116.37	0.000
8	83.00	0.000	22	97.21	2.062	36	102.82	1.994	50	118.06	0.006
9	84.55	0.000	23	97.38	1.972	37	103.31	1.720	51	120.17	0.006
10	85.03	0.000	24	97.73	2.565	38	103.54	1.641	52	121.43	0.000
11	87.38	0.028	25	97.84	2.632	39	104.16	1.368	53	121.78	0.000
12	90.37	0.005	26	99.07	0.000	40	105.91	0.000	54	122.44	0.
13	91.41	0.000	27	99.53	0.000	41	106.37	0.000	55	122.77	0.000
14	92.67	0.000	28	99.78	0.000	42	106.55	0.000	56	126.50	0.001

5-346

$J_{AA'}$	J_{AB}	$J_{AB'}$	$J_{BB'}$
4	-2	6	2
4	6	-2	2
2	-2	6	4
2	6	-2	4

The maximum summed intensity is 7.221

LINE	FREQ	INTEN	LINE	FREQ	INTEN	LINE	FREQ	INTEN	LINE	FREQ	INTEN
1	83.30	0.003	15	95.27	0.000	29	100.35	1.759	43	105.61	0.891
2	84.25	0.000	16	95.56	0.000	30	100.53	0.000	44	105.62	0.000
3	86.89	0.000	17	95.83	0.000	31	100.66	0.000	45	106.02	0.000
4	89.27	0.000	18	96.48	0.000	32	100.94	1.935	46	108.15	0.127
5	89.34	0.	19	97.08	0.000	33	101.53	1.857	47	108.60	0.241
6	90.22	0.143	20	97.52	0.000	34	101.61	2.488	48	109.25	0.007
7	90.51	0.236	21	97.96	2.492	35	101.61	3.109	49	109.47	0.
8	90.53	0.000	22	98.39	2.488	36	102.04	2.492	50	109.49	0.236
9	90.75	0.007	23	98.39	3.109	37	102.48	0.000	51	109.78	0.143
10	91.40	0.241	24	98.47	1.857	38	102.99	0.000	52	110.66	0.000
11	91.85	0.127	25	99.06	1.935	39	103.52	0.000	53	110.73	0.000
12	92.80	0.000	26	99.34	0.000	40	104.11	0.000	54	114.30	0.000
13	94.39	0.712	27	99.47	0.000	41	104.73	0.000	55	114.57	0.000
14	94.39	0.891	28	99.65	1.759	42	105.61	0.712	56	116.70	0.003

5-347

$J_{AA'}$	J_{AB}	$J_{AB'}$	$J_{BB'}$
4	-2	6	4
4	6	-2	4

The maximum summed intensity is 4.906.

LINE	FREQ	INTEN	LINE	FREQ	INTEN	LINE	FREQ	INTEN	LINE	FREQ	INTEN
1	82.34	0.003	15	94.95	0.000	29	100.64	0.000	43	105.24	0.851
2	84.95	0.000	16	95.51	0.000	30	101.00	1.800	44	105.61	0.891
3	85.51	0.000	17	95.61	0.000	31	101.00	1.800	45	106.07	0.000
4	88.39	0.000	18	96.07	0.000	32	101.00	0.000	46	108.68	0.087
5	89.00	0.000	19	96.39	0.000	33	101.47	1.869	47	109.00	0.200
6	89.36	0.000	20	96.39	0.000	34	101.61	3.109	48	109.00	0.200
7	89.55	0.168	21	98.03	2.244	35	101.88	2.776	49	109.09	0.003
8	90.91	0.003	22	98.12	2.776	36	101.97	2.244	50	110.45	0.168
9	91.00	0.200	23	98.39	3.109	37	103.61	0.000	51	110.64	0.000
10	91.00	0.200	24	98.53	1.869	38	103.61	0.000	52	111.00	0.000
11	91.32	0.087	25	99.00	1.800	39	103.93	0.000	53	111.61	0.000
12	93.93	0.000	26	99.00	1.800	40	104.39	0.000	54	114.49	0.000
13	94.39	0.891	27	99.00	0.000	41	104.49	0.000	55	115.05	0.000
14	94.76	0.851	28	99.36	0.000	42	105.05	0.000	56	117.66	0.003

−11 −10 −9 −8 −7 −6 −5 −4 −3 −2 −1 0 +1 +2 +3 +4 +5 +6 +7 +8 +9 +10 +11

5-348

$J_{AA'}$	J_{AB}	$J_{AB'}$	$J_{BB'}$
4	-2	6	6
4	6	-2	6
6	6	-2	4
6	-2	6	4

The maximum summed intensity is 5.970.

LINE	FREQ	INTEN	LINE	FREQ	INTEN	LINE	FREQ	INTEN	LINE	FREQ	INTEN
1	81.21	0.003	15	94.88	0.000	29	100.35	1.759	43	105.61	0.891
2	83.96	0.000	16	94.99	0.000	30	101.34	0.000	44	105.91	0.000
3	85.34	0.	17	95.05	0.971	31	101.53	1.857	45	106.20	0.000
4	87.27	0.000	18	95.28	0.000	32	101.61	3.109	46	108.60	0.241
5	88.00	0.000	19	95.52	0.000	33	101.78	2.977	47	108.99	0.001
6	88.42	0.114	20	97.27	0.000	34	101.87	0.000	48	109.15	0.060
7	88.53	0.	21	97.47	0.000	35	101.94	1.804	49	109.78	0.143
8	90.22	0.143	22	97.74	2.070	36	102.26	2.070	50	110.81	0.000
9	90.85	0.060	23	98.06	1.804	37	102.73	0.000	51	111.58	0.114
10	91.01	0.001	24	98.22	2.977	38	103.93	0.	52	112.66	0.000
11	91.40	0.241	25	98.39	3.109	39	104.48	0.000	53	112.73	0.000
12	94.29	0.000	26	98.47	1.857	40	104.53	0.000	54	114.85	0.000
13	94.39	0.891	27	99.31	0.000	41	104.95	0.971	55	115.84	0.000
14	94.48	0.000	28	99.65	1.759	42	105.52	0.000	56	118.79	0.003

−11 −10 −9 −8 −7 −6 −5 −4 −3 −2 −1 0 +1 +2 +3 +4 +5 +6 +7 +8 +9 +10 +11

5-349

$J_{AA'}$	J_{AB}	$J_{AB'}$	$J_{BB'}$
4	-2	9	2
4	9	-2	2
2	9	-2	4
2	-2	9	4

The maximum summed intensity is 7.742

LINE	FREQ	INTEN	LINE	FREQ	INTEN	LINE	FREQ	INTEN	LINE	FREQ	INTEN
1	78.33	0.001	15	92.74	0.000	29	100.26	1.864	43	107.98	0.000
2	79.14	0.000	16	92.80	0.000	30	100.30	0.000	44	108.11	0.481
3	85.21	0.000	17	96.02	0.000	31	100.52	1.934	45	108.20	0.000
4	86.70	0.	18	96.27	0.000	32	100.65	0.000	46	109.74	0.130
5	86.80	0.000	19	96.92	0.000	33	101.11	3.519	47	110.54	0.003
6	87.55	0.163	20	97.98	0.000	34	101.21	1.901	48	111.44	0.136
7	87.61	0.099	21	98.64	2.181	35	101.32	3.207	49	112.35	0.000
8	87.90	0.000	22	98.68	3.207	36	101.36	2.181	50	112.39	0.099
9	88.56	0.136	23	98.79	1.901	37	102.02	0.000	51	112.45	0.163
10	89.46	0.003	24	98.89	3.519	38	102.13	0.000	52	113.05	0.000
11	90.26	0.130	25	99.45	0.000	39	103.98	0.000	53	113.20	0.000
12	91.07	0.000	26	99.48	1.934	40	104.67	0.000	54	115.73	0.000
13	91.89	0.481	27	99.60	0.000	41	107.20	0.000	55	119.91	0.000
14	92.14	0.381	28	99.74	1.864	42	107.86	0.381	56	121.67	0.001

−11 −10 −9 −8 −7 −6 −5 −4 −3 −2 −1 0 +1 +2 +3 +4 +5 +6 +7 +8 +9 +10 +11

5-350

$J_{AA'}$	J_{AB}	$J_{AB'}$	$J_{BB'}$
4	-2	9	4
4	9	-2	4

The maximum summed intensity is 7.827.

LINE	FREQ	INTEN	LINE	FREQ	INTEN	LINE	FREQ	INTEN	LINE	FREQ	INTEN
1	77.49	0.001	15	92.72	0.472	29	100.40	0.000	43	107.64	0.000
2	79.83	0.000	16	93.89	0.000	30	100.76	1.878	44	107.78	0.000
3	83.99	0.000	17	95.11	0.000	31	100.76	1.878	45	108.11	0.481
4	85.89	0.000	18	95.25	0.000	32	100.91	1.878	46	110.13	0.106
5	86.24	0.000	19	96.52	0.000	33	101.11	3.519	47	110.36	0.000
6	86.71	0.131	20	96.89	0.000	34	101.14	3.766	48	111.76	0.122
7	87.07	0.000	21	98.06	1.646	35	101.24	0.000	49	111.76	0.122
8	88.24	0.122	22	98.76	0.000	36	101.94	1.646	50	112.93	0.000
9	88.24	0.122	23	98.86	3.766	37	103.11	0.000	51	113.29	0.131
10	89.64	0.000	24	98.89	3.519	38	103.48	0.000	52	113.76	0.000
11	89.87	0.106	25	99.09	1.878	39	104.75	0.000	53	114.11	0.000
12	91.89	0.481	26	99.24	1.878	40	104.89	0.000	54	116.01	0.000
13	92.22	0.000	27	99.24	1.878	41	106.11	0.000	55	120.17	0.000
14	92.36	0.000	28	99.60	0.000	42	107.28	0.472	56	122.51	0.001

−11 −10 −9 −8 −7 −6 −5 −4 −3 −2 −1 0 +1 +2 +3 +4 +5 +6 +7 +8 +9 +10 +11

5-351

$J_{AA'}$	J_{AB}	$J_{AB'}$	$J_{BB'}$
4	-2	9	9
4	9	-2	9
9	9	-2	4
9	-2	9	4

The maximum summed intensity is 6.134.

LINE	FREQ	INTEN	LINE	FREQ	INTEN	LINE	FREQ	INTEN	LINE	FREQ	INTEN
1	74.87	0.001	15	92.21	0.000	29	100.52	1.869	43	107.77	0.000
2	80.19	0.000	16	93.92	0.701	30	100.93	4.384	44	107.93	0.000
3	80.46	0.000	17	94.49	0.	31	101.11	3.519	45	108.11	0.481
4	82.85	0.000	18	94.93	0.000	32	101.74	1.936	46	110.15	0.003
5	84.09	0.069	19	95.52	0.	33	101.88	1.708	47	111.10	0.061
6	84.25	0.000	20	95.74	0.000	34	102.22	0.000	48	111.56	0.131
7	84.48	0.	21	95.85	0.000	35	102.45	0.000	49	113.50	0.000
8	86.18	0.064	22	96.86	1.072	36	103.14	1.072	50	113.82	0.064
9	88.44	0.131	23	98.12	1.708	37	104.15	0.000	51	115.91	0.069
10	88.90	0.061	24	98.26	1.936	38	105.07	0.000	52	117.15	0.000
11	89.85	0.003	25	98.89	3.519	39	105.53	0.	53	117.56	0.000
12	91.50	0.000	26	99.07	4.384	40	106.08	0.701	54	117.78	0.
13	91.89	0.481	27	99.48	1.869	41	106.24	0.000	55	121.80	0.000
14	92.07	0.000	28	99.80	0.000	42	106.51	0.	56	125.13	0.001

-11 -10 -9 -8 -7 -6 -5 -4 -3 -2 -1 0 +1 +2 +3 +4 +5 +6 +7 +8 +9 +10 +11

5-352

$J_{AA'}$	J_{AB}	$J_{AB'}$	$J_{BB'}$
4	-2	12	4
4	12	-2	4

The maximum summed intensity is 10.941.

LINE	FREQ	INTEN	LINE	FREQ	INTEN	LINE	FREQ	INTEN	LINE	FREQ	INTEN
1	72.20	0.000	15	90.39	0.267	29	100.16	0.000	43	109.96	0.000
2	74.41	0.000	16	91.17	0.000	30	100.51	1.916	44	110.36	0.000
3	81.85	0.000	17	94.72	0.000	31	100.62	1.919	45	110.83	0.285
4	83.17	0.000	18	94.83	0.000	32	100.62	1.919	46	112.17	0.093
5	83.38	0.	19	97.08	0.000	33	100.71	4.594	47	112.37	0.002
6	83.86	0.100	20	97.17	0.000	34	100.83	3.715	48	114.62	0.081
7	84.61	0.000	21	97.94	1.028	35	101.38	0.000	49	114.62	0.081
8	85.38	0.081	22	98.62	0.000	36	102.06	1.028	50	115.39	0.000
9	85.38	0.081	23	99.17	3.715	37	102.83	0.000	51	116.14	0.100
10	87.63	0.002	24	99.29	4.594	38	102.92	0.000	52	116.62	0.
11	87.83	0.093	25	99.38	1.919	39	105.17	0.000	53	116.83	0.000
12	89.17	0.285	26	99.38	1.919	40	105.28	0.000	54	118.15	0.000
13	89.64	0.000	27	99.49	1.916	41	108.83	0.000	55	125.59	0.000
14	90.04	0.000	28	99.84	0.000	42	109.61	0.267	56	127.80	0.000

-11 -10 -9 -8 -7 -6 -5 -4 -3 -2 -1 0 +1 +2 +3 +4 +5 +6 +7 +8 +9 +10 +11

5-353

$J_{AA'}$	J_{AB}	$J_{AB'}$	$J_{BB'}$
4	-2	12	12
4	12	-2	12
12	12	-2	4
12	-2	12	4

The maximum summed intensity is 5.310.

LINE	FREQ	INTEN	LINE	FREQ	INTEN	LINE	FREQ	INTEN	LINE	FREQ	INTEN
1	68.22	0.000	15	89.77	0.000	29	100.74	0.000	43	109.46	0.000
2	74.98	0.000	16	93.01	0.530	30	100.83	3.715	44	110.23	0.000
3	75.75	0.000	17	93.37	0.000	31	100.99	1.930	45	110.83	0.285
4	78.11	0.000	18	94.07	0.000	32	101.73	1.696	46	112.18	0.013
5	79.88	0.046	19	94.11	0.000	33	101.84	1.965	47	113.39	0.053
6	79.93	0.	20	94.23	0.000	34	102.08	0.000	48	115.13	0.070
7	80.94	0.000	21	95.32	0.426	35	103.10	0.000	49	116.23	0.000
8	82.04	0.035	22	95.55	0.000	36	104.68	0.426	50	117.96	0.035
9	84.87	0.070	23	98.16	1.965	37	105.77	0.000	51	120.12	0.046
10	86.61	0.053	24	98.27	1.696	38	105.89	0.000	52	121.42	0.000
11	87.82	0.013	25	99.01	1.930	39	106.99	0.530	53	121.89	0.000
12	89.12	0.000	26	99.17	3.715	40	107.28	0.000	54	122.90	0.
13	89.17	0.285	27	99.48	5.236	41	107.51	0.000	55	127.85	0.
14	89.66	0.000	28	100.52	5.236	42	108.05	0.000	56	131.78	0.000

5-354

$J_{AA'}$	J_{AB}	$J_{AB'}$	$J_{BB'}$
4	-2	15	4
4	15	-2	4

The maximum summed intensity is 11.000.

LINE	FREQ	INTEN	LINE	FREQ	INTEN	LINE	FREQ	INTEN	LINE	FREQ	INTEN
1	66.67	0.000	15	87.88	0.159	29	100.05	0.000	43	112.44	0.000
2	68.81	0.000	16	88.34	0.000	30	100.27	1.944	44	113.16	0.000
3	79.35	0.000	17	94.41	0.000	31	100.47	5.119	45	113.66	0.184
4	80.34	0.000	18	94.66	0.000	32	100.51	1.943	46	114.59	0.072
5	80.49	0.	19	97.34	0.000	33	100.51	1.943	47	114.79	0.004
6	80.99	0.077	20	97.38	0.000	34	100.66	3.816	48	117.51	0.057
7	82.02	0.000	21	97.81	0.624	35	101.49	0.000	49	117.51	0.057
8	82.49	0.057	22	98.51	0.000	36	102.19	0.624	50	117.98	0.000
9	82.49	0.057	23	99.34	3.816	37	102.62	0.000	51	119.01	0.077
10	85.21	0.004	24	99.49	1.943	38	102.66	0.000	52	119.51	0.000
11	85.41	0.072	25	99.49	1.943	39	105.34	0.000	53	119.66	0.000
12	86.34	0.184	26	99.53	5.119	40	105.59	0.000	54	120.65	0.000
13	86.84	0.000	27	99.73	1.944	41	111.66	0.000	55	131.19	0.000
14	87.56	0.000	28	99.95	0.000	42	112.12	0.159	56	133.33	0.000

5-355

$J_{AA'}$	J_{AB}	$J_{AB'}$	$J_{BB'}$
4	-2	15	15
4	15	-2	15
15	15	-2	4
15	-2	15	4

The maximum summed intensity is 5.435.

LINE	FREQ	INTEN	LINE	FREQ	INTEN	LINE	FREQ	INTEN	LINE	FREQ	INTEN
1	61.42	0.000	15	87.53	0.000	29	100.66	3.816	43	111.24	0.
2	69.22	0.	16	91.92	0.	30	101.26	1.959	44	112.47	0.000
3	70.98	0.000	17	92.20	0.418	31	101.28	0.000	45	113.66	0.184
4	73.22	0.000	18	92.22	0.000	32	101.56	1.718	46	114.65	0.015
5	75.14	0.	19	92.86	0.	33	101.88	0.000	47	115.88	0.044
6	75.74	0.033	20	93.47	0.000	34	101.90	1.978	48	118.98	0.041
7	77.83	0.000	21	93.49	0.181	35	103.98	0.000	49	119.00	0.000
8	77.85	0.022	22	95.02	0.000	36	106.51	0.181	50	122.15	0.022
9	81.02	0.041	23	98.10	1.978	37	106.53	0.000	51	124.26	0.033
10	84.12	0.044	24	98.44	1.718	38	107.78	0.000	52	125.86	0.000
11	85.35	0.015	25	98.74	1.959	39	107.80	0.418	53	126.78	0.000
12	86.34	0.184	26	99.34	3.816	40	108.14	0.000	54	128.02	0.000
13	86.94	0.000	27	99.66	5.591	41	109.64	0.000	55	133.94	0.000
14	87.20	0.000	28	100.34	5.591	42	109.90	0.	56	138.58	0.000

5-356

$J_{AA'}$	J_{AB}	$J_{AB'}$	$J_{BB'}$
4	-2	18	4
4	18	-2	4

The maximum summed intensity is 10.873.

LINE	FREQ	INTEN	LINE	FREQ	INTEN	LINE	FREQ	INTEN	LINE	FREQ	INTEN
1	61.01	0.000	15	85.23	0.100	29	100.12	1.961	43	115.11	0.000
2	63.11	0.000	16	85.46	0.000	30	100.21	0.000	44	116.01	0.000
3	76.67	0.000	17	94.23	0.000	31	100.34	5.423	45	116.54	0.127
4	77.46	0.000	18	94.54	0.000	32	100.44	1.958	46	117.21	0.055
5	77.56	0.	19	97.46	0.000	33	100.44	1.958	47	117.43	0.006
6	78.10	0.061	20	97.55	0.000	34	100.54	3.873	48	120.44	0.042
7	79.33	0.000	21	97.68	0.394	35	101.56	0.	49	120.44	0.042
8	79.56	0.042	22	98.44	0.	36	102.32	0.394	50	120.67	0.000
9	79.56	0.042	23	99.46	3.873	37	102.45	0.000	51	121.90	0.061
10	82.57	0.006	24	99.56	1.958	38	102.54	0.000	52	122.44	0.
11	82.79	0.055	25	99.56	1.958	39	105.46	0.000	53	122.54	0.000
12	83.46	0.127	26	99.66	5.423	40	105.77	0.000	54	123.33	0.000
13	83.99	0.000	27	99.79	0.000	41	114.54	0.000	55	136.89	0.000
14	84.89	0.	28	99.88	1.961	42	114.77	0.100	56	138.99	0.000

5-357

$J_{AA'}$	J_{AB}	$J_{AB'}$	$J_{BB'}$
4	-2	18	18
4	18	-2	18
18	18	-2	4
18	-2	18	4

The maximum summed intensity is 5.870.

LINE	FREQ	INTEN	LINE	FREQ	INTEN	LINE	FREQ	INTEN	LINE	FREQ	INTEN
1	54.53	0.000	15	85.34	0.000	29	100.31	0.000	43	113.09	0.000
2	63.30	0.000	16	90.25	0.000	30	100.54	3.873	44	114.66	0.000
3	66.07	0.000	17	90.29	0.000	31	101.40	1.750	45	116.54	0.127
4	68.25	0.000	18	91.37	0.339	32	101.44	1.974	46	117.33	0.014
5	70.23	0.000	19	91.54	0.087	33	101.94	1.985	47	118.49	0.036
6	71.61	0.025	20	91.77	0.000	34	103.06	0.000	48	121.85	0.000
7	73.65	0.015	21	92.66	0.000	35	104.86	0.	49	122.98	0.026
8	74.77	0.000	22	94.35	0.000	36	107.34	0.000	50	126.35	0.015
9	77.02	0.026	23	98.06	1.985	37	108.46	0.087	51	128.39	0.025
10	81.51	0.036	24	98.56	1.974	38	108.63	0.339	52	130.56	0.000
11	82.67	0.014	25	98.60	1.750	39	109.02	0.000	53	131.75	0.000
12	83.46	0.127	26	99.46	3.873	40	109.75	0.000	54	133.14	0.
13	84.80	0.000	27	99.75	5.749	41	111.79	0.000	55	140.07	0.000
14	84.84	0.000	28	100.25	5.749	42	111.83	0.000	56	145.47	0.000

-11 -10 -9 -8 -7 -6 -5 -4 -3 -2 -1 0 +1 +2 +3 +4 +5 +6 +7 +8 +9 +10 +11

5-358

$J_{AA'}$	J_{AB}	$J_{AB'}$	$J_{BB'}$
6	-1	1	1
6	1	-1	1
1	-1	1	6
1	1	-1	6

The maximum summed intensity is 9.187

LINE	FREQ	INTEN	LINE	FREQ	INTEN	LINE	FREQ	INTEN	LINE	FREQ	INTEN
1	89.23	0.005	15	96.81	0.000	29	101.57	0.917	43	103.64	0.000
2	89.30	0.000	16	96.86	1.871	30	102.09	0.000	44	103.81	0.000
3	90.14	0.000	17	96.92	1.937	31	102.19	0.000	45	103.81	1.083
4	90.81	0.000	18	97.00	2.000	32	102.38	0.000	46	103.99	0.000
5	90.91	0.000	19	97.00	2.000	33	102.45	1.844	47	104.62	0.000
6	90.92	0.000	20	97.10	1.980	34	102.86	2.054	48	104.77	0.285
7	91.54	0.000	21	97.14	2.054	35	102.90	1.980	49	105.39	0.000
8	91.55	0.004	22	97.48	0.000	36	103.00	2.000	50	108.28	0.020
9	91.72	0.020	23	97.55	1.844	37	103.00	2.000	51	108.45	0.004
10	92.46	0.000	24	97.81	0.000	38	103.07	0.000	52	109.08	0.000
11	95.23	0.285	25	98.05	0.000	39	103.08	1.937	53	109.19	0.000
12	95.24	0.000	26	98.43	0.917	40	103.14	1.871	54	109.23	0.000
13	96.19	1.083	27	100.83	0.000	41	103.15	0.000	55	110.77	0.005
14	96.19	0.000	28	101.32	0.000	42	103.19	0.000	56	115.17	0.000

-11 -10 -9 -8 -7 -6 -5 -4 -3 -2 -1 0 +1 +2 +3 +4 +5 +6 +7 +8 +9 +10 +11

5-359

$J_{AA'}$	J_{AB}	$J_{AB'}$	$J_{BB'}$
6	-1	1	2
6	1	-1	2
2	-1	1	6
2	1	-1	6

The maximum summed intensity is 9.252

LINE	FREQ	INTEN	LINE	FREQ	INTEN	LINE	FREQ	INTEN	LINE	FREQ	INTEN
1	88.43	0.004	15	96.76	0.000	29	100.82	0.684	43	103.48	0.000
2	88.51	0.000	16	96.88	1.890	30	101.10	0.000	44	103.65	1.316
3	90.33	0.000	17	96.93	1.942	31	101.24	0.000	45	104.76	0.
4	90.76	0.000	18	97.00	2.000	32	102.59	0.000	46	104.97	0.000
5	90.90	0.000	19	97.00	2.000	33	102.62	1.983	47	105.41	0.000
6	90.93	0.000	20	97.12	2.052	34	102.86	1.965	48	105.57	0.126
7	91.34	0.000	21	97.14	1.965	35	102.88	2.052	49	105.99	0.000
8	91.38	0.002	22	97.29	0.000	36	103.00	2.000	50	107.34	0.035
9	92.66	0.035	23	97.38	1.983	37	103.00	2.000	51	108.62	0.002
10	93.28	0.000	24	98.76	0.000	38	103.04	0.000	52	109.07	0.000
11	94.43	0.126	25	99.02	0.000	39	103.07	1.942	53	109.22	0.000
12	94.46	0.000	26	99.18	0.684	40	103.12	1.890	54	109.24	0.000
13	95.24	0.	27	100.21	0.000	41	103.16	0.	55	111.57	0.004
14	96.35	1.316	28	100.53	0.000	42	103.24	0.000	56	115.17	0.000

−11 −10 −9 −8 −7 −6 −5 −4 −3 −2 −1 0 +1 +2 +3 +4 +5 +6 +7 +8 +9 +10 +11

5-360

$J_{AA'}$	J_{AB}	$J_{AB'}$	$J_{BB'}$
6	-1	2	1
6	2	-1	1
1	-1	2	6
1	2	-1	6

The maximum summed intensity is 6.776

LINE	FREQ	INTEN	LINE	FREQ	INTEN	LINE	FREQ	INTEN	LINE	FREQ	INTEN
1	88.32	0.005	15	96.46	1.671	29	101.33	1.217	43	103.56	0.000
2	89.16	0.000	16	96.63	0.000	30	101.70	0.000	44	103.63	0.000
3	89.22	0.000	17	96.65	1.709	31	102.33	1.608	45	103.83	0.000
4	90.30	0.000	18	97.21	1.963	32	102.42	0.000	46	104.50	0.783
5	90.54	0.000	19	97.26	2.090	33	102.46	0.000	47	105.58	0.000
6	91.26	0.000	20	97.34	2.219	34	102.54	2.329	48	105.60	0.354
7	91.38	0.037	21	97.46	2.329	35	102.66	2.219	49	106.72	0.000
8	91.59	0.014	22	97.54	0.000	36	102.74	2.090	50	108.41	0.014
9	92.38	0.000	23	97.67	1.608	37	102.79	1.963	51	108.62	0.037
10	92.43	0.000	24	97.77	0.000	38	103.35	1.709	52	108.74	0.000
11	94.40	0.354	25	98.11	0.000	39	103.37	0.000	53	109.46	0.000
12	94.61	0.000	26	98.67	1.217	40	103.45	0.000	54	109.51	0.000
13	95.50	0.783	27	100.29	0.000	41	103.50	0.000	55	111.68	0.005
14	96.37	0.000	28	100.56	0.000	42	103.54	1.671	56	114.90	0.000

−11 −10 −9 −8 −7 −6 −5 −4 −3 −2 −1 0 +1 +2 +3 +4 +5 +6 +7 +8 +9 +10 +11

5-361

$J_{AA'}$	J_{AB}	$J_{AB'}$	$J_{BB'}$
6	-1	2	2
6	2	-1	2
2	-1	2	6
2	2	-1	6

The maximum summed intensity is 8.110

LINE	FREQ	INTEN	LINE	FREQ	INTEN	LINE	FREQ	INTEN	LINE	FREQ	INTEN
1	87.65	0.005	15	96.46	1.671	29	100.70	1.055	43	103.57	0.000
2	88.51	0.000	16	96.54	0.000	30	100.72	0.000	44	104.30	0.945
3	89.47	0.000	17	96.69	1.744	31	101.54	0.000	45	104.47	0.000
4	90.28	0.000	18	97.23	2.083	32	102.54	2.329	46	104.54	0.000
5	90.46	0.000	19	97.28	1.939	33	102.60	1.719	47	106.27	0.207
6	91.27	0.000	20	97.35	2.233	34	102.65	2.233	48	106.30	0.000
7	91.31	0.009	21	97.40	1.719	35	102.70	0.000	49	107.11	0.000
8	92.12	0.000	22	97.46	2.329	36	102.72	1.939	50	107.72	0.061
9	92.28	0.061	23	97.53	0.000	37	102.77	2.083	51	108.69	0.009
10	93.13	0.000	24	98.46	0.000	38	103.31	1.744	52	108.73	0.000
11	93.73	0.207	25	99.05	0.000	39	103.45	0.000	53	109.49	0.000
12	93.93	0.000	26	99.30	1.055	40	103.46	0.000	54	109.54	0.000
13	95.46	0.000	27	99.84	0.000	41	103.51	0.000	55	112.35	0.005
14	95.70	0.945	28	99.91	0.000	42	103.54	1.671	56	114.91	0.000

−11 −10 −9 −8 −7 −6 −5 −4 −3 −2 −1 0 +1 +2 +3 +4 +5 +6 +7 +8 +9 +10 +11

5-362

$J_{AA'}$	J_{AB}	$J_{AB'}$	$J_{BB'}$
6	-1	2	4
6	2	-1	4
4	-1	2	6
4	2	-1	6

The maximum summed intensity is 5.872

LINE	FREQ	INTEN	LINE	FREQ	INTEN	LINE	FREQ	INTEN	LINE	FREQ	INTEN
1	86.04	0.004	15	96.24	0.000	29	100.16	0.000	43	103.76	0.000
2	86.83	0.000	16	96.46	1.671	30	100.70	1.055	44	104.30	0.945
3	89.81	0.000	17	96.74	1.794	31	100.95	0.000	45	106.07	0.188
4	90.16	0.000	18	97.07	1.806	32	102.47	1.812	46	106.24	0.000
5	90.23	0.000	19	97.18	2.068	33	102.54	2.329	47	106.40	0.000
6	90.99	0.004	20	97.28	0.000	34	102.63	2.254	48	107.88	0.071
7	91.29	0.000	21	97.37	2.254	35	102.82	2.068	49	108.00	0.000
8	91.83	0.000	22	97.46	2.329	36	102.93	1.806	50	108.42	0.000
9	92.12	0.071	23	97.53	1.812	37	103.00	0.000	51	108.71	0.000
10	92.28	0.000	24	98.35	0.000	38	103.26	1.794	52	109.01	0.004
11	93.76	0.000	25	98.47	0.000	39	103.30	0.000	53	109.49	0.000
12	93.93	0.188	26	98.77	0.	40	103.42	0.000	54	109.84	0.000
13	94.76	0.000	27	99.30	1.055	41	103.47	0.000	55	113.96	0.004
14	95.70	0.945	28	99.84	0.000	42	103.54	1.671	56	114.94	0.000

−11 −10 −9 −8 −7 −6 −5 −4 −3 −2 −1 0 +1 +2 +3 +4 +5 +6 +7 +8 +9 +10 +11

5-363

$J_{AA'}$	J_{AB}	$J_{AB'}$	$J_{BB'}$
6	-1	2	6
6	2	-1	6

The maximum summed intensity is 4.608.

LINE	FREQ	INTEN	LINE	FREQ	INTEN	LINE	FREQ	INTEN	LINE	FREQ	INTEN
1	84.25	0.002	15	96.46	1.671	29	101.46	0.000	43	104.46	0.
2	84.99	0.000	16	96.52	0.000	30	101.85	1.447	44	104.85	0.553
3	89.46	0.000	17	96.65	0.000	31	101.85	1.447	45	104.85	0.553
4	89.94	0.000	18	96.78	0.000	32	102.54	2.329	46	107.54	0.000
5	90.15	0.000	19	96.78	1.826	33	102.61	2.270	47	108.30	0.000
6	90.34	0.028	20	96.85	0.000	34	102.83	0.000	48	108.70	0.000
7	90.46	0.000	21	96.91	1.816	35	102.86	2.055	49	109.17	0.002
8	90.83	0.002	22	97.14	2.055	36	103.09	1.816	50	109.54	0.
9	91.30	0.000	23	97.17	0.000	37	103.15	0.000	51	109.66	0.028
10	91.70	0.000	24	97.39	2.270	38	103.22	1.826	52	109.85	0.000
11	92.46	0.000	25	97.46	2.329	39	103.22	0.	53	110.06	0.000
12	95.15	0.553	26	98.15	1.447	40	103.35	0.000	54	110.54	0.000
13	95.15	0.553	27	98.15	1.447	41	103.48	0.000	55	115.01	0.000
14	95.54	0.000	28	98.54	0.000	42	103.54	1.671	56	115.75	0.002

−11 −10 −9 −8 −7 −6 −5 −4 −3 −2 −1 0 +1 +2 +3 +4 +5 +6 +7 +8 +9 +10 +11

5-364

$J_{AA'}$	J_{AB}	$J_{AB'}$	$J_{BB'}$
6	-2	1	1
6	1	-2	1
1	-2	1	6
1	1	-2	6

The maximum summed intensity is 4.661

LINE	FREQ	INTEN	LINE	FREQ	INTEN	LINE	FREQ	INTEN	LINE	FREQ	INTEN
1	88.18	0.000	15	96.37	0.000	29	101.33	1.217	43	103.69	1.582
2	88.79	0.010	16	96.46	1.671	30	101.42	0.000	44	104.32	0.000
3	89.63	0.000	17	96.63	0.000	31	101.84	2.427	45	104.50	0.783
4	90.22	0.000	18	96.64	1.676	32	102.46	0.000	46	104.53	0.000
5	90.54	0.000	19	97.21	1.963	33	102.54	2.329	47	104.58	0.000
6	91.30	0.000	20	97.27	2.067	34	102.70	0.000	48	105.13	0.225
7	91.35	0.000	21	97.46	2.329	35	102.73	2.067	49	106.25	0.000
8	91.38	0.037	22	97.54	0.000	36	102.79	1.963	50	107.92	0.013
9	92.08	0.013	23	97.77	0.000	37	102.96	0.000	51	108.62	0.037
10	92.92	0.000	24	98.11	0.000	38	103.09	0.000	52	109.46	0.000
11	94.60	0.000	25	98.16	2.427	39	103.36	1.676	53	109.52	0.000
12	94.87	0.225	26	98.67	1.217	40	103.37	0.000	54	109.78	0.000
13	95.50	0.783	27	99.80	0.000	41	103.54	1.671	55	111.21	0.010
14	96.31	1.582	28	101.03	0.000	42	103.63	0.000	56	115.94	0.000

−11 −10 −9 −8 −7 −6 −5 −4 −3 −2 −1 0 +1 +2 +3 +4 +5 +6 +7 +8 +9 +10 +11

5-365

$J_{AA'}$	J_{AB}	$J_{AB'}$	$J_{BB'}$
6	-2	2	2
6	2	-2	2
2	-2	2	6
2	2	-2	6

The maximum summed intensity is 4.120

LINE	FREQ	INTEN	LINE	FREQ	INTEN	LINE	FREQ	INTEN	LINE	FREQ	INTEN
1	87.26	0.009	15	96.17	0.000	29	100.59	1.316	43	104.17	0.000
2	87.46	0.000	16	96.53	1.614	30	101.39	0.000	44	104.35	0.000
3	88.88	0.000	17	96.70	1.769	31	101.76	0.000	45	104.91	0.000
4	90.17	0.000	18	97.00	2.000	32	101.83	0.000	46	105.06	0.684
5	90.61	0.000	19	97.00	2.000	33	102.03	2.223	47	106.24	0.000
6	90.70	0.001	20	97.44	1.919	34	102.53	2.204	48	106.74	0.162
7	91.79	0.081	21	97.47	2.204	35	102.56	1.919	49	107.97	0.000
8	91.94	0.000	22	97.77	0.000	36	103.00	2.000	50	108.03	0.017
9	91.97	0.017	23	97.97	2.223	37	103.00	2.000	51	108.21	0.081
10	93.26	0.162	24	98.17	0.000	38	103.27	0.000	52	109.30	0.001
11	93.30	0.000	25	98.79	0.000	39	103.30	1.769	53	109.83	0.000
12	93.58	0.000	26	99.08	0.000	40	103.47	1.614	54	109.85	0.000
13	94.94	0.684	27	99.41	1.316	41	103.50	0.000	55	112.74	0.009
14	95.83	0.000	28	99.65	0.000	42	103.83	0.000	56	115.69	0.000

5-366

$J_{AA'}$	J_{AB}	$J_{AB'}$	$J_{BB'}$
6	-2	2	4
6	2	-2	4
4	-2	2	6
4	2	-2	6

The maximum summed intensity is 4.262

LINE	FREQ	INTEN	LINE	FREQ	INTEN	LINE	FREQ	INTEN	LINE	FREQ	INTEN
1	85.67	0.006	15	95.76	0.000	29	100.24	0.000	43	104.24	0.000
2	85.91	0.000	16	96.62	1.692	30	100.59	1.316	44	105.06	0.684
3	89.19	0.000	17	96.74	1.802	31	100.91	0.000	45	105.76	0.000
4	89.76	0.000	18	97.00	2.000	32	102.17	0.000	46	106.71	0.200
5	90.53	0.	19	97.00	2.000	33	102.24	1.800	47	106.79	0.000
6	90.74	0.001	20	97.38	2.184	34	102.31	2.241	48	107.83	0.000
7	91.57	0.000	21	97.45	0.000	35	102.62	2.184	49	108.31	0.008
8	91.67	0.067	22	97.48	0.000	36	103.00	2.000	50	108.33	0.067
9	91.69	0.008	23	97.69	2.241	37	103.00	2.000	51	109.16	0.
10	91.79	0.000	24	97.76	1.800	38	103.14	0.	52	109.26	0.001
11	93.29	0.200	25	98.14	0.000	39	103.26	1.802	53	109.85	0.000
12	94.24	0.000	26	99.41	1.316	40	103.38	1.692	54	110.24	0.000
13	94.94	0.684	27	99.47	0.000	41	103.51	0.000	55	114.33	0.006
14	95.22	0.000	28	99.76	0.000	42	104.16	0.000	56	115.73	0.

5-367

$J_{AA'}$	J_{AB}	$J_{AB'}$	$J_{BB'}$
6	-2	4	2
6	4	-2	2
2	-2	4	6
2	4	-2	6

The maximum summed intensity is 6.732

LINE	FREQ	INTEN	LINE	FREQ	INTEN	LINE	FREQ	INTEN	LINE	FREQ	INTEN
1	85.12	0.006	15	95.84	1.231	29	100.44	1.614	43	104.44	0.000
2	86.45	0.000	16	95.84	1.368	30	100.83	0.000	44	104.56	0.000
3	87.12	0.000	17	96.44	0.000	31	101.84	1.949	45	104.83	0.000
4	89.17	0.000	18	97.23	0.000	32	101.84	0.000	46	106.77	0.386
5	89.23	0.000	19	97.44	2.206	33	102.16	2.369	47	108.16	0.051
6	90.56	0.096	20	97.77	1.904	34	102.16	2.632	48	108.16	0.000
7	91.12	0.004	21	97.84	2.369	35	102.23	1.904	49	108.56	0.184
8	91.44	0.184	22	97.84	0.000	36	102.56	2.206	50	108.88	0.004
9	91.84	0.051	23	97.84	2.632	37	102.77	0.000	51	109.44	0.096
10	91.84	0.000	24	98.11	0.000	38	103.56	0.000	52	110.77	0.000
11	93.17	0.000	25	98.16	1.949	39	103.89	0.000	53	110.83	0.000
12	93.23	0.386	26	98.16	0.000	40	104.16	1.231	54	110.88	0.000
13	93.44	0.000	27	99.17	0.000	41	104.16	0.000	55	114.88	0.006
14	95.56	0.000	28	99.56	1.614	42	104.16	1.368	56	115.55	0.000

-11 -10 -9 -8 -7 -6 -5 -4 -3 -2 -1 0 +1 +2 +3 +4 +5 +6 +7 +8 +9 +10 +11

5-368

$J_{AA'}$	J_{AB}	$J_{AB'}$	$J_{BB'}$
6	-2	4	4
6	4	-2	4
4	-2	4	6
4	4	-2	6

The maximum summed intensity is 6.403

LINE	FREQ	INTEN	LINE	FREQ	INTEN	LINE	FREQ	INTEN	LINE	FREQ	INTEN
1	83.80	0.005	15	95.00	0.000	29	100.44	1.614	43	105.00	0.000
2	85.75	0.000	16	95.84	1.368	30	100.83	0.000	44	105.00	0.000
3	86.96	0.000	17	96.01	1.344	31	101.32	0.000	45	105.64	0.000
4	88.68	0.000	18	96.83	0.000	32	101.84	1.822	46	106.77	0.386
5	89.00	0.000	19	96.96	0.000	33	102.16	2.632	47	108.16	0.178
6	90.13	0.105	20	97.52	2.301	34	102.27	1.916	48	108.60	0.031
7	90.57	0.000	21	97.67	2.295	35	102.33	2.295	49	108.80	0.003
8	91.20	0.003	22	97.73	1.916	36	102.39	0.000	50	109.61	0.000
9	91.40	0.031	23	97.78	0.000	37	102.48	2.301	51	109.87	0.105
10	91.84	0.178	24	97.84	2.632	38	103.99	1.344	52	110.83	0.000
11	92.96	0.000	25	98.16	1.822	39	104.04	0.000	53	111.32	0.000
12	93.23	0.386	26	98.68	0.000	40	104.16	1.368	54	111.64	0.000
13	94.57	0.000	27	99.00	0.000	41	104.43	0.000	55	115.64	0.000
14	95.00	0.000	28	99.56	1.614	42	104.57	0.000	56	116.20	0.005

-11 -10 -9 -8 -7 -6 -5 -4 -3 -2 -1 0 +1 +2 +3 +4 +5 +6 +7 +8 +9 +10 +11

5-369

$J_{AA'}$	J_{AB}	$J_{AB'}$	$J_{BB'}$
6	-2	4	6
6	4	-2	6

The maximum summed intensity is 5.662.

LINE	FREQ	INTEN	LINE	FREQ	INTEN	LINE	FREQ	INTEN	LINE	FREQ	INTEN
1	82.30	0.004	15	95.51	0.000	29	100.16	0.000	43	105.84	0.000
2	84.17	0.000	16	95.71	0.000	30	101.24	1.707	44	106.16	0.000
3	87.22	0.000	17	95.84	1.368	31	101.24	1.707	45	107.24	0.293
4	87.84	0.000	18	96.01	0.000	32	102.16	2.632	46	107.24	0.293
5	88.63	0.059	19	96.14	1.429	33	102.42	2.374	47	107.34	0.000
6	88.76	0.000	20	97.24	0.000	34	102.46	0.000	48	108.75	0.002
7	89.06	0.000	21	97.41	1.878	35	102.46	2.235	49	108.91	0.020
8	91.09	0.020	22	97.54	2.235	36	102.59	1.878	50	110.94	0.000
9	91.25	0.002	23	97.54	0.000	37	102.76	0.000	51	111.24	0.000
10	92.66	0.000	24	97.58	2.374	38	103.86	1.429	52	111.37	0.059
11	92.76	0.293	25	97.84	2.632	39	103.99	0.000	53	112.16	0.000
12	92.76	0.293	26	98.76	1.707	40	104.16	1.368	54	112.78	0.000
13	93.84	0.000	27	98.76	1.707	41	104.29	0.000	55	115.83	0.000
14	94.16	0.000	28	99.84	0.000	42	104.49	0.000	56	117.70	0.004

−11 −10 −9 −8 −7 −6 −5 −4 −3 −2 −1 0 +1 +2 +3 +4 +5 +6 +7 +8 +9 +10 +11

5-370

$J_{AA'}$	J_{AB}	$J_{AB'}$	$J_{BB'}$
6	-4	2	2
6	2	-4	2
2	-4	2	6
2	2	-4	6

The maximum summed intensity is 6.485

LINE	FREQ	INTEN	LINE	FREQ	INTEN	LINE	FREQ	INTEN	LINE	FREQ	INTEN
1	84.88	0.000	15	95.56	0.000	29	99.84	0.000	43	104.80	1.110
2	86.22	0.017	16	95.84	1.140	30	100.44	1.614	44	105.49	0.000
3	87.55	0.000	17	95.84	1.368	31	101.18	3.389	45	106.13	0.000
4	88.88	0.001	18	96.44	0.000	32	102.16	2.194	46	106.16	0.000
5	89.23	0.000	19	97.18	0.000	33	102.16	2.632	47	106.77	0.386
6	90.56	0.096	20	97.23	0.000	34	102.23	1.904	48	107.46	0.102
7	91.17	0.000	21	97.77	1.904	35	102.77	0.000	49	107.50	0.046
8	91.20	0.000	22	97.84	2.194	36	102.83	0.000	50	109.44	0.096
9	91.84	0.000	23	97.84	2.632	37	103.46	0.000	51	109.78	0.000
10	92.50	0.046	24	98.16	0.000	38	103.50	0.000	52	110.77	0.000
11	92.54	0.102	25	98.82	3.389	39	103.56	0.000	53	110.83	0.000
12	93.23	0.386	26	99.17	0.000	40	104.16	1.140	54	111.12	0.001
13	93.83	0.000	27	99.21	0.000	41	104.15	1.368	55	113.78	0.017
14	95.20	1.110	28	99.56	1.614	42	104.44	0.000	56	117.79	0.000

−11 −10 −9 −8 −7 −6 −5 −4 −3 −2 −1 0 +1 +2 +3 +4 +5 +6 +7 +8 +9 +10 +11

5-371

$J_{AA'}$	J_{AB}	$J_{AB'}$	$J_{BB'}$
6	-4	2	4
6	2	-4	4
4	-4	2	6
4	2	-4	6

The maximum summed intensity is 4.085

LINE	FREQ	INTEN	LINE	FREQ	INTEN	LINE	FREQ	INTEN	LINE	FREQ	INTEN
1	83.53	0.000	15	95.30	1.154	29	100.44	1.614	43	105.00	0.000
2	84.63	0.012	16	95.49	0.000	30	100.86	0.000	44	105.49	0.000
3	87.79	0.000	17	95.84	1.368	31	101.00	0.000	45	106.77	0.386
4	88.68	0.000	18	95.91	0.000	32	101.32	0.000	46	107.61	0.000
5	88.97	0.001	19	95.98	1.236	33	101.35	3.345	47	107.68	0.030
6	90.54	0.000	20	97.69	2.172	34	101.84	1.822	48	107.87	0.000
7	90.74	0.000	21	97.75	0.000	35	102.16	2.632	49	108.16	0.178
8	90.95	0.050	22	97.79	0.000	36	102.31	2.172	50	109.05	0.050
9	91.00	0.000	23	97.84	2.632	37	103.12	0.000	51	110.81	0.000
10	91.84	0.178	24	98.16	1.822	38	103.60	0.000	52	110.86	0.000
11	92.32	0.030	25	98.65	3.345	39	104.02	1.236	53	111.03	0.001
12	93.23	0.386	26	98.68	0.000	40	104.16	1.368	54	111.32	0.000
13	95.00	0.000	27	99.56	1.614	41	104.70	1.154	55	115.37	0.012
14	95.00	0.000	28	100.39	0.000	42	105.00	0.000	56	117.87	0.000

5-372

$J_{AA'}$	J_{AB}	$J_{AB'}$	$J_{BB'}$
6	-4	4	4
6	4	-4	4
4	-4	4	6
4	4	-4	6

The maximum summed intensity is 5.303

LINE	FREQ	INTEN	LINE	FREQ	INTEN	LINE	FREQ	INTEN	LINE	FREQ	INTEN
1	83.04	0.011	15	95.02	0.000	29	100.53	0.000	43	106.12	0.000
2	83.36	0.000	16	95.72	1.124	30	100.63	0.000	44	106.17	0.000
3	85.38	0.000	17	95.83	1.252	31	100.66	0.000	45	106.51	0.000
4	87.88	0.000	18	96.12	0.000	32	101.49	2.798	46	107.49	0.058
5	89.04	0.068	19	96.70	0.000	33	101.53	1.857	47	108.60	0.241
6	89.25	0.000	20	97.00	2.000	34	101.72	2.679	48	109.47	0.000
7	89.34	0.000	21	97.00	2.000	35	102.12	0.000	49	109.78	0.143
8	89.83	0.010	22	97.88	0.000	36	103.00	2.000	50	110.17	0.010
9	90.22	0.143	23	98.19	0.000	37	103.00	2.000	51	110.96	0.068
10	91.40	0.241	24	98.28	2.679	38	103.88	0.000	52	111.94	0.000
11	92.31	0.000	25	98.47	1.857	39	103.96	0.000	53	112.12	0.000
12	92.51	0.058	26	98.51	2.798	40	104.17	1.252	54	113.43	0.000
13	93.88	0.000	27	99.65	1.759	41	104.28	1.124	55	116.96	0.011
14	94.85	0.000	28	100.35	1.759	42	104.49	0.000	56	117.82	0.000

5-373

$J_{AA'}$	J_{AB}	$J_{AB'}$	$J_{BB'}$
6	-4	4	6
6	4	-4	6

The maximum summed intensity is 4.128

LINE	FREQ	INTEN	LINE	FREQ	INTEN	LINE	FREQ	INTEN	LINE	FREQ	INTEN
1	81.53	0.008	15	95.00	0.000	29	101.00	1.800	43	106.31	0.000
2	81.97	0.000	16	95.53	0.000	30	101.00	1.800	44	107.00	0.000
3	85.53	0.000	17	95.87	1.223	31	101.00	0.000	45	107.69	0.041
4	87.00	0.	18	95.97	1.331	32	101.00	0.000	46	108.03	0.000
5	87.53	0.042	19	96.31	0.000	33	101.69	2.727	47	109.00	0.200
6	87.87	0.000	20	97.00	2.000	34	101.87	2.620	48	109.00	0.200
7	89.00	0.000	21	97.00	2.000	35	102.13	0.000	49	110.03	0.008
8	89.97	0.008	22	97.87	0.000	36	103.00	2.000	50	111.00	0.000
9	91.00	0.200	23	98.13	2.620	37	103.00	2.000	51	112.13	0.000
10	91.00	0.200	24	98.31	2.727	38	103.69	0.000	52	112.47	0.042
11	91.97	0.000	25	99.00	1.800	39	104.03	1.331	53	113.00	0.000
12	92.31	0.041	26	99.00	1.800	40	104.13	1.223	54	114.47	0.000
13	93.00	0.000	27	99.00	0.000	41	104.47	0.000	55	118.03	0.000
14	93.69	0.000	28	99.00	0.000	42	105.00	0.000	56	118.47	0.008

−11 −10 −9 −8 −7 −6 −5 −4 −3 −2 −1 0 +1 +2 +3 +4 +5 +6 +7 +8 +9 +10 +11

5-374

$J_{AA'}$	J_{AB}	$J_{AB'}$	$J_{BB'}$
6	-4	6	6
6	6	-4	6

The maximum summed intensity is 3.607

LINE	FREQ	INTEN	LINE	FREQ	INTEN	LINE	FREQ	INTEN	LINE	FREQ	INTEN
1	79.43	0.005	15	94.43	0.000	29	100.83	1.857	43	106.70	0.000
2	81.64	0.000	16	95.11	0.928	30	100.83	1.857	44	106.98	0.000
3	82.77	0.000	17	95.32	0.000	31	101.17	0.000	45	107.84	0.000
4	85.76	0.053	18	95.84	0.000	32	101.44	3.048	46	108.01	0.073
5	85.84	0.000	19	95.84	1.368	33	101.69	2.365	47	109.69	0.022
6	86.44	0.000	20	96.63	1.507	34	101.89	0.000	48	110.83	0.143
7	87.17	0.000	21	97.84	0.000	35	102.16	0.000	49	110.83	0.143
8	89.17	0.143	22	97.84	2.632	36	102.16	2.632	50	112.83	0.000
9	89.17	0.143	23	98.11	0.000	37	103.37	1.507	51	113.56	0.000
10	90.31	0.022	24	98.31	2.365	38	104.16	0.000	52	114.16	0.000
11	91.99	0.073	25	98.56	3.048	39	104.16	1.368	53	114.24	0.053
12	92.16	0.000	26	98.83	0.000	40	104.68	0.000	54	117.23	0.000
13	93.02	0.000	27	99.17	1.857	41	104.89	0.928	55	118.36	0.000
14	93.30	0.000	28	99.17	1.857	42	105.57	0.000	56	120.57	0.005

−11 −10 −9 −8 −7 −6 −5 −4 −3 −2 −1 0 +1 +2 +3 +4 +5 +6 +7 +8 +9 +10 +11

5-375

$J_{AA'}$	J_{AB}	$J_{AB'}$	$J_{BB'}$
6	-4	6	9
6	6	-4	9
9	6	-4	6
9	-4	6	6

The maximum summed intensity is 4.075.

LINE	FREQ	INTEN	LINE	FREQ	INTEN	LINE	FREQ	INTEN	LINE	FREQ	INTEN
1	77.23	0.004	15	93.11	0.000	29	100.00	1.835	43	107.55	0.000
2	79.48	0.000	16	94.56	0.000	30	100.88	0.000	44	108.33	0.050
3	82.67	0.000	17	95.36	1.054	31	101.51	1.904	45	108.57	0.000
4	83.55	0.031	18	95.84	1.368	32	101.68	2.875	46	109.46	0.017
5	84.12	0.000	19	96.72	0.000	33	101.77	0.000	47	109.56	0.000
6	84.29	0.000	20	96.87	1.703	34	102.01	2.266	48	110.44	0.165
7	86.28	0.000	21	97.11	0.000	35	102.16	2.632	49	111.95	0.096
8	88.05	0.096	22	97.75	0.000	36	103.13	1.703	50	114.20	0.000
9	89.56	0.165	23	97.84	2.632	37	103.76	0.000	51	115.23	0.000
10	90.44	0.000	24	97.99	2.266	38	104.16	1.368	52	115.88	0.000
11	90.54	0.017	25	98.32	2.875	39	104.40	0.000	53	116.45	0.031
12	90.94	0.000	26	98.49	1.904	40	104.64	1.054	54	118.83	0.000
13	91.67	0.050	27	99.12	0.000	41	105.38	0.000	55	119.01	0.000
14	92.93	0.000	28	100.00	1.835	42	105.44	0.000	56	122.77	0.004

−11 −10 −9 −8 −7 −6 −5 −4 −3 −2 −1 0 +1 +2 +3 +4 +5 +6 +7 +8 +9 +10 +11

5-376

$J_{AA'}$	J_{AB}	$J_{AB'}$	$J_{BB'}$
6	-4	6	12
6	6	-4	12
12	6	-4	6
12	-4	6	6

The maximum summed intensity is 5.137.

LINE	FREQ	INTEN	LINE	FREQ	INTEN	LINE	FREQ	INTEN	LINE	FREQ	INTEN
1	74.85	0.003	15	92.68	0.000	29	100.01	0.000	43	108.58	0.000
2	77.06	0.000	16	93.67	0.000	30	100.83	1.857	44	108.59	0.035
3	81.18	0.018	17	95.00	0.000	31	101.88	2.736	45	109.29	0.013
4	81.90	0.000	18	95.55	1.159	32	101.98	1.944	46	110.13	0.000
5	82.01	0.000	19	95.84	1.368	33	102.16	2.632	47	110.83	0.143
6	82.01	0.000	20	97.04	1.859	34	102.19	0.000	48	111.67	0.000
7	85.00	0.000	21	97.52	0.000	35	102.26	2.177	49	113.64	0.056
8	86.36	0.056	22	97.74	2.177	36	102.96	1.859	50	115.29	0.000
9	88.33	0.000	23	97.84	2.632	37	104.16	1.368	51	117.81	0.000
10	88.61	0.000	24	98.02	1.944	38	104.23	0.000	52	117.99	0.000
11	89.17	0.143	25	98.12	2.736	39	104.45	1.159	53	118.82	0.018
12	90.71	0.013	26	98.58	0.000	40	105.18	0.000	54	120.13	0.000
13	91.41	0.035	27	99.17	1.857	41	105.29	0.000	55	120.80	0.000
14	92.01	0.000	28	99.99	0.000	42	106.33	0.000	56	125.15	0.003

−11 −10 −9 −8 −7 −6 −5 −4 −3 −2 −1 0 +1 +2 +3 +4 +5 +6 +7 +8 +9 +10 +11

5-377

$J_{AA'}$	J_{AB}	$J_{AB'}$	$J_{BB'}$
6	-4	6	15
6	6	-4	15
15	6	-4	6
15	-4	6	6

The maximum summed intensity is 5.436.

LINE	FREQ	INTEN	LINE	FREQ	INTEN	LINE	FREQ	INTEN	LINE	FREQ	INTEN
1	72.34	0.002	15	92.52	0.000	29	100.61	0.000	43	108.79	0.026
2	74.49	0.000	16	93.06	0.000	30	101.51	1.904	44	109.16	0.010
3	78.67	0.011	17	93.72	0.000	31	102.03	2.623	45	110.09	0.000
4	79.36	0.000	18	95.71	1.245	32	102.16	2.632	46	111.28	0.000
5	79.61	0.000	19	95.84	1.368	33	102.29	1.969	47	111.95	0.096
6	80.78	0.000	20	97.16	1.982	34	102.47	2.102	48	114.06	0.000
7	83.28	0.000	21	97.39	0.000	35	102.49	0.000	49	115.74	0.031
8	84.26	0.031	22	97.53	2.102	36	102.84	1.982	50	116.85	0.000
9	85.94	0.000	23	97.71	1.969	37	104.14	0.000	51	120.39	0.000
10	86.12	0.000	24	97.84	2.632	38	104.16	1.368	52	120.51	0.000
11	88.05	0.096	25	97.97	2.623	39	104.29	1.245	53	121.33	0.011
12	90.84	0.010	26	98.49	1.904	40	104.98	0.000	54	121.72	0.000
13	91.21	0.026	27	99.39	0.000	41	106.41	0.000	55	123.01	0.000
14	91.22	0.000	28	99.65	0.000	42	106.94	0.000	56	127.66	0.002

5-378

$J_{AA'}$	J_{AB}	$J_{AB'}$	$J_{BB'}$
6	-4	9	6
6	9	-4	6

The maximum summed intensity is 5.527.

LINE	FREQ	INTEN	LINE	FREQ	INTEN	LINE	FREQ	INTEN	LINE	FREQ	INTEN
1	75.31	0.002	15	93.28	0.534	29	100.66	1.908	43	107.62	0.000
2	78.06	0.000	16	93.55	0.000	30	100.66	1.908	44	107.87	0.
3	80.58	0.000	17	93.59	0.720	31	101.09	3.247	45	108.59	0.000
4	83.12	0.058	18	94.90	0.000	32	101.34	0.	46	109.20	0.103
5	83.59	0.000	19	95.59	0.000	33	101.39	2.099	47	110.16	0.029
6	84.02	0.000	20	96.59	0.000	34	101.41	3.280	48	113.66	0.092
7	84.34	0.	21	97.65	1.928	35	101.66	0.000	49	113.66	0.092
8	86.34	0.092	22	98.34	0.000	36	102.35	1.928	50	115.66	0.000
9	86.34	0.092	23	98.59	3.280	37	103.41	0.000	51	115.98	0.000
10	89.84	0.029	24	98.61	2.099	38	104.41	0.000	52	116.41	0.000
11	90.80	0.103	25	98.66	0.	39	105.10	0.000	53	116.88	0.058
12	91.41	0.000	26	98.91	3.247	40	106.41	0.720	54	119.42	0.000
13	92.13	0.000	27	99.34	1.908	41	106.45	0.000	55	121.94	0.000
14	92.38	0.000	28	99.34	1.908	42	106.72	0.534	56	124.69	0.002

5-379

$J_{AA'}$	J_{AB}	$J_{AB'}$	$J_{BB'}$
6	-4	9	9
6	9	-4	9
9	9	-4	6
9	-4	9	6

The maximum summed intensity is 6.509.

LINE	FREQ	INTEN	LINE	FREQ	INTEN	LINE	FREQ	INTEN	LINE	FREQ	INTEN
1	73.40	0.002	15	93.59	0.720	29	100.00	1.899	43	107.29	0.000
2	78.14	0.000	16	93.67	0.649	30	101.23	1.929	44	108.51	0.000
3	78.67	0.000	17	94.48	0.000	31	101.41	3.280	45	109.56	0.080
4	81.21	0.039	18	95.17	0.000	32	101.48	2.771	46	109.83	0.016
5	81.92	0.000	19	95.27	0.000	33	101.75	2.015	47	110.27	0.000
6	82.17	0.000	20	96.67	0.000	34	102.02	2.428	48	113.34	0.101
7	83.33	0.000	21	96.92	0.000	35	102.09	0.000	49	114.58	0.071
8	85.42	0.071	22	97.98	2.428	36	103.08	0.000	50	116.59	0.000
9	86.66	0.101	23	97.98	0.000	37	103.25	0.000	51	117.91	0.000
10	89.73	0.000	24	98.25	2.015	38	104.73	0.000	52	118.08	0.000
11	90.17	0.016	25	98.52	2.771	39	106.06	0.000	53	118.79	0.039
12	90.25	0.000	26	98.59	3.280	40	106.33	0.649	54	120.10	0.000
13	90.44	0.080	27	98.77	1.929	41	106.41	0.720	55	123.10	0.000
14	91.48	0.000	28	100.00	1.899	42	106.76	0.000	56	126.60	0.002

−11 −10 −9 −8 −7 −6 −5 −4 −3 −2 −1 0 +1 +2 +3 +4 +5 +6 +7 +8 +9 +10 +11

5-380

$J_{AA'}$	J_{AB}	$J_{AB'}$	$J_{BB'}$
6	-4	12	6
6	12	-4	6

The maximum summed intensity is 8.498.

LINE	FREQ	INTEN	LINE	FREQ	INTEN	LINE	FREQ	INTEN	LINE	FREQ	INTEN
1	70.48	0.001	15	91.00	0.400	29	100.54	1.936	43	109.00	0.320
2	72.93	0.000	16	91.46	0.000	30	100.54	1.936	44	109.00	0.400
3	78.93	0.000	17	91.46	0.	31	101.00	2.011	45	109.98	0.000
4	80.48	0.054	18	93.00	0.000	32	101.00	2.880	46	111.00	0.099
5	81.00	0.000	19	96.02	0.	33	101.00	3.600	47	111.52	0.015
6	81.46	0.000	20	97.00	0.000	34	101.46	0.000	48	116.54	0.064
7	81.46	0.000	21	98.48	2.620	35	101.46	0.000	49	116.54	0.064
8	83.46	0.064	22	98.54	0.000	36	101.52	2.620	50	118.54	0.000
9	83.46	0.064	23	98.54	0.000	37	103.00	0.000	51	118.54	0.
10	88.48	0.015	24	99.00	2.880	38	103.98	0.	52	119.00	0.000
11	89.00	0.099	25	99.00	2.011	39	107.00	0.000	53	119.52	0.054
12	90.02	0.000	26	99.00	3.600	40	108.54	0.	54	121.07	0.000
13	91.00	0.320	27	99.46	1.936	41	108.54	0.000	55	127.07	0.000
14	91.00	0.000	28	99.46	1.936	42	109.00	0.000	56	129.52	0.001

−11 −10 −9 −8 −7 −6 −5 −4 −3 −2 −1 0 +1 +2 +3 +4 +5 +6 +7 +8 +9 +10 +11

5-381

$J_{AA'}$	J_{AB}	$J_{AB'}$	$J_{BB'}$
6	-4	12	12
6	12	-4	12
12	12	-4	6
12	-4	12	6

The maximum summed intensity is 7.697.

LINE	FREQ	INTEN	LINE	FREQ	INTEN	LINE	FREQ	INTEN	LINE	FREQ	INTEN
1	66.93	0.001	15	91.00	0.400	29	100.54	1.936	43	109.07	0.000
2	72.93	0.000	16	92.26	0.492	30	101.00	4.091	44	110.34	0.000
3	75.00	0.000	17	94.34	0.000	31	101.00	3.600	45	111.00	0.000
4	76.93	0.030	18	94.54	0.000	32	101.46	1.960	46	111.66	0.070
5	77.46	0.000	19	95.00	0.000	33	101.66	1.878	47	112.54	0.000
6	78.26	0.000	20	95.00	0.000	34	102.26	1.438	48	116.54	0.064
7	79.00	0.000	21	95.46	0.000	35	103.00	0.000	49	118.54	0.040
8	81.46	0.040	22	97.74	1.438	36	103.74	0.000	50	119.74	0.000
9	83.46	0.064	23	98.26	0.000	37	104.54	0.000	51	122.54	0.000
10	87.46	0.000	24	98.34	1.878	38	105.46	0.000	52	123.00	0.000
11	87.66	0.000	25	98.54	1.960	39	107.00	0.000	53	123.00	0.000
12	88.34	0.070	26	99.00	4.091	40	107.66	0.000	54	123.07	0.030
13	88.93	0.000	27	99.00	3.600	41	107.74	0.492	55	129.07	0.000
14	89.00	0.000	28	99.46	1.936	42	109.00	0.400	56	133.07	0.001

5-382

$J_{AA'}$	J_{AB}	$J_{AB'}$	$J_{BB'}$
6	-4	15	6
6	15	-4	6

The maximum summed intensity is 6.848.

LINE	FREQ	INTEN	LINE	FREQ	INTEN	LINE	FREQ	INTEN	LINE	FREQ	INTEN
1	65.25	0.000	15	89.09	0.000	29	100.46	1.954	43	111.47	0.206
2	67.55	0.	16	90.24	0.000	30	100.46	1.954	44	111.76	0.244
3	76.81	0.000	17	90.76	0.000	31	100.68	1.988	45	112.52	0.000
4	77.78	0.047	18	90.99	0.	32	100.76	3.756	46	113.21	0.081
5	78.24	0.000	19	96.73	0.000	33	100.96	3.508	47	113.49	0.003
6	78.54	0.	20	97.24	0.000	34	101.06	2.166	48	119.46	0.046
7	78.83	0.000	21	98.46	0.000	35	101.24	0.000	49	119.46	0.046
8	80.54	0.046	22	98.76	0.000	36	101.54	0.000	50	121.17	0.000
9	80.54	0.046	23	98.94	2.166	37	102.76	0.000	51	121.46	0.000
10	86.51	0.003	24	99.04	3.508	38	103.27	0.000	52	121.76	0.000
11	86.79	0.081	25	99.24	3.756	39	109.01	0.000	53	122.22	0.047
12	87.48	0.000	26	99.32	1.988	40	109.24	0.000	54	123.19	0.000
13	88.24	0.244	27	99.54	1.954	41	109.76	0.000	55	132.45	0.000
14	88.53	0.206	28	99.54	1.954	42	110.91	0.000	56	134.75	0.000

5-383

$J_{AA'}$	J_{AB}	$J_{AB'}$	$J_{BB'}$
6	-4	15	15
6	15	-4	15
15	15	-4	6
15	-4	15	6

The maximum summed intensity is 6.112.

LINE	FREQ	INTEN	LINE	FREQ	INTEN	LINE	FREQ	INTEN	LINE	FREQ	INTEN
1	60.23	0.000	15	88.24	0.244	29	100.52	5.189	43	111.76	0.244
2	67.37	0.	16	91.22	0.379	30	100.76	3.756	44	112.33	0.000
3	70.61	0.000	17	93.09	0.000	31	100.89	1.959	45	113.05	0.007
4	72.72	0.000	18	93.62	0.000	32	101.53	1.835	46	114.06	0.057
5	72.76	0.023	19	93.72	0.000	33	101.59	1.975	47	114.75	0.000
6	74.38	0.000	20	93.75	0.000	34	103.39	0.000	48	120.13	0.041
7	74.88	0.000	21	94.81	0.000	35	103.75	0.509	49	122.62	0.025
8	77.38	0.025	22	96.25	0.509	36	103.90	0.000	50	122.63	0.000
9	79.87	0.041	23	98.41	1.975	37	106.25	0.000	51	126.91	0.000
10	85.19	0.000	24	98.47	1.835	38	106.28	0.000	52	127.24	0.023
11	85.25	0.000	25	99.09	0.000	39	107.67	0.000	53	127.28	0.000
12	85.94	0.057	26	99.11	1.959	40	108.78	0.379	54	128.10	0.000
13	86.61	0.000	27	99.24	3.756	41	109.39	0.000	55	135.11	0.000
14	86.95	0.007	28	99.48	5.189	42	110.91	0.000	56	139.77	0.000

5-384

$J_{AA'}$	J_{AB}	$J_{AB'}$	$J_{BB'}$
9	-1	2	9
9	2	-1	9

The maximum summed intensity is 4.462.

LINE	FREQ	INTEN	LINE	FREQ	INTEN	LINE	FREQ	INTEN	LINE	FREQ	INTEN
1	78.54	0.001	15	93.97	0.000	29	100.68	0.000	43	106.07	0.000
2	82.02	0.000	16	94.23	0.000	30	101.85	1.447	44	106.15	0.000
3	84.62	0.004	17	95.15	0.553	31	101.85	1.447	45	107.46	0.000
4	86.46	0.000	18	95.15	0.553	32	102.54	2.329	46	108.67	0.000
5	87.15	0.000	19	95.54	0.000	33	102.58	2.300	47	109.37	0.001
6	87.22	0.000	20	96.46	1.671	34	102.92	2.028	48	110.54	0.000
7	87.53	0.000	21	96.72	1.790	35	103.16	1.878	49	111.27	0.000
8	88.73	0.000	22	96.84	1.878	36	103.28	1.790	50	112.47	0.000
9	89.46	0.000	23	97.08	2.028	37	103.54	1.671	51	112.78	0.000
10	90.63	0.001	24	97.42	2.300	38	104.46	0.000	52	112.85	0.000
11	91.33	0.000	25	97.46	2.329	39	104.85	0.553	53	113.54	0.000
12	92.54	0.000	26	98.15	1.447	40	104.85	0.553	54	115.38	0.004
13	93.85	0.000	27	98.15	1.447	41	105.77	0.000	55	117.98	0.000
14	93.93	0.000	28	99.32	0.000	42	106.03	0.	56	121.46	0.001

5-385

$J_{AA'}$	J_{AB}	$J_{AB'}$	$J_{BB'}$
9	-2	4	9
9	4	-2	9

The maximum summed intensity is 4.212.

LINE	FREQ	INTEN	LINE	FREQ	INTEN	LINE	FREQ	INTEN	LINE	FREQ	INTEN
1	77.18	0.002	15	93.04	0.000	29	101.24	1.707	43	107.24	0.293
2	81.28	0.000	16	93.59	0.000	30	101.24	1.707	44	107.24	0.293
3	83.51	0.013	17	94.24	0.000	31	101.53	0.000	45	108.64	0.001
4	84.84	0.000	18	94.78	0.000	32	102.16	2.632	46	108.84	0.000
5	85.10	0.000	19	95.84	1.368	33	102.31	2.510	47	109.16	0.000
6	85.76	0.000	20	96.37	1.583	34	102.70	2.113	48	109.45	0.007
7	86.29	0.000	21	96.88	1.771	35	102.84	0.000	49	110.23	0.000
8	89.77	0.000	22	97.16	0.000	36	103.12	1.771	50	113.71	0.000
9	90.55	0.007	23	97.30	2.113	37	103.63	1.583	51	114.24	0.000
10	90.84	0.000	24	97.69	2.510	38	104.16	1.368	52	114.90	0.000
11	91.16	0.000	25	97.84	2.632	39	105.22	0.000	53	115.16	0.000
12	91.36	0.001	26	98.47	0.000	40	105.76	0.000	54	116.49	0.013
13	92.76	0.293	27	98.76	1.707	41	106.41	0.000	55	118.72	0.000
14	92.76	0.293	28	98.76	1.707	42	106.96	0.	56	122.82	0.002

5-386

$J_{AA'}$	J_{AB}	$J_{AB'}$	$J_{BB'}$
9	-4	6	9
9	6	-4	9

The maximum summed intensity is 4.563.

LINE	FREQ	INTEN	LINE	FREQ	INTEN	LINE	FREQ	INTEN	LINE	FREQ	INTEN
1	74.85	0.003	15	92.84	0.000	29	100.83	1.857	43	108.59	0.035
2	79.04	0.000	16	92.84	0.000	30	100.83	1.857	44	109.29	0.013
3	81.18	0.018	17	95.55	0.000	31	100.84	0.000	45	109.29	0.000
4	81.18	0.000	18	95.55	1.159	32	101.88	2.736	46	109.41	0.
5	82.84	0.000	19	95.83	0.000	33	102.16	2.632	47	110.83	0.143
6	83.88	0.000	20	95.84	1.368	34	102.26	0.000	48	110.83	0.143
7	84.17	0.000	21	97.04	1.859	35	102.26	2.177	49	110.84	0.000
8	89.16	0.000	22	97.74	2.177	36	102.96	1.859	50	115.83	0.000
9	89.17	0.143	23	97.74	0.000	37	104.16	1.368	51	116.12	0.000
10	89.17	0.143	24	97.84	2.632	38	104.17	0.000	52	117.16	0.000
11	90.59	0.000	25	98.12	2.736	39	104.45	1.159	53	118.82	0.000
12	90.71	0.000	26	99.16	0.000	40	104.45	0.000	54	118.82	0.018
13	90.71	0.013	27	99.17	1.857	41	107.16	0.000	55	120.96	0.000
14	91.41	0.035	28	99.17	1.857	42	107.16	0.000	56	125.15	0.003

5-387

$J_{AA'}$	J_{AB}	$J_{AB'}$	$J_{BB'}$
9	-6	9	12
9	9	-6	12
12	9	-6	9
12	-6	9	9

The maximum summed intensity is 5.471.

LINE	FREQ	INTEN	LINE	FREQ	INTEN	LINE	FREQ	INTEN	LINE	FREQ	INTEN
1	68.64	0.002	15	91.48	0.076	29	100.00	1.923	43	108.76	0.000
2	73.84	0.000	16	93.79	0.000	30	100.50	0.000	44	109.77	0.000
3	74.85	0.000	17	94.39	0.734	31	101.09	3.533	45	110.27	0.043
4	75.35	0.014	18	95.15	1.106	32	101.10	1.942	46	112.98	0.000
5	78.49	0.000	19	95.65	0.000	33	101.82	2.315	47	114.79	0.000
6	78.50	0.000	20	95.99	0.000	34	101.85	2.894	48	115.30	0.077
7	80.35	0.000	21	96.44	1.284	35	103.25	0.000	49	116.39	0.058
8	83.61	0.058	22	97.68	0.000	36	103.42	0.000	50	120.41	0.000
9	84.70	0.077	23	98.15	2.894	37	103.56	1.284	51	120.75	0.000
10	85.21	0.000	24	98.18	2.315	38	104.85	1.106	52	121.50	0.000
11	85.92	0.000	25	98.90	1.942	39	105.11	0.000	53	124.65	0.014
12	89.73	0.043	26	98.91	3.533	40	105.61	0.734	54	125.06	0.000
13	90.14	0.000	27	99.50	0.000	41	106.21	0.000	55	126.25	0.000
14	91.33	0.000	28	100.00	1.923	42	108.52	0.076	56	131.36	0.002

5-388

$J_{AA'}$	J_{AB}	$J_{AB'}$	$J_{BB'}$
9	-6	9	15
9	9	-6	15
15	9	-6	9
15	-6	9	9

The maximum summed intensity is 4.383.

LINE	FREQ	INTEN	LINE	FREQ	INTEN	LINE	FREQ	INTEN	LINE	FREQ	INTEN
1	66.28	0.002	15	91.29	0.063	29	100.57	0.000	43	108.76	0.000
2	71.75	0.000	16	92.72	0.000	30	100.58	1.928	44	109.99	0.036
3	72.99	0.010	17	94.00	0.000	31	101.28	3.348	45	111.14	0.000
4	74.14	0.000	18	94.57	0.812	32	101.53	1.957	46	114.15	0.000
5	76.32	0.000	19	95.15	1.106	33	101.85	2.894	47	115.58	0.072
6	76.57	0.000	20	95.53	0.000	34	102.00	2.247	48	116.72	0.000
7	79.00	0.000	21	96.71	1.482	35	102.96	0.000	49	117.68	0.043
8	82.32	0.043	22	98.00	2.247	36	103.29	1.482	50	121.58	0.000
9	83.28	0.000	23	98.15	2.894	37	103.90	0.000	51	123.10	0.000
10	83.75	0.000	24	98.47	1.957	38	104.85	1.106	52	123.43	0.000
11	84.42	0.072	25	98.72	3.348	39	105.43	0.812	53	126.14	0.000
12	89.14	0.000	26	99.15	0.000	40	106.58	0.000	54	127.01	0.010
13	90.01	0.036	27	99.42	1.928	41	107.28	0.000	55	127.97	0.000
14	90.96	0.000	28	99.43	0.000	42	108.71	0.063	56	133.72	0.002

5-389

$J_{AA'}$	J_{AB}	$J_{AB'}$	$J_{BB'}$
9	-6	12	9
9	12	-6	9

The maximum summed intensity is 6.124.

LINE	FREQ	INTEN	LINE	FREQ	INTEN	LINE	FREQ	INTEN	LINE	FREQ	INTEN
1	66.75	0.001	15	92.18	0.375	29	100.49	1.949	43	109.88	0.101
2	70.50	0.000	16	92.76	0.586	30	100.49	1.949	44	110.52	0.000
3	74.45	0.	17	93.42	0.000	31	100.67	4.001	45	111.31	0.056
4	75.23	0.024	18	93.88	0.000	32	101.24	3.414	46	112.85	0.000
5	77.76	0.000	19	95.76	0.000	33	101.39	2.132	47	113.76	0.000
6	77.94	0.000	20	95.76	0.000	34	102.51	0.000	48	118.49	0.051
7	78.51	0.000	21	96.91	0.000	35	102.82	1.310	49	118.49	0.051
8	81.51	0.051	22	97.18	1.310	36	103.09	0.000	50	121.49	0.
9	81.51	0.051	23	97.49	0.000	37	104.24	0.000	51	122.06	0.000
10	86.24	0.000	24	98.61	2.132	38	104.24	0.000	52	122.24	0.000
11	87.15	0.000	25	98.76	3.414	39	106.12	0.000	53	124.77	0.024
12	88.69	0.056	26	99.33	4.001	40	106.58	0.000	54	125.55	0.000
13	89.48	0.000	27	99.51	1.949	41	107.24	0.586	55	129.50	0.000
14	90.12	0.101	28	99.51	1.949	42	107.82	0.375	56	133.25	0.001

5-390

$J_{AA'}$	J_{AB}	$J_{AB'}$	$J_{BB'}$
9	-6	12	12
9	12	-6	12
12	12	-6	9
12	-6	12	9

The maximum summed intensity is 5.518.

LINE	FREQ	INTEN	LINE	FREQ	INTEN	LINE	FREQ	INTEN	LINE	FREQ	INTEN
1	64.71	0.001	15	92.46	0.451	29	100.00	1.946	43	110.10	0.087
2	70.33	0.000	16	92.76	0.586	30	100.94	1.956	44	110.49	0.000
3	72.82	0.000	17	92.95	0.000	31	100.95	3.532	45	110.86	0.041
4	73.19	0.018	18	94.38	0.000	32	101.24	3.414	46	113.76	0.000
5	76.13	0.000	19	95.51	0.000	33	101.62	2.076	47	115.38	0.000
6	76.14	0.000	20	95.62	0.000	34	102.37	1.794	48	118.25	0.054
7	77.38	0.	21	96.27	0.000	35	102.87	0.000	49	119.19	0.044
8	80.81	0.044	22	97.13	0.000	36	103.44	0.000	50	122.92	0.000
9	81.75	0.054	23	97.63	1.794	37	104.67	0.000	51	123.56	0.000
10	84.62	0.000	24	98.38	2.076	38	105.42	0.000	52	123.87	0.000
11	85.30	0.000	25	98.76	3.414	39	105.62	0.000	53	126.24	0.000
12	88.58	0.000	26	99.05	3.532	40	107.24	0.586	54	126.81	0.018
13	89.14	0.041	27	99.06	1.956	41	107.54	0.451	55	130.61	0.000
14	89.90	0.087	28	100.00	1.946	42	107.99	0.000	56	135.29	0.001

5-391

$J_{AA'}$	J_{AB}	$J_{AB'}$	$J_{BB'}$
9	-6	15	9
9	15	-6	9

The maximum summed intensity is 5.598.

LINE	FREQ	INTEN	LINE	FREQ	INTEN	LINE	FREQ	INTEN	LINE	FREQ	INTEN
1	62.02	0.000	15	89.81	0.238	29	100.42	1.962	43	111.91	0.088
2	65.51	0.000	16	90.09	0.336	30	100.42	1.962	44	112.65	0.000
3	72.79	0.000	17	91.58	0.	31	100.62	3.760	45	112.70	0.037
4	72.84	0.024	18	93.09	0.000	32	100.91	3.664	46	113.42	0.000
5	75.09	0.000	19	94.63	0.000	33	101.10	2.037	47	114.09	0.000
6	75.29	0.000	20	96.09	0.000	34	101.88	1.816	48	121.42	0.038
7	75.58	0.000	21	97.14	0.000	35	102.58	0.000	49	121.42	0.038
8	78.58	0.038	22	97.42	0.000	36	102.86	0.000	50	124.42	0.
9	78.58	0.038	23	98.12	1.816	37	103.91	0.000	51	124.71	0.000
10	85.91	0.000	24	98.90	2.037	38	105.37	0.000	52	124.91	0.000
11	86.58	0.000	25	99.09	3.664	39	106.91	0.000	53	127.16	0.024
12	87.30	0.037	26	99.38	3.760	40	108.42	0.000	54	127.21	0.000
13	87.35	0.000	27	99.58	1.962	41	109.91	0.336	55	134.49	0.000
14	88.09	0.088	28	99.58	1.962	42	110.19	0.238	56	137.98	0.000

5-392

$J_{AA'}$	J_{AB}	$J_{AB'}$	$J_{BB'}$
9	-6	15	15
9	15	-6	15
15	15	-6	9
15	-6	15	9

The maximum summed intensity is 6.428.

LINE	FREQ	INTEN	LINE	FREQ	INTEN	LINE	FREQ	INTEN	LINE	FREQ	INTEN
1	58.18	0.000	15	90.09	0.336	29	100.42	1.962	43	111.94	0.004
2	65.09	0.000	16	90.77	0.369	30	100.91	3.664	44	112.32	0.000
3	69.00	0.015	17	93.51	0.000	31	101.12	3.612	45	112.34	0.071
4	69.38	0.000	18	93.56	0.000	32	101.17	1.971	46	115.56	0.000
5	71.67	0.000	19	94.00	0.000	33	101.53	1.949	47	117.51	0.000
6	72.09	0.000	20	94.56	0.000	34	101.59	1.980	48	121.42	0.038
7	73.00	0.000	21	95.67	0.000	35	104.33	0.000	49	123.01	0.029
8	76.99	0.029	22	96.28	0.000	36	104.41	0.000	50	126.32	0.000
9	78.58	0.038	23	98.41	1.980	37	105.32	0.000	51	128.33	0.000
10	82.49	0.000	24	98.47	1.949	38	106.49	0.000	52	128.59	0.000
11	82.84	0.000	25	98.83	1.971	39	107.03	0.000	53	129.03	0.000
12	86.09	0.000	26	98.88	3.612	40	108.03	0.000	54	131.00	0.015
13	87.66	0.071	27	99.09	3.664	41	109.23	0.369	55	136.50	0.000
14	88.06	0.004	28	99.58	1.962	42	109.91	0.336	56	141.82	0.000

5-393

$J_{AA'}$	J_{AB}	$J_{AB'}$	$J_{BB'}$
12	-1	2	12
12	2	-1	12

The maximum summed intensity is 4.383.

LINE	FREQ	INTEN	LINE	FREQ	INTEN	LINE	FREQ	INTEN	LINE	FREQ	INTEN
1	72.66	0.000	15	91.27	0.000	29	101.85	1.447	43	108.95	0.000
2	78.74	0.001	16	91.35	0.000	30	101.85	1.447	44	108.96	0.
3	79.04	0.000	17	92.54	0.000	31	102.25	0.000	45	109.15	0.000
4	83.46	0.000	18	95.15	0.553	32	102.54	2.329	46	109.44	0.000
5	84.15	0.000	19	95.15	0.553	33	102.57	2.317	47	110.46	0.000
6	84.34	0.000	20	96.46	1.671	34	102.95	2.011	48	113.54	0.000
7	84.56	0.000	21	96.65	1.769	35	103.13	1.902	49	114.26	0.000
8	85.74	0.000	22	96.87	1.902	36	103.35	1.769	50	115.44	0.000
9	86.46	0.000	23	97.05	2.011	37	103.54	1.671	51	115.66	0.000
10	89.54	0.000	24	97.43	2.317	38	104.85	0.553	52	115.85	0.000
11	90.56	0.000	25	97.46	2.329	39	104.85	0.553	53	116.54	0.000
12	90.85	0.000	26	97.75	0.000	40	107.46	0.000	54	120.96	0.000
13	91.04	0.000	27	98.15	1.447	41	108.65	0.000	55	121.26	0.001
14	91.05	0.000	28	98.15	1.447	42	108.73	0.000	56	127.34	0.000

5-394

$J_{AA'}$	J_{AB}	$J_{AB'}$	$J_{BB'}$
12	-2	4	12
12	4	-2	12

The maximum summed intensity is 4.904.

LINE	FREQ	INTEN	LINE	FREQ	INTEN	LINE	FREQ	INTEN	LINE	FREQ	INTEN
1	71.62	0.001	15	91.42	0.000	29	101.22	0.000	43	108.76	0.000
2	77.95	0.004	16	91.90	0.000	30	101.24	1.707	44	108.97	0.000
3	78.34	0.000	17	92.76	0.293	31	101.24	1.707	45	109.70	0.004
4	81.84	0.000	18	92.76	0.293	32	102.16	2.632	46	109.71	0.
5	82.54	0.000	19	94.16	0.000	33	102.25	2.586	47	111.84	0.
6	82.76	0.000	20	95.84	1.368	34	102.82	2.042	48	112.16	0.000
7	83.42	0.000	21	96.50	1.663	35	103.37	1.700	49	113.17	0.000
8	86.83	0.000	22	96.63	1.700	36	103.50	1.663	50	116.58	0.000
9	87.84	0.000	23	97.18	2.042	37	104.16	1.368	51	117.24	0.000
10	88.16	0.000	24	97.75	2.586	38	105.84	0.000	52	117.46	0.000
11	90.29	0.000	25	97.84	2.632	39	107.24	0.293	53	118.16	0.000
12	90.30	0.004	26	98.76	1.707	40	107.24	0.293	54	121.66	0.000
13	91.03	0.000	27	98.76	1.707	41	108.10	0.000	55	122.05	0.004
14	91.24	0.000	28	98.78	0.000	42	108.58	0.000	56	128.38	0.001

5-395

$J_{AA'}$	J_{AB}	$J_{AB'}$	$J_{BB'}$
12	-4	6	12
12	6	-4	12

The maximum summed intensity is 4.949.

LINE	FREQ	INTEN	LINE	FREQ	INTEN	LINE	FREQ	INTEN	LINE	FREQ	INTEN
1	69.73	0.001	15	90.94	0.008	29	100.37	0.	43	109.27	0.000
2	76.06	0.007	16	91.04	0.020	30	100.83	1.857	44	110.16	0.000
3	76.27	0.000	17	92.83	0.000	31	100.83	1.857	45	110.83	0.143
4	79.07	0.000	18	92.83	0.000	32	102.16	2.531	46	110.83	0.143
5	79.84	0.000	19	95.84	1.315	33	102.16	2.632	47	112.03	0.
6	81.17	0.000	20	95.84	1.368	34	102.63	2.038	48	112.07	0.000
7	81.17	0.000	21	96.16	0.000	35	102.74	2.080	49	113.84	0.000
8	86.16	0.000	22	97.26	2.080	36	103.84	0.000	50	118.83	0.000
9	87.93	0.000	23	97.37	2.038	37	104.16	1.315	51	118.83	0.000
10	87.97	0.000	24	97.84	2.531	38	104.16	1.368	52	120.16	0.000
11	89.17	0.143	25	97.84	2.632	39	107.17	0.000	53	120.93	0.000
12	89.17	0.143	26	99.17	1.857	40	107.17	0.000	54	123.73	0.000
13	89.84	0.000	27	99.17	1.857	41	108.96	0.020	55	123.94	0.007
14	90.73	0.000	28	99.63	0.000	42	109.06	0.008	56	130.27	0.001

5-396

$J_{AA'}$	J_{AB}	$J_{AB'}$	$J_{BB'}$
12	-6	9	12
12	9	-6	12

The maximum summed intensity is 4.356.

LINE	FREQ	INTEN	LINE	FREQ	INTEN	LINE	FREQ	INTEN	LINE	FREQ	INTEN
1	66.28	0.002	15	91.29	0.063	29	100.58	1.928	43	109.99	0.036
2	72.99	0.010	16	92.15	0.000	30	100.58	1.928	44	110.29	0.000
3	73.28	0.000	17	94.00	0.000	31	101.15	0.000	45	110.56	0.000
4	73.56	0.000	18	94.57	0.812	32	101.28	3.348	46	114.72	0.
5	77.15	0.000	19	94.58	0.000	33	101.43	0.000	47	115.58	0.072
6	77.85	0.000	20	95.15	1.106	34	101.85	2.894	48	115.58	0.072
7	78.42	0.000	21	96.71	1.482	35	102.00	2.247	49	116.15	0.000
8	83.85	0.000	22	98.00	2.247	36	103.29	1.482	50	121.58	0.000
9	84.42	0.072	23	98.15	2.894	37	104.85	1.106	51	122.15	0.000
10	84.42	0.072	24	98.57	0.000	38	105.42	0.000	52	122.85	0.000
11	85.28	0.	25	98.72	3.348	39	105.43	0.812	53	126.44	0.000
12	89.44	0.000	26	98.85	0.000	40	106.00	0.000	54	126.72	0.000
13	89.71	0.000	27	99.42	1.928	41	107.85	0.000	55	127.01	0.010
14	90.01	0.036	28	99.42	1.928	42	108.71	0.063	56	133.72	0.002

5-397

$J_{AA'}$	J_{AB}	$J_{AB'}$	$J_{BB'}$
12	-9	12	15
12	12	-9	15
15	12	-9	12
15	-9	12	12

The maximum summed intensity is 4.305.

LINE	FREQ	INTEN	LINE	FREQ	INTEN	LINE	FREQ	INTEN	LINE	FREQ	INTEN
1	59.70	0.001	15	91.82	0.109	29	100.00	1.960	43	111.82	0.000
2	65.95	0.000	16	93.75	0.000	30	100.46	0.000	44	112.02	0.000
3	66.15	0.000	17	93.80	0.506	31	100.51	4.227	45	112.28	0.069
4	66.41	0.008	18	94.43	0.557	32	100.82	1.966	46	119.28	0.000
5	72.23	0.000	19	95.08	0.000	33	101.47	2.523	47	120.75	0.000
6	72.54	0.000	20	95.15	1.106	34	101.85	2.894	48	121.21	0.040
7	74.39	0.000	21	95.61	0.000	35	102.75	0.000	49	122.03	0.034
8	77.97	0.034	22	98.06	0.000	36	103.58	0.000	50	126.42	0.000
9	78.79	0.040	23	98.15	2.894	37	104.85	1.106	51	126.95	0.000
10	79.25	0.000	24	98.53	2.523	38	105.57	0.557	52	127.46	0.000
11	79.91	0.000	25	99.18	1.966	39	105.74	0.000	53	133.04	0.000
12	87.16	0.000	26	99.49	4.227	40	106.20	0.506	54	133.59	0.008
13	87.72	0.069	27	99.54	0.000	41	106.25	0.000	55	134.87	0.000
14	88.99	0.000	28	100.00	1.960	42	108.18	0.109	56	140.30	0.001

5-398

$J_{AA'}$	J_{AB}	$J_{AB'}$	$J_{BB'}$
12	-9	15	12
12	15	-9	12

The maximum summed intensity is 6.996.

LINE	FREQ	INTEN	LINE	FREQ	INTEN	LINE	FREQ	INTEN	LINE	FREQ	INTEN
1	57.90	0.001	15	91.08	0.000	29	100.20	4.874	43	109.71	0.116
2	61.77	0.000	16	91.72	0.245	30	100.37	1.970	44	113.49	0.
3	66.34	0.000	17	92.76	0.586	31	100.37	1.970	45	113.53	0.083
4	66.38	0.012	18	94.16	0.	32	101.23	2.246	46	118.90	0.000
5	71.59	0.000	19	94.95	0.424	33	101.24	3.414	47	119.76	0.000
6	71.76	0.000	20	95.76	0.000	34	102.63	0.000	48	124.37	0.030
7	72.63	0.	21	95.76	0.000	35	103.67	0.000	49	124.37	0.030
8	75.63	0.030	22	96.33	0.000	36	104.24	0.000	50	127.37	0.
9	75.63	0.030	23	97.37	0.000	37	104.24	0.000	51	128.24	0.000
10	80.24	0.000	24	98.76	3.414	38	105.05	0.424	52	128.41	0.000
11	81.10	0.000	25	98.77	2.246	39	105.84	0.000	53	133.62	0.012
12	86.47	0.083	26	99.63	1.970	40	107.24	0.586	54	133.66	0.000
13	86.51	0.000	27	99.63	1.970	41	108.28	0.245	55	138.23	0.000
14	90.29	0.116	28	99.80	4.874	42	108.92	0.000	56	142.10	0.001

5-399

$J_{AA'}$	J_{AB}	$J_{AB'}$	$J_{BB'}$
12	-9	15	15
12	15	-9	15
15	15	-9	12
15	-9	15	12

The maximum summed intensity is 5.038.

LINE	FREQ	INTEN	LINE	FREQ	INTEN	LINE	FREQ	INTEN	LINE	FREQ	INTEN
1	55.79	0.001	15	90.67	0.000	29	100.00	1.969	43	110.05	0.000
2	61.44	0.000	16	91.83	0.280	30	100.31	4.728	44	112.89	0.083
3	64.27	0.009	17	92.76	0.586	31	100.72	1.973	45	113.65	0.000
4	65.04	0.000	18	94.35	0.000	32	101.24	3.414	46	119.99	0.000
5	69.75	0.000	19	95.38	0.000	33	101.36	2.213	47	121.35	0.000
6	70.16	0.000	20	95.59	0.000	34	102.84	0.000	48	124.19	0.031
7	71.41	0.000	21	95.60	0.579	35	103.68	0.000	49	124.91	0.027
8	75.09	0.027	22	95.80	0.000	36	104.40	0.579	50	129.32	0.
9	75.81	0.031	23	97.16	0.000	37	104.92	0.	51	129.53	0.000
10	78.65	0.000	24	98.64	2.213	38	105.34	0.000	52	129.84	0.000
11	79.29	0.000	25	98.76	3.414	39	105.65	0.000	53	134.24	0.000
12	85.63	0.000	26	99.28	1.973	40	107.24	0.586	54	135.73	0.009
13	87.11	0.083	27	99.69	4.728	41	108.17	0.280	55	139.28	0.000
14	90.15	0.107	28	100.00	1.969	42	109.85	0.107	56	144.21	0.001

-11 -10 -9 -8 -7 -6 -5 -4 -3 -2 -1 0 +1 +2 +3 +4 +5 +6 +7 +8 +9 +10 +11

5-400

$J_{AA'}$	J_{AB}	$J_{AB'}$	$J_{BB'}$
15	-1	2	15
15	4	-2	15

The maximum summed intensity is 4.323.

LINE	FREQ	INTEN	LINE	FREQ	INTEN	LINE	FREQ	INTEN	LINE	FREQ	INTEN
1	66.72	0.000	15	89.54	0.000	29	101.85	1.447	43	111.71	0.000
2	72.80	0.000	16	90.53	0.000	30	101.85	1.447	44	111.88	0.000
3	76.05	0.000	17	91.36	0.000	31	102.54	2.329	45	111.92	0.
4	80.46	0.000	18	94.78	0.000	32	102.56	2.328	46	112.15	0.000
5	81.15	0.000	19	95.15	0.553	33	102.97	2.001	47	113.46	0.000
6	81.41	0.000	20	95.15	0.553	34	103.11	1.916	48	116.54	0.000
7	81.58	0.000	21	96.46	1.671	35	103.39	1.755	49	117.24	0.000
8	82.76	0.000	22	96.61	1.755	36	103.54	1.671	50	118.42	0.000
9	83.46	0.000	23	96.89	1.916	37	104.85	0.553	51	118.59	0.000
10	86.54	0.000	24	97.03	2.001	38	104.85	0.553	52	118.85	0.000
11	87.85	0.000	25	97.44	2.328	39	105.22	0.000	53	119.54	0.000
12	88.08	0.000	26	97.46	2.329	40	108.64	0.000	54	123.95	0.000
13	88.12	0.000	27	98.15	1.447	41	109.47	0.000	55	127.20	0.000
14	88.29	0.000	28	98.15	1.447	42	110.46	0.000	56	133.28	0.000

-11 -10 -9 -8 -7 -6 -5 -4 -3 -2 -1 0 +1 +2 +3 +4 +5 +6 +7 +8 +9 +10 +11

5-401

$J_{AA'}$	J_{AB}	$J_{AB'}$	$J_{BB'}$
15	-2	4	15
15	4	-2	15

The maximum summed intensity is 5.142.

LINE	FREQ	INTEN	LINE	FREQ	INTEN	LINE	FREQ	INTEN	LINE	FREQ	INTEN
1	65.88	0.000	15	90.16	0.003	29	101.24	1.707	43	111.02	0.000
2	72.20	0.002	16	91.16	0.000	30	101.24	1.707	44	111.72	0.000
3	75.38	0.000	17	91.46	0.000	31	102.16	2.632	45	111.76	0.000
4	78.84	0.000	18	92.76	0.293	32	102.21	2.634	46	112.57	0.
5	79.76	0.000	19	92.76	0.293	33	102.90	1.996	47	114.84	0.000
6	79.80	0.000	20	95.84	1.368	34	103.42	1.711	48	115.16	0.000
7	80.50	0.000	21	95.92	0.000	35	103.51	1.655	49	116.13	0.000
8	83.87	0.000	22	96.49	1.655	36	104.08	0.000	50	119.50	0.000
9	84.84	0.000	23	96.58	1.711	37	104.16	1.368	51	120.20	0.000
10	85.16	0.000	24	97.10	1.996	38	107.24	0.293	52	120.24	0.000
11	87.43	0.000	25	97.79	2.634	39	107.24	0.293	53	121.16	0.000
12	88.24	0.000	26	97.84	2.632	40	108.54	0.000	54	124.62	0.000
13	88.28	0.000	27	98.76	1.707	41	108.84	0.000	55	127.80	0.002
14	88.98	0.000	28	98.76	1.707	42	109.84	0.003	56	134.12	0.000

5-402

$J_{AA'}$	J_{AB}	$J_{AB'}$	$J_{BB'}$
15	-4	6	15
15	6	-4	15

The maximum summed intensity is 3.799.

LINE	FREQ	INTEN	LINE	FREQ	INTEN	LINE	FREQ	INTEN	LINE	FREQ	INTEN
1	64.32	0.001	15	89.83	0.000	29	100.83	1.857	43	110.83	0.143
2	70.64	0.003	16	90.02	0.000	30	100.83	1.857	44	110.83	0.143
3	73.41	0.000	17	90.79	0.013	31	102.16	2.632	45	111.69	0.000
4	76.65	0.000	18	91.08	0.005	32	102.35	2.394	46	113.16	0.000
5	76.84	0.000	19	93.16	0.000	33	102.60	2.225	47	114.78	0.
6	78.17	0.000	20	95.84	1.368	34	102.88	1.938	48	114.93	0.000
7	78.36	0.000	21	96.03	1.421	35	103.12	0.000	49	116.84	0.000
8	83.16	0.000	22	96.88	0.000	36	103.97	1.421	50	121.64	0.000
9	85.07	0.000	23	97.12	1.938	37	104.16	1.368	51	121.83	0.000
10	85.22	0.000	24	97.40	2.225	38	106.84	0.000	52	123.16	0.000
11	86.84	0.000	25	97.65	2.394	39	108.92	0.005	53	123.35	0.
12	88.31	0.000	26	97.84	2.632	40	109.21	0.013	54	126.59	0.000
13	89.17	0.143	27	99.17	1.857	41	109.98	0.000	55	129.36	0.003
14	89.17	0.143	28	99.17	1.857	42	110.17	0.000	56	135.68	0.001

5-403

$J_{AA'}$	J_{AB}	$J_{AB'}$	$J_{BB'}$
15	-6	9	15
15	9	-6	15

The maximum summed intensity is 3.799.

LINE	FREQ	INTEN	LINE	FREQ	INTEN	LINE	FREQ	INTEN	LINE	FREQ	INTEN
1	61.31	0.001	15	90.40	0.025	29	100.58	1.928	43	110.85	0.000
2	68.02	0.005	16	90.97	0.044	30	100.58	1.928	44	112.26	0.000
3	70.67	0.000	17	91.32	0.000	31	101.25	0.000	45	113.17	0.000
4	71.59	0.000	18	91.58	0.000	32	101.60	3.030	46	115.58	0.072
5	74.15	0.000	19	94.89	0.950	33	101.85	2.894	47	115.58	0.072
6	75.16	0.000	20	95.15	1.106	34	102.32	2.125	48	117.41	0.
7	75.42	0.000	21	95.85	0.000	35	102.90	1.820	49	119.15	0.000
8	80.85	0.000	22	97.10	1.820	36	104.15	0.000	50	124.58	0.000
9	82.59	0.000	23	97.68	2.125	37	104.85	1.106	51	124.84	0.000
10	84.42	0.072	24	98.15	2.894	38	105.11	0.950	52	125.85	0.000
11	84.42	0.072	25	98.40	3.030	39	108.42	0.000	53	128.41	0.000
12	86.83	0.000	26	98.75	0.000	40	108.68	0.000	54	129.33	0.000
13	87.74	0.000	27	99.42	1.928	41	109.03	0.044	55	131.98	0.005
14	89.15	0.000	28	99.42	1.928	42	109.60	0.025	56	138.69	0.001

−11 −10 −9 −8 −7 −6 −5 −4 −3 −2 −1 0 +1 +2 +3 +4 +5 +6 +7 +8 +9 +10 +11

5-404

$J_{AA'}$	J_{AB}	$J_{AB'}$	$J_{BB'}$
15	-9	12	15
15	12	-9	15

The maximum summed intensity is 5.869.

LINE	FREQ	INTEN	LINE	FREQ	INTEN	LINE	FREQ	INTEN	LINE	FREQ	INTEN
1	57.37	0.001	15	91.70	0.098	29	100.42	1.962	43	111.85	0.067
2	64.07	0.006	16	92.15	0.000	30	100.42	1.962	44	112.57	0.000
3	64.80	0.000	17	93.19	0.000	31	100.62	4.130	45	113.36	0.000
4	65.59	0.000	18	93.91	0.553	32	100.87	0.000	46	120.97	0.000
5	71.15	0.000	19	94.42	0.000	33	101.15	0.000	47	121.42	0.038
6	71.35	0.000	20	94.86	0.666	34	101.59	2.479	48	121.42	0.038
7	72.58	0.000	21	95.15	1.106	35	101.85	2.894	49	122.15	0.000
8	77.85	0.000	22	98.15	2.894	36	104.85	1.106	50	127.42	0.000
9	78.58	0.038	23	98.41	2.479	37	105.14	0.666	51	128.65	0.000
10	78.58	0.038	24	98.85	0.000	38	105.58	0.000	52	128.85	0.000
11	79.03	0.000	25	99.13	0.000	39	106.09	0.553	53	134.41	0.000
12	86.64	0.000	26	99.38	4.130	40	106.81	0.000	54	135.20	0.000
13	87.43	0.000	27	99.58	1.962	41	107.85	0.000	55	135.93	0.006
14	88.15	0.067	28	99.58	1.962	42	108.30	0.098	56	142.63	0.001

−11 −10 −9 −8 −7 −6 −5 −4 −3 −2 −1 0 +1 +2 +3 +4 +5 +6 +7 +8 +9 +10 +11

5-405

$J_{AA'}$	J_{AB}	$J_{AB'}$	$J_{BB'}$
18	-1	2	18
18	2	-1	18

The maximum summed intensity is 4.337.

LINE	FREQ	INTEN	LINE	FREQ	INTEN	LINE	FREQ	INTEN	LINE	FREQ	INTEN
1	60.76	0.000	15	86.54	0.000	29	101.85	1.447	43	114.70	0.000
2	66.85	0.000	16	90.51	0.000	30	101.85	1.447	44	114.84	0.000
3	73.06	0.000	17	91.37	0.000	31	102.54	2.329	45	114.90	0.000
4	77.46	0.000	18	91.81	0.000	32	102.55	2.335	46	115.15	0.000
5	78.15	0.000	19	95.15	0.553	33	102.98	1.993	47	116.46	0.000
6	78.45	0.000	20	95.15	0.553	34	103.10	1.924	48	119.54	0.000
7	78.59	0.000	21	96.46	1.671	35	103.41	1.747	49	120.24	0.000
8	79.76	0.000	22	96.59	1.747	36	103.54	1.671	50	121.41	0.000
9	80.46	0.000	23	96.90	1.924	37	104.85	0.553	51	121.55	0.000
10	83.54	0.000	24	97.02	1.993	38	104.85	0.553	52	121.85	0.000
11	84.85	0.000	25	97.45	2.335	39	108.19	0.000	53	122.54	0.000
12	85.10	0.000	26	97.46	2.329	40	108.63	0.000	54	126.94	0.000
13	85.16	0.000	27	98.15	1.447	41	109.49	0.000	55	133.15	0.000
14	85.30	0.000	28	98.15	1.447	42	113.46	0.000	56	139.24	0.000

5-406

$J_{AA'}$	J_{AB}	$J_{AB'}$	$J_{BB'}$
18	-2	4	18
18	4	-2	18

The maximum summed intensity is 5.166.

LINE	FREQ	INTEN	LINE	FREQ	INTEN	LINE	FREQ	INTEN	LINE	FREQ	INTEN
1	60.05	0.000	15	88.16	0.000	29	101.24	1.707	43	113.97	0.000
2	66.37	0.001	16	90.07	0.002	30	101.24	1.707	44	114.55	0.000
3	72.41	0.000	17	91.49	0.000	31	102.16	2.632	45	114.76	0.000
4	75.84	0.000	18	92.76	0.293	32	102.18	2.666	46	115.48	0.
5	76.76	0.000	19	92.76	0.293	33	102.95	1.964	47	117.84	0.000
6	76.97	0.000	20	93.01	0.000	34	103.37	1.742	48	118.16	0.000
7	77.55	0.000	21	95.84	1.368	35	103.60	1.624	49	119.10	0.000
8	80.90	0.000	22	96.40	1.624	36	104.16	1.368	50	122.45	0.000
9	81.84	0.000	23	96.63	1.742	37	106.99	0.000	51	123.03	0.000
10	82.16	0.000	24	97.05	1.964	38	107.24	0.293	52	123.24	0.000
11	84.52	0.000	25	97.82	2.666	39	107.24	0.293	53	124.16	0.000
12	85.24	0.000	26	97.84	2.632	40	108.51	0.000	54	127.59	0.000
13	85.45	0.000	27	98.76	1.707	41	109.93	0.002	55	133.63	0.001
14	86.03	0.000	28	98.76	1.707	42	111.84	0.000	56	139.95	0.000

5-407

$J_{AA'}$	J_{AB}	$J_{AB'}$	$J_{BB'}$
-1	2	4	2
-1	4	2	2
2	4	2	-1
2	2	4	-1

The maximum summed intensity is 4.555.

LINE	FREQ	INTEN	LINE	FREQ	INTEN	LINE	FREQ	INTEN	LINE	FREQ	INTEN
1	85.59	0.001	15	95.85	0.459	29	100.00	0.615	43	104.33	0.582
2	88.53	0.000	16	96.39	1.385	30	100.00	0.615	44	105.06	0.000
3	89.82	0.000	17	96.71	0.000	31	100.31	0.000	45	105.55	0.000
4	90.69	0.017	18	96.88	0.000	32	100.83	4.646	46	105.92	0.875
5	92.14	0.	19	97.06	0.000	33	101.24	3.414	47	106.10	0.000
6	92.76	0.586	20	97.19	1.933	34	101.94	0.000	48	106.23	0.307
7	93.45	0.000	21	97.75	1.111	35	102.25	1.111	49	106.41	0.067
8	93.59	0.067	22	98.06	0.000	36	102.39	0.000	50	106.55	0.000
9	93.77	0.307	23	98.30	0.	37	102.81	1.933	51	107.24	0.586
10	94.08	0.875	24	98.76	3.414	38	102.94	0.000	52	107.37	0.000
11	94.45	0.000	25	98.78	0.000	39	103.61	1.385	53	108.11	0.000
12	94.70	0.000	26	98.89	0.	40	103.77	0.000	54	109.31	0.017
13	94.80	0.000	27	99.04	0.000	41	104.02	0.000	55	114.27	0.000
14	95.67	0.582	28	99.17	4.646	42	104.15	0.459	56	114.41	0.001

5-408

$J_{AA'}$	J_{AB}	$J_{AB'}$	$J_{BB'}$
-1	2	4	4
-1	4	2	4
4	4	2	-1
4	2	4	-1

The maximum summed intensity is 4.788.

LINE	FREQ	INTEN	LINE	FREQ	INTEN	LINE	FREQ	INTEN	LINE	FREQ	INTEN
1	85.54	0.001	15	96.17	0.000	29	99.79	0.000	43	104.83	0.671
2	87.85	0.000	16	96.19	1.083	30	99.95	0.000	44	105.44	0.000
3	90.16	0.000	17	96.35	1.215	31	100.05	0.000	45	105.44	0.000
4	90.69	0.018	18	96.62	0.000	32	100.82	4.666	46	105.98	0.853
5	91.56	0.000	19	96.95	0.000	33	100.99	0.500	47	107.24	0.586
6	91.72	0.020	20	97.10	1.980	34	101.24	3.414	48	107.35	0.000
7	92.40	0.000	21	97.13	0.000	35	101.57	0.917	49	107.50	0.076
8	92.50	0.076	22	98.43	0.917	36	102.03	0.000	50	107.68	0.000
9	92.76	0.586	23	98.76	3.414	37	102.90	1.980	51	108.28	0.020
10	93.50	0.000	24	98.91	0.000	38	103.05	0.000	52	108.44	0.000
11	94.02	0.853	25	99.01	0.500	39	103.13	0.000	53	109.31	0.018
12	94.38	0.000	26	99.03	0.000	40	103.65	1.215	54	110.09	0.000
13	94.56	0.000	27	99.18	4.666	41	103.81	1.083	55	114.31	0.000
14	95.17	0.671	28	99.36	0.000	42	104.68	0.000	56	114.46	0.001

5-409

$J_{AA'}$	J_{AB}	$J_{AB'}$	$J_{BB'}$
-1	2	6	2
-1	6	2	2
2	6	2	-1
2	2	6	-1

The maximum summed intensity is 5.096.

LINE	FREQ	INTEN	LINE	FREQ	INTEN	LINE	FREQ	INTEN	LINE	FREQ	INTEN
1	82.74	0.001	15	94.74	0.000	29	99.74	0.000	43	105.93	.0.307
2	85.74	0.000	16	95.00	0.720	30	100.00	1.280	44	106.83	0.000
3	88.99	0.000	17	95.93	0.296	31	100.00	1.280	45	107.00	0.000
4	89.41	0.020	18	97.00	0.000	32	100.59	5.088	46	107.26	0.626
5	90.74	0.000	19	97.58	1.873	33	101.00	3.600	47	107.42	0.127
6	91.00	0.400	20	97.84	0.000	34	101.74	1.447	48	107.69	0.000
7	91.74	0.216	21	98.00	0.000	35	102.00	0.000	49	108.00	0.000
8	92.00	0.000	22	98.00	0.000	36	102.42	1.873	50	108.26	0.216
9	92.58	0.127	23	98.26	1.447	37	103.00	0.000	51	108.59	0.
10	92.74	0.626	24	98.84	0.000	38	103.49	0.000	52	109.00	0.400
11	93.00	0.000	25	98.93	0.000	39	103.59	0.000	53	109.42	0.000
12	93.00	0.000	26	99.00	3.600	40	103.93	0.000	54	110.59	0.020
13	93.64	0.000	27	99.41	5.088	41	104.07	0.296	55	116.68	0.000
14	94.07	0.307	28	99.58	0.000	42	105.00	0.720	56	117.26	0.001

5-410

$J_{AA'}$	J_{AB}	$J_{AB'}$	$J_{BB'}$
-1	2	6	6
-1	6	2	6
6	6	2	-1
6	2	6	-1

The maximum summed intensity is 5.035.

LINE	FREQ	INTEN	LINE	FREQ	INTEN	LINE	FREQ	INTEN	LINE	FREQ	INTEN
1	82.38	0.000	15	94.15	0.393	29	99.70	0.000	43	106.01	0.000
2	85.13	0.000	16	95.33	0.000	30	99.89	0.879	44	106.09	0.308
3	87.82	0.000	17	95.56	0.000	31	100.11	0.879	45	106.53	0.000
4	88.47	0.000	18	95.81	0.000	32	100.57	5.144	46	107.62	0.541
5	89.17	0.024	19	95.85	0.958	33	101.00	3.600	47	109.00	0.400
6	89.43	0.022	20	96.53	0.000	34	101.53	0.000	48	109.41	0.000
7	89.89	0.063	21	97.23	1.976	35	101.97	1.692	49	110.11	0.063
8	91.00	0.400	22	98.03	1.692	36	102.77	1.976	50	110.13	0.000
9	91.44	0.000	23	98.47	0.000	37	103.32	0.000	51	110.57	0.022
10	91.55	0.000	24	98.73	0.000	38	103.47	0.000	52	110.83	0.024
11	91.95	0.000	25	99.00	3.600	39	103.71	0.000	53	111.53	0.000
12	92.38	0.541	26	99.43	5.144	40	104.15	0.958	54	113.30	0.000
13	93.47	0.000	27	99.45	0.000	41	105.15	0.000	55	116.92	0.000
14	93.91	0.308	28	99.59	0.000	42	105.85	0.393	56	117.62	0.000

5-411

$J_{AA'}$	J_{AB}	$J_{AB'}$	$J_{BB'}$
-1	2	9	2
-1	9	2	2
2	9	2	-1
2	2	9	-1

The maximum summed intensity is 5.531.

LINE	FREQ	INTEN	LINE	FREQ	INTEN	LINE	FREQ	INTEN	LINE	FREQ	INTEN
1	77.83	0.000	15	91.65	0.000	29	100.00	1.690	43	108.55	0.154
2	80.79	0.000	16	92.38	0.310	30	100.00	1.690	44	109.51	0.125
3	87.07	0.018	17	96.02	0.183	31	100.30	0.000	45	109.57	0.000
4	87.13	0.000	18	97.04	0.000	32	100.40	5.445	46	109.64	0.376
5	88.24	0.244	19	97.81	0.	33	100.76	3.756	47	109.70	0.000
6	88.40	0.000	20	98.04	0.000	34	101.22	1.696	48	110.24	0.000
7	88.69	0.128	21	98.11	1.875	35	101.89	1.875	49	110.57	0.000
8	89.43	0.000	22	98.54	0.000	36	101.96	0.000	50	110.97	0.000
9	90.19	0.	23	98.78	1.696	37	102.92	0.000	51	111.31	0.128
10	90.36	0.376	24	98.84	0.000	38	102.96	0.000	52	111.70	0.000
11	90.43	0.000	25	98.97	0.000	39	103.36	0.000	53	111.76	0.244
12	90.49	0.125	26	99.24	3.756	40	103.98	0.183	54	112.93	0.018
13	91.45	0.154	27	99.26	0.000	41	106.59	0.000	55	121.10	0.000
14	91.52	0.000	28	99.60	5.445	42	107.62	0.310	56	122.17	0.000

5-412

$J_{AA'}$	J_{AB}	$J_{AB'}$	$J_{BB'}$
-1	2	9	9
-1	9	2	9
9	9	2	-1
9	2	9	-1

The maximum summed intensity is 5.460.

LINE	FREQ	INTEN	LINE	FREQ	INTEN	LINE	FREQ	INTEN	LINE	FREQ	INTEN
1	76.57	0.000	15	92.36	0.184	29	100.37	5.523	43	107.64	0.184
2	80.63	0.000	16	92.87	0.000	30	100.76	3.756	44	108.37	0.000
3	82.80	0.000	17	94.37	0.000	31	100.77	0.000	45	110.13	0.096
4	83.63	0.000	18	94.53	0.000	32	100.84	1.249	46	110.90	0.253
5	85.16	0.020	19	95.11	0.721	33	100.93	0.000	47	111.76	0.244
6	86.47	0.000	20	95.84	0.000	34	102.07	1.904	48	111.83	0.000
7	86.63	0.049	21	96.16	0.000	35	102.63	1.980	49	112.90	0.022
8	87.10	0.022	22	97.37	1.980	36	103.84	0.000	50	113.37	0.049
9	88.24	0.244	23	97.93	1.904	37	104.16	0.000	51	114.67	0.000
10	88.64	0.000	24	98.09	0.000	38	104.43	0.000	52	114.84	0.020
11	89.10	0.253	25	98.60	0.000	39	104.89	0.721	53	116.37	0.000
12	89.87	0.096	26	99.16	1.249	40	106.10	0.000	54	118.23	0.000
13	90.87	0.000	27	99.24	3.756	41	106.61	0.000	55	121.90	0.000
14	91.63	0.000	28	99.63	5.523	42	106.66	0.000	56	123.43	0.000

5-413

$J_{AA'}$	J_{AB}	$J_{AB'}$	$J_{BB'}$
-1	2	12	2
-1	12	2	12
12	12	2	-1
12	2	12	-1

The maximum summed intensity is 6.037.

LINE	FREQ	INTEN	LINE	FREQ	INTEN	LINE	FREQ	INTEN	LINE	FREQ	INTEN
1	72.49	0.000	15	89.09	0.000	29	100.00	1.835	43	111.30	0.091
2	75.38	0.	16	89.56	0.165	30	100.00	1.835	44	111.95	0.096
3	84.47	0.015	17	96.07	0.124	31	100.30	5.631	45	112.28	0.238
4	84.86	0.000	18	97.10	0.000	32	100.62	3.838	46	112.34	0.000
5	85.38	0.162	19	97.72	0.	33	100.77	0.	47	112.67	0.000
6	85.68	0.083	20	98.10	0.000	34	100.91	1.818	48	112.93	0.000
7	85.82	0.000	21	98.31	0.000	35	101.51	1.904	49	113.34	0.000
8	86.66	0.000	22	98.49	1.904	36	101.90	0.000	50	113.63	0.000
9	87.28	0.	23	98.97	0.000	37	102.54	0.000	51	114.23	0.
10	87.66	0.000	24	99.02	0.000	38	102.90	0.000	52	114.32	0.083
11	87.72	0.238	25	99.09	1.818	39	103.19	0.000	53	114.62	0.162
12	88.05	0.096	26	99.38	3.838	40	103.93	0.124	54	115.53	0.015
13	88.58	0.	27	99.48	0.000	41	109.41	0.000	55	126.12	0.000
14	88.70	0.091	28	99.70	5.631	42	110.44	0.165	56	127.51	0.000

−11 −10 −9 −8 −7 −6 −5 −4 −3 −2 −1 0 +1 +2 +3 +4 +5 +6 +7 +8 +9 +10 +11

5-414

$J_{AA'}$	J_{AB}	$J_{AB'}$	$J_{BB'}$
-1	2	12	12
-1	12	2	12
12	12	2	-1
12	2	12	-1

The maximum summed intensity is 5.728.

LINE	FREQ	INTEN	LINE	FREQ	INTEN	LINE	FREQ	INTEN	LINE	FREQ	INTEN
1	70.11	0.000	15	90.43	0.094	29	100.27	5.705	43	109.65	0.000
2	75.88	0.000	16	90.73	0.000	30	100.62	3.838	44	110.32	0.000
3	77.13	0.	17	92.43	0.000	31	101.05	1.447	45	113.90	0.000
4	78.68	0.000	18	93.60	0.000	32	101.76	0.000	46	114.30	0.046
5	81.06	0.015	19	93.92	0.000	33	102.10	1.954	47	114.62	0.162
6	81.40	0.000	20	94.34	0.563	34	102.53	1.985	48	114.65	0.133
7	83.72	0.039	21	95.08	0.000	35	102.94	0.000	49	115.50	0.018
8	84.50	0.018	22	97.35	0.000	36	104.92	0.000	50	116.28	0.039
9	85.35	0.133	23	97.44	0.000	37	105.66	0.563	51	118.94	0.015
10	85.38	0.162	24	97.47	1.985	38	106.03	0.000	52	119.49	0.000
11	85.70	0.046	25	97.90	1.954	39	106.08	0.000	53	121.32	0.000
12	85.72	0.000	26	98.95	1.447	40	107.19	0.000	54	123.24	0.000
13	89.33	0.000	27	99.38	3.838	41	107.28	0.000	55	127.51	0.
14	89.68	0.000	28	99.73	5.705	42	109.57	0.094	56	129.89	0.000

−11 −10 −9 −8 −7 −6 −5 −4 −3 −2 −1 0 +1 +2 +3 +4 +5 +6 +7 +8 +9 +10 +11

5-415

$J_{AA'}$	J_{AB}	$J_{AB'}$	$J_{BB'}$
-1	2	15	2
-1	15	2	2
2	15	2	-1
2	2	15	-1

The maximum summed intensity is 6.836.

LINE	FREQ	INTEN	LINE	FREQ	INTEN	LINE	FREQ	INTEN	LINE	FREQ	INTEN
1	66.91	0.000	15	86.48	0.000	29	100.00	1.899	43	114.13	0.059
2	69.76	0.000	16	86.66	0.101	30	100.00	1.899	44	114.58	0.071
3	81.74	0.012	17	96.10	0.089	31	100.24	5.739	45	115.06	0.160
4	82.35	0.	18	97.16	0.000	32	100.51	3.886	46	115.18	0.000
5	82.49	0.114	19	97.67	0.	33	100.72	1.883	47	115.67	0.000
6	82.69	0.058	20	98.16	0.000	34	101.09	0.000	48	115.70	0.000
7	83.10	0.000	21	98.16	0.000	35	101.23	1.929	49	116.18	0.000
8	83.82	0.000	22	98.77	1.929	36	101.84	0.000	50	116.42	0.000
9	84.33	0.	23	98.88	0.000	37	102.29	0.000	51	116.91	0.
10	84.82	0.000	24	98.95	0.000	38	102.84	0.000	52	117.31	0.058
11	84.94	0.160	25	99.28	1.883	39	103.08	0.000	53	117.51	0.114
12	85.42	0.071	26	99.49	3.886	40	103.90	0.089	54	118.26	0.012
13	85.53	0.000	27	99.76	5.739	41	112.29	0.000	55	131.48	0.000
14	85.87	0.059	28	99.89	0.000	42	113.34	0.101	56	133.09	0.000

5-416

$J_{AA'}$	J_{AB}	$J_{AB'}$	$J_{BB'}$
-1	2	15	15
-1	15	2	15
15	15	2	-1
15	2	15	-1

The maximum summed intensity is 6.001.

LINE	FREQ	INTEN	LINE	FREQ	INTEN	LINE	FREQ	INTEN	LINE	FREQ	INTEN
1	63.39	0.000	15	88.45	0.052	29	100.21	5.801	43	112.32	0.000
2	71.00	0.000	16	88.71	0.000	30	100.51	3.886	44	112.66	0.000
3	71.20	0.000	17	90.31	0.000	31	101.07	1.571	45	115.86	0.000
4	73.68	0.000	18	91.71	0.000	32	102.11	1.973	46	117.51	0.114
5	76.30	0.000	19	92.70	0.000	33	102.47	1.989	47	118.24	0.014
6	76.92	0.011	20	93.52	0.449	34	102.72	0.000	48	118.51	0.027
7	80.90	0.032	21	94.29	0.000	35	105.11	0.000	49	118.59	0.080
8	81.41	0.080	22	96.26	0.000	36	105.71	0.000	50	119.10	0.032
9	81.49	0.027	23	96.55	0.000	37	106.48	0.449	51	123.08	0.011
10	81.76	0.014	24	97.53	1.989	38	107.82	0.000	52	124.42	0.000
11	82.49	0.114	25	97.89	1.973	39	108.02	0.000	53	126.32	0.000
12	82.76	0.000	26	98.93	1.571	40	108.29	0.000	54	128.28	0.000
13	87.60	0.000	27	99.49	3.886	41	108.31	0.000	55	133.38	0.000
14	87.68	0.000	28	99.79	5.801	42	111.55	0.052	56	136.61	0.000

5-417

$J_{AA'}$	J_{AB}	$J_{AB'}$	$J_{BB'}$
-1	2	18	2
-1	18	2	2
2	18	2	-1
2	2	18	-1

The maximum summed intensity is 7.798.

LINE	FREQ	INTEN	LINE	FREQ	INTEN	LINE	FREQ	INTEN	LINE	FREQ	INTEN
1	61.21	0.000	15	83.72	0.068	29	100.00	1.932	43	117.01	0.041
2	64.01	0.	16	83.75	0.000	30	100.17	0.000	44	117.32	0.053
3	78.93	0.010	17	96.13	0.067	31	100.19	5.806	45	117.91	0.114
4	79.56	0.084	18	97.20	0.000	32	100.44	3.916	46	118.08	0.000
5	79.69	0.000	19	97.64	0.000	33	100.59	1.920	47	118.53	0.000
6	79.71	0.043	20	98.05	0.000	34	101.04	1.947	48	118.67	0.000
7	80.29	0.000	21	98.20	0.000	35	101.32	0.000	49	119.08	0.000
8	80.92	0.000	22	98.79	0.000	36	101.80	0.000	50	119.27	0.000
9	81.36	0.	23	98.93	0.000	37	102.11	0.000	51	119.68	0.
10	81.92	0.000	24	98.96	1.947	38	102.80	0.000	52	120.29	0.043
11	82.09	0.114	25	99.41	1.920	39	102.99	0.000	53	120.44	0.084
12	82.51	0.000	26	99.56	3.916	40	103.87	0.067	54	121.07	0.010
13	82.68	0.053	27	99.81	5.806	41	115.21	0.000	55	137.03	0.000
14	82.99	0.041	28	100.00	1.932	42	116.28	0.068	56	138.79	0.000

5-418

$J_{AA'}$	J_{AB}	$J_{AB'}$	$J_{BB'}$
-1	2	18	18
-1	18	2	18
18	18	2	-1
18	2	18	-1

The maximum summed intensity is 6.462.

LINE	FREQ	INTEN	LINE	FREQ	INTEN	LINE	FREQ	INTEN	LINE	FREQ	INTEN
1	56.53	0.000	15	86.45	0.031	29	100.17	5.858	43	114.36	0.000
2	65.16	0.000	16	86.72	0.000	30	100.44	3.916	44	115.70	0.000
3	66.05	0.000	17	88.13	0.	31	101.03	1.657	45	117.81	0.000
4	68.64	0.000	18	89.52	0.000	32	102.11	1.982	46	120.44	0.084
5	71.19	0.000	19	91.81	0.000	33	102.42	1.991	47	121.05	0.011
6	72.74	0.009	20	92.67	0.363	34	103.66	0.000	48	121.91	0.027
7	77.27	0.018	21	93.48	0.000	35	106.52	0.000	49	122.59	0.053
8	77.41	0.053	22	95.09	0.000	36	107.33	0.363	50	122.73	0.018
9	78.09	0.027	23	95.73	0.000	37	107.33	0.000	51	127.26	0.009
10	78.95	0.011	24	97.58	1.991	38	108.80	0.000	52	129.42	0.000
11	79.56	0.084	25	97.89	1.982	39	109.45	0.000	53	131.36	0.000
12	79.77	0.000	26	98.97	1.657	40	109.69	0.000	54	133.34	0.
13	85.64	0.000	27	99.56	3.916	41	110.48	0.000	55	139.37	0.000
14	85.78	0.000	28	99.83	5.858	42	113.55	0.031	56	143.47	0.000

5-419

$J_{AA'}$	J_{AB}	$J_{AB'}$	$J_{BB'}$
-2	4	6	4
-2	6	4	4
4	6	4	-2
4	4	6	-2

The maximum summed intensity is 5.473.

LINE	FREQ	INTEN	LINE	FREQ	INTEN	LINE	FREQ	INTEN	LINE	FREQ	INTEN
1	80.80	0.001	15	95.00	0.	29	99.60	5.463	43	106.40	0.000
2	86.63	0.000	16	95.49	0.271	30	99.92	0.000	44	107.15	0.077
3	86.68	0.000	17	95.84	0.684	31	100.40	5.463	45	107.54	0.618
4	87.93	0.025	18	96.33	0.000	32	100.68	0.000	46	107.99	0.000
5	88.63	0.000	19	96.45	0.000	33	100.83	3.715	47	108.23	0.000
6	89.17	0.285	20	96.46	0.000	34	101.67	0.000	48	108.63	0.000
7	90.01	0.000	21	97.08	1.988	35	102.16	1.316	49	109.25	0.012
8	90.62	0.174	22	97.71	1.371	36	102.29	1.371	50	109.38	0.174
9	90.75	0.012	23	97.84	1.316	37	102.92	1.988	51	109.99	0.000
10	92.01	0.000	24	98.33	0.000	38	103.67	0.000	52	110.83	0.285
11	92.46	0.618	25	98.45	0.000	39	104.16	0.684	53	112.07	0.025
12	92.85	0.077	26	98.68	0.000	40	104.51	0.271	54	112.08	0.000
13	93.00	0.	27	98.85	0.000	41	106.23	0.000	55	118.46	0.000
14	94.23	0.000	28	99.17	3.715	42	106.29	0.000	56	119.20	0.001

5-420

$J_{AA'}$	J_{AB}	$J_{AB'}$	$J_{BB'}$
-2	4	6	6
-2	6	4	6
6	6	4	-2
6	4	6	-2

The maximum summed intensity is 5.472.

LINE	FREQ	INTEN	LINE	FREQ	INTEN	LINE	FREQ	INTEN	LINE	FREQ	INTEN
1	80.76	0.001	15	94.41	0.000	29	99.71	0.000	43	107.48	0.000
2	84.70	0.	16	94.46	0.143	30	99.93	0.000	44	107.58	0.608
3	87.17	0.000	17	95.34	0.000	31	100.29	0.000	45	107.95	0.000
4	87.94	0.025	18	96.17	0.000	32	100.40	5.465	46	108.24	0.186
5	88.05	0.000	19	96.29	0.000	33	100.83	3.715	47	109.48	0.000
6	88.81	0.005	20	96.58	0.983	34	101.00	0.000	48	109.65	0.000
7	89.17	0.285	21	97.05	1.995	35	101.42	0.669	49	110.24	0.063
8	89.76	0.063	22	97.29	1.857	36	102.71	1.857	50	110.83	0.285
9	90.00	0.000	23	98.18	0.000	37	102.95	1.995	51	111.19	0.005
10	91.59	0.000	24	98.58	0.669	38	103.42	0.983	52	111.95	0.000
11	91.76	0.186	25	98.84	0.000	39	103.71	0.000	53	112.06	0.025
12	92.05	0.000	26	99.00	0.000	40	104.34	0.	54	114.07	0.000
13	92.42	0.608	27	99.17	3.715	41	105.54	0.143	55	118.48	0.000
14	93.34	0.000	28	99.60	5.465	42	106.82	0.000	56	119.24	0.001

5-421

$J_{AA'}$	J_{AB}	$J_{AB'}$	$J_{BB'}$
-2	4	9	4
-2	9	4	4
4	9	4	-2
4	4	9	-2

The maximum summed intensity is 5.721.

LINE	FREQ	INTEN	LINE	FREQ	INTEN	LINE	FREQ	INTEN	LINE	FREQ	INTEN
1	76.10	0.001	15	92.91	0.000	29	99.71	5.667	43	107.28	0.048
2	81.76	0.000	16	92.96	0.145	30	100.29	5.667	44	109.24	0.000
3	85.05	0.000	17	93.59	0.360	31	100.66	3.816	45	109.58	0.402
4	85.39	0.020	18	95.00	0.	32	101.00	0.000	46	110.06	0.000
5	86.34	0.184	19	95.75	0.000	33	101.41	1.640	47	110.41	0.045
6	86.76	0.000	20	97.41	1.955	34	101.57	1.617	48	110.95	0.000
7	87.25	0.101	21	97.75	0.000	35	102.25	0.000	49	111.09	0.000
8	87.94	0.000	22	97.91	0.000	36	102.59	1.955	50	112.06	0.000
9	89.59	0.045	23	98.05	0.000	37	103.38	0.000	51	112.75	0.101
10	89.94	0.000	24	98.09	0.000	38	104.25	0.000	52	113.66	0.184
11	90.00	0.	25	98.38	0.000	39	105.62	0.000	53	114.00	0.000
12	90.42	0.402	26	98.43	1.617	40	105.95	0.000	54	114.61	0.020
13	92.62	0.000	27	98.59	1.640	41	106.41	0.360	55	122.24	0.000
14	92.72	0.048	28	99.34	3.816	42	107.04	0.145	56	123.90	0.001

5-422

$J_{AA'}$	J_{AB}	$J_{AB'}$	$J_{BB'}$
-2	4	9	9
-2	9	4	9
9	9	4	-2
9	4	9	-2

The maximum summed intensity is 5.846.

LINE	FREQ	INTEN	LINE	FREQ	INTEN	LINE	FREQ	INTEN	LINE	FREQ	INTEN
1	75.65	0.000	15	90.72	0.000	29	99.99	1.033	43	109.58	0.064
2	80.19	0.000	16	92.79	0.000	30	100.01	1.033	44	109.70	0.000
3	82.77	0.000	17	93.54	0.000	31	100.29	5.674	45	110.04	0.347
4	83.30	0.000	18	94.81	0.000	32	100.66	3.816	46	110.24	0.100
5	85.10	0.010	19	95.38	0.000	33	101.14	0.000	47	112.53	0.000
6	85.40	0.020	20	95.92	0.784	34	102.38	0.000	48	113.66	0.184
7	85.67	0.041	21	96.88	0.000	35	102.51	1.936	49	114.33	0.041
8	86.34	0.184	22	97.18	1.990	36	102.82	1.990	50	114.48	0.000
9	86.46	0.000	23	97.49	1.936	37	103.96	0.000	51	114.60	0.020
10	89.76	0.100	24	97.62	0.000	38	104.08	0.784	52	114.90	0.010
11	89.84	0.000	25	97.91	0.000	39	104.62	0.000	53	116.70	0.000
12	89.96	0.347	26	99.34	3.816	40	104.83	0.000	54	118.86	0.000
13	90.30	0.000	27	99.71	5.674	41	107.41	0.000	55	122.55	0.000
14	90.42	0.064	28	99.87	0.000	42	108.44	0.000	56	124.35	0.000

5-423

$J_{AA'}$	J_{AB}	$J_{AB'}$	$J_{BB'}$
-2	4	12	4
-2	12	4	4
4	12	4	-2
4	4	12	-2

The maximum summed intensity is 5.779.

LINE	FREQ	INTEN	LINE	FREQ	INTEN	LINE	FREQ	INTEN	LINE	FREQ	INTEN
1	70.89	0.000	15	90.59	0.000	29	99.77	5.774	43	109.74	0.088
2	76.44	0.000	16	91.00	0.200	30	100.23	5.774	44	112.02	0.260
3	82.69	0.016	17	92.65	0.032	31	100.54	3.873	45	112.21	0.057
4	83.02	0.000	18	95.00	0.000	32	101.00	1.800	46	112.35	0.000
5	83.46	0.127	19	95.46	0.000	33	101.14	1.764	47	112.54	0.000
6	84.05	0.067	20	97.44	0.000	34	101.79	0.	48	113.62	0.000
7	84.44	0.000	21	97.46	0.000	35	102.21	1.943	49	113.77	0.000
8	85.46	0.000	22	97.59	0.000	36	102.54	0.000	50	114.54	0.000
9	87.00	0.	23	97.79	1.943	37	104.54	0.000	51	115.95	0.067
10	87.46	0.000	24	98.20	0.000	38	105.01	0.000	52	116.21	0.
11	87.79	0.057	25	98.86	1.764	39	105.77	0.000	53	116.54	0.127
12	87.98	0.260	26	99.00	1.800	40	106.20	0.000	54	117.31	0.016
13	89.59	0.000	27	99.19	0.000	41	107.35	0.032	55	126.77	0.000
14	90.26	0.088	28	99.46	3.873	42	109.00	0.200	56	129.11	0.000

5-424

$J_{AA'}$	J_{AB}	$J_{AB'}$	$J_{BB'}$
-2	4	12	12
-2	12	4	12
12	12	4	-2
12	4	12	-2

The maximum summed intensity is 5.835.

LINE	FREQ	INTEN	LINE	FREQ	INTEN	LINE	FREQ	INTEN	LINE	FREQ	INTEN
1	69.62	0.000	15	88.82	0.000	29	100.22	5.783	43	111.61	0.000
2	75.46	0.000	16	90.17	0.000	30	100.54	3.873	44	112.30	0.057
3	77.50	0.000	17	92.66	0.000	31	100.63	1.293	45	113.30	0.187
4	78.39	0.000	18	93.40	0.000	32	101.49	0.000	46	113.72	0.035
5	81.17	0.010	19	94.52	0.000	33	102.23	0.000	47	114.94	0.000
6	81.34	0.000	20	95.21	0.631	34	102.41	1.965	48	116.54	0.127
7	82.29	0.032	21	95.48	0.000	35	102.71	1.990	49	117.31	0.016
8	82.69	0.016	22	95.59	0.000	36	104.52	0.000	50	117.71	0.032
9	83.46	0.127	23	97.01	0.000	37	104.79	0.631	51	118.83	0.010
10	86.28	0.035	24	97.29	1.990	38	105.48	0.000	52	119.42	0.000
11	86.70	0.187	25	97.59	1.965	39	106.07	0.000	53	121.61	0.000
12	87.70	0.057	26	99.37	1.293	40	106.90	0.000	54	123.77	0.
13	87.99	0.000	27	99.46	3.873	41	108.11	0.000	55	127.61	0.000
14	88.39	0.000	28	99.78	5.783	42	109.53	0.000	56	130.38	0.000

5-425

$J_{AA'}$	J_{AB}	$J_{AB'}$	$J_{BB'}$
-2	4	15	4
-2	15	4	4
4	15	4	-2
4	4	15	-2

The maximum summed intensity is 6.325.

LINE	FREQ	INTEN	LINE	FREQ	INTEN	LINE	FREQ	INTEN	LINE	FREQ	INTEN
1	65.40	0.000	15	88.24	0.122	29	99.95	0.000	43	112.54	0.058
2	70.87	0.000	16	88.29	0.000	30	100.18	5.837	44	114.40	0.054
3	79.89	0.012	17	92.61	0.023	31	100.46	3.907	45	114.67	0.176
4	80.54	0.093	18	95.00	0.	32	100.76	1.878	46	115.23	0.000
5	80.71	0.000	19	95.30	0.000	33	100.87	1.847	47	115.49	0.000
6	80.95	0.048	20	96.99	0.000	34	101.87	1.946	48	116.23	0.000
7	81.87	0.000	21	97.30	0.000	35	102.36	0.000	49	116.65	0.000
8	82.77	0.000	22	97.41	0.000	36	102.70	0.000	50	117.23	0.000
9	84.00	0.000	23	98.07	0.000	37	104.56	0.000	51	118.64	0.
10	84.77	0.000	24	98.13	1.946	38	104.70	0.000	52	119.05	0.048
11	85.33	0.176	25	99.13	1.847	39	105.65	0.000	53	119.46	0.093
12	85.60	0.054	26	99.24	1.878	40	107.39	0.023	54	120.11	0.012
13	86.41	0.000	27	99.54	3.907	41	109.07	0.000	55	131.77	0.000
14	87.46	0.058	28	99.82	5.837	42	111.76	0.122	56	134.60	0.000

-11 -10 -9 -8 -7 -6 -5 -4 -3 -2 -1 0 +1 +2 +3 +4 +5 +6 +7 +8 +9 +10 +11

5-426

$J_{AA'}$	J_{AB}	$J_{AB'}$	$J_{BB'}$
-2	4	15	15
-2	15	4	15
15	15	4	-2
15	4	15	-2

The maximum summed intensity is 6.309.

LINE	FREQ	INTEN	LINE	FREQ	INTEN	LINE	FREQ	INTEN	LINE	FREQ	INTEN
1	63.12	0.000	15	87.36	0.000	29	100.18	5.846	43	113.59	0.000
2	70.61	0.000	16	87.91	0.000	30	100.46	3.907	44	114.37	0.034
3	71.80	0.000	17	91.56	0.000	31	100.85	1.461	45	116.96	0.109
4	73.41	0.000	18	91.78	0.000	32	102.35	1.978	46	117.06	0.000
5	76.22	0.000	19	93.34	0.000	33	102.62	1.992	47	117.90	0.022
6	77.13	0.008	20	93.66	0.000	34	103.25	0.000	48	119.46	0.093
7	79.23	0.027	21	94.31	0.000	35	103.47	0.000	49	120.10	0.013
8	79.90	0.013	22	94.45	0.510	36	105.55	0.510	50	120.77	0.027
9	80.54	0.093	23	96.11	0.000	37	106.34	0.000	51	122.87	0.008
10	82.10	0.022	24	97.38	1.992	38	106.66	0.000	52	124.42	0.000
11	83.04	0.109	25	97.65	1.978	39	107.67	0.000	53	126.59	0.000
12	85.16	0.000	26	99.15	1.461	40	108.86	0.000	54	128.75	0.000
13	85.63	0.034	27	99.54	3.907	41	109.87	0.000	55	133.17	0.000
14	86.41	0.000	28	99.82	5.846	42	110.66	0.000	56	136.88	0.000

-11 -10 -9 -8 -7 -6 -5 -4 -3 -2 -1 0 +1 +2 +3 +4 +5 +6 +7 +8 +9 +10 +11

5-427

$J_{AA'}$	J_{AB}	$J_{AB'}$	$J_{BB'}$
-2	4	18	4
-2	18	4	4
4	18	4	-2
4	4	18	-2

The maximum summed intensity is 6.791.

LINE	FREQ	INTEN	LINE	FREQ	INTEN	LINE	FREQ	INTEN	LINE	FREQ	INTEN
1	59.75	0.000	15	85.38	0.081	29	100.16	5.877	43	115.39	0.040
2	65.16	0.	16	85.79	0.000	30	100.40	3.930	44	116.84	0.046
3	77.04	0.010	17	92.59	0.017	31	100.48	0.000	45	117.44	0.124
4	77.60	0.070	18	95.00	0.000	32	100.62	1.919	46	118.02	0.000
5	77.90	0.036	19	95.21	0.000	33	100.70	1.896	47	118.62	0.000
6	78.22	0.000	20	96.66	0.000	34	101.60	1.954	48	118.92	0.
7	79.16	0.000	21	97.21	0.000	35	102.78	0.000	49	119.56	0.000
8	79.98	0.000	22	97.30	0.000	36	102.79	0.000	50	120.02	0.000
9	81.00	0.	23	97.99	0.000	37	104.23	0.000	51	121.22	0.
10	81.98	0.000	24	98.40	1.954	38	104.79	0.000	52	122.10	0.036
11	82.56	0.124	25	99.30	1.896	39	105.56	0.000	53	122.40	0.070
12	83.16	0.046	26	99.38	1.919	40	107.41	0.017	54	122.96	0.010
13	83.30	0.000	27	99.60	3.930	41	111.99	0.000	55	137.06	0.
14	84.61	0.040	28	99.84	5.877	42	114.62	0.081	56	140.25	0.000

5-428

$J_{AA'}$	J_{AB}	$J_{AB'}$	$J_{BB'}$
-2	4	18	18
-2	18	4	18
18	18	4	-2
18	4	18	-2

The maximum summed intensity is 6.722

LINE	FREQ	INTEN	LINE	FREQ	INTEN	LINE	FREQ	INTEN	LINE	FREQ	INTEN
1	56.39	0.000	15	85.69	0.000	29	100.15	5.885	43	115.61	0.000
2	65.68	0.000	16	85.79	0.	30	100.40	3.930	44	116.43	0.022
3	65.89	0.000	17	89.55	0.000	31	100.91	1.577	45	119.08	0.000
4	68.39	0.000	18	90.90	0.	32	102.31	1.985	46	120.81	0.069
5	71.10	0.000	19	91.20	0.000	33	102.56	1.993	47	122.11	0.015
6	73.03	0.007	20	92.80	0.000	34	104.24	0.000	48	122.40	0.070
7	76.29	0.022	21	93.07	0.000	35	105.59	0.000	49	122.95	0.010
8	77.05	0.010	22	93.63	0.415	36	106.37	0.415	50	123.71	0.022
9	77.60	0.070	23	95.21	0.000	37	107.20	0.000	51	126.97	0.007
10	77.89	0.015	24	97.44	1.993	38	108.80	0.000	52	129.45	0.000
11	79.19	0.069	25	97.69	1.985	39	109.45	0.	53	131.61	0.000
12	82.26	0.000	26	99.09	1.577	40	109.65	0.000	54	133.76	0.000
13	83.57	0.022	27	99.60	3.930	41	111.79	0.000	55	138.98	0.000
14	84.39	0.000	28	99.85	5.885	42	112.87	0.000	56	143.61	0.000

5-429

$J_{AA'}$	J_{AB}	$J_{AB'}$	$J_{BB'}$
-4	6	9	6
-4	9	6	6
6	9	6	-4
6	6	9	-4

The maximum summed intensity is 5.602.

LINE	FREQ	INTEN	LINE	FREQ	INTEN	LINE	FREQ	INTEN	LINE	FREQ	INTEN
1	74.07	0.001	15	92.28	0.061	29	99.76	5.758	43	108.72	0.000
2	80.65	0.000	16	92.40	0.000	30	100.24	5.758	44	109.43	0.011
3	82.55	0.000	17	93.28	0.060	31	100.36	0.000	45	109.78	0.406
4	83.61	0.018	18	94.00	0.	32	100.58	3.857	46	111.81	0.000
5	84.42	0.143	19	96.14	0.000	33	101.86	0.000	47	112.30	0.000
6	85.65	0.000	20	96.97	0.000	34	101.97	1.660	48	113.24	0.000
7	85.70	0.000	21	97.08	1.994	35	102.15	0.000	49	113.36	0.006
8	85.82	0.087	22	97.15	0.000	36	102.72	1.939	50	114.18	0.087
9	86.64	0.006	23	97.28	1.939	37	102.92	1.994	51	114.30	0.000
10	87.70	0.000	24	97.40	0.000	38	103.86	0.000	52	115.58	0.143
11	89.00	0.	25	98.03	1.660	39	106.72	0.060	53	116.39	0.018
12	90.22	0.406	26	98.14	0.000	40	106.81	0.000	54	116.64	0.
13	90.57	0.011	27	98.83	0.000	41	107.72	0.061	55	124.99	0.000
14	92.21	0.000	28	99.42	3.857	42	108.49	0.000	56	125.93	0.001

5-430

$J_{AA'}$	J_{AB}	$J_{AB'}$	$J_{BB'}$
-4	6	9	9
-4	9	6	9
9	9	6	-4
9	6	9	-4

The maximum summed intensity is 5.607.

LINE	FREQ	INTEN	LINE	FREQ	INTEN	LINE	FREQ	INTEN	LINE	FREQ	INTEN
1	73.99	0.001	15	91.76	0.000	29	99.80	0.000	43	110.48	0.016
2	79.57	0.000	16	92.19	0.000	30	100.24	5.759	44	110.99	0.000
3	80.76	0.000	17	93.81	0.000	31	100.38	0.000	45	111.95	0.031
4	82.75	0.000	18	94.39	0.000	32	100.58	3.857	46	112.25	0.000
5	83.61	0.018	19	94.82	0.000	33	101.09	0.000	47	113.62	0.000
6	83.71	0.002	20	95.80	0.341	34	101.57	1.388	48	114.58	0.066
7	84.42	0.143	21	96.09	0.000	35	102.43	0.000	49	114.62	0.000
8	85.42	0.066	22	97.05	1.998	36	102.86	1.984	50	115.58	0.143
9	86.19	0.000	23	97.14	1.984	37	102.95	1.998	51	116.29	0.002
10	87.75	0.000	24	98.43	1.388	38	103.91	0.000	52	116.39	0.018
11	88.05	0.031	25	98.80	0.000	39	104.20	0.341	53	117.25	0.000
12	88.38	0.000	26	98.91	0.000	40	105.81	0.	54	119.62	0.000
13	89.52	0.016	27	99.42	3.857	41	107.01	0.000	55	125.05	0.
14	90.15	0.396	28	99.76	5.759	42	109.85	0.396	56	126.01	0.001

5-431

$J_{AA'}$	J_{AB}	$J_{AB'}$	$J_{BB'}$
-4	6	12	6
-4	12	6	6
6	12	6	-4
6	6	12	-4

The maximum summed intensity is 6.174.

LINE	FREQ	INTEN	LINE	FREQ	INTEN	LINE	FREQ	INTEN	LINE	FREQ	INTEN
1	69.12	0.000	15	90.56	0.096	29	99.81	5.830	43	109.73	0.011
2	76.00	0.000	16	90.70	0.000	30	100.19	5.830	44	111.85	0.000
3	80.78	0.000	17	90.76	0.056	31	100.49	3.897	45	111.91	0.279
4	80.84	0.014	18	93.61	0.000	32	101.45	1.754	46	114.28	0.000
5	81.51	0.103	19	95.34	0.000	33	101.46	0.000	47	114.32	0.000
6	82.47	0.057	20	96.56	0.000	34	102.23	1.904	48	114.37	0.016
7	83.21	0.000	21	97.15	0.000	35	102.66	0.000	49	115.58	0.000
8	83.68	0.000	22	97.29	1.984	36	102.71	1.984	50	116.32	0.000
9	85.63	0.016	23	97.34	0.000	37	104.36	0.000	51	117.53	0.057
10	85.68	0.000	24	97.77	1.904	38	104.66	0.000	52	118.49	0.103
11	86.39	0.	25	97.87	0.000	39	107.07	0.000	53	118.54	0.000
12	88.09	0.279	26	98.50	0.000	40	107.79	0.000	54	119.16	0.014
13	89.35	0.000	27	98.55	1.754	41	109.24	0.056	55	128.94	0.000
14	90.27	0.011	28	99.51	3.897	42	109.44	0.096	56	130.88	0.000

−11 −10 −9 −8 −7 −6 −5 −4 −3 −2 −1 0 +1 +2 +3 +4 +5 +6 +7 +8 +9 +10 +11

5-432

$J_{AA'}$	J_{AB}	$J_{AB'}$	$J_{BB'}$
-4	6	12	12
-4	12	6	12
12	12	6	-4
12	6	12	-4

The maximum summed intensity is 6.284.

LINE	FREQ	INTEN	LINE	FREQ	INTEN	LINE	FREQ	INTEN	LINE	FREQ	INTEN
1	68.64	0.000	15	89.17	0.000	29	100.19	5.831	43	112.38	0.246
2	74.92	0.000	16	89.40	0.	30	100.49	1.392	44	114.03	0.000
3	76.30	0.000	17	92.83	0.000	31	100.49	3.897	45	114.29	0.029
4	77.97	0.000	18	93.36	0.000	32	100.83	0.000	46	114.37	0.016
5	80.05	0.004	19	93.60	0.000	33	101.60	0.000	47	116.40	0.000
6	80.84	0.014	20	95.06	0.000	34	102.71	1.984	48	118.49	0.037
7	81.17	0.000	21	95.32	0.450	35	102.86	1.996	49	118.49	0.103
8	81.51	0.037	22	96.94	0.000	36	103.06	0.000	50	119.16	0.014
9	81.51	0.103	23	97.14	1.996	37	104.68	0.450	51	119.51	0.000
10	85.63	0.016	24	97.29	1.984	38	104.94	0.000	52	119.95	0.004
11	85.71	0.029	25	97.73	0.000	39	105.02	0.000	53	122.03	0.000
12	85.97	0.000	26	99.51	1.392	40	106.47	0.000	54	124.40	0.000
13	87.62	0.246	27	99.51	3.897	41	107.84	0.000	55	129.27	0.000
14	87.96	0.000	28	99.81	5.831	42	112.21	0.000	56	131.36	0.000

−11 −10 −9 −8 −7 −6 −5 −4 −3 −2 −1 0 +1 +2 +3 +4 +5 +6 +7 +8 +9 +10 +11

5-433

$J_{AA'}$	J_{AB}	$J_{AB'}$	$J_{BB'}$
-4	6	15	6
-4	15	6	6
6	15	6	6
6	6	15	-4

The maximum summed intensity is 6.574.

LINE	FREQ	INTEN	LINE	FREQ	INTEN	LINE	FREQ	INTEN	LINE	FREQ	INTEN
1	63.81	0.000	15	88.35	0.087	29	99.84	5.873	43	111.94	0.044
2	70.80	0.000	16	88.80	0.000	30	100.16	5.873	44	114.35	0.193
3	78.00	0.011	17	90.10	0.009	31	100.42	3.923	45	115.09	0.000
4	78.58	0.077	18	93.42	0.	32	101.10	1.830	46	115.91	0.024
5	78.74	0.000	19	94.81	0.000	33	101.80	1.913	47	116.65	0.000
6	79.26	0.041	20	96.10	0.000	34	102.32	0.000	48	117.00	0.000
7	80.65	0.000	21	96.81	0.000	35	102.45	1.976	49	118.00	0.000
8	81.35	0.000	22	97.09	0.000	36	103.19	0.000	50	118.65	0.000
9	83.35	0.000	23	97.10	0.000	37	105.19	0.000	51	120.68	0.
10	83.58	0.	24	97.55	1.976	38	106.94	0.000	52	120.74	0.041
11	84.09	0.024	25	98.20	1.913	39	107.16	0.000	53	121.42	0.077
12	85.65	0.193	26	98.90	1.830	40	107.16	0.000	54	122.00	0.011
13	86.25	0.000	27	99.58	3.923	41	109.90	0.009	55	133.45	0.000
14	88.06	0.044	28	99.64	0.000	42	111.65	0.087	56	136.19	0.000

−11 −10 −9 −8 −7 −6 −5 −4 −3 −2 −1 0 +1 +2 +3 +4 +5 +6 +7 +8 +9 +10 +11

5-434

$J_{AA'}$	J_{AB}	$J_{AB'}$	$J_{BB'}$
-4	6	15	15
-4	15	6	15
15	15	6	-4
15	6	15	-4

The maximum summed intensity is 8.033.

LINE	FREQ	INTEN	LINE	FREQ	INTEN	LINE	FREQ	INTEN	LINE	FREQ	INTEN
1	62.62	0.000	15	86.79	0.000	29	100.12	1.496	43	115.54	0.149
2	70.14	0.000	16	86.94	0.000	30	100.16	5.876	44	115.93	0.000
3	71.13	0.000	17	91.91	0.	31	100.42	3.923	45	116.49	0.021
4	73.07	0.000	18	92.02	0.000	32	102.36	0.000	46	118.42	0.013
5	76.09	0.	19	92.26	0.000	33	102.61	1.987	47	118.83	0.000
6	76.20	0.005	20	94.09	0.000	34	102.71	0.	48	121.42	0.077
7	78.00	0.011	21	94.65	0.421	35	102.77	1.995	49	121.96	0.027
8	78.04	0.027	22	94.91	0.000	36	105.09	0.000	50	122.00	0.011
9	78.58	0.077	23	96.71	0.000	37	105.35	0.421	51	123.80	0.005
10	81.58	0.013	24	97.23	1.995	38	105.91	0.000	52	124.48	0.000
11	83.51	0.021	25	97.39	1.987	39	107.68	0.000	53	126.93	0.000
12	84.07	0.000	26	99.58	3.923	40	107.83	0.000	54	129.29	0.000
13	84.46	0.149	27	99.84	5.876	41	108.67	0.000	55	134.25	0.000
14	86.55	0.000	28	99.88	1.496	42	113.36	0.000	56	137.38	0.000

−11 −10 −9 −8 −7 −6 −5 −4 −3 −2 −1 0 +1 +2 +3 +4 +5 +6 +7 +8 +9 +10 +11

5-435

$J_{AA'}$	J_{AB}	$J_{AB'}$	$J_{BB'}$
-6	9	12	9
-6	12	9	9
9	12	9	-6
9	9	12	-6

The maximum summed intensity is 6.540.

LINE	FREQ	INTEN	LINE	FREQ	INTEN	LINE	FREQ	INTEN	LINE	FREQ	INTEN
1	65.81	0.000	15	87.65	0.273	29	99.84	5.877	43	112.35	0.273
2	73.49	0.000	16	90.46	0.000	30	100.16	5.877	44	112.39	0.008
3	76.82	0.000	17	91.65	0.018	31	100.42	3.923	45	113.49	0.002
4	78.00	0.011	18	92.74	0.000	32	101.39	0.000	46	117.07	0.000
5	78.58	0.077	19	94.19	0.000	33	101.68	1.774	47	117.32	0.000
6	79.84	0.044	20	95.23	0.000	34	101.77	0.000	48	118.26	0.002
7	79.93	0.000	21	97.00	0.000	35	102.91	1.992	49	118.35	0.000
8	81.74	0.002	22	97.04	1.998	36	102.96	1.998	50	120.07	0.000
9	82.93	0.000	23	97.09	1.992	37	103.67	0.000	51	120.16	0.044
10	82.98	0.000	24	97.13	0.000	38	104.77	0.000	52	121.42	0.077
11	83.26	0.000	25	98.03	0.000	39	107.83	0.000	53	122.00	0.011
12	86.51	0.002	26	98.23	0.000	40	108.35	0.018	54	122.61	0.
13	87.52	0.000	27	98.32	1.774	41	111.16	0.000	55	132.37	0.000
14	87.61	0.008	28	99.58	3.923	42	111.68	0.000	56	134.19	0.000

−11 −10 −9 −8 −7 −6 −5 −4 −3 −2 −1 0 +1 +2 +3 +4 +5 +6 +7 +8 +9 +10 +11

5-436

$J_{AA'}$	J_{AB}	$J_{AB'}$	$J_{BB'}$
-6	9	12	12
-6	12	9	12
12	12	9	-6
12	9	12	-6

The maximum summed intensity is 6.540.

LINE	FREQ	INTEN	LINE	FREQ	INTEN	LINE	FREQ	INTEN	LINE	FREQ	INTEN
1	65.76	0.000	15	87.60	0.270	29	99.84	5.877	43	114.51	0.000
2	73.50	0.000	16	90.32	0.000	30	100.16	5.877	44	115.31	0.003
3	73.83	0.000	17	91.40	0.000	31	100.42	3.923	45	116.33	0.004
4	76.96	0.000	18	92.68	0.000	32	101.20	0.000	46	117.04	0.000
5	78.00	0.011	19	94.26	0.000	33	101.41	0.000	47	118.44	0.000
6	78.58	0.077	20	94.49	0.072	34	101.57	1.724	48	120.26	0.000
7	78.78	0.001	21	95.20	0.000	35	102.94	1.997	49	120.27	0.042
8	79.73	0.042	22	97.03	1.999	36	102.97	1.999	50	121.22	0.001
9	80.32	0.000	23	97.06	1.997	37	103.77	0.000	51	121.42	0.077
10	82.96	0.000	24	98.02	0.000	38	104.80	0.000	52	122.00	0.011
11	83.67	0.004	25	98.43	1.724	39	105.51	0.072	53	123.04	0.000
12	84.69	0.003	26	98.80	0.000	40	107.89	0.000	54	125.59	0.000
13	85.87	0.000	27	99.58	3.923	41	108.22	0.000	55	132.41	0.000
14	87.47	0.000	28	99.84	0.000	42	112.40	0.270	56	134.24	0.000

−11 −10 −9 −8 −7 −6 −5 −4 −3 −2 −1 0 +1 +2 +3 +4 +5 +6 +7 +8 +9 +10 +11

5-437

$J_{AA'}$	J_{AB}	$J_{AB'}$	$J_{BB'}$
-6	9	15	9
-6	15	9	9
9	15	9	-6
9	9	15	-6

The maximum summed intensity is 7.201.

LINE	FREQ	INTEN	LINE	FREQ	INTEN	LINE	FREQ	INTEN	LINE	FREQ	INTEN
1	60.84	0.000	15	86.51	0.021	29	99.87	5.906	43	114.03	0.002
2	69.30	0.	16	89.24	0.000	30	100.13	5.906	44	114.37	0.000
3	75.08	0.000	17	89.29	0.026	31	100.37	3.940	45	114.42	0.201
4	75.13	0.009	18	91.91	0.000	32	101.32	1.824	46	118.95	0.000
5	75.63	0.060	19	94.21	0.000	33	102.58	0.000	47	119.00	0.005
6	76.58	0.032	20	94.43	0.000	34	102.67	1.979	48	119.41	0.000
7	78.05	0.000	21	95.86	0.000	35	102.79	0.000	49	120.47	0.000
8	80.12	0.000	22	96.92	0.000	36	102.84	1.995	50	121.95	0.000
9	81.00	0.005	23	97.16	1.995	37	105.25	0.000	51	123.42	0.032
10	81.05	0.000	24	97.21	0.000	38	105.79	0.000	52	124.37	0.060
11	81.09	0.000	25	97.33	1.979	39	108.60	0.000	53	124.42	0.000
12	85.04	0.000	26	98.63	0.000	40	110.71	0.026	54	124.87	0.009
13	85.58	0.201	27	98.68	1.824	41	111.08	0.000	55	136.21	0.000
14	85.97	0.002	28	99.63	3.940	42	113.49	0.021	56	139.16	0.000

5-438

$J_{AA'}$	J_{AB}	$J_{AB'}$	$J_{BB'}$
-6	9	15	15
-6	15	9	15
15	15	9	-6
15	9	15	-6

The maximum summed intensity is 7.207.

LINE	FREQ	INTEN	LINE	FREQ	INTEN	LINE	FREQ	INTEN	LINE	FREQ	INTEN
1	60.52	0.000	15	85.47	0.000	29	100.13	5.906	43	116.24	0.000
2	69.17	0.000	16	88.58	0.000	30	100.37	3.940	44	118.79	0.000
3	69.31	0.000	17	89.51	0.000	31	100.88	1.667	45	119.00	0.005
4	72.21	0.000	18	91.58	0.000	32	101.09	0.000	46	119.28	0.007
5	75.13	0.009	19	93.16	0.000	33	102.67	0.	47	120.81	0.000
6	75.25	0.002	20	94.05	0.000	34	102.84	1.995	48	123.85	0.027
7	75.42	0.000	21	94.54	0.196	35	102.91	1.998	49	124.37	0.060
8	75.63	0.060	22	96.83	0.000	36	103.05	0.000	50	124.75	0.002
9	76.15	0.027	23	96.95	0.000	37	105.46	0.196	51	124.87	0.009
10	80.72	0.007	24	97.09	1.998	38	105.67	0.000	52	125.08	0.000
11	81.00	0.005	25	97.16	1.995	39	105.95	0.000	53	127.79	0.000
12	81.21	0.000	26	99.12	1.667	40	108.78	0.000	54	130.33	0.
13	84.94	0.000	27	99.63	3.940	41	108.93	0.000	55	136.44	0.000
14	85.26	0.188	28	99.87	5.906	42	114.74	0.188	56	139.48	0.000

5-439

$J_{AA'}$	J_{AB}	$J_{AB'}$	$J_{BB'}$
-9	12	15	15
-9	15	12	15
15	15	12	-9
15	12	15	-9

The maximum summed intensity is 8.045.

LINE	FREQ	INTEN	LINE	FREQ	INTEN	LINE	FREQ	INTEN	LINE	FREQ	INTEN
1	57.29	0.000	15	84.95	0.192	29	99.88	5.926	43	117.71	0.000
2	64.99	0.000	16	87.56	0.000	30	100.12	5.926	44	119.47	0.001
3	67.98	0.000	17	88.24	0.000	31	100.33	3.952	45	121.22	0.001
4	71.08	0.000	18	91.81	0.013	32	101.26	0.000	46	122.92	0.000
5	72.22	0.007	19	92.62	0.000	33	101.40	1.835	47	124.50	0.000
6	72.67	0.048	20	94.35	0.000	34	101.43	0.000	48	126.07	0.000
7	72.83	0.000	21	95.26	0.000	35	102.97	1.999	49	126.26	0.026
8	73.74	0.026	22	97.02	2.000	36	102.98	2.000	50	127.17	0.000
9	74.38	0.000	23	97.03	1.999	37	104.74	0.000	51	127.33	0.048
10	77.08	0.000	24	98.13	0.000	38	106.49	0.000	52	127.78	0.007
11	78.78	0.001	25	98.60	1.835	39	107.82	0.000	53	128.92	0.000
12	80.53	0.001	26	98.74	0.000	40	108.19	0.013	54	131.57	0.000
13	81.45	0.000	27	99.67	3.952	41	110.81	0.000	55	140.96	0.000
14	83.24	0.000	28	99.70	0.000	42	115.05	0.192	56	142.71	0.000

5-440

$J_{AA'}$	J_{AB}	$J_{AB'}$	$J_{BB'}$
-1	2	4	-1
-1	4	2	-1

The maximum summed intensity is 4.334.

LINE	FREQ	INTEN	LINE	FREQ	INTEN	LINE	FREQ	INTEN	LINE	FREQ	INTEN
1	85.64	0.001	15	95.76	0.000	29	100.78	0.000	43	104.24	0.000
2	85.72	0.000	16	95.84	0.684	30	100.85	4.539	44	104.56	0.000
3	90.66	0.015	17	95.84	0.684	31	100.93	0.000	45	105.16	0.
4	92.05	0.000	18	97.14	1.598	32	101.16	0.000	46	105.54	0.000
5	92.74	0.000	19	97.76	0.000	33	101.24	3.414	47	105.62	0.594
6	92.76	0.586	20	97.84	1.316	34	101.76	0.000	48	105.87	0.893
7	93.36	0.081	21	97.84	1.316	35	101.84	0.281	49	106.24	0.000
8	93.76	0.000	22	98.16	0.281	36	102.16	1.316	50	106.64	0.081
9	94.13	0.893	23	98.24	0.000	37	102.16	1.316	51	107.24	0.586
10	94.38	0.594	24	98.76	3.414	38	102.24	0.000	52	107.26	0.000
11	94.46	0.000	25	98.84	0.000	39	102.86	1.598	53	107.95	0.000
12	94.84	0.	26	99.07	0.000	40	104.16	0.684	54	109.34	0.015
13	95.44	0.000	27	99.15	4.539	41	104.16	0.684	55	114.28	0.000
14	95.76	0.000	28	99.22	0.000	42	104.24	0.000	56	114.36	0.001

5-441

$J_{AA'}$	J_{AB}	$J_{AB'}$	$J_{BB'}$
-1	2	6	-1
-1	6	2	-1

The maximum summed intensity is 4.668.

LINE	FREQ	INTEN	LINE	FREQ	INTEN	LINE	FREQ	INTEN	LINE	FREQ	INTEN
1	82.89	0.001	15	94.39	0.445	29	100.11	0.000	43	105.79	0.000
2	83.29	0.000	16	94.39	0.445	30	100.61	0.000	44	106.00	0.000
3	89.36	0.015	17	96.00	0.000	31	100.64	4.871	45	106.61	0.000
4	90.50	0.000	18	97.72	1.622	32	101.00	3.600	46	107.11	0.661
5	91.00	0.400	19	98.00	0.000	33	101.03	0.000	47	107.32	0.000
6	91.75	0.000	20	98.19	0.427	34	101.42	0.000	48	107.72	0.302
7	91.81	0.103	21	98.39	1.555	35	101.61	1.555	49	108.00	0.000
8	92.00	0.000	22	98.39	1.555	36	101.61	1.555	50	108.19	0.103
9	92.28	0.302	23	98.58	0.000	37	101.81	0.427	51	108.25	0.000
10	92.68	0.000	24	98.97	0.000	38	102.00	0.000	52	109.00	0.400
11	92.89	0.661	25	99.00	3.600	39	102.28	1.622	53	109.50	0.000
12	93.39	0.000	26	99.36	4.871	40	104.00	0.000	54	110.64	0.015
13	94.00	0.000	27	99.39	0.000	41	105.61	0.445	55	116.71	0.000
14	94.21	0.000	28	99.89	0.000	42	105.61	0.445	56	117.11	0.001

−11 −10 −9 −8 −7 −6 −5 −4 −3 −2 −1 0 +1 +2 +3 +4 +5 +6 +7 +8 +9 +10 +11

5-442

$J_{AA'}$	J_{AB}	$J_{AB'}$	$J_{BB'}$
-1	2	9	-1
-1	9	2	-1

The maximum summed intensity is 5.337.

LINE	FREQ	INTEN	LINE	FREQ	INTEN	LINE	FREQ	INTEN	LINE	FREQ	INTEN
1	78.13	0.000	15	91.89	0.241	29	100.11	0.000	43	108.15	0.000
2	78.79	0.000	16	91.89	0.241	30	100.46	5.175	44	108.76	0.000
3	87.01	0.012	17	96.24	0.000	31	100.76	3.756	45	109.11	0.000
4	88.01	0.000	18	98.24	0.000	32	101.05	0.000	46	109.34	0.410
5	88.24	0.244	19	98.27	0.433	33	101.07	0.000	47	110.27	0.000
6	89.08	0.148	20	98.39	1.741	34	101.11	1.759	48	110.33	0.000
7	89.20	0.081	21	98.89	0.000	35	101.11	1.759	49	110.76	0.000
8	89.24	0.000	22	98.89	1.759	36	101.11	0.000	50	110.80	0.081
9	89.67	0.000	23	98.89	1.759	37	101.61	1.741	51	110.92	0.148
10	89.73	0.000	24	98.93	0.000	38	101.73	0.433	52	111.76	0.244
11	90.66	0.410	25	98.95	0.000	39	101.76	0.000	53	111.99	0.000
12	90.89	0.	26	99.24	3.756	40	103.76	0.000	54	112.99	0.012
13	91.24	0.000	27	99.54	5.175	41	108.11	0.241	55	121.21	0.000
14	91.85	0.000	28	99.89	0.000	42	108.11	0.241	56	121.87	0.000

−11 −10 −9 −8 −7 −6 −5 −4 −3 −2 −1 0 +1 +2 +3 +4 +5 +6 +7 +8 +9 +10 +11

5-443

$J_{AA'}$	J_{AB}	$J_{AB'}$	$J_{BB'}$
-1	2	12	-1
-1	12	2	-1

The maximum summed intensity is 5.916.

LINE	FREQ	INTEN	LINE	FREQ	INTEN	LINE	FREQ	INTEN	LINE	FREQ	INTEN
1	72.90	0.000	15	89.17	0.143	29	100.17	0.	43	110.83	0.143
2	73.68	0.000	16	89.22	0.000	30	100.35	5.373	44	111.62	0.000
3	84.42	0.010	17	96.38	0.000	31	100.62	3.838	45	111.83	0.
4	85.35	0.000	18	98.34	0.376	32	100.83	1.857	46	111.87	0.262
5	85.38	0.162	19	98.38	0.000	33	100.83	1.857	47	112.80	0.000
6	85.95	0.090	20	98.40	0.000	34	100.88	0.000	48	113.27	0.000
7	86.38	0.000	21	98.82	1.832	35	101.14	0.000	49	113.57	0.058
8	86.43	0.058	22	98.86	0.000	36	101.18	1.832	50	113.62	0.000
9	86.73	0.000	23	99.12	0.000	37	101.60	0.000	51	114.05	0.090
10	87.20	0.000	24	99.17	1.857	38	101.62	0.000	52	114.62	0.162
11	88.13	0.262	25	99.17	1.857	39	101.66	0.376	53	114.65	0.000
12	88.17	0.	26	99.38	3.838	40	103.62	0.000	54	115.58	0.010
13	88.38	0.000	27	99.65	5.373	41	110.78	0.000	55	126.32	0.000
14	89.17	0.143	28	99.83	0.	42	110.83	0.143	56	127.10	0.000

5-444

$J_{AA'}$	J_{AB}	$J_{AB'}$	$J_{BB'}$
-1	2	15	-1
-1	15	2	-1

The maximum summed intensity is 6.877.

LINE	FREQ	INTEN	LINE	FREQ	INTEN	LINE	FREQ	INTEN	LINE	FREQ	INTEN
1	67.40	0.000	15	86.34	0.092	29	100.28	5.511	43	113.66	0.092
2	68.26	0.000	16	86.45	0.000	30	100.34	0.	44	114.51	0.000
3	81.69	0.008	17	96.49	0.000	31	100.51	3.886	45	114.57	0.176
4	82.49	0.114	18	98.06	0.000	32	100.66	1.908	46	114.66	0.
5	82.57	0.000	19	98.38	0.315	33	100.66	1.908	47	115.45	0.000
6	82.88	0.060	20	98.49	0.000	34	100.76	0.000	48	116.26	0.000
7	83.49	0.000	21	98.86	0.000	35	100.91	1.888	49	116.41	0.042
8	83.59	0.042	22	99.09	1.888	36	101.14	0.000	50	116.51	0.000
9	83.74	0.000	23	99.24	0.000	37	101.51	0.000	51	117.12	0.060
10	84.55	0.000	24	99.34	1.908	38	101.62	0.315	52	117.43	0.000
11	85.34	0.	25	99.34	1.908	39	101.94	0.000	53	117.51	0.114
12	85.43	0.176	26	99.49	3.886	40	103.51	0.000	54	118.31	0.008
13	85.49	0.000	27	99.66	0.	41	113.55	0.000	55	131.74	0.000
14	86.34	0.092	28	99.72	5.511	42	113.66	0.092	56	132.60	0.000

5-445

$J_{AA'}$	J_{AB}	$J_{AB'}$	$J_{BB'}$
-1	2	18	-1
-1	18	2	-1

The maximum summed intensity is 8.177.

LINE	FREQ	INTEN	LINE	FREQ	INTEN	LINE	FREQ	INTEN	LINE	FREQ	INTEN
1	61.75	0.000	15	83.46	0.064	29	100.23	5.610	43	116.54	0.064
2	62.64	0.000	16	83.61	0.000	30	100.44	3.916	44	117.37	0.124
3	78.89	0.007	17	96.56	0.000	31	100.46	0.000	45	117.44	0.000
4	79.56	0.084	18	97.83	0.000	32	100.54	1.936	46	117.54	0.000
5	79.73	0.000	19	98.41	0.262	33	100.54	1.936	47	118.22	0.000
6	79.85	0.044	20	98.56	0.000	34	100.69	0.000	48	119.25	0.
7	80.56	0.000	21	98.87	0.000	35	100.73	1.922	49	119.29	0.032
8	80.71	0.032	22	99.27	1.922	36	101.13	0.000	50	119.44	0.000
9	80.75	0.000	23	99.31	0.000	37	101.44	0.000	51	120.15	0.044
10	81.78	0.	24	99.46	1.936	38	101.59	0.262	52	120.27	0.000
11	82.46	0.	25	99.46	1.936	39	102.17	0.000	53	120.44	0.084
12	82.56	0.000	26	99.54	0.000	40	103.44	0.000	54	121.11	0.007
13	82.63	0.124	27	99.56	3.916	41	116.39	0.000	55	137.36	0.
14	83.46	0.064	28	99.77	5.610	42	116.54	0.064	56	138.25	0.000

-11 -10 -9 -8 -7 -6 -5 -4 -3 -2 -1 0 +1 +2 +3 +4 +5 +6 +7 +8 +9 +10 +11

5-446

$J_{AA'}$	J_{AB}	$J_{AB'}$	$J_{BB'}$
-1	-1	2	4
-1	2	-1	4
4	2	-1	-1
4	-1	2	-1

The maximum summed intensity is 4.891.

LINE	FREQ	INTEN	LINE	FREQ	INTEN	LINE	FREQ	INTEN	LINE	FREQ	INTEN
1	87.03	0.000	15	96.34	1.372	29	99.92	0.000	43	103.70	0.000
2	89.73	0.002	16	96.42	0.000	30	100.03	0.000	44	104.19	1.168
3	91.19	0.001	17	96.46	1.671	31	100.12	1.131	45	104.46	0.000
4	91.38	0.037	18	96.76	0.000	32	100.54	0.000	46	104.50	0.783
5	92.18	0.000	19	97.21	1.963	33	101.33	1.217	47	105.69	0.000
6	92.54	0.000	20	97.27	2.128	34	101.37	0.000	48	106.20	0.124
7	92.69	0.000	21	97.46	2.329	35	101.63	0.000	49	107.36	0.000
8	93.80	0.124	22	97.58	2.074	36	102.42	2.074	50	107.46	0.000
9	95.50	0.783	23	98.37	0.000	37	102.54	2.329	51	107.70	0.000
10	95.54	0.000	24	98.43	0.000	38	102.73	2.128	52	108.62	0.037
11	95.81	1.168	25	98.63	0.000	39	102.79	1.963	53	108.81	0.001
12	95.85	0.000	26	98.67	1.217	40	103.54	1.671	54	108.85	0.000
13	95.96	0.000	27	99.58	0.000	41	103.58	0.000	55	110.27	0.002
14	96.30	0.000	28	99.88	1.131	42	103.66	1.372	56	111.43	0.000

-11 -10 -9 -8 -7 -6 -5 -4 -3 -2 -1 0 +1 +2 +3 +4 +5 +6 +7 +8 +9 +10 +11

5-447

$J_{AA'}$	J_{AB}	$J_{AB'}$	$J_{BB'}$
-1	-1	2	6
-1	2	-1	6
6	2	-1	-1
6	-1	2	-1

The maximum summed intensity is 6.131.

LINE	FREQ	INTEN	LINE	FREQ	INTEN	LINE	FREQ	INTEN	LINE	FREQ	INTEN
1	85.10	0.000	15	96.39	0.000	29	98.59	1.274	43	104.35	0.000
2	89.26	0.004	16	96.46	1.671	30	99.63	0.000	44	104.50	0.000
3	89.52	0.016	17	96.47	0.000	31	101.33	0.000	45	104.65	0.801
4	90.41	0.000	18	96.54	1.596	32	101.41	1.274	46	105.39	0.336
5	90.65	0.000	19	96.73	0.000	33	101.73	0.000	47	106.65	0.000
6	91.23	0.000	20	97.14	1.984	34	102.23	1.664	48	107.49	0.041
7	92.51	0.041	21	97.31	2.183	35	102.54	2.329	49	108.62	0.000
8	93.22	0.000	22	97.37	2.100	36	102.63	2.100	50	108.77	0.000
9	94.61	0.336	23	97.46	2.329	37	102.69	2.183	51	109.35	0.000
10	95.28	0.000	24	97.77	1.664	38	102.86	1.984	52	109.67	0.000
11	95.35	0.801	25	98.27	0.000	39	103.27	0.000	53	109.81	0.000
12	95.42	0.000	26	98.44	0.000	40	103.46	1.596	54	110.48	0.016
13	95.65	0.000	27	98.52	0.000	41	103.54	1.671	55	110.74	0.004
14	96.33	0.000	28	98.58	0.000	42	103.76	0.000	56	111.86	0.000

5-448

$J_{AA'}$	J_{AB}	$J_{AB'}$	$J_{BB'}$
-1	-1	2	9
-1	2	-1	9
9	2	-1	-1
9	-1	2	-1

The maximum summed intensity is 8.564.

LINE	FREQ	INTEN	LINE	FREQ	INTEN	LINE	FREQ	INTEN	LINE	FREQ	INTEN
1	82.17	0.000	15	95.85	0.000	29	98.45	0.000	43	106.18	0.000
2	86.64	0.006	16	96.36	0.000	30	100.85	0.000	44	106.27	0.207
3	87.59	0.000	17	96.46	1.671	31	101.77	0.000	45	106.77	0.000
4	87.65	0.005	18	96.69	1.744	32	101.82	0.000	46	107.19	0.000
5	87.74	0.000	19	97.08	1.994	33	102.54	2.329	47	107.72	0.061
6	91.27	0.000	20	97.17	0.000	34	102.60	1.719	48	108.69	0.009
7	91.31	0.009	21	97.19	0.000	35	102.65	2.233	49	108.73	0.000
8	92.19	0.000	22	97.23	2.083	36	102.72	1.939	50	109.79	0.000
9	92.28	0.061	23	97.28	1.939	37	102.77	2.083	51	112.19	0.000
10	93.00	0.000	24	97.35	2.233	38	102.92	1.994	52	112.26	0.000
11	93.51	0.	25	97.40	1.719	39	103.31	1.744	53	112.35	0.005
12	93.73	0.207	26	97.46	2.329	40	103.54	1.671	54	112.64	0.000
13	93.82	0.000	27	98.00	0.000	41	103.87	0.000	55	113.36	0.006
14	95.74	0.000	28	98.18	0.000	42	104.26	0.000	56	113.45	0.000

5-449

$J_{AA'}$	J_{AB}	$J_{AB'}$	$J_{BB'}$
-1	-1	2	12
-1	2	-1	12
12	2	-1	-1
12	-1	2	-1

The maximum summed intensity is 7.098.

LINE	FREQ	INTEN	LINE	FREQ	INTEN	LINE	FREQ	INTEN	LINE	FREQ	INTEN
1	79.22	0.000	15	95.79	0.000	29	98.46	0.000	43	107.35	0.000
2	83.71	0.002	16	96.38	0.000	30	101.87	0.000	44	108.70	0.000
3	84.68	0.000	17	96.46	1.671	31	101.89	0.000	45	108.76	0.044
4	84.79	0.000	18	96.68	0.000	32	102.54	2.329	46	109.10	0.003
5	85.16	0.003	19	96.76	1.812	33	102.62	2.262	47	109.13	0.000
6	89.52	0.016	20	96.98	1.815	34	102.84	2.061	48	109.51	0.000
7	89.90	0.000	21	97.05	1.998	35	102.86	1.984	49	110.18	0.000
8	90.19	0.000	22	97.14	1.984	36	102.95	1.998	50	110.48	0.016
9	90.87	0.000	23	97.16	2.061	37	103.02	1.815	51	114.84	0.003
10	90.90	0.003	24	97.38	2.262	38	103.24	1.812	52	114.97	0.000
11	90.94	0.000	25	97.46	2.329	39	103.25	0.000	53	115.21	0.000
12	91.24	0.044	26	97.51	0.000	40	103.54	1.671	54	115.62	0.
13	91.30	0.000	27	97.81	0.000	41	103.92	0.000	55	115.91	0.000
14	95.63	0.000	28	98.13	0.000	42	104.21	0.000	56	116.29	0.002

−11 −10 −9 −8 −7 −6 −5 −4 −3 −2 −1 0 +1 +2 +3 +4 +5 +6 +7 +8 +9 +10 +11

5-450

$J_{AA'}$	J_{AB}	$J_{AB'}$	$J_{BB'}$
-1	-1	2	15
-1	2	-1	15
15	2	-1	-1
15	-1	2	-1

The maximum summed intensity is 6.247.

LINE	FREQ	INTEN	LINE	FREQ	INTEN	LINE	FREQ	INTEN	LINE	FREQ	INTEN
1	76.26	0.000	15	95.82	0.000	29	98.46	0.000	43	107.42	0.000
2	80.76	0.001	16	96.40	0.000	30	101.90	0.000	44	108.68	0.000
3	81.74	0.000	17	96.46	1.671	31	101.93	0.000	45	109.27	0.001
4	81.82	0.000	18	96.47	0.000	32	102.54	2.329	46	110.33	0.000
5	82.38	0.001	19	96.80	1.849	33	102.60	2.282	47	111.53	0.013
6	86.64	0.006	20	96.82	1.809	34	102.89	2.044	48	112.10	0.000
7	87.21	0.000	21	97.04	1.999	35	102.92	1.994	49	112.37	0.000
8	87.28	0.000	22	97.08	1.994	36	102.96	1.999	50	113.36	0.006
9	87.90	0.000	23	97.11	2.044	37	103.18	1.809	51	117.62	0.001
10	88.12	0.000	24	97.40	2.282	38	103.20	1.849	52	117.86	0.000
11	88.47	0.013	25	97.46	2.329	39	103.54	1.671	53	118.18	0.000
12	90.73	0.001	26	97.65	0.000	40	103.95	0.000	54	118.60	0.
13	91.32	0.000	27	97.72	0.000	41	104.18	0.000	55	118.68	0.000
14	95.56	0.000	28	98.10	0.000	42	106.00	0.000	56	119.24	0.001

−11 −10 −9 −8 −7 −6 −5 −4 −3 −2 −1 0 +1 +2 +3 +4 +5 +6 +7 +8 +9 +10 +11

5-451

$J_{AA'}$	J_{AB}	$J_{AB'}$	$J_{BB'}$
-1	-1	2	18
-1	2	-1	18
18	2	-1	-1
18	-1	2	-1

The maximum summed intensity is 6.416.

LINE	FREQ	INTEN	LINE	FREQ	INTEN	LINE	FREQ	INTEN	LINE	FREQ	INTEN
1	73.28	0.000	15	95.84	0.000	29	98.46	0.000	43	108.67	0.000
2	77.79	0.001	16	96.36	0.000	30	101.92	0.000	44	108.87	0.000
3	78.78	0.000	17	96.41	0.000	31	101.96	0.000	45	109.35	0.001
4	78.84	0.000	18	96.46	1.671	32	102.54	2.329	46	110.40	0.000
5	79.51	0.001	19	96.74	1.794	33	102.59	2.296	47	114.41	0.005
6	83.71	0.002	20	96.83	1.872	34	102.91	2.031	48	115.08	0.000
7	84.33	0.000	21	97.03	1.999	35	102.95	1.998	49	115.30	0.000
8	84.38	0.000	22	97.05	1.998	36	102.97	1.999	50	116.29	0.002
9	84.92	0.000	23	97.09	2.031	37	103.17	1.872	51	120.49	0.001
10	85.22	0.000	24	97.41	2.296	38	103.26	1.794	52	120.80	0.000
11	85.59	0.005	25	97.46	2.329	39	103.54	1.671	53	121.16	0.000
12	90.65	0.001	26	97.67	0.000	40	103.96	0.000	54	121.54	0.000
13	91.33	0.000	27	97.72	0.000	41	104.16	0.000	55	121.59	0.000
14	95.52	0.000	28	98.08	0.000	42	107.46	0.000	56	122.21	0.001

5-452

$J_{AA'}$	J_{AB}	$J_{AB'}$	$J_{BB'}$
-1	-1	4	2
-1	4	-1	2
2	4	-1	-1
2	-1	4	-1

The maximum summed intensity is 4.030.

LINE	FREQ	INTEN	LINE	FREQ	INTEN	LINE	FREQ	INTEN	LINE	FREQ	INTEN
1	87.58	0.001	15	95.08	0.000	29	100.00	1.471	43	105.37	0.578
2	88.52	0.000	16	95.15	1.106	30	100.06	0.000	44	105.43	0.000
3	88.75	0.000	17	96.85	0.000	31	100.80	1.728	45	105.71	0.795
4	91.05	0.005	18	96.90	0.000	32	100.87	0.000	46	105.77	0.000
5	91.94	0.134	19	97.76	2.281	33	100.92	0.000	47	105.83	0.529
6	92.34	0.000	20	97.77	1.866	34	100.94	0.000	48	105.90	0.351
7	93.23	0.000	21	98.15	2.894	35	101.34	2.262	49	106.77	0.000
8	94.10	0.351	22	98.66	2.262	36	101.85	2.894	50	107.15	0.000
9	94.17	0.529	23	99.05	0.000	37	102.23	1.866	51	107.20	0.000
10	94.23	0.000	24	99.06	0.000	38	102.24	2.281	52	108.06	0.134
11	94.29	0.795	25	99.20	1.728	39	102.63	0.000	53	108.95	0.005
12	94.35	0.000	26	99.60	0.000	40	103.18	0.000	54	109.01	0.000
13	94.63	0.578	27	99.94	0.000	41	103.41	0.000	55	112.42	0.001
14	95.03	0.000	28	100.00	1.471	42	104.85	1.106	56	113.71	0.000

5-453

$J_{AA'}$	J_{AB}	$J_{AB'}$	$J_{BB'}$
-1	-1	6	2
-1	6	-1	2
2	6	-1	-1
2	-1	6	-1

The maximum summed intensity is 3.977.

LINE	FREQ	INTEN	LINE	FREQ	INTEN	LINE	FREQ	INTEN	LINE	FREQ	INTEN
1	84.63	0.001	15	93.44	0.000	29	100.00	1.690	43	106.89	0.365
2	85.22	0.000	16	93.59	0.720	30	100.40	0.000	44	107.16	0.275
3	88.06	0.000	17	97.05	0.000	31	100.60	0.000	45	107.21	0.000
4	90.35	0.008	18	97.30	0.	32	100.65	1.845	46	107.29	0.000
5	90.49	0.125	19	98.11	1.875	33	100.81	0.000	47	107.56	0.501
6	90.82	0.000	20	98.16	2.389	34	100.92	2.616	48	107.62	0.310
7	91.79	0.000	21	98.59	3.280	35	101.05	0.000	49	108.21	0.000
8	92.38	0.310	22	99.08	2.616	36	101.41	3.280	50	108.46	0.000
9	92.44	0.501	23	99.35	1.845	37	101.84	2.389	51	108.70	0.
10	92.79	0.000	24	99.40	0.000	38	101.89	1.875	52	109.51	0.125
11	92.84	0.000	25	99.46	0.000	39	102.22	0.000	53	109.65	0.008
12	92.84	0.275	26	99.60	0.000	40	102.43	0.000	54	110.05	0.000
13	93.11	0.365	27	99.68	0.000	41	105.27	0.000	55	115.37	0.001
14	93.19	0.000	28	100.00	1.690	42	106.41	0.720	56	116.67	0.000

5-454

$J_{AA'}$	J_{AB}	$J_{AB'}$	$J_{BB'}$
-1	-1	9	2
-1	9	-1	2
2	9	-1	-1
2	-1	9	-1

The maximum summed intensity is 4.686.

LINE	FREQ	INTEN	LINE	FREQ	INTEN	LINE	FREQ	INTEN	LINE	FREQ	INTEN
1	79.58	0.000	15	90.82	0.000	29	100.00	1.835	43	109.45	0.196
2	79.86	0.	16	91.00	0.400	30	100.28	0.000	44	109.46	0.176
3	86.34	0.000	17	97.24	0.000	31	100.54	1.908	45	109.72	0.000
4	88.05	0.096	18	97.77	0.000	32	100.55	3.082	46	110.17	0.000
5	88.32	0.000	19	98.49	1.904	33	100.72	0.000	47	110.42	0.286
6	88.56	0.010	20	98.56	2.342	34	100.72	0.000	48	110.44	0.165
7	89.28	0.000	21	99.00	3.600	35	101.00	3.600	49	110.69	0.000
8	89.56	0.165	22	99.28	0.000	36	101.26	0.000	50	110.72	0.000
9	89.58	0.286	23	99.45	3.082	37	101.44	2.342	51	111.23	0.000
10	90.28	0.000	24	99.46	1.908	38	101.51	1.904	52	111.44	0.010
11	90.28	0.	25	99.72	0.000	39	101.72	0.000	53	111.95	0.096
12	90.30	0.000	26	99.73	0.000	40	101.78	0.000	54	112.16	0.000
13	90.54	0.176	27	99.79	0.000	41	108.20	0.000	55	120.42	0.000
14	90.55	0.196	28	100.00	1.835	42	109.00	0.400	56	121.65	0.000

5-455

$J_{AA'}$	J_{AB}	$J_{AB'}$	$J_{BB'}$
-1	-1	12	2
-1	12	-1	2
2	12	-1	-1
2	-1	12	-1

The maximum summed intensity is 4.986.

LINE	FREQ	INTEN	LINE	FREQ	INTEN	LINE	FREQ	INTEN	LINE	FREQ	INTEN
1	74.15	0.000	15	88.03	0.	29	100.00	1.899	43	112.07	0.114
2	74.24	0.000	16	88.24	0.244	30	100.09	0.000	44	112.18	0.115
3	84.13	0.000	17	97.40	0.000	31	100.35	3.490	45	112.44	0.000
4	85.42	0.071	18	98.09	0.000	32	100.46	1.936	46	113.09	0.000
5	85.67	0.000	19	98.77	1.929	33	100.67	0.	47	113.21	0.000
6	86.27	0.010	20	98.80	2.152	34	100.76	3.756	48	113.32	0.183
7	86.56	0.000	21	99.09	0.000	35	100.91	0.000	49	113.34	0.101
8	86.66	0.101	22	99.24	3.756	36	101.20	2.152	50	113.44	0.000
9	86.68	0.183	23	99.54	1.936	37	101.23	1.929	51	113.73	0.010
10	87.33	0.	24	99.65	3.490	38	101.30	0.000	52	113.91	0.
11	87.56	0.000	25	99.75	0.000	39	101.37	0.000	53	114.58	0.071
12	87.59	0.000	26	99.91	0.000	40	101.49	0.000	54	114.64	0.000
13	87.82	0.115	27	99.94	0.000	41	111.18	0.000	55	125.85	0.000
14	87.93	0.114	28	100.00	1.899	42	111.76	0.244	56	126.99	0.000

5-456

$J_{AA'}$	J_{AB}	$J_{AB'}$	$J_{BB'}$
-1	-1	15	2
-1	15	-1	2
2	15	-1	-1
2	-1	15	-1

The maximum summed intensity is 5.551

LINE	FREQ	INTEN	LINE	FREQ	INTEN	LINE	FREQ	INTEN	LINE	FREQ	INTEN
1	68.50	0.000	15	85.18	0.078	29	100.01	0.000	43	114.82	0.078
2	68.53	0.000	16	85.38	0.162	30	100.02	0.000	44	115.01	0.073
3	81.65	0.	17	97.53	0.000	31	100.22	3.854	45	115.26	0.000
4	82.68	0.053	18	98.32	0.000	32	100.41	1.953	46	115.89	0.000
5	82.93	0.000	19	98.94	1.906	33	100.62	3.838	47	116.03	0.000
6	83.71	0.009	20	98.96	1.947	34	100.64	0.000	48	116.24	0.126
7	83.72	0.068	21	98.98	0.000	35	101.02	0.000	49	116.26	0.000
8	83.74	0.000	22	99.38	3.838	36	101.03	0.000	50	116.28	0.068
9	83.76	0.126	23	99.59	1.953	37	101.04	1.947	51	116.29	0.009
10	84.36	0.000	24	99.75	0.000	38	101.06	1.906	52	116.68	0.
11	84.74	0.000	25	99.78	3.854	39	101.29	0.000	53	117.31	0.000
12	84.78	0.000	26	99.98	0.000	40	101.43	0.000	54	117.32	0.053
13	84.99	0.073	27	100.00	1.932	41	114.18	0.	55	131.47	0.000
14	85.15	0.000	28	100.00	1.932	42	114.62	0.162	56	132.54	0.000

5-457

$J_{AA'}$	J_{AB}	$J_{AB'}$	$J_{BB'}$
-1	-1	18	2
-1	18	-1	2
2	18	-1	-1
2	-1	18	-1

The maximum summed intensity is 8.292.

LINE	FREQ	INTEN	LINE	FREQ	INTEN	LINE	FREQ	INTEN	LINE	FREQ	INTEN
1	62.69	0.000	15	82.34	0.056	29	100.03	0.000	43	117.66	0.056
2	62.79	0.000	16	82.49	0.114	30	100.10	0.000	44	117.88	0.050
3	79.01	0.000	17	97.64	0.000	31	100.15	4.176	45	118.13	0.000
4	79.87	0.041	18	98.49	0.000	32	100.36	1.964	46	118.66	0.000
5	80.12	0.000	19	98.90	0.000	33	100.51	3.886	47	118.99	0.000
6	80.76	0.049	20	99.04	1.654	34	100.62	0.000	48	118.99	0.009
7	80.82	0.092	21	99.11	1.959	35	100.86	0.000	49	119.13	0.000
8	80.87	0.000	22	99.49	3.886	36	100.89	1.959	50	119.18	0.092
9	81.01	0.009	23	99.64	1.964	37	100.96	1.654	51	119.24	0.049
10	81.38	0.	24	99.75	0.000	38	101.10	0.000	52	119.51	0.
11	81.87	0.000	25	99.85	4.176	39	101.14	0.000	53	120.10	0.000
12	81.92	0.000	26	99.90	0.000	40	101.47	0.000	54	120.13	0.041
13	82.12	0.050	27	100.00	1.951	41	117.18	0.000	55	137.21	0.000
14	82.23	0.000	28	100.00	1.951	42	117.51	0.114	56	138.21	0.000

5-458

$J_{AA'}$	J_{AB}	$J_{AB'}$	$J_{BB'}$
-2	4	6	-2
-2	6	4	-2

The maximum summed intensity is 5.389.

LINE	FREQ	INTEN	LINE	FREQ	INTEN	LINE	FREQ	INTEN	LINE	FREQ	INTEN
1	80.86	0.001	15	95.17	0.000	29	100.16	0.000	43	105.39	0.000
2	81.53	0.000	16	95.84	0.684	30	100.41	5.412	44	106.16	0.000
3	87.85	0.	17	95.84	0.684	31	100.83	3.715	45	106.83	0.000
4	87.92	0.023	18	97.17	0.000	32	100.94	0.000	46	107.41	0.000
5	89.17	0.285	19	97.33	1.618	33	101.08	0.000	47	107.48	0.631
6	89.94	0.012	20	97.84	1.316	34	101.60	0.067	48	108.32	0.000
7	91.01	0.234	21	97.84	1.316	35	102.00	0.000	49	108.83	0.000
8	91.17	0.000	22	98.00	0.000	36	102.16	1.316	50	108.99	0.234
9	91.68	0.000	23	98.40	0.067	37	102.16	1.316	51	110.06	0.012
10	92.52	0.631	24	98.92	0.000	38	102.67	1.618	52	110.83	0.285
11	92.59	0.000	25	99.06	0.000	39	102.83	0.000	53	112.08	0.023
12	93.17	0.000	26	99.17	3.715	40	104.16	0.684	54	112.15	0.
13	93.84	0.000	27	99.59	5.412	41	104.16	0.684	55	118.47	0.000
14	94.61	0.000	28	99.84	0.000	42	104.83	0.000	56	119.14	0.001

5-459

$J_{AA'}$	J_{AB}	$J_{AB'}$	$J_{BB'}$
-2	4	9	-2
-2	6	4	-2

The maximum summed intensity is 5.634.

LINE	FREQ	INTEN	LINE	FREQ	INTEN	LINE	FREQ	INTEN	LINE	FREQ	INTEN
1	76.38	0.001	15	93.34	0.000	29	100.31	5.582	43	107.01	0.000
2	77.64	0.000	16	93.59	0.360	30	100.59	0.000	44	107.66	0.000
3	85.37	0.018	17	93.59	0.360	31	100.66	3.816	45	108.41	0.000
4	85.45	0.000	18	96.79	0.000	32	100.80	0.000	46	109.30	0.435
5	86.34	0.184	19	97.34	0.000	33	101.41	1.640	47	109.37	0.000
6	87.72	0.121	20	97.95	0.112	34	101.41	1.640	48	111.02	0.000
7	87.73	0.025	21	97.96	1.706	35	101.56	0.000	49	111.66	0.000
8	88.34	0.000	22	98.44	0.000	36	102.04	1.706	50	112.27	0.025
9	88.98	0.000	23	98.59	1.640	37	102.05	0.112	51	112.28	0.121
10	90.63	0.000	24	98.59	1.640	38	102.66	0.000	52	113.66	0.184
11	90.70	0.435	25	99.20	0.000	39	103.21	0.000	53	114.55	0.000
12	91.59	0.000	26	99.34	3.816	40	106.41	0.360	54	114.63	0.018
13	92.34	0.000	27	99.41	0.000	41	106.41	0.360	55	122.36	0.000
14	92.99	0.000	28	99.69	5.582	42	106.66	0.000	56	123.62	0.001

−11 −10 −9 −8 −7 −6 −5 −4 −3 −2 −1 0 +1 +2 +3 +4 +5 +6 +7 +8 +9 +10 +11

5-460

$J_{AA'}$	J_{AB}	$J_{AB'}$	$J_{BB'}$
-2	4	12	-2
-2	12	4	-2

The maximum summed intensity is 5.843.

LINE	FREQ	INTEN	LINE	FREQ	INTEN	LINE	FREQ	INTEN	LINE	FREQ	INTEN
1	71.40	0.000	15	91.00	0.200	29	100.25	5.692	43	109.27	0.000
2	72.94	0.000	16	91.00	0.200	30	100.54	3.873	44	110.54	0.000
3	82.66	0.013	17	93.46	0.000	31	100.73	0.000	45	111.00	0.
4	82.94	0.000	18	96.00	0.000	32	101.00	1.800	46	111.51	0.293
5	83.46	0.127	19	97.46	0.000	33	101.00	1.800	47	111.79	0.000
6	84.45	0.075	20	97.73	0.106	34	101.00	0.	48	114.00	0.000
7	85.19	0.026	21	98.21	0.000	35	101.54	1.795	49	114.54	0.000
8	85.46	0.000	22	98.46	1.795	36	101.79	0.000	50	114.81	0.026
9	86.00	0.000	23	99.00	1.800	37	102.27	0.106	51	115.55	0.075
10	88.21	0.000	24	99.00	1.800	38	102.54	0.000	52	116.54	0.127
11	88.49	0.293	25	99.00	0.	39	104.00	0.000	53	117.06	0.
12	89.00	0.	26	99.27	0.000	40	106.54	0.000	54	117.34	0.013
13	89.46	0.000	27	99.46	3.873	41	109.00	0.200	55	127.06	0.000
14	90.73	0.000	28	99.75	5.692	42	109.00	0.200	56	128.60	0.000

−11 −10 −9 −8 −7 −6 −5 −4 −3 −2 −1 0 +1 +2 +3 +4 +5 +6 +7 +8 +9 +10 +11

5-461

$J_{AA'}$	J_{AB}	$J_{AB'}$	$J_{BB'}$
-2	4	15	-2
-2	15	4	-2

The maximum summed intensity is 6.270.

LINE	FREQ	INTEN	LINE	FREQ	INTEN	LINE	FREQ	INTEN	LINE	FREQ	INTEN
1	66.09	0.000	15	88.24	0.122	29	100.20	5.767	43	111.82	0.000
2	67.78	0.000	16	88.24	0.122	30	100.46	3.907	44	113.46	0.000
3	79.87	0.010	17	93.54	0.000	31	100.71	0.000	45	113.76	0.
4	80.31	0.000	18	95.49	0.000	32	100.76	1.878	46	113.99	0.201
5	80.54	0.093	19	97.54	0.000	33	100.76	1.878	47	114.43	0.000
6	81.27	0.051	20	97.59	0.089	34	101.19	1.858	48	117.04	0.000
7	82.48	0.023	21	98.10	0.000	35	101.24	0.	49	117.46	0.000
8	82.54	0.000	22	98.76	0.	36	101.90	0.000	50	117.52	0.023
9	82.96	0.000	23	98.81	1.858	37	102.41	0.089	51	118.73	0.051
10	85.57	0.000	24	99.24	1.878	38	102.46	0.000	52	119.46	0.093
11	86.01	0.201	25	99.24	1.878	39	104.51	0.000	53	119.69	0.000
12	86.24	0.	26	99.29	0.000	40	106.46	0.000	54	120.13	0.010
13	86.54	0.000	27	99.54	3.907	41	111.76	0.122	55	132.22	0.
14	88.18	0.000	28	99.80	5.767	42	111.76	0.122	56	133.91	0.000

−11 −10 −9 −8 −7 −6 −5 −4 −3 −2 −1 0 +1 +2 +3 +4 +5 +6 +7 +8 +9 +10 +11

5-462

$J_{AA'}$	J_{AB}	$J_{AB'}$	$J_{BB'}$
-2	4	18	-2
-2	18	4	-2

The maximum summed intensity is 6.909.

LINE	FREQ	INTEN	LINE	FREQ	INTEN	LINE	FREQ	INTEN	LINE	FREQ	INTEN
1	60.57	0.000	15	85.38	0.081	29	100.17	5.818	43	114.62	0.081
2	62.36	0.000	16	85.48	0.000	30	100.40	3.930	44	116.40	0.000
3	77.02	0.008	17	93.60	0.000	31	100.62	1.919	45	116.62	0.000
4	77.59	0.000	18	95.16	0.000	32	100.62	1.919	46	116.62	0.143
5	77.60	0.070	19	97.50	0.074	33	100.71	0.000	47	117.19	0.000
6	78.14	0.038	20	97.60	0.000	34	100.95	1.900	48	120.07	0.000
7	79.60	0.000	21	98.04	0.000	35	101.38	0.000	49	120.31	0.019
8	79.69	0.019	22	98.62	0.000	36	101.96	0.000	50	120.40	0.000
9	79.93	0.000	23	99.05	1.900	37	102.40	0.000	51	121.86	0.038
10	82.81	0.000	24	99.29	0.000	38	102.50	0.074	52	122.40	0.070
11	83.38	0.143	25	99.38	1.919	39	104.84	0.000	53	122.41	0.000
12	83.38	0.	26	99.38	1.919	40	106.40	0.000	54	122.98	0.008
13	83.60	0.000	27	99.60	3.930	41	114.52	0.000	55	137.64	0.000
14	85.38	0.081	28	99.83	5.818	42	114.62	0.081	56	139.43	0.000

−11 −10 −9 −8 −7 −6 −5 −4 −3 −2 −1 0 +1 +2 +3 +4 +5 +6 +7 +8 +9 +10 +11

5-463

$J_{AA'}$	J_{AB}	$J_{AB'}$	$J_{BB'}$
-2	-2	4	6
-2	4	-2	6
6	4	-2	-2
6	-2	4	-2

The maximum summed intensity is 2.892.

LINE	FREQ	INTEN	LINE	FREQ	INTEN	LINE	FREQ	INTEN	LINE	FREQ	INTEN
1	84.41	0.000	15	95.27	0.886	29	100.16	0.000	43	104.81	0.000
2	87.05	0.006	16	95.37	0.000	30	100.17	0.000	44	106.16	0.000
3	87.38	0.028	17	95.38	0.000	31	100.40	0.000	45	106.63	0.466
4	88.82	0.000	18	95.84	1.368	32	100.59	2.007	46	106.73	0.000
5	89.05	0.000	19	96.16	0.000	33	101.41	0.000	47	106.91	0.162
6	89.84	0.000	20	97.19	1.891	34	101.60	2.573	48	108.16	0.178
7	90.87	0.009	21	97.38	1.972	35	101.84	1.822	49	109.13	0.009
8	91.84	0.178	22	97.84	2.632	36	102.16	2.632	50	109.36	0.000
9	93.09	0.162	23	98.16	1.822	37	102.62	1.972	51	110.16	0.000
10	93.37	0.466	24	98.40	2.573	38	102.81	1.891	52	110.62	0.000
11	93.84	0.000	25	99.41	2.007	39	103.84	0.000	53	111.13	0.000
12	93.84	0.000	26	99.64	0.000	40	104.05	0.000	54	112.62	0.028
13	94.13	0.000	27	99.84	0.000	41	104.16	1.368	55	112.95	0.006
14	95.09	0.000	28	100.16	0.000	42	104.73	0.886	56	115.41	0.000

−11 −10 −9 −8 −7 −6 −5 −4 −3 −2 −1 0 +1 +2 +3 +4 +5 +6 +7 +8 +9 +10 +11

5-464

$J_{AA'}$	J_{AB}	$J_{AB'}$	$J_{BB'}$
-2	-2	4	9
-2	4	-2	9
9	4	-2	-2
9	-2	4	-2

The maximum summed intensity is 4.837.

LINE	FREQ	INTEN	LINE	FREQ	INTEN	LINE	FREQ	INTEN	LINE	FREQ	INTEN
1	81.72	0.000	15	94.86	0.000	29	99.75	0.000	43	105.93	0.000
2	84.72	0.013	16	95.49	0.000	30	100.40	0.000	44	106.60	0.000
3	85.70	0.007	17	95.73	1.161	31	100.70	0.000	45	107.89	0.068
4	86.38	0.000	18	95.84	1.368	32	101.57	1.962	46	107.98	0.240
5	87.07	0.000	19	96.26	0.000	33	102.05	2.413	47	108.51	0.000
6	88.45	0.000	20	97.25	1.987	34	102.16	2.632	48	108.93	0.005
7	89.83	0.070	21	97.40	2.145	35	102.36	1.930	49	110.17	0.070
8	91.07	0.005	22	97.64	1.930	36	102.60	2.145	50	110.25	0.000
9	91.59	0.000	23	97.84	2.632	37	102.67	0.000	51	112.93	0.000
10	92.02	0.240	24	97.95	2.413	38	102.75	1.987	52	113.17	0.000
11	92.11	0.068	25	98.43	1.962	39	104.16	1.368	53	113.51	0.000
12	92.22	0.000	26	98.63	0.000	40	104.27	1.161	54	114.30	0.007
13	93.40	0.000	27	99.41	0.000	41	104.41	0.000	55	115.28	0.013
14	94.07	0.000	28	99.60	0.000	42	105.36	0.000	56	116.66	0.000

−11 −10 −9 −8 −7 −6 −5 −4 −3 −2 −1 0 +1 +2 +3 +4 +5 +6 +7 +8 +9 +10 +11

5-465

$J_{AA'}$	J_{AB}	$J_{AB'}$	$J_{BB'}$
-2	-2	4	12
-2	4	-2	12
12	4	-2	-2
12	-2	4	-2

The maximum summed intensity is 6.492.

LINE	FREQ	INTEN	LINE	FREQ	INTEN	LINE	FREQ	INTEN	LINE	FREQ	INTEN
1	78.92	0.000	15	94.57	0.000	29	99.80	0.000	43	105.78	0.000
2	81.94	0.006	16	95.56	0.000	30	100.55	0.000	44	108.60	0.031
3	83.73	0.000	17	95.84	1.368	31	100.83	0.000	45	108.80	0.003
4	83.80	0.005	18	96.01	1.344	32	102.16	2.632	46	109.45	0.000
5	84.22	0.000	19	96.96	0.000	33	102.27	1.916	47	109.87	0.105
6	86.96	0.000	20	97.18	1.994	34	102.33	2.295	48	110.83	0.000
7	87.38	0.028	21	97.38	1.972	35	102.48	2.301	49	110.87	0.000
8	89.00	0.000	22	97.52	2.301	36	102.62	1.972	50	112.62	0.028
9	89.99	0.000	23	97.60	0.000	37	102.82	1.994	51	115.64	0.000
10	90.13	0.105	24	97.67	2.295	38	103.99	1.344	52	115.78	0.000
11	90.55	0.000	25	97.73	1.916	39	104.16	1.368	53	116.20	0.005
12	91.20	0.003	26	97.84	2.632	40	104.57	0.000	54	116.44	0.000
13	91.40	0.031	27	99.00	0.000	41	104.61	0.000	55	118.06	0.006
14	94.22	0.000	28	99.45	0.000	42	105.64	0.000	56	118.48	0.000

5-466

$J_{AA'}$	J_{AB}	$J_{AB'}$	$J_{BB'}$
-2	-2	4	15
-2	4	-2	15
15	4	-2	-2
15	-2	4	-2

The maximum summed intensity is 5.410.

LINE	FREQ	INTEN	LINE	FREQ	INTEN	LINE	FREQ	INTEN	LINE	FREQ	INTEN
1	76.05	0.000	15	94.36	0.000	29	99.82	0.000	43	106.89	0.000
2	79.10	0.004	16	95.62	0.000	30	100.65	0.000	44	108.72	0.002
3	80.97	0.000	17	95.84	1.368	31	100.88	0.000	45	109.04	0.016
4	81.32	0.000	18	96.19	1.463	32	102.16	2.632	46	111.26	0.000
5	81.50	0.004	19	96.95	0.000	33	102.40	2.403	47	112.17	0.045
6	84.72	0.013	20	97.13	1.996	34	102.51	2.210	48	112.35	0.000
7	84.90	0.000	21	97.25	1.987	35	102.71	1.858	49	113.41	0.000
8	86.24	0.000	22	97.29	1.858	36	102.75	1.987	50	115.28	0.013
9	87.49	0.000	23	97.43	0.000	37	102.87	1.996	51	118.33	0.000
10	87.65	0.000	24	97.49	2.210	38	103.81	1.463	52	118.50	0.004
11	87.83	0.045	25	97.60	2.403	39	104.16	1.368	53	118.68	0.000
12	90.96	0.016	26	97.84	2.632	40	104.74	0.000	54	119.38	0.000
13	91.28	0.002	27	98.76	0.000	41	105.68	0.000	55	120.72	0.000
14	94.32	0.000	28	99.35	0.000	42	105.80	0.000	56	120.90	0.004

5-467

$J_{AA'}$	J_{AB}	$J_{AB'}$	$J_{BB'}$
-2	-2	4	18
-2	4	-2	18
18	4	-2	-2
18	-2	4	-2

The maximum summed intensity is 5.296.

LINE	FREQ	INTEN	LINE	FREQ	INTEN	LINE	FREQ	INTEN	LINE	FREQ	INTEN
1	73.15	0.000	15	94.40	0.000	29	99.84	0.000	43	108.67	0.001
2	76.22	0.002	16	95.66	0.000	30	100.72	0.000	44	109.32	0.010
3	78.13	0.000	17	95.84	1.368	31	100.91	0.000	45	109.46	0.000
4	78.40	0.000	18	96.31	1.543	32	102.16	2.632	46	111.50	0.000
5	78.96	0.002	19	96.53	0.000	33	102.34	2.474	47	114.71	0.021
6	81.94	0.006	20	97.01	1.803	34	102.64	2.147	48	115.28	0.000
7	82.51	0.000	21	97.10	1.998	35	102.82	1.994	49	116.14	0.000
8	83.38	0.000	22	97.18	1.994	36	102.90	1.998	50	118.06	0.006
9	84.72	0.000	23	97.36	2.147	37	102.99	1.803	51	121.04	0.002
10	84.81	0.000	24	97.66	2.474	38	103.69	1.543	52	121.12	0.000
11	85.29	0.021	25	97.74	0.000	39	104.16	1.368	53	121.60	0.000
12	90.68	0.010	26	97.84	2.632	40	104.82	0.000	54	122.34	0.000
13	91.33	0.001	27	98.62	0.000	41	105.60	0.000	55	123.22	0.000
14	94.23	0.000	28	99.28	0.000	42	105.89	0.000	56	123.78	0.002

5-468

$J_{AA'}$	J_{AB}	$J_{AB'}$	$J_{BB'}$
-2	-2	6	4
-2	6	-2	4
4	6	-2	-2
4	-2	6	-2

The maximum summed intensity is 3.391.

LINE	FREQ	INTEN	LINE	FREQ	INTEN	LINE	FREQ	INTEN	LINE	FREQ	INTEN
1	84.71	0.002	15	93.53	0.000	29	100.14	2.053	43	106.51	0.414
2	85.32	0.000	16	94.39	0.891	30	100.39	0.000	44	107.08	0.257
3	85.54	0.000	17	95.26	0.000	31	100.70	3.278	45	107.61	0.000
4	87.79	0.057	18	95.79	0.000	32	101.00	1.800	46	107.91	0.000
5	88.88	0.000	19	97.36	1.571	33	101.00	0.000	47	108.08	0.398
6	90.15	0.025	20	97.61	0.000	34	101.53	0.000	48	109.00	0.200
7	90.39	0.000	21	97.79	1.943	35	101.61	3.109	49	109.61	0.000
8	91.00	0.200	22	98.39	3.109	36	102.21	1.943	50	109.68	0.000
9	91.92	0.398	23	99.00	1.800	37	102.39	0.000	51	109.85	0.025
10	92.39	0.000	24	99.30	3.278	38	102.64	1.571	52	110.21	0.000
11	92.92	0.257	25	99.61	0.000	39	103.25	0.000	53	111.25	0.000
12	93.00	0.	26	99.86	2.053	40	103.31	0.000	54	112.21	0.057
13	93.32	0.	27	99.91	0.000	41	103.47	0.000	55	115.29	0.002
14	93.49	0.414	28	99.96	0.000	42	105.61	0.891	56	117.89	0.000

5-469

$J_{AA'}$	J_{AB}	$J_{AB'}$	$J_{BB'}$
-2	-2	9	4
-2	9	-2	4
4	9	-2	-2
4	-2	9	-2

The maximum summed intensity is 5.299.

LINE	FREQ	INTEN	LINE	FREQ	INTEN	LINE	FREQ	INTEN	LINE	FREQ	INTEN
1	79.69	0.001	15	91.11	0.209	29	100.30	0.000	43	108.89	0.209
2	79.80	0.000	16	91.89	0.481	30	100.33	3.992	44	109.03	0.184
3	84.03	0.000	17	95.28	0.000	31	100.66	0.000	45	109.87	0.000
4	85.60	0.054	18	96.36	0.	32	100.76	1.878	46	110.78	0.000
5	86.58	0.000	19	97.34	0.000	33	101.00	0.000	47	111.09	0.235
6	88.13	0.000	20	97.78	1.342	34	101.11	3.519	48	111.44	0.032
7	88.24	0.122	21	98.13	1.946	35	101.87	1.946	49	111.56	0.000
8	88.56	0.032	22	98.89	3.519	36	102.08	0.000	50	111.76	0.122
9	88.91	0.235	23	99.24	1.878	37	102.22	1.342	51	111.87	0.000
10	90.00	0.	24	99.34	0.000	38	102.33	0.000	52	112.64	0.000
11	90.13	0.000	25	99.67	3.992	39	102.66	0.000	53	113.33	0.
12	90.80	0.000	26	99.78	0.000	40	102.86	0.000	54	114.40	0.054
13	90.97	0.184	27	99.81	2.006	41	106.56	0.000	55	120.31	0.001
14	91.08	0.000	28	100.19	2.006	42	108.11	0.481	56	122.84	0.000

−11 −10 −9 −8 −7 −6 −5 −4 −3 −2 −1 0 +1 +2 +3 +4 +5 +6 +7 +8 +9 +10 +11

5-470

$J_{AA'}$	J_{AB}	$J_{AB'}$	$J_{BB'}$
-2	-2	12	4
-2	12	-2	4
4	12	-2	-2
4	-2	12	-2

The maximum summed intensity is 6.244.

LINE	FREQ	INTEN	LINE	FREQ	INTEN	LINE	FREQ	INTEN	LINE	FREQ	INTEN
1	74.11	0.000	15	88.57	0.124	29	100.23	1.986	43	111.43	0.124
2	74.28	0.000	16	89.17	0.285	30	100.41	0.000	44	111.51	0.114
3	81.97	0.000	17	95.38	0.000	31	100.62	1.919	45	112.45	0.000
4	83.16	0.046	18	96.78	0.	32	100.78	0.000	46	113.64	0.030
5	84.10	0.000	19	97.22	0.000	33	100.83	3.715	47	113.68	0.000
6	85.38	0.081	20	98.03	1.064	34	101.00	0.000	48	113.82	0.000
7	85.55	0.000	21	98.40	1.954	35	101.60	1.954	49	114.05	0.155
8	85.95	0.155	22	99.17	3.715	36	101.81	0.000	50	114.45	0.000
9	86.36	0.030	23	99.22	0.000	37	101.97	1.064	51	114.62	0.081
10	87.00	0.000	24	99.38	1.919	38	102.40	0.000	52	115.22	0.000
11	87.55	0.000	25	99.68	0.000	39	102.54	0.000	53	115.81	0.000
12	88.11	0.	26	99.77	1.986	40	102.78	0.000	54	116.84	0.046
13	88.40	0.000	27	99.85	4.527	41	109.67	0.000	55	125.72	0.000
14	88.49	0.114	28	100.15	4.527	42	110.83	0.285	56	128.10	0.000

−11 −10 −9 −8 −7 −6 −5 −4 −3 −2 −1 0 +1 +2 +3 +4 +5 +6 +7 +8 +9 +10 +11

5-471

$J_{AA'}$	J_{AB}	$J_{AB'}$	$J_{BB'}$
-2	-2	15	4
-2	15	-2	4
4	15	-2	-2
4	-2	15	-2

The maximum summed intensity is 9.430.

LINE	FREQ	INTEN	LINE	FREQ	INTEN	LINE	FREQ	INTEN	LINE	FREQ	INTEN
1	68.33	0.	15	85.92	0.085	29	100.24	1.981	43	114.08	0.085
2	68.67	0.000	16	86.34	0.184	30	100.42	0.000	44	114.26	0.068
3	79.61	0.000	17	95.51	0.000	31	100.51	1.943	45	115.17	0.000
4	80.58	0.038	18	97.10	0.000	32	100.66	3.816	46	116.14	0.026
5	81.50	0.000	19	97.15	0.000	33	100.85	0.000	47	116.32	0.000
6	82.49	0.057	20	98.17	0.819	34	101.00	0.000	48	116.60	0.000
7	82.83	0.000	21	98.61	1.962	35	101.39	1.962	49	117.01	0.110
8	82.99	0.110	22	99.15	0.000	36	101.48	0.000	50	117.17	0.000
9	83.86	0.026	23	99.34	3.816	37	101.83	0.819	51	117.51	0.057
10	84.00	0.	24	99.49	1.943	38	102.31	0.000	52	117.90	0.000
11	84.83	0.000	25	99.60	0.000	39	102.58	0.000	53	118.48	0.
12	85.33	0.000	26	99.76	1.981	40	102.85	0.000	54	119.42	0.038
13	85.58	0.	27	99.94	4.912	41	112.76	0.000	55	131.33	0.000
14	85.74	0.068	28	100.06	4.912	42	113.66	0.184	56	133.57	0.

```
                             X
                             X
                             X
                             X
                            XXX
                            XXX
                            XXX
                            XXX
                            XXX
                            XXX
                            XXX
                           XXXXX
                      X    XXXXX    X
                      X    XXXXX    X
                     XX    XXXXX    XX
                     XXX   XXXXX   XXX
                     XXX   XXXXX   XXX
                     XXX  XXXXXXX  XXX
                     XXXXXXXXXXXXXXXXX
                    XXXXXXXXXXXXXXXXXXX
           X        XXXXXXXXXXXXXXXXXXX        X
          XXX       XXXXXXXXXXXXXXXXXXX       XXX
          XXX       XXXXXXXXXXXXXXXXXXX       XXX
       XXXXXXXX    XXXXXXXXXXXXXXXXXXXXX    XXXXXXXX
      XXXXXXXXX    XXXXXXXXXXXXXXXXXXXXX    XXXXXXXXX
```

−11 −10 −9 −8 −7 −6 −5 −4 −3 −2 −1 0 +1 +2 +3 +4 +5 +6 +7 +8 +9 +10 +11

5-472

$J_{AA'}$	J_{AB}	$J_{AB'}$	$J_{BB'}$
-2	-2	18	4
-2	18	-2	4
4	18	-2	-2
4	-2	18	-2

The maximum summed intensity is 10.977.

LINE	FREQ	INTEN	LINE	FREQ	INTEN	LINE	FREQ	INTEN	LINE	FREQ	INTEN
1	62.49	0.000	15	83.15	0.061	29	100.24	1.981	43	116.85	0.061
2	62.95	0.000	16	83.46	0.127	30	100.38	0.000	44	117.08	0.043
3	77.06	0.000	17	95.64	0.000	31	100.44	1.958	45	117.98	0.000
4	77.90	0.031	18	97.10	0.000	32	100.54	3.873	46	118.82	0.022
5	78.81	0.000	19	97.34	0.000	33	100.90	0.000	47	118.96	0.000
6	79.56	0.042	20	98.27	0.629	34	101.00	0.000	48	119.53	0.000
7	80.02	0.000	21	98.78	1.969	35	101.22	1.969	49	119.96	0.081
8	80.04	0.081	22	99.10	0.000	36	101.28	0.000	50	119.98	0.000
9	81.00	0.	23	99.46	3.873	37	101.73	0.629	51	120.44	0.042
10	81.18	0.022	24	99.53	0.000	38	102.13	0.000	52	120.66	0.
11	82.02	0.000	25	99.56	1.958	39	102.70	0.000	53	121.28	0.000
12	82.49	0.000	26	99.76	1.981	40	102.90	0.000	54	122.10	0.031
13	82.70	0.000	27	99.99	5.183	41	115.85	0.000	55	137.05	0.000
14	82.92	0.043	28	100.01	5.183	42	116.54	0.127	56	139.17	0.000

```
                              X
                              X
                              X
                              X
                              X
                             XXX
                             XXX
                             XXX
                             XXX
                             XXX
                             XXX
                             XXX
                             XXX
                        X    XXX    X
                        X   XXXXX   X
                        XX  XXXXX  XX
                       XXX  XXXXX  XXX
                       XXXXXXXXXXXXXXX
                       XXXXXXXXXXXXXXX
                       XXXXXXXXXXXXXXX
                       XXXXXXXXXXXXXXX
                       XXXXXXXXXXXXXXX
                      XXXXXXXXXXXXXXXXX
             XX       XXXXXXXXXXXXXXXXX       XX
             XXX      XXXXXXXXXXXXXXXXX      XXX
            XXXX      XXXXXXXXXXXXXXXXX      XXXX
      XXXXXXXXXX XXXXXXXXXXXXXXXXXX XXXXXXXXXX
```

−11 −10 −9 −8 −7 −6 −5 −4 −3 −2 −1 0 +1 +2 +3 +4 +5 +6 +7 +8 +9 +10 +11

5-473

$J_{AA'}$	J_{AB}	$J_{AB'}$	$J_{BB'}$
-4	6	9	-4
-4	9	6	-4

The maximum summed intensity is 4.736.

LINE	FREQ	INTEN	LINE	FREQ	INTEN	LINE	FREQ	INTEN	LINE	FREQ	INTEN
1	74.20	0.001	15	93.46	0.000	29	100.11	2.873	43	106.85	0.000
2	74.92	0.000	16	94.42	0.000	30	100.15	0.000	44	107.54	0.000
3	81.63	0.	17	95.15	0.553	31	100.35	2.889	45	107.79	0.000
4	83.49	0.004	18	95.15	0.553	32	100.58	3.857	46	109.65	0.420
5	83.74	0.017	19	97.42	0.000	33	100.83	0.000	47	110.58	0.000
6	84.42	0.143	20	97.82	1.702	34	101.08	0.000	48	113.25	0.000
7	86.03	0.094	21	98.15	1.447	35	101.85	1.447	49	113.58	0.000
8	86.42	0.000	22	98.15	1.447	36	101.85	1.447	50	113.97	0.094
9	86.75	0.000	23	98.92	0.000	37	102.18	1.702	51	115.58	0.143
10	89.42	0.000	24	99.17	0.000	38	102.58	0.000	52	116.26	0.017
11	90.35	0.420	25	99.42	3.857	39	104.85	0.553	53	116.51	0.004
12	92.21	0.000	26	99.65	2.889	40	104.85	0.553	54	118.37	0.000
13	92.46	0.000	27	99.85	0.000	41	105.58	0.000	55	125.08	0.000
14	93.15	0.000	28	99.89	2.873	42	106.54	0.000	56	125.80	0.001

5-474

$J_{AA'}$	J_{AB}	$J_{AB'}$	$J_{BB'}$
-4	6	12	-4
-4	12	6	-4

The maximum summed intensity is 6.166.

LINE	FREQ	INTEN	LINE	FREQ	INTEN	LINE	FREQ	INTEN	LINE	FREQ	INTEN
1	69.51	0.000	15	91.51	0.000	29	100.23	5.446	43	109.24	0.000
2	70.76	0.000	16	92.52	0.000	30	100.49	0.390	44	109.24	0.000
3	79.24	0.000	17	92.76	0.293	31	100.49	3.897	45	109.96	0.000
4	80.80	0.010	18	92.76	0.293	32	100.76	0.000	46	110.49	0.000
5	81.51	0.010	19	97.51	0.000	33	100.76	0.000	47	111.51	0.305
6	81.51	0.103	20	98.23	1.777	34	101.24	1.707	48	115.96	0.000
7	82.80	0.061	21	98.52	0.000	35	101.24	1.707	49	116.49	0.000
8	83.51	0.000	22	98.76	1.707	36	101.48	0.000	50	117.20	0.061
9	84.04	0.000	23	98.76	1.707	37	101.77	1.777	51	118.49	0.010
10	88.49	0.305	24	99.24	0.000	38	102.49	0.000	52	118.49	0.103
11	89.51	0.000	25	99.24	0.000	39	107.24	0.293	53	119.20	0.010
12	90.04	0.000	26	99.51	0.390	40	107.24	0.293	54	120.76	0.000
13	90.76	0.000	27	99.51	3.897	41	107.48	0.000	55	129.24	0.000
14	90.76	0.000	28	99.77	5.446	42	108.49	0.000	56	130.49	0.000

5-475

$J_{AA'}$	J_{AB}	$J_{AB'}$	$J_{BB'}$
-4	6	15	-4
-4	15	6	-4

The maximum summed intensity is 6.597.

LINE	FREQ	INTEN	LINE	FREQ	INTEN	LINE	FREQ	INTEN	LINE	FREQ	INTEN
1	64.47	0.000	15	89.58	0.000	29	100.19	5.683	43	111.40	0.000
2	65.98	0.000	16	90.09	0.168	30	100.42	3.923	44	111.42	0.000
3	76.80	0.	17	90.09	0.168	31	100.59	0.000	45	111.91	0.000
4	77.97	0.008	18	91.91	0.000	32	100.91	1.832	46	112.52	0.000
5	78.58	0.077	19	97.58	0.000	33	100.91	1.832	47	113.69	0.220
6	79.08	0.010	20	98.30	0.000	34	100.93	0.197	48	118.91	0.000
7	79.58	0.043	21	98.58	1.839	35	101.09	0.000	49	119.42	0.000
8	80.58	0.000	22	98.91	0.000	36	101.42	1.839	50	120.42	0.043
9	81.09	0.000	23	99.07	0.197	37	101.70	0.000	51	120.92	0.010
10	86.31	0.220	24	99.09	1.832	38	102.42	0.000	52	121.42	0.077
11	87.48	0.000	25	99.09	1.832	39	108.09	0.	53	122.03	0.008
12	88.09	0.000	26	99.41	0.000	40	109.91	0.168	54	123.20	0.000
13	88.58	0.000	27	99.58	3.923	41	109.91	0.168	55	134.01	0.000
14	88.60	0.000	28	99.81	5.683	42	110.42	0.000	56	135.53	0.000

−11 −10 −9 −8 −7 −6 −5 −4 −3 −2 −1 0 +1 +2 +3 +4 +5 +6 +7 +8 +9 +10 +11

5-476

$J_{AA'}$	J_{AB}	$J_{AB'}$	$J_{BB'}$
-4	-4	6	9
-4	6	-4	9
9	6	-4	-4
9	-4	6	-4

The maximum summed intensity is 5.801.

LINE	FREQ	INTEN	LINE	FREQ	INTEN	LINE	FREQ	INTEN	LINE	FREQ	INTEN
1	79.22	0.000	15	92.76	0.000	29	100.65	3.559	43	107.00	0.195
2	81.06	0.015	16	93.00	0.195	30	100.68	2.593	44	107.54	0.000
3	83.17	0.000	17	94.32	0.558	31	100.69	0.000	45	108.86	0.000
4	83.61	0.009	18	95.38	0.000	32	102.10	1.954	46	110.06	0.180
5	84.25	0.000	19	95.61	0.870	33	102.16	2.632	47	110.71	0.037
6	85.70	0.046	20	95.84	1.368	34	102.53	1.985	48	111.12	0.000
7	86.14	0.000	21	97.46	0.000	35	102.54	0.000	49	112.08	0.000
8	89.29	0.037	22	97.47	1.985	36	102.60	0.000	50	113.86	0.000
9	89.94	0.180	23	97.84	2.632	37	103.95	0.000	51	114.24	0.000
10	90.40	0.000	24	97.90	1.954	38	104.16	1.368	52	114.30	0.046
11	90.60	0.000	25	98.91	0.000	39	104.39	0.870	53	116.15	0.000
12	91.14	0.000	26	99.32	2.593	40	104.76	0.000	54	116.39	0.009
13	92.46	0.000	27	99.35	3.559	41	105.68	0.558	55	118.94	0.015
14	92.56	0.000	28	99.99	0.000	42	105.72	0.000	56	121.46	0.000

−11 −10 −9 −8 −7 −6 −5 −4 −3 −2 −1 0 +1 +2 +3 +4 +5 +6 +7 +8 +9 +10 +11

5-477

$J_{AA'}$	J_{AB}	$J_{AB'}$	$J_{BB'}$
-4	-4	6	12
-4	6	-4	12
12	6	-4	-4
12	-4	6	-4

The maximum summed intensity is 5.039.

LINE	FREQ	INTEN	LINE	FREQ	INTEN	LINE	FREQ	INTEN	LINE	FREQ	INTEN
1	76.92	0.000	15	92.61	0.000	29	101.02	3.329	43	107.48	0.127
2	78.48	0.009	16	92.92	0.000	30	101.08	0.000	44	108.60	0.000
3	81.78	0.000	17	94.70	0.725	31	101.15	2.503	45	110.16	0.031
4	82.01	0.008	18	95.84	1.368	32	102.07	0.000	46	110.27	0.000
5	82.10	0.000	19	96.16	1.169	33	102.16	2.632	47	111.66	0.109
6	83.40	0.000	20	96.25	0.000	34	102.27	0.000	48	112.40	0.000
7	83.49	0.026	21	97.35	1.991	35	102.36	1.974	49	113.21	0.000
8	87.93	0.000	22	97.64	1.974	36	102.65	1.991	50	116.51	0.026
9	88.23	0.000	23	97.73	0.000	37	103.84	1.169	51	116.60	0.000
10	88.34	0.109	24	97.84	2.632	38	103.93	0.000	52	117.08	0.000
11	89.73	0.000	25	98.74	0.000	39	104.16	1.368	53	117.99	0.008
12	89.84	0.031	26	98.85	2.503	40	105.30	0.725	54	118.07	0.000
13	91.40	0.000	27	98.98	3.329	41	105.94	0.000	55	121.52	0.009
14	92.52	0.127	28	99.07	0.000	42	106.76	0.000	56	122.91	0.000

5-478

$J_{AA'}$	J_{AB}	$J_{AB'}$	$J_{BB'}$
-4	-4	6	15
-4	6	-4	15
15	6	-4	-4
15	-4	6	-4

The maximum summed intensity is 3.834.

LINE	FREQ	INTEN	LINE	FREQ	INTEN	LINE	FREQ	INTEN	LINE	FREQ	INTEN
1	74.41	0.000	15	92.57	0.000	29	101.34	0.000	43	108.40	0.000
2	75.80	0.005	16	93.04	0.000	30	101.34	3.113	44	108.97	0.000
3	79.22	0.000	17	95.02	0.880	31	101.57	2.400	45	109.79	0.024
4	80.12	0.006	18	95.84	1.368	32	101.70	0.000	46	112.69	0.000
5	80.58	0.000	19	96.54	1.431	33	102.07	0.000	47	113.07	0.000
6	80.60	0.000	20	96.98	0.000	34	102.16	2.632	48	113.55	0.063
7	81.06	0.015	21	97.27	1.995	35	102.53	1.985	49	115.52	0.000
8	85.30	0.000	22	97.47	1.985	36	102.73	1.995	50	118.94	0.015
9	85.77	0.000	23	97.75	0.000	37	103.46	1.431	51	119.40	0.000
10	86.45	0.063	24	97.84	2.632	38	103.92	0.000	52	119.88	0.006
11	86.93	0.000	25	97.93	0.000	39	104.16	1.368	53	119.96	0.000
12	90.21	0.024	26	98.43	2.400	40	104.98	0.880	54	120.33	0.000
13	91.60	0.000	27	98.66	3.113	41	106.14	0.000	55	124.20	0.005
14	92.11	0.083	28	99.12	0.000	42	107.89	0.083	56	124.68	0.000

5-479

$J_{AA'}$	J_{AB}	$J_{AB'}$	$J_{BB'}$
-4	-4	9	6
-4	9	-4	6
6	9	-4	-4
6	-4	9	-4

The maximum summed intensity is 12.971.

LINE	FREQ	INTEN	LINE	FREQ	INTEN	LINE	FREQ	INTEN	LINE	FREQ	INTEN
1	78.24	0.000	15	92.16	0.200	29	100.08	2.286	43	107.84	0.200
2	79.69	0.	16	92.67	0.000	30	100.30	0.000	44	107.89	0.233
3	80.14	0.003	17	93.19	0.	31	101.40	1.937	45	111.11	0.000
4	81.49	0.027	18	93.59	0.720	32	101.41	3.280	46	111.74	0.000
5	84.76	0.000	19	94.70	0.000	33	102.11	1.973	47	112.05	0.177
6	85.00	0.063	20	94.90	0.343	34	103.20	0.000	48	112.91	0.057
7	86.89	0.000	21	96.70	0.000	35	103.30	0.000	49	113.11	0.000
8	87.09	0.057	22	97.89	1.973	36	103.30	0.000	50	113.29	0.000
9	87.95	0.177	23	98.13	0.000	37	103.82	0.000	51	113.81	0.000
10	88.89	0.000	24	98.59	3.280	38	104.65	0.000	52	115.00	0.063
11	89.70	0.000	25	98.60	1.937	39	105.10	0.343	53	116.80	0.000
12	90.22	0.000	26	99.92	2.286	40	105.30	0.000	54	118.51	0.027
13	91.84	0.000	27	99.97	4.702	41	105.37	0.000	55	119.86	0.003
14	92.11	0.233	28	100.03	4.702	42	106.41	0.720	56	125.26	0.000

5-480

$J_{AA'}$	J_{AB}	$J_{AB'}$	$J_{BB'}$
-4	-4	12	6
-4	12	-4	6
6	12	-4	-4
6	-4	12	-4

The maximum summed intensity is 11.515.

LINE	FREQ	INTEN	LINE	FREQ	INTEN	LINE	FREQ	INTEN	LINE	FREQ	INTEN
1	72.63	0.	15	90.02	0.159	29	100.11	5.231	43	109.98	0.159
2	74.87	0.001	16	91.00	0.400	30	100.31	0.000	44	110.11	0.103
3	77.69	0.000	17	92.67	0.000	31	101.00	3.600	45	113.43	0.000
4	79.25	0.026	18	93.69	0.000	32	101.19	1.951	46	114.35	0.000
5	82.32	0.049	19	94.57	0.000	33	101.88	1.974	47	115.00	0.052
6	82.58	0.000	20	95.00	0.209	34	102.75	0.000	48	115.13	0.123
7	84.57	0.000	21	96.57	0.000	35	103.25	0.000	49	115.29	0.000
8	84.87	0.123	22	97.86	0.000	36	103.43	0.000	50	115.43	0.000
9	85.00	0.052	23	98.12	1.974	37	104.27	0.000	51	116.31	0.
10	86.57	0.000	24	98.81	1.951	38	105.00	0.209	52	117.68	0.049
11	86.75	0.000	25	99.00	3.600	39	105.21	0.000	53	119.25	0.000
12	87.77	0.000	26	99.89	5.231	40	105.43	0.000	54	120.75	0.026
13	89.12	0.000	27	99.98	2.122	41	107.81	0.000	55	125.13	0.001
14	89.89	0.103	28	100.02	2.122	42	109.00	0.400	56	130.44	0.000

5-481

$J_{AA'}$	J_{AB}	$J_{AB'}$	$J_{BB'}$
-4	-4	15	6
-4	15	-4	6
6	15	-4	-4
6	-4	15	-4

The maximum summed intensity is 10.200.

LINE	FREQ	INTEN	LINE	FREQ	INTEN	LINE	FREQ	INTEN	LINE	FREQ	INTEN
1	66.90	0.	15	87.55	0.107	29	100.12	5.514	43	112.45	0.107
2	69.34	0.000	16	88.24	0.244	30	100.24	0.000	44	112.65	0.058
3	75.40	0.000	17	92.76	0.000	31	100.76	3.756	45	116.00	0.000
4	76.84	0.023	18	94.08	0.000	32	101.03	1.962	46	117.10	0.000
5	79.56	0.038	19	94.53	0.000	33	101.68	1.977	47	117.45	0.042
6	80.19	0.000	20	95.08	0.134	34	102.48	0.000	48	117.60	0.000
7	81.87	0.090	21	96.53	0.000	35	103.21	0.000	49	118.00	0.000
8	82.00	0.000	22	97.68	0.000	36	103.47	0.000	50	118.13	0.090
9	82.55	0.042	23	98.32	1.977	37	104.53	0.000	51	118.92	0.000
10	83.79	0.	24	98.97	1.962	38	104.92	0.134	52	120.44	0.038
11	84.00	0.000	25	99.24	3.756	39	105.03	0.000	53	121.89	0.000
12	85.11	0.000	26	99.88	5.514	40	105.47	0.000	54	123.16	0.023
13	86.32	0.000	27	99.92	2.054	41	110.97	0.000	55	130.66	0.000
14	87.35	0.058	28	100.08	2.054	42	111.76	0.244	56	135.81	0.000

5-482

$J_{AA'}$	J_{AB}	$J_{AB'}$	$J_{BB'}$
-6	9	12	-6
-6	12	9	-6

The maximum summed intensity is 6.473.

LINE	FREQ	INTEN	LINE	FREQ	INTEN	LINE	FREQ	INTEN	LINE	FREQ	INTEN
1	65.93	0.000	15	92.15	0.	29	100.15	5.861	43	108.43	0.000
2	67.50	0.000	16	93.58	0.000	30	100.42	3.923	44	109.57	0.000
3	74.21	0.000	17	95.15	0.553	31	101.15	0.000	45	111.79	0.000
4	76.87	0.000	18	95.15	0.553	32	101.29	0.017	46	112.22	0.281
5	78.01	0.011	19	96.58	0.000	33	101.72	0.000	47	115.42	0.000
6	78.58	0.077	20	97.14	0.000	34	101.78	1.784	48	118.42	0.000
7	79.94	0.045	21	98.15	1.447	35	101.85	1.447	49	118.49	0.000
8	81.51	0.000	22	98.15	1.447	36	101.85	1.447	50	120.06	0.045
9	81.58	0.000	23	98.22	1.784	37	102.86	0.000	51	121.42	0.077
10	84.58	0.000	24	98.28	0.000	38	103.42	0.000	52	121.99	0.011
11	87.78	0.281	25	98.71	0.017	39	104.85	0.553	53	123.13	0.000
12	88.21	0.000	26	98.85	0.000	40	104.85	0.553	54	125.79	0.000
13	90.43	0.000	27	99.58	3.923	41	106.42	0.000	55	132.50	0.000
14	91.57	0.000	28	99.85	5.861	42	107.85	0.000	56	134.07	0.000

5-483

$J_{AA'}$	J_{AB}	$J_{AB'}$	$J_{BB'}$
-6	9	15	-6
-6	15	9	-6

The maximum summed intensity is 7.920.

LINE	FREQ	INTEN	LINE	FREQ	INTEN	LINE	FREQ	INTEN	LINE	FREQ	INTEN
1	61.22	0.000	15	89.76	0.000	29	100.10	5.284	43	110.71	0.000
2	63.35	0.000	16	90.63	0.000	30	100.37	3.940	44	111.03	0.000
3	71.84	0.000	17	92.76	0.293	31	100.42	0.622	45	112.61	0.000
4	74.84	0.000	18	92.76	0.293	32	101.24	1.707	46	114.04	0.217
5	75.16	0.010	19	96.63	0.000	33	101.24	1.707	47	115.37	0.000
6	75.63	0.060	20	97.45	0.000	34	101.52	1.832	48	121.09	0.000
7	76.78	0.033	21	97.77	0.000	35	101.76	0.000	49	121.37	0.000
8	78.63	0.000	22	98.24	0.000	36	102.23	0.000	50	123.22	0.033
9	78.91	0.000	23	98.48	1.832	37	102.55	0.000	51	124.37	0.060
10	84.63	0.000	24	98.76	1.707	38	103.37	0.000	52	124.84	0.010
11	85.96	0.217	25	98.76	1.707	39	107.24	0.293	53	125.16	0.000
12	87.39	0.000	26	99.58	0.622	40	107.24	0.293	54	128.16	0.
13	88.97	0.000	27	99.63	3.940	41	109.37	0.000	55	136.65	0.000
14	89.29	0.000	28	99.90	5.284	42	110.24	0.000	56	138.78	0.000

5-484

$J_{AA'}$	J_{AB}	$J_{AB'}$	$J_{BB'}$
-6	-6	9	12
-6	9	-6	12
12	9	-6	-6
12	-6	9	-6

The maximum summed intensity is 7.006.

LINE	FREQ	INTEN	LINE	FREQ	INTEN	LINE	FREQ	INTEN	LINE	FREQ	INTEN
1	72.89	0.000	15	90.35	0.000	29	100.62	2.639	43	108.63	0.000
2	74.13	0.009	16	92.67	0.214	30	101.10	0.000	44	111.36	0.000
3	75.14	0.000	17	93.38	0.326	31	101.19	0.000	45	112.07	0.000
4	78.39	0.006	18	93.39	0.313	32	101.85	2.894	46	113.32	0.056
5	78.68	0.020	19	94.35	0.000	33	102.11	1.980	47	114.90	0.085
6	79.58	0.000	20	94.64	0.000	34	102.44	1.991	48	115.13	0.000
7	81.93	0.000	21	95.15	1.106	35	103.36	0.000	49	115.87	0.000
8	85.10	0.085	22	96.67	0.000	36	104.85	1.106	50	118.07	0.000
9	85.90	0.000	23	97.56	1.991	37	105.10	0.000	51	118.65	0.000
10	86.68	0.056	24	97.89	1.980	38	105.36	0.000	52	121.32	0.020
11	86.82	0.000	25	98.15	2.894	39	106.61	0.313	53	121.61	0.006
12	87.93	0.000	26	99.38	2.639	40	106.62	0.326	54	122.57	0.000
13	88.64	0.000	27	99.92	4.362	41	107.33	0.214	55	125.87	0.009
14	89.42	0.000	28	100.08	4.362	42	107.88	0.000	56	129.41	0.000

5-485

$J_{AA'}$	J_{AB}	$J_{AB'}$	$J_{BB'}$
-6	-6	9	15
-6	9	-6	15
15	9	-6	-6
15	-6	9	-6

The maximum summed intensity is 4.193.

LINE	FREQ	INTEN	LINE	FREQ	INTEN	LINE	FREQ	INTEN	LINE	FREQ	INTEN
1	71.02	0.000	15	90.56	0.000	29	100.28	4.254	43	110.86	0.000
2	71.65	0.006	16	92.40	0.174	30	100.89	2.588	44	111.76	0.000
3	74.02	0.	17	93.57	0.398	31	101.85	2.894	45	112.39	0.060
4	76.49	0.014	18	94.32	0.461	32	101.91	0.000	46	114.05	0.000
5	76.78	0.005	19	94.95	0.000	33	102.30	1.986	47	115.19	0.000
6	76.98	0.000	20	95.15	1.106	34	102.54	1.994	48	116.52	0.060
7	79.24	0.000	21	95.24	0.000	35	102.93	0.000	49	118.18	0.000
8	83.39	0.000	22	96.97	0.000	36	104.61	0.000	50	120.76	0.000
9	83.48	0.060	23	97.46	1.994	37	104.85	1.106	51	121.44	0.000
10	84.30	0.000	24	97.70	1.986	38	105.05	0.000	52	123.22	0.005
11	85.95	0.000	25	98.15	2.894	39	105.68	0.461	53	123.51	0.014
12	87.61	0.060	26	99.11	2.588	40	106.43	0.398	54	124.14	0.000
13	88.24	0.000	27	99.72	4.254	41	107.60	0.174	55	128.35	0.006
14	89.65	0.000	28	99.93	0.000	42	107.87	0.000	56	130.81	0.000

5-486

$J_{AA'}$	J_{AB}	$J_{AB'}$	$J_{BB'}$
-6	-6	12	9
-6	12	-6	9
9	12	-6	-6
9	-6	12	-6

The maximum summed intensity is 7.330.

LINE	FREQ	INTEN	LINE	FREQ	INTEN	LINE	FREQ	INTEN	LINE	FREQ	INTEN
1	70.51	0.	15	90.67	0.	29	100.22	2.310	43	108.71	0.197
2	72.69	0.000	16	91.03	0.000	30	100.35	0.000	44	108.97	0.000
3	74.46	0.014	17	91.29	0.197	31	101.24	3.414	45	114.46	0.000
4	74.83	0.002	18	91.34	0.135	32	101.65	1.973	46	115.98	0.000
5	78.22	0.027	19	92.26	0.116	33	102.11	1.986	47	116.22	0.052
6	80.26	0.000	20	92.76	0.586	34	103.42	0.000	48	116.69	0.089
7	82.54	0.000	21	94.03	0.000	35	105.56	0.000	49	116.79	0.000
8	83.31	0.089	22	95.85	0.000	36	105.60	0.000	50	117.46	0.000
9	83.78	0.052	23	97.89	1.986	37	105.97	0.000	51	118.33	0.000
10	85.44	0.000	24	98.35	1.973	38	107.10	0.000	52	121.78	0.027
11	85.54	0.000	25	98.76	3.414	39	107.24	0.586	53	123.54	0.000
12	86.97	0.000	26	99.78	2.310	40	107.74	0.116	54	125.17	0.002
13	89.14	0.000	27	99.83	5.099	41	107.92	0.000	55	125.54	0.014
14	90.63	0.000	28	100.17	5.099	42	108.66	0.135	56	133.26	0.

5-487

$J_{AA'}$	J_{AB}	$J_{AB'}$	$J_{BB'}$
-6	-6	15	9
-6	15	-6	9
9	15	-6	-6
9	-6	15	-6

The maximum summed intensity is 7.827.

LINE	FREQ	INTEN	LINE	FREQ	INTEN	LINE	FREQ	INTEN	LINE	FREQ	INTEN
1	64.94	0.000	15	89.07	0.135	29	100.17	5.458	43	110.93	0.135
2	69.46	0.001	16	89.17	0.000	30	100.28	0.000	44	110.99	0.073
3	70.58	0.000	17	90.09	0.336	31	100.91	3.664	45	116.81	0.000
4	72.25	0.014	18	91.00	0.000	32	101.48	1.977	46	118.48	0.044
5	75.67	0.023	19	91.15	0.000	33	101.95	1.986	47	118.51	0.000
6	78.07	0.000	20	92.34	0.071	34	103.14	0.000	48	118.87	0.000
7	80.19	0.000	21	94.00	0.000	35	105.42	0.000	49	119.72	0.070
8	80.28	0.070	22	95.66	0.000	36	106.00	0.000	50	119.81	0.000
9	81.52	0.044	23	98.05	1.986	37	107.40	0.000	51	120.85	0.
10	82.58	0.	24	98.52	1.977	38	107.66	0.071	52	124.33	0.023
11	83.19	0.000	25	99.09	3.664	39	107.77	0.000	53	125.99	0.000
12	84.56	0.000	26	99.83	5.458	40	108.78	0.	54	127.75	0.014
13	87.79	0.000	27	99.89	2.149	41	109.00	0.000	55	130.54	0.001
14	89.01	0.073	28	100.11	2.149	42	109.91	0.336	56	138.48	0.000

−11 −10 −9 −8 −7 −6 −5 −4 −3 −2 −1 0 +1 +2 +3 +4 +5 +6 +7 +8 +9 +10 +11

5-488

$J_{AA'}$	J_{AB}	$J_{AB'}$	$J_{BB'}$
-9	12	15	-9
-9	15	12	-9

The maximum summed intensity is 8.056.

LINE	FREQ	INTEN	LINE	FREQ	INTEN	LINE	FREQ	INTEN	LINE	FREQ	INTEN
1	57.42	0.000	15	92.15	0.000	29	100.12	5.926	43	108.30	0.000
2	58.90	0.000	16	93.67	0.000	30	100.33	3.952	44	112.51	0.000
3	65.61	0.000	17	94.20	0.000	31	101.15	0.000	45	114.92	0.197
4	68.02	0.000	18	95.15	0.553	32	101.48	1.844	46	118.00	0.000
5	72.22	0.007	19	95.15	0.553	33	101.59	0.000	47	121.33	0.000
6	72.67	0.048	20	95.68	0.000	34	101.85	1.447	48	124.33	0.000
7	73.82	0.026	21	96.67	0.000	35	101.85	1.447	49	124.70	0.000
8	75.30	0.000	22	98.15	1.447	36	103.33	0.000	50	126.18	0.026
9	75.67	0.000	23	98.15	1.447	37	104.32	0.000	51	127.33	0.048
10	78.67	0.000	24	98.41	0.000	38	104.85	0.553	52	127.78	0.007
11	82.00	0.	25	98.52	1.844	39	104.85	0.553	53	131.98	0.000
12	85.08	0.197	26	98.85	0.000	40	105.80	0.000	54	134.39	0.000
13	87.49	0.000	27	99.67	3.952	41	106.33	0.000	55	141.10	0.000
14	91.70	0.000	28	99.88	5.926	42	107.85	0.000	56	142.58	0.000

−11 −10 −9 −8 −7 −6 −5 −4 −3 −2 −1 0 +1 +2 +3 +4 +5 +6 +7 +8 +9 +10 +11

5-489

$J_{AA'}$	J_{AB}	$J_{AB'}$	$J_{BB'}$
-9	-9	12	15
-9	12	-9	15
15	12	-9	-9
15	-9	12	-9

The maximum summed intensity is 4.668.

LINE	FREQ	INTEN	LINE	FREQ	INTEN	LINE	FREQ	INTEN	LINE	FREQ	INTEN
1	64.07	0.000	15	86.19	0.000	29	100.53	2.776	43	112.95	0.000
2	65.74	0.006	16	88.73	0.092	30	100.69	0.000	44	115.59	0.000
3	65.90	0.000	17	90.41	0.000	31	101.85	2.894	45	116.30	0.000
4	70.23	0.010	18	92.71	0.000	32	101.96	0.000	46	117.97	0.041
5	73.37	0.005	19	92.76	0.240	33	102.12	1.990	47	119.19	0.000
6	75.15	0.000	20	93.11	0.241	34	102.36	1.994	48	119.92	0.047
7	77.70	0.000	21	93.56	0.000	35	103.79	0.000	49	120.37	0.000
8	80.08	0.047	22	95.15	1.106	36	104.85	1.106	50	122.30	0.000
9	81.67	0.000	23	97.64	1.994	37	106.89	0.241	51	122.81	0.000
10	82.03	0.041	24	97.88	1.990	38	107.24	0.240	52	126.63	0.005
11	82.57	0.	25	98.15	2.894	39	109.33	0.000	53	129.77	0.010
12	83.70	0.000	26	99.47	2.776	40	109.59	0.000	54	131.45	0.000
13	84.41	0.000	27	99.82	4.557	41	111.27	0.092	55	134.26	0.006
14	85.29	0.000	28	100.18	4.557	42	111.77	0.000	56	138.58	0.000

−11 −10 −9 −8 −7 −6 −5 −4 −3 −2 −1 0 +1 +2 +3 +4 +5 +6 +7 +8 +9 +10 +11

5-490

$J_{AA'}$	J_{AB}	$J_{AB'}$	$J_{BB'}$
-9	-9	15	12
-9	15	-9	12
12	15	-9	-9
12	-9	15	-9

The maximum summed intensity is 7.192.

LINE	FREQ	INTEN	LINE	FREQ	INTEN	LINE	FREQ	INTEN	LINE	FREQ	INTEN
1	61.43	0.000	15	86.80	0.000	29	100.26	5.176	43	112.69	0.037
2	63.51	0.000	16	87.31	0.037	30	100.27	2.385	44	113.20	0.000
3	65.99	0.008	17	89.73	0.000	31	101.24	3.414	45	118.69	0.000
4	69.84	0.002	18	89.80	0.000	32	101.79	1.987	46	120.15	0.000
5	69.90	0.013	19	91.24	0.199	33	102.12	1.992	47	121.08	0.000
6	75.94	0.000	20	91.26	0.115	34	104.28	0.000	48	121.17	0.035
7	78.31	0.000	21	91.85	0.000	35	106.35	0.000	49	121.67	0.051
8	78.33	0.051	22	92.76	0.586	36	107.24	0.586	50	121.69	0.000
9	78.83	0.035	23	97.88	1.992	37	108.74	0.115	51	122.56	0.000
10	81.31	0.000	24	98.21	1.987	38	108.76	0.199	52	130.10	0.013
11	81.35	0.	25	98.76	3.414	39	109.65	0.	53	130.16	0.002
12	82.84	0.	26	99.63	0.000	40	110.20	0.000	54	132.58	0.000
13	84.95	0.000	27	99.73	2.385	41	111.14	0.000	55	134.01	0.008
14	86.44	0.	28	99.74	5.176	42	112.06	0.000	56	142.48	0.000

−11 −10 −9 −8 −7 −6 −5 −4 −3 −2 −1 0 +1 +2 +3 +4 +5 +6 +7 +8 +9 +10 +11

6

The AB_4 *Case*

For many AB_4 cases, all the A-B coupling constants are the same. Then the relative line positions are dependent only on the ratio $J_{AB}/\Delta\nu$. The changes in spectra accompanying an increase in this ratio are shown in Spectra 6-1 through 6-14. The most characteristic feature is that one of the lines of the A part is always at ν_A, and this line may usually be located by a comparison of the observed and calculated spectra.

The chemical shift for B is the average of the positions for several sets of lines, for example, those at 101.78 and 104.22 in Spectrum 6-7 ($J/\Delta\nu = 0.5$). However, there are many other lines in this vicinity, and it is usually only possible to pick out an approximate value for ν_B.

A detailed comparison of the observed spectrum with those given here will permit an assignment of a value to J_{AB} and, at the same time, will usually permit one to obtain a more accurate value for ν_B.

A common example of an AB_4 spectrum is provided by the $-SF_5$ group. Here, the chemical shifts are so large that most of the lines in the spectrum may be resolved. The spectrum will then look quite different from those presented here, and the frequencies and intensities given in the tables should be used for obtaining the spectral parameters rather than the plots.

6-1

J=0.0

Maximum summed intensity = 64.000

LINE	FREQ	INTEN	LINE	FREQ	INTEN	LINE	FREQ	INTEN	LINE	FREQ	INTEN
1	97.00	1.000	61	97.00	0.	121	103.00	1.000	181	103.00	1.000
2	97.00	1.000	62	97.00	0.	122	103.00	0.	182	103.00	1.000
3	97.00	0.	63	97.00	0.	123	103.00	1.000	183	109.00	0.
4	97.00	0.	64	97.00	1.000	124	103.00	0.	184	109.00	0.
5	97.00	0.	65	97.00	0.	125	103.00	1.000	185	109.00	0.
6	97.00	0.	66	97.00	0.	126	103.00	0.	186	109.00	0.
7	97.00	1.000	67	97.00	0.	127	103.00	1.000	187	109.00	0.
8	97.00	0.	68	97.00	0.	128	103.00	1.000	188	109.00	0.
9	97.00	0.	69	97.00	1.000	129	103.00	1.000	189	109.00	0.
10	97.00	0.	70	97.00	1.000	130	103.00	0.	190	109.00	0.
11	97.00	0.	71	103.00	0.	131	103.00	0.	191	109.00	0.
12	97.00	1.000	72	103.00	0.	132	103.00	1.000	192	109.00	0.
13	97.00	0.	73	103.00	1.000	133	103.00	0.	193	109.00	0.
14	97.00	0.	74	103.00	0.	134	103.00	0.	194	109.00	0.
15	97.00	0.	75	103.00	1.000	135	103.00	0.	195	109.00	0.
16	97.00	0.	76	103.00	0.	136	103.00	1.000	196	109.00	0.
17	97.00	1.000	77	103.00	1.000	137	103.00	1.000	197	109.00	0.
18	97.00	1.000	78	103.00	0.	138	103.00	1.000	198	109.00	0.
19	97.00	0.	79	103.00	0.	139	103.00	1.000	199	109.00	0.
20	97.00	0.	80	103.00	1.000	140	103.00	0.	200	109.00	0.
21	97.00	0.	81	103.00	0.	141	103.00	0.	201	109.00	0.
22	97.00	0.	82	103.00	1.000	142	103.00	1.000	202	109.00	0.
23	97.00	0.	83	103.00	1.000	143	103.00	0.	203	109.00	0.
24	97.00	0.	84	103.00	1.000	144	103.00	1.000	204	109.00	0.
25	97.00	1.000	85	103.00	1.000	145	103.00	0.	205	109.00	0.
26	97.00	0.	86	103.00	1.000	146	103.00	0.	206	109.00	0.
27	97.00	0.	87	103.00	1.000	147	103.00	1.000	207	109.00	0.
28	97.00	0.	88	103.00	1.000	148	103.00	1.000	208	109.00	0.
29	97.00	0.	89	103.00	0.	149	103.00	0.	209	109.00	0.
30	97.00	0.	90	103.00	1.000	150	103.00	1.000	210	109.00	0.
31	97.00	0.	91	103.00	1.000	151	103.00	0.	211	0.	0.
32	97.00	1.000	92	103.00	0.	152	103.00	0.	212	0.	0.
33	97.00	0.	93	103.00	0.	153	103.00	1.000	213	0.	0.
34	97.00	0.	94	103.00	0.	154	103.00	0.	214	0.	0.
35	97.00	0.	95	103.00	0.	155	103.00	1.000	215	0.	0.
36	97.00	0.	96	103.00	1.000	156	103.00	0.	216	0.	0.
37	97.00	0.	97	103.00	1.000	157	103.00	1.000	217	0.	0.
38	97.00	0.	98	103.00	1.000	158	103.00	0.	218	0.	0.
39	97.00	1.000	99	103.00	1.000	159	103.00	0.	219	0.	0.
40	97.00	0.	100	103.00	1.000	160	103.00	1.000	220	0.	0.
41	97.00	0.	101	103.00	0.	161	103.00	1.000	221	0.	0.
42	97.00	0.	102	103.00	1.000	162	103.00	1.000	222	0.	0.
43	97.00	0.	103	103.00	0.	163	103.00	1.000	223	0.	0.
44	97.00	0.	104	103.00	1.000	164	103.00	1.000	224	0.	0.
45	97.00	0.	105	103.00	0.	165	103.00	1.000	225	0.	0.
46	97.00	1.000	106	103.00	0.	166	103.00	1.000	226	0.	0.
47	97.00	0.	107	103.00	1.000	167	103.00	1.000	227	0.	0.
48	97.00	0.	108	103.00	1.000	168	103.00	0.	228	0.	0.
49	97.00	0.	109	103.00	0.	169	103.00	0.	229	0.	0.
50	97.00	0.	110	103.00	0.	170	103.00	0.	230	0.	0.
51	97.00	0.	111	103.00	1.000	171	103.00	1.000	231	0.	0.
52	97.00	0.	112	103.00	1.000	172	103.00	1.000	232	0.	0.
53	97.00	1.000	113	103.00	0.	173	103.00	1.000	233	0.	0.
54	97.00	1.000	114	103.00	0.	174	103.00	0.	234	0.	0.
55	97.00	0.	115	103.00	1.000	175	103.00	0.	235	0.	0.
56	97.00	0.	116	103.00	1.000	176	103.00	1.000	236	0.	0.
57	97.00	0.	117	103.00	0.	177	103.00	1.000	237	0.	0.
58	97.00	0.	118	103.00	0.	178	103.00	1.000	238	0.	0.
59	97.00	1.000	119	103.00	1.000	179	103.00	1.000	239	0.	0.
60	97.00	0.	120	103.00	0.	180	103.00	1.000	240	0.	0.

−11 −10 −9 −8 −7 −6 −5 −4 −3 −2 −1 0 +1 +2 +3 +4 +5 +6 +7 +8 +9 +10 +11

6-2

J=0.5

Maximum summed intensity = 32.940

LINE	FREQ	INTEN	LINE	FREQ	INTEN	LINE	FREQ	INTEN	LINE	FREQ	INTEN
1	95.96	0.723	61	97.48	0.097	121	102.79	0.000	181	103.31	0.000
2	96.40	0.815	62	97.48	0.786	122	102.81	0.000	182	103.31	0.000
3	96.44	0.000	63	97.48	1.056	123	102.81	0.000	183	108.55	0.000
4	96.44	0.000	64	97.48	0.120	124	102.81	0.000	184	108.55	0.000
5	96.44	0.000	65	97.48	0.023	125	102.81	0.000	185	108.57	0.000
6	96.44	0.000	66	97.48	0.271	126	102.81	0.000	186	108.57	0.000
7	96.44	0.000	67	97.48	0.294	127	103.20	0.000	187	108.57	0.000
8	96.44	0.000	68	97.48	0.001	128	103.20	0.000	188	108.61	0.000
9	96.48	0.071	69	97.48	0.882	129	103.21	0.000	189	109.04	0.000
10	96.48	0.427	70	97.95	1.401	130	103.21	0.000	190	109.04	0.000
11	96.48	0.563	71	102.71	0.000	131	103.21	0.000	191	109.04	0.000
12	96.48	0.240	72	102.71	0.000	132	103.22	0.000	192	109.04	0.000
13	96.48	0.211	73	102.71	0.000	133	103.22	0.000	193	109.04	0.000
14	96.48	0.178	74	102.71	0.000	134	103.22	0.000	194	109.04	0.000
15	96.48	0.346	75	102.71	0.000	135	103.23	3.723	195	109.04	0.000
16	96.48	0.042	76	102.73	4.401	136	103.24	5.538	196	109.04	0.000
17	96.48	0.456	77	102.73	0.000	137	103.25	0.590	197	109.04	0.000
18	96.88	0.941	78	102.73	0.000	138	103.25	0.863	198	109.08	0.000
19	96.92	0.000	79	102.73	0.000	139	103.25	0.391	199	109.08	0.000
20	96.92	0.000	80	102.75	0.000	140	103.25	0.717	200	109.08	0.000
21	96.92	0.000	81	102.75	0.000	141	103.25	0.000	201	109.08	0.000
22	96.92	0.000	82	102.75	0.000	142	103.25	1.127	202	109.08	0.000
23	96.92	0.000	83	102.75	0.000	143	103.25	0.981	203	109.08	0.000
24	96.92	0.000	84	102.75	0.000	144	103.25	0.536	204	109.12	0.000
25	96.94	0.000	85	102.75	0.000	145	103.25	0.327	205	109.54	0.000
26	96.94	0.000	86	102.75	0.000	146	103.25	0.000	206	109.54	0.000
27	96.94	0.000	87	102.75	0.000	147	103.25	0.000	207	109.56	0.000
28	96.94	0.000	88	102.75	0.000	148	103.25	0.000	208	109.56	0.000
29	96.96	0.843	89	102.75	1.013	149	103.25	0.000	209	109.56	0.000
30	96.96	0.136	90	102.75	1.124	150	103.25	0.000	210	109.60	0.000
31	96.96	0.107	91	102.75	0.595	151	103.25	0.000	211	0.	0.
32	96.96	0.612	92	102.75	0.568	152	103.25	0.000	212	0.	0.
33	96.96	0.001	93	102.75	0.269	153	103.25	0.000	213	0.	0.
34	96.96	0.261	94	102.75	0.783	154	103.25	0.000	214	0.	0.
35	96.96	0.029	95	102.75	0.039	155	103.27	0.000	215	0.	0.
36	96.96	0.232	96	102.75	1.312	156	103.27	0.000	216	0.	0.
37	96.96	0.718	97	102.75	0.825	157	103.27	0.000	217	0.	0.
38	96.98	0.000	98	102.76	6.521	158	103.27	5.479	218	0.	0.
39	96.98	0.000	99	102.77	0.354	159	103.27	0.000	219	0.	0.
40	96.98	0.000	100	102.77	1.802	160	103.27	0.000	220	0.	0.
41	96.98	0.000	101	102.77	0.211	161	103.27	0.000	221	0.	0.
42	96.98	0.000	102	102.77	0.049	162	103.27	0.000	222	0.	0.
43	96.98	0.000	103	102.77	1.591	163	103.27	0.000	223	0.	0.
44	96.98	0.000	104	102.77	0.305	164	103.27	0.000	224	0.	0.
45	96.98	0.000	105	102.77	0.000	165	103.27	0.688	225	0.	0.
46	96.98	0.000	106	102.77	1.896	166	103.27	0.282	226	0.	0.
47	96.98	0.000	107	102.77	0.260	167	103.27	0.625	227	0.	0.
48	96.98	0.000	108	102.77	0.000	168	103.27	0.229	228	0.	0.
49	96.98	0.000	109	102.77	0.000	169	103.27	0.510	229	0.	0.
50	97.00	0.969	110	102.77	0.000	170	103.27	1.313	230	0.	0.
51	97.00	0.031	111	102.77	0.000	171	103.27	0.854	231	0.	0.
52	97.00	0.031	112	102.77	0.000	172	103.27	0.970	232	0.	0.
53	97.00	0.969	113	102.77	0.000	173	103.27	0.000	233	0.	0.
54	97.39	1.121	114	102.77	6.462	174	103.29	0.000	234	0.	0.
55	97.43	0.000	115	102.78	0.000	175	103.29	0.000	235	0.	0.
56	97.43	0.000	116	102.78	0.000	176	103.29	0.000	236	0.	0.
57	97.43	0.000	117	102.78	0.000	177	103.30	3.599	237	0.	0.
58	97.44	0.000	118	102.79	4.277	178	103.31	0.000	238	0.	0.
59	97.44	0.000	119	102.79	0.000	179	103.31	0.000	239	0.	0.
60	97.44	0.000	120	102.79	0.000	180	103.31	0.000	240	0.	0.

−11 −10 −9 −8 −7 −6 −5 −4 −3 −2 −1 0 +1 +2 +3 +4 +5 +6 +7 +8 +9 +10 +11

6-3

J=1.0

Maximum summed intensity = 32.283

LINE	FREQ	INTEN	LINE	FREQ	INTEN	LINE	FREQ	INTEN	LINE	FREQ	INTEN
1	94.87	0.535	61	97.91	0.493	121	102.68	0.000	181	103.76	0.000
2	95.65	0.633	62	97.91	0.189	122	102.72	0.000	182	103.76	0.000
3	95.78	0.000	63	97.91	0.060	123	102.72	0.000	183	108.21	0.000
4	95.78	0.000	64	97.91	0.686	124	102.72	0.000	184	108.21	0.000
5	95.78	0.000	65	97.91	0.834	125	102.76	0.000	185	108.30	0.000
6	95.79	0.000	66	97.91	0.473	126	102.76	0.000	186	108.30	0.000
7	95.79	0.000	67	97.91	0.814	127	103.29	0.000	187	108.30	0.000
8	95.79	0.000	68	97.91	0.345	128	103.29	0.000	188	108.47	0.002
9	95.92	0.205	69	97.91	0.209	129	103.32	0.000	189	109.17	0.000
10	95.92	0.341	70	98.79	1.942	130	103.32	0.000	190	109.17	0.000
11	95.92	0.284	71	102.37	0.000	131	103.32	0.000	191	109.17	0.000
12	95.92	0.165	72	102.37	0.000	132	103.38	0.000	192	109.17	0.000
13	95.92	0.356	73	102.37	0.000	133	103.38	0.000	193	109.17	0.000
14	95.92	0.070	74	102.37	0.000	134	103.38	0.000	194	109.17	0.000
15	95.92	0.222	75	102.37	0.000	135	103.41	3.535	195	109.17	0.000
16	95.92	0.013	76	102.44	0.000	136	103.46	5.167	196	109.17	0.000
17	95.92	0.475	77	102.44	0.000	137	103.49	0.397	197	109.17	0.000
18	96.52	0.793	78	102.44	0.000	138	103.49	0.586	198	109.31	0.000
19	96.66	0.000	79	102.45	4.939	139	103.49	0.727	199	109.31	0.000
20	96.66	0.000	80	102.50	0.000	140	103.49	0.261	200	109.31	0.000
21	96.66	0.000	81	102.50	0.000	141	103.49	1.052	201	109.34	0.000
22	96.69	0.000	82	102.50	0.000	142	103.49	1.121	202	109.34	0.000
23	96.69	0.000	83	102.50	0.000	143	103.49	0.003	203	109.34	0.000
24	96.69	0.000	84	102.50	0.000	144	103.49	0.655	204	109.48	0.001
25	96.74	0.000	85	102.50	0.000	145	103.49	0.328	205	110.13	0.000
26	96.74	0.000	86	102.50	0.000	146	103.50	0.000	206	110.13	0.000
27	96.78	0.000	87	102.50	0.000	147	103.50	0.000	207	110.21	0.000
28	96.78	0.000	88	102.50	0.000	148	103.50	0.000	208	110.21	0.000
29	96.83	0.050	89	102.51	0.080	149	103.50	0.000	209	110.21	0.000
30	96.83	0.339	90	102.51	0.822	150	103.50	0.000	210	110.35	0.000
31	96.83	0.827	91	102.51	1.466	151	103.50	0.000	211	0.	0.
32	96.83	0.533	92	102.51	0.452	152	103.50	0.000	212	0.	0.
33	96.83	0.045	93	102.51	1.320	153	103.50	0.000	213	0.	0.
34	96.83	0.001	94	102.51	1.094	154	103.50	0.000	214	0.	0.
35	96.83	0.093	95	102.51	0.968	155	103.55	4.958	215	0.	0.
36	96.83	0.581	96	102.51	0.596	156	103.56	0.000	216	0.	0.
37	96.83	0.295	97	102.51	0.306	157	103.56	0.000	217	0.	0.
38	96.91	0.000	98	102.54	7.039	158	103.56	0.000	218	0.	0.
39	96.91	0.000	99	102.58	0.216	159	103.58	0.000	219	0.	0.
40	96.91	0.000	100	102.58	0.441	160	103.58	0.000	220	0.	0.
41	96.91	0.000	101	102.58	0.745	161	103.58	0.000	221	0.	0.
42	96.91	0.000	102	102.58	1.447	162	103.58	0.000	222	0.	0.
43	96.91	0.000	103	102.58	1.632	163	103.58	0.000	223	0.	0.
44	96.92	0.000	104	102.58	0.097	164	103.58	0.000	224	0.	0.
45	96.92	0.000	105	102.58	1.328	165	103.59	0.499	225	0.	0.
46	96.92	0.000	106	102.58	0.401	166	103.59	0.248	226	0.	0.
47	96.92	0.000	107	102.58	0.560	167	103.59	0.885	227	0.	0.
48	96.92	0.000	108	102.59	0.000	168	103.59	0.605	228	0.	0.
49	96.92	0.000	109	102.59	0.000	169	103.59	0.280	229	0.	0.
50	97.00	0.806	110	102.59	0.000	170	103.59	0.746	230	0.	0.
51	97.00	0.194	111	102.59	0.000	171	103.59	0.528	231	0.	0.
52	97.00	0.194	112	102.59	0.000	172	103.59	1.104	232	0.	0.
53	97.00	0.806	113	102.59	0.000	173	103.59	0.000	233	0.	0.
54	97.53	1.100	114	102.59	6.831	174	103.63	0.000	234	0.	0.
55	97.70	0.000	115	102.62	0.000	175	103.63	0.000	235	0.	0.
56	97.70	0.000	116	102.62	0.000	176	103.63	0.000	236	0.	0.
57	97.70	0.000	117	102.62	0.000	177	103.71	3.058	237	0.	0.
58	97.74	0.000	118	102.63	4.465	178	103.72	0.000	238	0.	0.
59	97.74	0.000	119	102.68	0.000	179	103.72	0.000	239	0.	0.
60	97.74	0.000	120	102.68	0.000	180	103.76	0.000	240	0.	0.

6 - 4

J= 1.5

Maximum summed intensity =30.897

LINE	FREQ	INTEN	LINE	FREQ	INTEN	LINE	FREQ	INTEN	LINE	FREQ	INTEN
1	93.74	0.407	61	98.29	0.826	121	102.67	0.000	181	104.33	0.000
2	94.77	0.484	62	98.29	0.431	122	102.72	0.000	182	104.33	0.000
3	95.03	0.000	63	98.29	0.617	123	102.72	0.000	183	108.03	0.000
4	95.03	0.000	64	98.29	0.309	124	102.72	0.000	184	108.03	0.000
5	95.03	0.000	65	98.29	0.092	125	102.83	0.000	185	108.23	0.000
6	95.07	0.000	66	98.29	0.858	126	102.83	0.000	186	108.23	0.000
7	95.07	0.000	67	98.29	0.124	127	103.22	0.000	187	108.23	0.000
8	95.07	0.000	68	98.29	1.043	128	103.22	0.000	188	108.61	0.011
9	95.34	0.447	69	98.29	0.399	129	103.33	0.000	189	109.37	0.000
10	95.34	0.133	70	99.47	2.578	130	103.33	0.000	190	109.37	0.001
11	95.34	0.018	71	101.99	0.000	131	103.33	0.000	191	109.37	0.001
12	95.34	0.151	72	101.99	0.000	132	103.43	0.000	192	109.37	0.000
13	95.34	0.000	73	101.99	0.000	133	103.43	0.000	193	109.37	0.000
14	95.34	0.399	74	101.99	0.000	134	103.43	0.000	194	109.37	0.000
15	95.34	0.067	75	101.99	0.000	135	103.55	3.406	195	109.37	0.000
16	95.34	0.048	76	102.15	0.000	136	103.64	4.886	196	109.37	0.000
17	95.34	0.532	77	102.15	0.000	137	103.71	1.066	197	109.37	0.001
18	95.95	0.619	78	102.15	0.000	138	103.71	0.104	198	109.67	0.000
19	96.26	0.000	79	102.20	5.567	139	103.71	0.428	199	109.67	0.000
20	96.26	0.000	80	102.25	0.000	140	103.71	1.143	200	109.67	0.000
21	96.26	0.000	81	102.25	0.000	141	103.71	0.321	201	109.74	0.000
22	96.33	0.000	82	102.25	0.000	142	103.71	0.211	202	109.74	0.000
23	96.33	0.000	83	102.25	0.000	143	103.71	0.352	203	109.74	0.000
24	96.33	0.000	84	102.25	0.000	144	103.71	0.135	204	110.05	0.004
25	96.42	0.000	85	102.25	0.000	145	103.71	1.035	205	110.76	0.000
26	96.42	0.000	86	102.25	0.000	146	103.75	0.000	206	110.76	0.000
27	96.53	0.000	87	102.25	0.000	147	103.75	0.000	207	110.93	0.000
28	96.53	0.000	88	102.25	0.000	148	103.75	0.000	208	110.93	0.000
29	96.63	0.003	89	102.29	1.704	149	103.75	0.000	209	110.93	0.000
30	96.63	0.205	90	102.29	0.005	150	103.75	0.000	210	111.23	0.001
31	96.63	0.627	91	102.29	0.337	151	103.75	0.000	211	0.	0.
32	96.63	0.751	92	102.29	0.856	152	103.75	0.000	212	0.	0.
33	96.63	0.049	93	102.29	1.710	153	103.75	0.000	213	0.	0.
34	96.63	0.036	94	102.29	0.525	154	103.75	0.000	214	0.	0.
35	96.63	0.081	95	102.29	0.850	155	103.80	4.494	215	0.	0.
36	96.63	0.581	96	102.29	0.518	156	103.85	0.000	216	0.	0.
37	96.63	0.173	97	102.29	1.191	157	103.85	0.000	217	0.	0.
38	96.79	0.000	98	102.36	7.491	158	103.85	0.000	218	0.	0.
39	96.79	0.000	99	102.41	0.796	159	103.91	0.000	219	0.	0.
40	96.79	0.000	100	102.41	1.348	160	103.91	0.000	220	0.	0.
41	96.79	0.000	101	102.41	0.257	161	103.91	0.000	221	0.	0.
42	96.79	0.000	102	102.41	1.369	162	103.91	0.000	222	0.	0.
43	96.79	0.000	103	102.41	0.236	163	103.91	0.000	223	0.	0.
44	96.84	0.000	104	102.41	0.268	164	103.91	0.000	224	0.	0.
45	96.84	0.000	105	102.41	0.786	165	103.96	0.355	225	0.	0.
46	96.84	0.000	106	102.41	0.764	166	103.96	0.774	226	0.	0.
47	96.84	0.000	107	102.41	1.380	167	103.96	0.609	227	0.	0.
48	96.84	0.000	108	102.45	7.109	168	103.96	0.638	228	0.	0.
49	96.84	0.000	109	102.46	0.000	169	103.96	0.470	229	0.	0.
50	97.00	0.740	110	102.46	0.000	170	103.96	0.021	230	0.	0.
51	97.00	0.260	111	102.46	0.000	171	103.96	0.305	231	0.	0.
52	97.00	0.260	112	102.46	0.000	172	103.96	0.186	232	0.	0.
53	97.00	0.740	113	102.46	0.000	173	103.96	0.943	233	0.	0.
54	97.39	0.928	114	102.46	0.000	174	104.01	0.000	234	0.	0.
55	97.77	0.000	115	102.51	4.593	175	104.01	0.000	235	0.	0.
56	97.77	0.000	116	102.57	0.000	176	104.01	0.000	236	0.	0.
57	97.77	0.000	117	102.57	0.000	177	104.22	0.000	237	0.	0.
58	97.92	0.000	118	102.57	0.000	178	104.22	0.000	238	0.	0.
59	97.92	0.000	119	102.67	0.000	179	104.28	2.422	239	0.	0.
60	97.92	0.000	120	102.67	0.000	180	104.33	0.000	240	0.	0.

-11 -10 -9 -8 -7 -6 -5 -4 -3 -2 -1 0 +1 +2 +3 +4 +5 +6 +7 +8 +9 +10 +11

6 - 5

J=2.0

Maximum summed intensity = 26.474

LINE	FREQ	INTEN	LINE	FREQ	INTEN	LINE	FREQ	INTEN	LINE	FREQ	INTEN
1	92.58	0.317	61	98.63	0.005	121	102.73	0.000	181	105.00	0.000
2	93.80	0.371	62	98.63	1.287	122	102.77	0.000	182	105.00	1.800
3	94.23	0.000	63	98.63	1.671	123	102.77	0.000	183	108.00	0.000
4	94.23	0.000	64	98.63	0.044	124	102.77	0.000	184	108.00	0.000
5	94.23	0.000	65	98.63	0.469	125	103.00	0.000	185	108.37	0.000
6	94.30	0.000	66	98.63	0.046	126	103.00	0.000	186	108.37	0.000
7	94.30	0.000	67	98.63	0.085	127	103.00	0.000	187	108.37	0.000
8	94.30	0.000	68	98.63	0.430	128	103.00	0.000	188	109.00	0.029
9	94.73	0.344	69	98.63	1.247	129	103.27	0.000	189	109.65	0.002
10	94.73	0.063	70	100.00	3.200	130	103.27	0.000	190	109.65	0.000
11	94.73	0.100	71	101.58	0.000	131	103.27	0.000	191	109.65	0.000
12	94.73	0.022	72	101.58	0.000	132	103.37	0.000	192	109.65	0.000
13	94.73	0.425	73	101.60	0.000	133	103.37	0.000	193	109.65	0.000
14	94.73	0.059	74	101.60	0.000	134	103.37	0.000	194	109.65	0.000
15	94.73	0.141	75	101.60	0.000	135	103.65	3.315	195	109.65	0.002
16	94.73	0.018	76	101.85	0.000	136	103.77	4.678	196	109.65	0.002
17	94.73	0.348	77	101.85	0.000	137	103.90	0.079	197	109.65	0.000
18	95.23	0.465	78	101.85	0.000	138	103.90	0.444	198	110.14	0.000
19	95.73	0.000	79	102.00	0.000	139	103.90	0.982	199	110.14	0.000
20	95.73	0.000	80	102.00	6.171	140	103.90	1.332	200	110.14	0.000
21	95.73	0.000	81	102.00	0.000	141	103.90	0.094	201	110.27	0.000
22	95.86	0.000	82	102.00	0.000	142	103.90	0.170	202	110.27	0.000
23	95.86	0.000	83	102.00	0.000	143	103.90	0.890	203	110.27	0.000
24	95.86	0.000	84	102.00	0.000	144	103.90	0.003	204	110.77	0.008
25	96.00	0.000	85	102.00	0.000	145	103.90	0.520	205	111.42	0.000
26	96.00	0.000	86	102.00	0.000	146	104.00	0.000	206	111.42	0.000
27	96.23	0.000	87	102.00	0.000	147	104.00	0.000	207	111.70	0.000
28	96.23	0.000	88	102.00	0.000	148	104.00	4.114	208	111.70	0.000
29	96.35	0.513	89	102.10	1.709	149	104.00	0.000	209	111.70	0.000
30	96.35	0.148	90	102.10	0.781	150	104.00	0.000	210	112.20	0.002
31	96.35	0.073	91	102.10	0.269	151	104.00	0.000	211	0.	0.
32	96.35	0.178	92	102.10	0.756	152	104.00	0.000	212	0.	0.
33	96.35	0.043	93	102.10	0.294	153	104.00	0.000	213	0.	0.
34	96.35	0.553	94	102.10	0.262	154	104.00	0.000	214	0.	0.
35	96.35	0.034	95	102.10	1.716	155	104.00	0.000	215	0.	0.
36	96.35	0.004	96	102.10	1.741	156	104.15	0.000	216	0.	0.
37	96.35	0.657	97	102.10	0.749	157	104.15	0.000	217	0.	0.
38	96.63	0.000	98	102.23	7.849	158	104.15	0.000	218	0.	0.
39	96.63	0.000	99	102.27	1.429	159	104.27	0.000	219	0.	0.
40	96.63	0.000	100	102.27	0.249	160	104.27	0.000	220	0.	0.
41	96.63	0.000	101	102.27	0.392	161	104.27	0.000	221	0.	0.
42	96.63	0.000	102	102.27	0.815	162	104.27	0.000	222	0.	0.
43	96.63	0.000	103	102.27	0.558	163	104.27	0.000	223	0.	0.
44	96.73	0.000	104	102.27	1.543	164	104.27	0.000	224	0.	0.
45	96.73	0.000	105	102.27	0.672	165	104.37	0.284	225	0.	0.
46	96.73	0.000	106	102.27	1.686	166	104.37	0.624	226	0.	0.
47	96.73	0.000	107	102.27	0.135	167	104.37	0.595	227	0.	0.
48	96.73	0.000	108	102.35	7.312	168	104.37	0.147	228	0.	0.
49	96.73	0.000	109	102.37	0.000	169	104.37	0.330	229	0.	0.
50	97.00	0.499	110	102.37	0.000	170	104.37	0.496	230	0.	0.
51	97.00	0.501	111	102.37	0.000	171	104.37	0.019	231	0.	0.
52	97.00	0.501	112	102.37	0.000	172	104.37	0.807	232	0.	0.
53	97.00	0.499	113	102.37	0.000	173	.04.37	0.412	233	0.	0.
54	97.00	0.686	114	102.37	0.000	174	104.40	0.000	234	0.	0.
55	97.63	0.000	115	102.42	4.683	175	104.40	0.000	235	0.	0.
56	97.63	0.000	116	102.63	0.000	176	104.40	0.000	236	0.	0.
57	97.63	0.000	117	102.63	0.000	177	104.77	0.000	237	0.	0.
58	98.00	0.000	118	102.63	0.000	178	104.77	0.000	238	0.	0.
59	98.00	0.000	119	102.73	0.000	179	105.00	0.000	239	0.	0.
60	98.00	0.000	120	102.73	0.000	180	105.00	0.000	240	0.	0.

6 - 6

J= 2.5

Maximum summed intensity = 24.198

LINE	FREQ	INTEN	LINE	FREQ	INTEN	LINE	FREQ	INTEN	LINE	FREQ	INTEN
1	91.40	0.253	61	98.91	1.395	121	102.84	0.000	181	105.75	0.000
2	92.78	0.287	62	98.91	0.188	122	102.84	0.000	182	105.87	1.292
3	93.38	0.000	63	98.91	0.115	123	102.84	0.000	183	108.12	0.000
4	93.38	0.000	64	98.91	0.360	124	102.87	0.000	184	108.12	0.000
5	93.38	0.000	65	98.91	0.474	125	102.87	0.000	185	108.70	0.000
6	93.49	0.000	66	98.91	1.355	126	102.87	0.000	186	108.70	0.000
7	93.49	0.000	67	98.91	0.434	127	103.16	0.000	187	108.70	0.000
8	93.49	0.000	68	98.91	1.281	128	103.16	0.000	188	109.62	0.047
9	94.09	0.383	69	98.91	0.228	129	103.16	0.000	189	109.99	0.004
10	94.09	0.000	70	100.38	3.708	130	103.22	0.000	190	109.99	0.000
11	94.09	0.048	71	101.15	0.000	131	103.22	0.000	191	109.99	0.000
12	94.09	0.033	72	101.15	0.000	132	103.22	0.000	192	109.99	0.000
13	94.09	0.110	73	101.22	0.000	133	103.25	0.000	193	109.99	0.001
14	94.09	0.287	74	101.22	0.000	134	103.25	0.000	194	109.99	0.003
15	94.09	0.015	75	101.22	0.000	135	103.73	3.250	195	109.99	0.000
16	94.09	0.320	76	101.55	0.000	136	103.87	4.526	196	109.99	0.003
17	94.09	0.096	77	101.55	0.000	137	104.07	0.193	197	109.99	0.001
18	94.38	0.345	78	101.55	0.000	138	104.07	0.922	198	110.71	0.000
19	95.09	0.000	79	101.75	0.000	139	104.07	0.956	199	110.71	0.000
20	95.09	0.000	80	101.75	0.000	140	104.07	0.312	200	110.71	0.000
21	95.09	0.000	81	101.75	0.000	141	104.07	0.279	201	110.91	0.000
22	95.29	0.000	82	101.75	0.000	142	104.07	0.384	202	110.91	0.000
23	95.29	0.000	83	101.75	0.000	143	104.07	0.121	203	110.91	0.000
24	95.29	0.000	84	101.75	0.000	144	104.07	0.088	204	111.62	0.011
25	95.50	0.000	85	101.75	0.000	145	104.07	1.027	205	112.10	0.000
26	95.50	0.000	86	101.75	0.000	146	104.13	3.824	206	112.10	0.000
27	95.88	0.000	87	101.75	0.000	147	104.25	0.000	207	112.51	0.000
28	95.88	0.000	88	101.87	6.661	148	104.25	0.000	208	112.51	0.000
29	96.01	0.011	89	101.93	0.388	149	104.25	0.000	209	112.51	0.000
30	96.01	0.065	90	101.93	1.436	150	104.25	0.000	210	113.22	0.002
31	96.01	0.608	91	101.93	1.115	151	104.25	0.000	211	0.	0.
32	96.01	0.004	92	101.93	0.043	152	104.25	0.000	212	0.	0.
33	96.01	0.553	93	101.93	1.827	153	104.25	0.000	213	0.	0.
34	96.01	0.018	94	101.93	1.069	154	104.25	0.000	214	0.	0.
35	96.01	0.011	95	101.93	1.460	155	104.25	0.000	215	0.	0.
36	96.01	0.561	96	101.93	0.724	156	104.45	0.000	216	0.	0.
37	96.01	0.058	97	101.93	0.756	157	104.45	0.000	217	0.	0.
38	96.38	0.468	98	102.13	8.118	158	104.45	0.000	218	0.	0.
39	96.41	0.000	99	102.16	0.477	159	104.66	0.000	219	0.	0.
40	96.41	0.000	100	102.16	0.623	160	104.66	0.000	220	0.	0.
41	96.41	0.000	101	102.16	1.469	161	104.66	0.000	221	0.	0.
42	96.41	0.000	102	102.16	0.009	162	104.66	0.000	222	0.	0.
43	96.41	0.000	103	102.16	1.729	163	104.66	0.000	223	0.	0.
44	96.41	0.000	104	102.16	0.831	164	104.66	0.000	224	0.	0.
45	96.59	0.000	105	102.16	2.083	165	104.78	0.000	225	0.	0.
46	96.59	0.000	106	102.16	0.217	166	104.78	0.000	226	0.	0.
47	96.59	0.000	107	102.16	0.269	167	104.78	0.000	227	0.	0.
48	96.59	0.000	108	102.27	7.460	168	104.84	0.019	228	0.	0.
49	96.59	0.000	109	102.34	0.000	169	104.84	0.944	229	0.	0.
50	96.59	0.000	110	102.34	0.000	170	104.84	0.094	230	0.	0.
51	97.00	0.724	111	102.34	0.000	171	104.84	0.006	231	0.	0.
52	97.00	0.276	112	102.34	0.000	172	104.84	0.680	232	0.	0.
53	97.00	0.276	113	102.34	0.000	173	104.84	0.107	233	0.	0.
54	97.00	0.724	114	102.34	0.000	174	104.84	0.358	234	0.	0.
55	97.30	0.000	115	102.35	4.747	175	104.84	0.371	235	0.	0.
56	97.30	0.000	116	102.63	0.000	176	104.84	0.591	236	0.	0.
57	97.30	0.000	117	102.63	0.000	177	105.37	0.000	237	0.	0.
58	98.00	0.000	118	102.78	0.000	178	105.37	0.000	238	0.	0.
59	98.00	0.000	119	102.78	0.000	179	105.75	0.000	239	0.	0.
60	98.00	0.000	120	102.78	0.000	180	105.75	0.000	240	0.	0.

-11 -10 -9 -8 -7 -6 -5 -4 -3 -2 -1 0 +1 +2 +3 +4 +5 +6 +7 +8 +9 +10 +11

6 - 7

J=3.0

Maximum summed intensity = 23.022

LINE	FREQ	INTEN	LINE	FREQ	INTEN	LINE	FREQ	INTEN	LINE	FREQ	INTEN
1	90.20	0.205	61	99.16	0.506	121	103.00	0.000	181	106.56	0.000
2	91.70	0.226	62	99.16	0.269	122	103.00	0.000	182	106.84	0.924
3	92.50	0.000	63	99.16	0.077	123	103.00	0.000	183	108.34	0.000
4	92.50	0.000	64	99.16	1.508	124	103.00	0.000	184	108.34	0.000
5	92.50	0.000	65	99.16	1.524	125	103.00	0.000	185	109.18	0.000
6	92.64	0.000	66	99.16	0.330	126	103.00	0.000	186	109.18	0.000
7	92.64	0.000	67	99.16	1.332	127	103.00	0.000	187	109.18	0.000
8	92.64	0.000	68	99.16	0.522	128	103.00	0.000	188	110.40	0.000
9	93.44	0.020	69	99.16	0.253	129	103.00	0.000	189	110.40	0.000
10	93.44	0.095	70	100.66	4.076	130	103.00	0.000	190	110.40	0.059
11	93.44	0.278	71	100.70	0.000	131	103.00	0.000	191	110.40	0.002
12	93.44	0.071	72	100.70	0.000	132	103.00	0.000	192	110.40	0.006
13	93.44	0.028	73	100.84	0.000	133	103.56	0.000	193	110.40	0.004
14	93.44	0.257	74	100.84	0.000	134	103.56	0.000	194	110.40	0.000
15	93.44	0.246	75	100.84	0.000	135	103.80	3.203	195	110.40	0.004
16	93.44	0.253	76	101.26	0.000	136	103.94	4.415	196	110.40	0.002
17	93.44	0.063	77	101.26	0.000	137	104.22	0.838	197	110.40	0.000
18	93.44	0.052	78	101.26	0.000	138	104.22	0.486	198	111.34	0.000
19	94.38	0.000	79	101.50	0.000	139	104.22	0.330	199	111.34	0.000
20	94.38	0.000	80	101.50	0.000	140	104.22	0.195	200	111.34	0.000
21	94.38	0.000	81	101.50	0.000	141	104.22	0.257	201	111.62	0.000
22	94.66	0.000	82	101.50	0.000	142	104.22	0.038	202	111.62	0.000
23	94.66	0.000	83	101.50	0.000	143	104.22	0.620	203	111.62	0.000
24	94.66	0.000	84	101.50	0.000	144	104.22	3.613	204	112.56	0.013
25	94.94	0.000	85	101.50	0.000	145	104.22	0.776	205	112.80	0.000
26	94.94	0.000	86	101.50	0.000	146	104.22	0.548	206	112.80	0.000
27	95.50	0.000	87	101.50	0.000	147	104.50	0.000	207	113.36	0.000
28	95.50	0.000	88	101.78	1.910	148	104.50	0.000	208	113.36	0.000
29	95.60	0.096	89	101.78	0.210	149	104.50	0.000	209	113.36	0.000
30	95.60	0.382	90	101.78	0.835	150	104.50	0.000	210	114.30	0.003
31	95.60	0.053	91	101.78	0.355	151	104.50	0.000	211	0.	0.
32	95.60	0.412	92	101.78	1.846	152	104.50	0.000	212	0.	0.
33	95.60	0.023	93	101.78	0.981	153	104.50	0.000	213	0.	0.
34	95.60	0.033	94	101.78	0.419	154	104.50	0.000	214	0.	0.
35	95.60	0.116	95	101.78	1.045	155	104.50	0.000	215	0.	0.
36	95.60	0.476	96	101.78	1.700	156	104.74	0.000	216	0.	0.
37	95.60	0.003	97	101.78	7.017	157	104.74	0.000	217	0.	0.
38	95.60	0.311	98	102.06	8.314	158	104.74	0.000	218	0.	0.
39	96.16	0.000	99	102.06	1.293	159	105.06	0.000	219	0.	0.
40	96.16	0.000	100	102.06	1.130	160	105.06	0.000	220	0.	0.
41	96.16	0.000	101	102.06	0.122	161	105.06	0.000	221	0.	0.
42	96.16	0.000	102	102.06	0.208	162	105.06	0.000	222	0.	0.
43	96.16	0.000	103	102.06	0.857	163	105.06	0.000	223	0.	0.
44	96.16	0.000	104	102.06	1.652	164	105.06	0.000	224	0.	0.
45	96.44	0.000	105	102.06	1.216	165	105.16	0.000	225	0.	0.
46	96.44	0.000	106	102.06	0.644	166	105.16	0.000	226	0.	0.
47	96.44	0.000	107	102.06	0.771	167	105.16	0.000	227	0.	0.
48	96.44	0.000	108	102.16	0.000	168	105.34	0.349	228	0.	0.
49	96.44	0.000	109	102.16	0.000	169	105.34	0.109	229	0.	0.
50	96.44	0.000	110	102.20	7.569	170	105.34	0.361	230	0.	0.
51	96.82	0.000	111	102.30	4.795	171	105.34	0.136	231	0.	0.
52	96.82	0.000	112	102.34	0.000	172	105.34	0.436	232	0.	0.
53	96.82	0.000	113	102.34	0.000	173	105.34	0.396	233	0.	0.
54	97.00	0.048	114	102.34	0.000	174	105.34	0.409	234	0.	0.
55	97.00	0.952	115	102.34	0.000	175	105.34	0.424	235	0.	0.
56	97.00	0.952	116	102.34	0.000	176	105.34	0.061	236	0.	0.
57	97.00	0.048	117	102.34	0.000	177	106.00	0.000	237	0.	0.
58	97.94	0.000	118	103.00	0.000	178	106.00	0.000	238	0.	0.
59	97.94	0.000	119	103.00	0.000	179	106.56	0.000	239	0.	0.
60	97.94	0.000	120	103.00	0.000	180	106.56	0.000	240	0.	0.

6 - 8

J=4.0

Maximum summed intensity = 21.238

LINE	FREQ	INTEN	LINE	FREQ	INTEN	LINE	FREQ	INTEN	LINE	FREQ	INTEN
1	87.79	0.143	61	99.54	0.261	121	102.61	0.000	181	108.29	0.000
2	89.46	0.147	62	99.54	0.014	122	102.61	0.000	182	109.00	0.000
3	90.68	0.000	63	99.54	2.091	123	102.61	0.000	183	109.00	0.000
4	90.68	0.000	64	99.54	1.053	124	103.32	0.000	184	109.00	0.500
5	90.68	0.000	65	99.54	1.052	125	103.32	0.000	185	110.46	0.000
6	90.89	0.000	66	99.54	1.239	126	103.32	0.000	186	110.46	0.000
7	90.89	0.000	67	99.54	0.074	127	103.39	0.000	187	110.46	0.000
8	90.89	0.000	68	99.54	1.113	128	103.39	0.000	188	111.36	0.000
9	91.38	0.150	69	99.54	0.201	129	103.39	0.000	189	111.36	0.000
10	92.10	0.111	70	99.79	0.000	130	103.54	0.000	190	111.36	0.010
11	92.10	0.110	71	99.79	0.000	131	103.54	0.000	191	111.36	0.000
12	92.10	0.000	72	100.14	0.000	132	103.54	0.000	192	111.36	0.010
13	92.10	0.095	73	100.14	0.000	133	103.89	3.139	193	111.36	0.010
14	92.10	0.054	74	100.14	0.000	134	104.03	4.271	194	111.36	0.000
15	92.10	0.164	75	100.69	0.000	135	104.29	0.000	195	111.36	0.000
16	92.10	0.180	76	100.69	0.000	136	104.29	0.000	196	111.36	0.000
17	92.10	0.070	77	100.69	0.000	137	104.29	3.356	197	112.29	0.065
18	92.10	0.042	78	101.00	0.000	138	104.43	0.208	198	112.79	0.000
19	92.81	0.000	79	101.00	0.000	139	104.43	0.363	199	112.79	0.000
20	92.81	0.000	80	101.00	0.000	140	104.43	0.694	200	112.79	0.000
21	92.81	0.000	81	101.00	0.000	141	104.43	0.848	201	113.19	0.000
22	93.21	0.000	82	101.00	0.000	142	104.43	0.210	202	113.19	0.000
23	93.21	0.000	83	101.00	0.000	143	104.43	0.028	203	113.19	0.000
24	93.21	0.000	84	101.00	0.000	144	104.43	0.390	204	114.21	0.000
25	93.71	0.000	85	101.00	0.000	145	104.43	0.181	205	114.21	0.000
26	93.71	0.000	86	101.00	0.000	146	104.43	0.874	206	114.62	0.015
27	93.71	0.144	87	101.00	0.000	147	105.00	0.000	207	115.11	0.000
28	94.64	0.331	88	101.00	4.500	148	105.00	0.000	208	115.11	0.000
29	94.64	0.030	89	101.00	0.000	149	105.00	0.	209	115.11	0.000
30	94.64	0.007	90	101.57	1.697	150	105.00	0.000	210	116.54	0.003
31	94.64	0.015	91	101.57	0.563	151	105.00	0.000	211	0.	0.
32	94.64	0.283	92	101.57	2.342	152	105.00	0.000	212	0.	0.
33	94.64	0.023	93	101.57	1.096	153	105.00	0.000	213	0.	0.
34	94.64	0.055	94	101.57	0.993	154	105.00	0.000	214	0.	0.
35	94.64	0.071	95	101.57	0.021	155	105.00	0.000	215	0.	0.
36	94.64	0.291	96	101.57	0.666	156	105.31	0.000	216	0.	0.
37	94.68	0.000	97	101.57	0.451	157	105.31	0.000	217	0.	0.
38	94.68	0.000	98	101.57	2.240	158	105.31	0.000	218	0.	0.
39	95.54	0.000	99	101.71	7.435	159	105.86	0.000	219	0.	0.
40	95.54	0.000	100	101.90	0.302	160	105.86	0.000	220	0.	0.
41	95.54	0.000	101	101.90	1.524	161	105.86	0.000	221	0.	0.
42	95.54	0.000	102	101.90	0.898	162	105.90	0.000	222	0.	0.
43	95.54	0.000	103	101.90	1.575	163	105.90	0.000	223	0.	0.
44	95.54	0.000	104	101.90	0.059	164	105.90	0.000	224	0.	0.
45	95.54	0.000	105	101.90	1.091	165	105.90	0.000	225	0.	0.
46	95.54	0.000	106	101.90	0.847	166	105.90	0.000	226	0.	0.
47	95.54	0.000	107	101.90	1.142	167	105.90	0.000	227	0.	0.
48	96.10	0.000	108	101.90	0.735	168	106.46	0.272	228	0.	0.
49	96.10	0.000	109	101.97	8.564	169	106.46	0.182	229	0.	0.
50	96.10	0.000	110	102.11	7.711	170	106.46	0.180	230	0.	0.
51	96.10	0.000	111	102.21	4.857	171	106.46	0.269	231	0.	0.
52	96.10	0.000	112	102.46	0.000	172	106.46	0.001	232	0.	0.
53	96.10	0.000	113	102.46	0.000	173	106.46	0.450	233	0.	0.
54	97.00	0.901	114	102.46	0.000	174	106.46	0.094	234	0.	0.
55	97.00	0.099	115	102.46	0.000	175	106.46	0.364	235	0.	0.
56	97.00	0.099	116	102.46	0.000	176	106.46	0.090	236	0.	0.
57	97.00	0.901	117	102.46	0.000	177	107.32	0.000	237	0.	0.
58	97.71	0.000	118	102.46	0.000	178	107.32	0.000	238	0.	0.
59	97.71	0.000	119	102.46	0.000	179	108.29	0.000	239	0.	0.
60	97.71	0.000	120	102.46	0.000	180	108.29	0.000	240	0.	0.

-11 -10 -9 -8 -7 -6 -5 -4 -3 -2 -1 0 +1 +2 +3 +4 +5 +6 +7 +8 +9 +10 +11

6 - 9

J=6.0

Maximum summed intensity = 20.146

LINE	FREQ	INTEN	LINE	FREQ	INTEN	LINE	FREQ	INTEN	LINE	FREQ	INTEN
1	82.90	0.079	61	97.90	0.000	121	103.00	0.000	181	112.00	0.000
2	84.78	0.073	62	97.90	0.000	122	103.00	0.000	182	112.00	0.000
3	86.88	0.063	63	98.32	0.000	123	103.00	0.000	183	112.00	0.000
4	86.88	0.000	64	98.32	0.000	124	103.99	3.076	184	113.68	0.000
5	86.88	0.000	65	98.88	0.000	125	104.12	4.137	185	113.68	0.014
6	86.88	0.000	66	98.88	0.000	126	104.12	0.000	186	113.68	0.000
7	87.21	0.000	67	98.88	0.000	127	104.12	0.000	187	113.68	0.000
8	87.21	0.000	68	99.58	0.000	128	104.12	0.000	188	113.68	0.006
9	87.21	0.000	69	99.58	0.000	129	104.32	3.152	189	113.68	0.000
10	89.32	0.044	70	99.58	0.000	130	104.32	0.000	190	113.68	0.000
11	89.32	0.000	71	100.00	0.049	131	104.32	0.000	191	113.68	0.008
12	89.32	0.000	72	100.00	1.761	132	104.32	0.000	192	113.68	0.000
13	89.32	0.118	73	100.00	0.000	133	104.68	0.087	193	113.68	0.008
14	89.32	0.000	74	100.00	2.275	134	104.68	0.986	194	113.68	0.000
15	89.32	0.030	75	100.00	0.000	135	104.68	0.000	195	113.68	0.006
16	89.32	0.018	76	100.00	0.000	136	104.68	0.156	196	113.68	0.196
17	89.32	0.010	77	100.00	0.856	137	104.68	0.267	197	116.12	0.000
18	89.32	0.120	78	100.00	0.258	138	104.68	0.079	198	116.12	0.000
19	89.32	0.037	79	100.00	0.343	139	104.68	0.729	199	116.12	0.000
20	89.32	0.038	80	100.00	0.000	140	104.68	0.000	200	116.68	0.000
21	89.32	0.017	81	100.00	0.134	141	104.68	0.798	201	116.68	0.000
22	89.32	0.111	82	100.00	0.648	142	104.68	0.010	202	116.68	0.000
23	89.88	0.000	83	100.00	0.000	143	104.68	0.344	203	116.68	0.048
24	89.88	0.000	84	100.00	0.000	144	104.68	0.000	204	117.10	0.000
25	89.88	0.000	85	100.00	1.676	145	106.00	0.000	205	117.10	0.000
26	91.00	0.000	86	100.00	0.000	146	106.00	0.000	206	118.79	0.000
27	91.00	0.000	87	100.00	0.000	147	106.00	0.000	207	118.79	0.000
28	92.32	0.000	88	100.00	0.000	148	106.00	0.000	208	118.79	0.000
29	92.32	0.000	89	101.32	0.000	149	106.00	0.000	209	119.12	0.013
30	92.32	0.138	90	101.32	2.431	150	106.00	0.000	210	121.22	0.003
31	92.32	0.000	91	101.32	0.000	151	106.00	0.000	211	0.	0.
32	92.32	0.005	92	101.32	0.524	152	106.00	0.000	212	0.	0.
33	92.32	0.000	93	101.32	0.000	153	106.00	0.000	213	0.	0.
34	92.32	0.164	94	101.32	0.232	154	106.00	0.000	214	0.	0.
35	92.32	0.039	95	101.32	3.045	155	106.00	0.000	215	0.	0.
36	92.32	0.044	96	101.32	0.990	156	106.42	0.000	216	0.	0.
37	92.32	0.018	97	101.32	0.698	157	106.42	0.000	217	0.	0.
38	92.32	0.013	98	101.32	0.084	158	106.42	0.000	218	0.	0.
39	92.32	0.124	99	101.32	0.375	159	107.12	0.000	219	0.	0.
40	92.88	0.000	100	101.32	2.579	160	107.12	0.000	220	0.	0.
41	92.88	0.000	101	101.32	4.804	161	107.12	0.000	221	0.	0.
42	94.00	0.000	102	101.68	0.000	162	107.68	0.000	222	0.	0.
43	94.00	0.000	103	101.68	0.000	163	107.68	0.000	223	0.	0.
44	94.00	0.000	104	101.68	1.412	164	107.68	0.000	224	0.	0.
45	94.00	0.000	105	101.68	0.000	165	107.68	0.000	225	0.	0.
46	94.00	0.000	106	101.68	0.392	166	107.68	0.000	226	0.	0.
47	94.00	0.000	107	101.68	7.756	167	107.68	0.000	227	0.	0.
48	95.32	0.000	108	101.68	0.280	168	109.00	0.001	228	0.	0.
49	95.32	0.000	109	101.68	1.141	169	109.00	0.266	229	0.	0.
50	95.32	0.000	110	101.68	2.436	170	109.00	0.179	230	0.	0.
51	95.32	0.000	111	101.68	1.029	171	109.00	0.067	231	0.	0.
52	95.32	0.000	112	101.68	0.006	172	109.00	0.037	232	0.	0.
53	95.32	0.000	113	101.68	0.118	173	109.00	0.154	233	0.	0.
54	97.00	0.058	114	101.68	1.687	174	109.00	0.031	234	0.	0.
55	97.00	0.942	115	101.88	8.787	175	109.00	0.117	235	0.	0.
56	97.00	0.942	116	102.01	7.847	176	109.00	0.149	236	0.	0.
57	97.00	0.058	117	102.10	4.921	177	110.12	0.000	237	0.	0.
58	97.00	0.000	118	103.00	0.000	178	110.12	0.000	238	0.	0.
59	97.00	0.000	119	103.00	0.000	179	110.68	0.000	239	0.	0.
60	97.00	0.000	120	103.00	0.000	180	110.68	0.000	240	0.	0.

```
                                                                                                                     X
                                                                                                                    XX
                                                                                                                    XXX
                                                                                                                    XXXX
                                                                                                                    XXXX
                                                                                                                    XXXX
                                                                                                                X   XXXX
                                                                                                                X  XXXXX
                                                                                                                XX XXXXX
                                                                                                                XX XXXXXX
                                                                                                                XX XXXXXX
                                                                                                                XXXXXXXXX
                                                                                                               XXXXXXXXXX
                                                                                                               XXXXXXXXXX
                                                                                                               XXXXXXXXXX
                                                                                                    X          XXXXXXXXXX
                                                                                                    X          XXXXXXXXXX
                                                                                                    X          XXXXXXXXXXX             XX
                                                                                                   XXX         XXXXXXXXXXX            XXX
                                                                                                   XXX         XXXXXXXXXXX            XXXX
                                                                                                   XXX        XXXXXXXXXXXX            XXXX
                                                                                                   XXX        XXXXXXXXXXXX            XXXXXX XX
                                                                                                  XXXXX       XXXXXXXXXXXXX           XXXXXXXXXX
                                                                        XXX                       XXXXX       XXXXXXXXXXXXX          XXXXXXXXXXX
  XX                         XX                                        XXXXX                     XXXXXXX      XXXXXXXXXXXXXXX        XXXXXXXXXXXX                                             XXX
-11      -10      -9       -8       -7       -6       -5       -4       -3       -2       -1        0       +1       +2       +3       +4       +5       +6       +7       +8       +9      +10      +11
```

6 - 10

J=8.0

Maximum summed intensity = 20.343

LINE	FREQ	INTEN	LINE	FREQ	INTEN	LINE	FREQ	INTEN	LINE	FREQ	INTEN
1	77.96	0.050	61	97.00	0.994	121	103.74	0.000	181	115.85	0.000
2	79.96	0.043	62	97.00	0.006	122	103.74	0.000	182	115.85	0.000
3	82.15	0.033	63	97.00	0.006	123	103.74	0.000	183	115.85	0.000
4	83.00	0.000	64	97.00	0.994	124	104.04	3.048	184	116.29	0.002
5	83.00	0.000	65	97.74	0.000	125	104.15	4.081	185	116.29	0.013
6	83.00	0.000	66	97.74	0.000	126	104.30	3.082	186	116.29	0.013
7	83.41	0.000	67	97.74	0.000	127	104.81	1.035	187	116.29	0.002
8	83.41	0.000	68	98.51	0.000	128	104.81	0.048	188	116.29	0.000
9	83.41	0.000	69	98.51	0.000	129	104.81	0.051	189	116.29	0.000
10	84.61	0.019	70	98.51	0.000	130	104.81	0.442	190	116.29	0.000
11	85.60	0.000	71	99.00	0.000	131	104.81	0.012	191	116.29	0.000
12	85.60	0.000	72	99.00	0.000	132	104.81	0.009	192	116.29	0.014
13	85.60	0.000	73	99.00	0.000	133	104.81	0.605	193	117.29	0.000
14	86.26	0.000	74	99.00	0.000	134	104.81	0.601	194	117.29	0.000
15	86.26	0.000	75	99.00	0.000	135	104.81	0.482	195	117.29	0.000
16	86.26	0.000	76	99.00	0.000	136	105.00	0.000	196	118.54	0.101
17	86.45	0.023	77	99.00	0.000	137	105.00	0.000	197	119.74	0.000
18	86.45	0.073	78	99.00	0.000	138	105.00	0.000	198	119.74	0.000
19	86.45	0.055	79	99.00	0.000	139	105.30	0.000	199	119.74	0.000
20	86.45	0.031	80	100.20	0.000	140	105.30	0.000	200	120.04	0.000
21	86.45	0.001	81	100.20	0.000	141	105.30	0.000	201	120.04	0.000
22	86.45	0.035	82	100.20	0.000	142	105.80	0.000	202	120.40	0.000
23	86.45	0.013	83	100.26	0.924	143	105.80	0.000	203	120.40	0.000
24	86.45	0.053	84	100.26	0.328	144	105.80	0.000	204	120.40	0.000
25	86.45	0.043	85	100.26	1.554	145	107.00	0.000	205	121.39	0.032
26	88.15	0.000	86	100.26	0.033	146	107.00	0.000	206	122.59	0.000
27	88.15	0.000	87	100.26	1.849	147	107.00	0.000	207	122.59	0.000
28	88.71	0.000	88	100.26	2.118	148	107.00	0.000	208	122.59	0.000
29	88.71	0.000	89	100.26	0.360	149	107.00	0.000	209	123.85	0.010
30	88.71	0.000	90	100.26	0.654	150	107.00	0.000	210	126.04	0.002
31	89.71	0.096	91	100.26	0.597	151	107.00	0.000	211	0.	0.
32	89.71	0.003	92	100.70	0.000	152	107.00	0.000	212	0.	0.
33	89.71	0.000	93	100.70	0.000	153	107.00	0.000	213	0.	0.
34	89.71	0.011	94	100.70	0.000	154	107.49	0.000	214	0.	0.
35	89.71	0.000	95	101.19	1.916	155	107.49	0.000	215	0.	0.
36	89.71	0.088	96	101.19	1.523	156	107.49	0.000	216	0.	0.
37	89.71	0.003	97	101.19	2.264	157	107.85	0.000	217	0.	0.
38	89.71	0.085	98	101.19	1.357	158	107.85	0.000	218	0.	0.
39	89.71	0.011	99	101.19	0.352	159	108.26	0.000	219	0.	0.
40	91.00	0.000	100	101.19	0.170	160	108.26	0.000	220	0.	0.
41	91.00	0.000	101	101.19	0.518	161	108.26	0.000	221	0.	0.
42	92.26	0.000	102	101.19	0.004	162	109.55	0.000	222	0.	0.
43	92.26	0.000	103	101.19	3.269	163	109.55	0.	223	0.	0.
44	92.26	0.000	104	101.46	4.899	164	109.55	0.000	224	0.	0.
45	92.26	0.000	105	101.55	1.588	165	109.55	0.000	225	0.	0.
46	92.26	0.000	106	101.55	0.198	166	109.55	0.000	226	0.	0.
47	92.26	0.000	107	101.55	1.105	167	109.55	0.000	227	0.	0.
48	94.45	0.000	108	101.55	1.246	168	111.74	0.192	228	0.	0.
49	94.45	0.000	109	101.55	0.651	169	111.74	0.002	229	0.	0.
50	94.45	0.000	110	101.55	0.994	170	111.74	0.001	230	0.	0.
51	94.45	0.000	111	101.55	0.057	171	111.74	0.002	231	0.	0.
52	94.45	0.000	112	101.55	2.042	172	111.74	0.001	232	0.	0.
53	94.45	0.000	113	101.55	0.792	173	111.74	0.000	233	0.	0.
54	95.46	0.000	114	101.70	7.867	174	111.74	0.192	234	0.	0.
55	95.46	0.000	115	101.85	8.876	175	111.74	0.194	235	0.	0.
56	95.96	0.000	116	101.96	7.907	176	111.74	0.000	236	0.	0.
57	95.96	0.000	117	102.04	4.950	177	112.54	0.000	237	0.	0.
58	96.15	0.000	118	103.74	0.000	178	112.54	0.000	238	0.	0.
59	96.15	0.000	119	103.74	0.000	179	113.00	0.000	239	0.	0.
60	96.15	0.000	120	103.74	0.000	180	113.00	0.000	240	0.	0.

−11 −10 −9 −8 −7 −6 −5 −4 −3 −2 −1 0 +1 +2 +3 +4 +5 +6 +7 +8 +9 +10 +11

6 - 11

J=10.0

Maximum summed intensity = 21.875

LINE	FREQ	INTEN	LINE	FREQ	INTEN	LINE	FREQ	INTEN	LINE	FREQ	INTEN
1	73.00	0.034	61	96.66	0.000	121	104.59	0.000	181	119.05	0.002
2	75.07	0.028	62	96.66	0.000	122	104.59	0.000	182	119.05	0.010
3	77.32	0.020	63	96.66	0.000	123	104.59	0.000	183	119.05	0.000
4	79.07	0.000	64	97.00	0.686	124	104.59	0.000	184	119.05	0.000
5	79.07	0.000	65	97.00	0.314	125	104.59	0.000	185	119.05	0.000
6	79.07	0.000	66	97.00	0.314	126	104.59	0.000	186	119.05	0.011
7	79.54	0.000	67	97.00	0.686	127	104.87	0.930	187	119.05	0.012
8	79.54	0.000	68	97.46	0.000	128	104.87	0.007	188	119.05	0.002
9	79.54	0.000	69	97.46	0.000	129	104.87	0.043	189	119.05	0.000
10	79.78	0.010	70	97.46	0.000	130	104.87	0.127	190	119.76	0.000
11	81.78	0.000	71	98.00	0.000	131	104.87	0.495	191	119.76	0.000
12	81.78	0.000	72	98.00	0.000	132	104.87	0.526	192	119.76	0.000
13	81.78	0.000	73	98.00	0.000	133	104.87	0.091	193	121.05	0.000
14	82.49	0.000	74	98.00	0.000	134	104.87	0.563	194	121.05	0.000
15	82.49	0.000	75	98.00	0.000	135	104.87	0.411	195	121.05	0.000
16	82.49	0.000	76	98.00	0.000	136	105.93	0.000	196	123.00	0.000
17	83.54	0.052	77	98.00	0.000	137	105.93	0.000	197	123.00	0.000
18	83.54	0.011	78	98.00	0.000	138	105.93	0.000	198	123.47	0.061
19	83.54	0.014	79	98.00	0.000	139	106.30	0.000	199	123.51	0.000
20	83.54	0.024	80	99.12	0.000	140	106.30	0.000	200	123.51	0.000
21	83.54	0.034	81	99.12	0.000	141	106.30	0.000	201	123.51	0.000
22	83.54	0.001	82	99.12	0.000	142	106.88	0.000	202	124.22	0.000
23	83.54	0.032	83	99.70	0.000	143	106.88	0.000	203	124.22	0.000
24	83.54	0.019	84	99.70	0.000	144	106.88	0.000	204	124.22	0.000
25	83.54	0.044	85	99.70	0.000	145	108.00	0.000	205	126.22	0.023
26	84.95	0.000	86	100.41	1.997	146	108.00	0.000	206	126.46	0.000
27	84.95	0.000	87	100.41	0.718	147	108.00	0.000	207	126.46	0.000
28	84.95	0.000	88	100.41	0.161	148	108.00	0.000	208	126.46	0.000
29	85.24	0.000	89	100.41	0.060	149	108.00	0.000	209	128.68	0.008
30	85.24	0.000	90	100.41	0.135	150	108.00	0.000	210	130.93	0.002
31	86.95	0.029	91	100.41	2.681	151	108.00	0.000	211	0.	0.
32	86.95	0.001	92	100.41	0.819	152	108.00	0.000	212	0.	0.
33	86.95	0.030	93	100.41	2.023	153	108.00	0.000	213	0.	0.
34	86.95	0.003	94	100.41	0.034	154	108.54	0.000	214	0.	0.
35	86.95	0.028	95	101.13	1.653	155	108.54	0.000	215	0.	0.
36	86.95	0.002	96	101.13	0.129	156	108.54	0.000	216	0.	0.
37	86.95	0.057	97	101.13	1.472	157	109.34	0.000	217	0.	0.
38	86.95	0.030	98	101.13	0.738	158	109.34	0.000	218	0.	0.
39	86.95	0.000	99	101.13	2.080	159	109.34	0.000	219	0.	0.
40	89.07	0.000	100	101.13	0.720	160	109.76	0.000	220	0.	0.
41	89.07	0.000	101	101.13	3.014	161	109.76	0.000	221	0.	0.
42	90.41	0.000	102	101.13	1.671	162	111.46	0.000	222	0.	0.
43	90.41	0.000	103	101.13	0.111	163	111.46	0.000	223	0.	0.
44	90.41	0.000	104	101.46	1.841	164	111.46	0.000	224	0.	0.
45	90.41	0.000	105	101.46	1.024	165	111.46	0.000	225	0.	0.
46	90.41	0.000	106	101.46	0.334	166	111.46	0.000	226	0.	0.
47	90.41	0.000	107	101.46	1.130	167	111.46	0.000	227	0.	0.
48	92.53	0.000	108	101.46	0.748	168	114.47	0.000	228	0.	0.
49	92.53	0.000	109	101.46	0.769	169	114.47	0.000	229	0.	0.
50	93.54	0.000	110	101.46	0.058	170	114.59	0.000	230	0.	0.
51	93.54	0.000	111	101.46	1.459	171	114.59	0.005	231	0.	0.
52	93.54	0.000	112	101.46	1.406	172	114.59	0.120	232	0.	0.
53	93.54	0.000	113	101.53	4.939	173	114.59	0.109	233	0.	0.
54	93.54	0.000	114	101.71	7.917	174	114.59	0.014	234	0.	0.
55	93.54	0.000	115	101.83	8.919	175	114.59	0.001	235	0.	0.
56	94.00	0.000	116	101.93	7.937	176	114.59	0.015	236	0.	0.
57	94.00	0.000	117	102.00	4.966	177	114.59	0.105	237	0.	0.
58	95.24	0.000	118	104.07	3.033	178	114.59	0.004	238	0.	0.
59	95.24	0.000	119	104.17	4.053	179	115.93	0.000	239	0.	0.
60	95.24	0.000	120	104.29	3.050	180	115.93	0.000	240	0.	0.

```
                                                      X
                                                      XX
                                                      XX
                                                      XX
                                                     XXX
                                                     XXX
                                                    XXXX
                                                   XXXXXX
                                                   XXXXXX
                                                   XXXXXX
                                                   XXXXXX
                                                  XXXXXXX
                                               XX XXXXXXX
                                               XX XXXXXXX
                                               XXXXXXXXXX
                                               XXXXXXXXXX
                                        X      XXXXXXXXXX
                                        X      XXXXXXXXXXX                      X
                                        XX    XXXXXXXXXXXX                     XX
                                       XXX    XXXXXXXXXXXX                     XXX
                                       XXX    XXXXXXXXXXXX                     XXX
                                       XXX    XXXXXXXXXXXX                    XXXX
                                       XXX    XXXXXXXXXXXX                    XXXX
                                       XXXX  XXXXXXXXXXXXXX                   XXXXX   XX
   XXX                                XXXXX  XXXXXXXXXXXXXXX                 XXXXXX  XXXX
  XXXXX                               XXXXXXXXXXXXXXXXXXXXXX                 XXXXXXXXXXXXX
```

−11 −10 −9 −8 −7 −6 −5 −4 −3 −2 −1 0 +1 +2 +3 +4 +5 +6 +7 +8 +9 +10 +11

6 - 12

J=12.0

Maximum summed intensity = 24.268

LINE	FREQ	INTEN	LINE	FREQ	INTEN	LINE	FREQ	INTEN	LINE	FREQ	INTEN
1	68.03	0.025	61	95.61	0.000	121	104.91	0.916	181	121.88	0.001
2	70.15	0.020	62	95.61	0.000	122	104.91	0.023	182	121.88	0.009
3	72.43	0.013	63	95.61	0.000	123	104.91	0.110	183	121.88	0.001
4	74.89	0.006	64	96.42	0.000	124	104.91	0.107	184	121.88	0.000
5	75.13	0.000	65	96.42	0.000	125	104.91	0.000	185	121.88	0.009
6	75.13	0.000	66	96.42	0.000	126	104.91	0.935	186	121.88	0.002
7	75.13	0.000	67	97.00	0.019	127	104.91	0.019	187	121.88	0.001
8	75.64	0.000	68	97.00	0.981	128	104.91	1.023	188	121.88	0.001
9	75.64	0.000	69	97.00	0.000	129	104.91	0.004	189	121.88	0.009
10	75.64	0.000	70	97.00	0.981	130	105.49	0.000	190	123.70	0.000
11	77.91	0.000	71	97.00	0.000	131	105.49	0.000	191	123.70	0.000
12	77.91	0.000	72	97.00	0.019	132	105.49	0.000	192	123.70	0.000
13	77.91	0.000	73	97.00	0.000	133	105.49	0.000	193	124.90	0.000
14	78.64	0.000	74	97.00	0.000	134	105.49	0.000	194	124.90	0.000
15	78.64	0.000	75	97.00	0.000	135	105.49	0.000	195	124.90	0.000
16	78.64	0.000	76	97.00	0.000	136	106.87	0.000	196	125.97	0.000
17	80.61	0.014	77	97.00	0.000	137	106.87	0.000	197	125.97	0.000
18	80.61	0.013	78	97.00	0.000	138	106.87	0.000	198	127.36	0.000
19	80.61	0.042	79	97.00	0.000	139	107.30	0.000	199	127.36	0.000
20	80.61	0.001	80	98.07	0.000	140	107.30	0.000	200	127.36	0.000
21	80.61	0.002	81	98.07	0.000	141	107.30	0.000	201	128.09	0.000
22	80.61	0.041	82	98.07	0.000	142	107.93	0.000	202	128.09	0.000
23	80.61	0.029	83	98.70	0.000	143	107.93	0.000	203	128.09	0.000
24	80.61	0.013	84	98.70	0.000	144	107.93	0.000	204	128.42	0.040
25	80.61	0.015	85	98.70	0.000	145	109.00	0.000	205	130.36	0.000
26	81.10	0.000	86	100.51	0.296	146	109.00	0.000	206	130.36	0.000
27	81.10	0.000	87	100.51	2.368	147	109.00	0.000	207	130.36	0.000
28	81.10	0.000	88	100.51	0.001	148	109.00	0.000	208	131.11	0.016
29	82.30	0.000	89	100.51	0.287	149	109.00	0.000	209	133.57	0.006
30	82.30	0.000	90	100.51	0.250	150	109.00	0.000	210	135.85	0.002
31	84.12	0.019	91	100.51	2.626	151	109.00	0.000	211	0.	0.
32	84.12	0.014	92	100.51	2.618	152	109.00	0.000	212	0.	0.
33	84.12	0.007	93	100.51	0.259	153	109.00	0.000	213	0.	0.
34	84.12	0.002	94	100.51	0.038	154	109.58	0.000	214	0.	0.
35	84.12	0.021	95	101.09	0.179	155	109.58	0.000	215	0.	0.
36	84.12	0.017	96	101.09	2.467	156	109.58	0.000	216	0.	0.
37	84.12	0.018	97	101.09	3.255	157	110.39	0.000	217	0.	0.
38	84.12	0.005	98	101.09	0.470	158	110.39	0.000	218	0.	0.
39	84.12	0.017	99	101.09	1.258	159	110.39	0.000	219	0.	0.
40	87.13	0.000	100	101.09	0.904	160	111.70	0.000	220	0.	0.
41	87.13	0.000	101	101.09	0.532	161	111.70	0.000	221	0.	0.
42	88.51	0.000	102	101.09	0.117	162	113.39	0.000	222	0.	0.
43	88.51	0.000	103	101.09	2.529	163	113.39	0.000	223	0.	0.
44	88.51	0.000	104	101.39	0.374	164	113.39	0.000	224	0.	0.
45	88.51	0.000	105	101.39	1.893	165	113.39	0.000	225	0.	0.
46	88.51	0.000	106	101.39	0.174	166	113.39	0.000	226	0.	0.
47	88.51	0.000	107	101.39	0.974	167	113.39	0.000	227	0.	0.
48	89.58	0.000	108	101.39	0.677	168	116.42	0.000	228	0.	0.
49	89.58	0.000	109	101.39	2.395	169	116.42	0.000	229	0.	0.
50	92.03	0.000	110	101.39	0.077	170	117.49	0.075	230	0.	0.
51	92.03	0.000	111	101.39	1.795	171	117.49	0.002	231	0.	0.
52	92.61	0.000	112	101.39	0.472	172	117.49	0.046	232	0.	0.
53	92.61	0.000	113	101.58	4.960	173	117.49	0.001	233	0.	0.
54	92.61	0.000	114	101.72	7.943	174	117.49	0.010	234	0.	0.
55	92.61	0.000	115	101.82	8.943	175	117.49	0.009	235	0.	0.
56	92.61	0.000	116	101.90	7.955	176	117.49	0.038	236	0.	0.
57	92.61	0.000	117	101.97	4.975	177	117.49	0.038	237	0.	0.
58	94.30	0.000	118	104.10	3.024	178	117.49	0.039	238	0.	0.
59	94.30	0.000	119	104.18	4.037	179	118.87	0.000	239	0.	0.
60	94.30	0.000	120	104.28	3.034	180	118.87	0.000	240	0.	0.

6 - 13

J=15.0

Maximum summed intensity = 27.101

LINE	FREQ	INTEN	LINE	FREQ	INTEN	LINE	FREQ	INTEN	LINE	FREQ	INTEN
1	60.56	0.017	61	94.06	0.000	121	104.94	0.385	181	126.21	0.001
2	62.74	0.013	62	94.06	0.000	122	104.94	0.616	182	126.21	0.000
3	65.04	0.008	63	94.06	0.000	123	104.94	0.030	183	126.21	0.007
4	67.49	0.004	64	94.88	0.000	124	104.94	0.461	184	126.21	0.008
5	69.18	0.000	65	94.88	0.000	125	104.94	0.184	185	126.21	0.000
6	69.18	0.000	66	94.88	0.000	126	104.94	0.174	186	126.21	0.000
7	69.18	0.000	67	95.50	0.000	127	104.94	0.395	187	126.21	0.008
8	69.74	0.000	68	95.50	0.000	128	104.94	0.827	188	126.21	0.001
9	69.74	0.000	69	95.50	0.000	129	104.94	0.019	189	126.21	0.000
10	69.74	0.000	70	95.50	0.000	130	106.88	0.000	190	129.64	0.000
11	72.04	0.000	71	95.50	0.000	131	106.88	0.000	191	129.64	0.000
12	72.04	0.000	72	95.50	0.000	132	106.88	0.000	192	129.64	0.000
13	72.04	0.000	73	95.50	0.000	133	106.88	0.000	193	130.44	0.000
14	72.79	0.000	74	95.50	0.000	134	106.88	0.000	194	130.44	0.000
15	72.79	0.000	75	95.50	0.000	135	106.88	0.000	195	130.75	0.000
16	72.79	0.000	76	96.51	0.000	136	108.32	0.000	196	130.75	0.000
17	75.25	0.000	77	96.51	0.000	137	108.32	0.000	197	130.75	0.000
18	75.25	0.000	78	96.51	0.000	138	108.32	0.000	198	133.21	0.000
19	75.25	0.000	79	97.00	0.324	139	108.81	0.000	199	133.21	0.000
20	76.18	0.016	80	97.00	0.676	140	108.81	0.000	200	133.21	0.000
21	76.18	0.014	81	97.00	0.676	141	108.81	0.000	201	133.96	0.000
22	76.18	0.006	82	97.00	0.324	142	109.49	0.000	202	133.96	0.000
23	76.18	0.003	83	97.19	0.000	143	109.49	0.000	203	133.96	0.000
24	76.18	0.008	84	97.19	0.000	144	109.49	0.000	204	135.87	0.025
25	76.18	0.030	85	97.19	0.000	145	110.50	0.000	205	136.26	0.000
26	76.18	0.017	86	100.62	0.308	146	110.50	0.000	206	136.26	0.000
27	76.18	0.021	87	100.62	1.472	147	110.50	0.000	207	136.26	0.000
28	76.18	0.000	88	100.62	2.470	148	110.50	0.000	208	138.51	0.011
29	77.86	0.000	89	100.62	0.168	149	110.50	0.000	209	140.96	0.004
30	77.86	0.000	90	100.62	0.013	150	110.50	0.000	210	143.26	0.001
31	79.79	0.000	91	100.62	1.461	151	110.50	0.000	211	0.	0.
32	79.79	0.008	92	100.62	1.166	152	110.50	0.000	212	0.	0.
33	79.79	0.016	93	100.62	1.317	153	110.50	0.000	213	0.	0.
34	79.79	0.001	94	100.62	0.463	154	111.12	0.000	214	0.	0.
35	79.79	0.023	95	101.06	2.070	155	111.12	0.000	215	0.	0.
36	79.79	0.015	96	101.06	1.861	156	111.12	0.000	216	0.	0.
37	79.79	0.008	97	101.06	0.470	157	111.94	0.000	217	0.	0.
38	79.79	0.001	98	101.06	0.006	158	111.94	0.000	218	0.	0.
39	79.79	0.000	99	101.06	1.397	159	111.94	0.000	219	0.	0.
40	84.18	0.000	100	101.06	0.672	160	114.64	0.000	220	0.	0.
41	84.18	0.000	101	101.06	1.404	161	114.64	0.000	221	0.	0.
42	85.13	0.000	102	101.06	2.795	162	116.32	0.000	222	0.	0.
43	85.13	0.000	103	101.06	1.136	163	116.32	0.000	223	0.	0.
44	85.62	0.000	104	101.32	0.422	164	116.32	0.000	224	0.	0.
45	85.62	0.000	105	101.32	1.259	165	116.32	0.000	225	0.	0.
46	85.62	0.000	106	101.32	0.401	166	116.32	0.000	226	0.	0.
47	85.62	0.000	107	101.32	0.883	167	116.32	0.000	227	0.	0.
48	85.62	0.000	108	101.32	1.281	168	119.37	0.000	228	0.	0.
49	85.62	0.000	109	101.32	1.678	169	119.37	0.000	229	0.	0.
50	89.06	0.000	110	101.32	2.139	170	121.88	0.029	230	0.	0.
51	89.06	0.000	111	101.32	0.819	171	121.88	0.012	231	0.	0.
52	91.18	0.000	112	101.32	0.003	172	121.88	0.003	232	0.	0.
53	91.18	0.000	113	101.63	4.975	173	121.88	0.022	233	0.	0.
54	91.18	0.000	114	101.73	7.964	174	121.88	0.013	234	0.	0.
55	91.18	0.000	115	101.81	8.964	175	121.88	0.012	235	0.	0.
56	91.18	0.000	116	101.88	7.971	176	121.88	0.028	236	0.	0.
57	91.18	0.000	117	101.94	4.983	177	121.88	0.004	237	0.	0.
58	92.86	0.000	118	104.12	3.016	178	121.88	0.038	238	0.	0.
59	92.86	0.000	119	104.19	4.024	179	123.32	0.000	239	0.	0.
60	92.86	0.000	120	104.27	3.021	180	123.32	0.000	240	0.	0.

-11 -10 -9 -8 -7 -6 -5 -4 -3 -2 -1 0 +1 +2 +3 +4 +5 +6 +7 +8 +9 +10 +11

6 - 14

J=18.0

Maximum summed intensity = 29.063

LINE	FREQ	INTEN	LINE	FREQ	INTEN	LINE	FREQ	INTEN	LINE	FREQ	INTEN
1	53.08	0.012	61	92.53	0.000	121	104.96	0.938	181	130.59	0.000
2	55.30	0.009	62	92.53	0.000	122	104.96	0.077	182	130.59	0.001
3	57.62	0.005	63	92.53	0.000	123	104.96	0.064	183	130.59	0.003
4	60.06	0.002	64	93.36	0.000	124	104.96	0.020	184	130.59	0.003
5	63.21	0.000	65	93.36	0.000	125	104.96	0.895	185	130.59	0.005
6	63.21	0.000	66	93.36	0.000	126	104.96	0.049	186	130.59	0.001
7	63.21	0.000	67	94.00	0.000	127	104.96	0.006	187	130.59	0.002
8	63.81	0.000	68	94.00	0.000	128	104.96	0.063	188	130.59	0.003
9	63.81	0.000	69	94.00	0.000	129	104.96	0.953	189	130.59	0.001
10	63.81	0.000	70	94.00	0.000	130	108.32	0.000	190	134.92	0.000
11	66.13	0.000	71	94.00	0.000	131	108.32	0.000	191	134.92	0.000
12	66.13	0.000	72	94.00	0.000	132	108.32	0.000	192	135.60	0.000
13	66.13	0.000	73	94.00	0.000	133	108.32	0.000	193	135.60	0.000
14	66.90	0.000	74	94.00	0.000	134	108.32	0.000	194	135.60	0.000
15	66.90	0.000	75	94.00	0.000	135	108.32	0.000	195	136.65	0.000
16	66.90	0.000	76	94.98	0.000	136	109.79	0.000	196	136.65	0.000
17	69.35	0.000	77	94.98	0.000	137	109.79	0.000	197	136.65	0.000
18	69.35	0.000	78	94.98	0.000	138	109.79	0.000	198	139.10	0.000
19	69.35	0.000	79	95.68	0.000	139	110.32	0.000	199	139.10	0.000
20	71.73	0.000	80	95.68	0.000	140	110.32	0.000	200	139.10	0.000
21	71.73	0.008	81	95.68	0.000	141	110.32	0.000	201	139.87	0.000
22	71.73	0.020	82	97.00	0.185	142	111.02	0.000	202	139.87	0.000
23	71.73	0.027	83	97.00	0.815	143	111.02	0.000	203	139.87	0.000
24	71.73	0.000	84	97.00	0.815	144	111.02	0.000	204	142.19	0.000
25	71.73	0.000	85	97.00	0.185	145	112.00	0.000	205	142.19	0.000
26	71.73	0.020	86	100.68	0.217	146	112.00	0.000	206	142.19	0.000
27	71.73	0.000	87	100.68	0.044	147	112.00	0.000	207	143.34	0.017
28	71.73	0.008	88	100.68	2.702	148	112.00	0.000	208	145.94	0.008
29	73.40	0.000	89	100.68	0.781	149	112.00	0.000	209	148.38	0.003
30	73.40	0.000	90	100.68	2.178	150	112.00	0.000	210	150.70	0.001
31	75.41	0.003	91	100.68	0.004	151	112.00	0.000	211	0.	0.
32	75.41	0.013	92	100.68	0.741	152	112.00	0.000	212	0.	0.
33	75.41	0.011	93	100.68	1.965	153	112.00	0.000	213	0.	0.
34	75.41	0.002	94	100.68	0.257	154	112.64	0.000	214	0.	0.
35	75.41	0.000	95	101.04	2.948	155	112.64	0.000	215	0.	0.
36	75.41	0.002	96	101.04	0.681	156	112.64	0.000	216	0.	0.
37	75.41	0.000	97	101.04	0.328	157	113.47	0.000	217	0.	0.
38	75.41	0.003	98	101.04	0.078	158	113.47	0.000	218	0.	0.
39	75.41	0.013	99	101.04	0.486	159	113.47	0.000	219	0.	0.
40	80.66	0.000	100	101.04	3.392	160	117.60	0.000	220	0.	0.
41	80.66	0.000	101	101.04	0.931	161	117.60	0.000	221	0.	0.
42	81.21	0.000	102	101.04	0.236	162	119.27	0.000	222	0.	0.
43	81.21	0.000	103	101.04	2.790	163	119.27	0.000	223	0.	0.
44	82.68	0.000	104	101.27	0.017	164	119.27	0.000	224	0.	0.
45	82.68	0.000	105	101.27	1.317	165	119.27	0.000	225	0.	0.
46	82.68	0.000	106	101.27	0.816	166	119.27	0.000	226	0.	0.
47	82.68	0.000	107	101.27	1.639	167	119.27	0.000	227	0.	0.
48	82.68	0.000	108	101.27	2.140	168	122.34	0.000	228	0.	0.
49	82.68	0.000	109	101.27	1.096	169	122.34	0.000	229	0.	0.
50	86.08	0.000	110	101.27	0.559	170	126.32	0.021	230	0.	0.
51	86.08	0.000	111	101.27	1.060	171	126.32	0.007	231	0.	0.
52	89.73	0.000	112	101.27	0.274	172	126.32	0.015	232	0.	0.
53	89.73	0.000	113	101.66	4.983	173	126.32	0.017	233	0.	0.
54	89.73	0.000	114	101.74	7.976	174	126.32	0.009	234	0.	0.
55	89.73	0.000	115	101.81	8.975	175	126.32	0.001	235	0.	0.
56	89.73	0.000	116	101.87	7.979	176	126.32	0.013	236	0.	0.
57	89.73	0.000	117	101.92	4.988	177	126.32	0.006	237	0.	0.
58	91.40	0.000	118	104.13	3.011	178	126.32	0.023	238	0.	0.
59	91.40	0.000	119	104.19	4.017	179	127.79	0.000	239	0.	0.
60	91.40	0.000	120	104.26	3.014	180	127.79	0.000	240	0.	0.

-11 -10 -9 -8 -7 -6 -5 -4 -3 -2 -1 0 +1 +2 +3 +4 +5 +6 +7 +8 +9 +10 +11

7

The A_2B_3 *Case*

The coupling of a group of two identical protons with a group of three identical protons involves only one chemical shift but involves the following spin-coupling constants:

$$J_{AA'}$$
$$J_{BB'} = J_{BB''} = J_{B'B''}$$
$$J_{AB} \quad J_{AB'} \quad J_{AB''} \quad J_{A'B} \quad J_{A'B'} \quad J_{A'B''}$$

It is obviously impractical to prepare a catalog showing how the spectrum varies with changes in each of these eight spin-coupling constants. A much simpler subgroup is one in which the spin constants are averaged, owing to the motion of the molecule. Thus, in an ethyl group there is usually relatively rapid rotation about the carbon-carbon single bond, which averages the AB-coupling constants. The spectra for this case are relatively simple in that $J_{AA'}$ and the three BB-coupling constants have no effect, and the spectrum is simply dependent on $J_{AB}/\Delta\nu_{AB}$. These spectra are presented as Spectra 7-1 through 7-14.

The main feature of these spectra is that one of the lines of the B group stays at ν_B. The value of ν_A is given by the average of several sets of lines in the A part, such as 95.57 and 98.43 in Spectrum 7-8 ($J/\Delta\nu = 0.67$). However, other lines come in this vicinity, and only the approximate value of ν_A may be obtained in this way.

The value of J_{AB}, and a better estimate of ν_A, may be obtained from a detailed comparison of the observed spectrum with those presented here.

7-1

J=0

Maximum summed intensity = 48.00

LINE	FREQ	INTEN	LINE	FREQ	INTEN	LINE	FREQ	INTEN	LINE	FREQ	INTEN
1	91.00	0.	61	97.00	0.	121	103.00	1.000	181	103.00	0.
2	91.00	0.	62	97.00	0.	122	103.00	1.000	182	103.00	1.000
3	91.00	0.	63	97.00	1.000	123	103.00	1.000	183	103.00	1.000
4	91.00	0.	64	97.00	0.	124	103.00	1.000	184	103.00	1.000
5	91.00	0.	65	97.00	0.	125	103.00	1.000	185	103.00	0.
6	91.00	0.	66	97.00	1.000	126	103.00	1.000	186	109.00	0.
7	91.00	0.	67	97.00	0.	127	103.00	1.000	187	109.00	0.
8	91.00	0.	68	97.00	0.	128	103.00	1.000	188	109.00	0.
9	91.00	0.	69	97.00	0.	129	103.00	1.000	189	109.00	0.
10	91.00	0.	70	97.00	1.000	130	103.00	1.000	190	109.00	0.
11	91.00	0.	71	97.00	0.	131	103.00	0.	191	109.00	0.
12	91.00	0.	72	97.00	0.	132	103.00	1.000	192	109.00	0.
13	91.00	0.	73	97.00	1.000	133	103.00	0.	193	109.00	0.
14	91.00	0.	74	97.00	1.000	134	103.00	0.	194	109.00	0.
15	91.00	0.	75	97.00	0.	135	103.00	0.	195	109.00	0.
16	97.00	1.000	76	97.00	0.	136	103.00	0.	196	109.00	0.
17	97.00	1.000	77	97.00	0.	137	103.00	1.000	197	109.00	0.
18	97.00	1.000	78	97.00	1.000	138	103.00	1.000	198	109.00	0.
19	97.00	0.	79	97.00	0.	139	103.00	0.	199	109.00	0.
20	97.00	0.	80	97.00	0.	140	103.00	0.	200	109.00	0.
21	97.00	1.000	81	97.00	0.	141	103.00	0.	201	109.00	0.
22	97.00	0.	82	97.00	1.000	142	103.00	1.000	202	109.00	0.
23	97.00	0.	83	97.00	1.000	143	103.00	1.000	203	109.00	0.
24	97.00	1.000	84	97.00	0.	144	103.00	1.000	204	109.00	0.
25	97.00	0.	85	97.00	0.	145	103.00	0.	205	109.00	0.
26	97.00	1.000	86	97.00	0.	146	103.00	1.000	206	109.00	0.
27	97.00	0.	87	97.00	1.000	147	103.00	0.	207	109.00	0.
28	97.00	0.	88	97.00	0.	148	103.00	1.000	208	109.00	0.
29	97.00	1.000	89	97.00	0.	149	103.00	0.	209	109.00	0.
30	97.00	0.	90	97.00	0.	150	103.00	1.000	210	115.00	0.
31	97.00	0.	91	97.00	1.000	151	103.00	1.000	211	0.	0.
32	97.00	0.	92	97.00	1.000	152	103.00	0.	212	0.	0.
33	97.00	1.000	93	97.00	1.000	153	103.00	0.	213	0.	0.
34	97.00	0.	94	97.00	1.000	154	103.00	1.000	214	0.	0.
35	97.00	0.	95	97.00	1.000	155	103.00	0.	215	0.	0.
36	97.00	1.000	96	103.00	1.000	156	103.00	1.000	216	0.	0.
37	97.00	1.000	97	103.00	1.000	157	103.00	1.000	217	0.	0.
38	97.00	0.	98	103.00	0.	158	103.00	1.000	218	0.	0.
39	97.00	0.	99	103.00	0.	159	103.00	1.000	219	0.	0.
40	97.00	0.	100	103.00	0.	160	103.00	0.	220	0.	0.
41	97.00	1.000	101	103.00	1.000	161	103.00	0.	221	0.	0.
42	97.00	0.	102	103.00	1.000	162	103.00	1.000	222	0.	0.
43	97.00	0.	103	103.00	0.	163	103.00	0.	223	0.	0.
44	97.00	0.	104	103.00	1.000	164	103.00	1.000	224	0.	0.
45	97.00	1.000	105	103.00	1.000	165	103.00	0.	225	0.	0.
46	97.00	1.000	106	103.00	0.	166	103.00	0.	226	0.	0.
47	97.00	0.	107	103.00	0.	167	103.00	0.	227	0.	0.
48	97.00	0.	108	103.00	0.	168	103.00	0.	228	0.	0.
49	97.00	0.	109	103.00	0.	169	103.00	1.000	229	0.	0.
50	97.00	1.000	110	103.00	1.000	170	103.00	1.000	230	0.	0.
51	97.00	0.	111	103.00	0.	171	103.00	0.	231	0.	0.
52	97.00	0.	112	103.00	1.000	172	103.00	1.000	232	0.	0.
53	97.00	0.	113	103.00	0.	173	103.00	0.	233	0.	0.
54	97.00	1.000	114	103.00	1.000	174	103.00	1.000	234	0.	0.
55	97.00	1.000	115	103.00	0.	175	103.00	0.	235	0.	0.
56	97.00	1.000	116	103.00	0.	176	103.00	1.000	236	0.	0.
57	97.00	0.	117	103.00	0.	177	103.00	1.000	237	0.	0.
58	97.00	0.	118	103.00	0.	178	103.00	0.	238	0.	0.
59	97.00	1.000	119	103.00	1.000	179	103.00	1.000	239	0.	0.
60	97.00	0.	120	103.00	1.000	180	103.00	0.	240	0.	0.

```
                                     X
                                     X
                                     X
                                     X
                                     X
                                     X
                                     X
                                    XXX
                                    XXX
       X                            XXX
       X                            XXX
       X                            XXX
       X                            XXX
      XXX                           XXX
      XXX                           XXX
      XXX                           XXX
      XXX                           XXX
      XXX                           XXX
      XXX                          XXXXX
      XXX                          XXXXX
     XXXXX                         XXXXX
     XXXXX                         XXXXX
     XXXXX                         XXXXX
     XXXXX                        XXXXXXX
    XXXXXXX                       XXXXXXX
```

−11 −10 −9 −8 −7 −6 −5 −4 −3 −2 −1 0 +1 +2 +3 +4 +5 +6 +7 +8 +9 +10 +11

7-2

J=0.5

Maximum summed intensity = 23.147

LINE	FREQ	INTEN	LINE	FREQ	INTEN	LINE	FREQ	INTEN	LINE	FREQ	INTEN
1	89.89	0.000	61	97.17	2.092	121	103.00	1.004	181	103.54	0.000
2	89.94	0.000	62	97.18	2.097	122	103.00	1.000	182	103.54	0.000
3	89.94	0.000	63	97.18	0.000	123	103.00	1.002	183	103.56	2.479
4	90.83	0.000	64	97.18	0.000	124	103.00	1.000	184	103.58	0.000
5	90.89	0.000	65	97.19	0.000	125	103.00	0.998	185	103.58	0.000
6	90.89	0.000	66	97.19	0.000	126	103.00	1.002	186	108.32	0.000
7	90.90	0.000	67	97.19	0.000	127	103.00	1.000	187	108.32	0.000
8	90.90	0.000	68	97.23	0.000	128	103.00	0.000	188	108.32	0.000
9	90.96	0.000	69	97.23	0.000	129	103.00	0.996	189	108.34	0.000
10	90.96	0.000	70	97.23	0.000	130	103.00	0.000	190	108.34	0.000
11	90.96	0.000	71	97.23	0.000	131	103.00	1.002	191	108.35	0.000
12	90.96	0.000	72	97.23	0.000	132	103.01	0.000	192	108.77	0.000
13	91.86	0.000	73	97.23	0.000	133	103.01	0.000	193	108.77	0.000
14	91.93	0.000	74	97.23	0.541	134	103.01	0.000	194	108.83	0.000
15	91.93	0.000	75	97.23	1.615	135	103.02	0.000	195	108.83	0.000
16	96.19	1.538	76	97.23	1.615	136	103.02	0.000	196	108.84	0.000
17	96.19	0.000	77	97.23	0.541	137	103.02	0.000	197	108.90	0.000
18	96.25	0.000	78	97.24	0.000	138	103.02	0.000	198	109.27	0.000
19	96.25	1.582	79	97.24	0.000	139	103.02	0.000	199	109.27	0.000
20	96.66	1.765	80	97.24	0.000	140	103.02	0.000	200	109.33	0.000
21	96.67	0.000	81	97.24	0.000	141	103.02	0.000	201	109.33	0.000
22	96.67	0.000	82	97.25	0.271	142	103.02	0.000	202	109.33	0.000
23	96.67	0.000	83	97.25	1.906	143	103.02	0.000	203	109.39	0.000
24	96.67	0.000	84	97.25	1.906	144	103.02	0.000	204	109.81	0.000
25	96.67	0.000	85	97.25	0.271	145	103.02	0.000	205	109.81	0.000
26	96.69	0.000	86	97.25	0.000	146	103.02	0.000	206	109.81	0.000
27	96.69	0.000	87	97.25	0.000	147	103.03	2.956	207	109.81	0.000
28	96.69	0.000	88	97.25	0.000	148	103.03	0.000	208	109.83	0.000
29	96.69	0.000	89	97.25	0.000	149	103.03	0.000	209	109.83	0.000
30	96.69	0.000	90	97.25	0.000	150	103.03	0.000	210	115.13	0.000
31	96.70	1.800	91	97.25	0.000	151	103.03	0.000	211	0.	0.
32	96.72	0.000	92	97.68	0.000	152	103.03	0.000	212	0.	0.
33	96.72	0.000	93	97.69	2.521	153	103.04	0.000	213	0.	0.
34	96.73	0.000	94	97.74	2.605	154	103.04	0.000	214	0.	0.
35	96.73	1.823	95	97.75	0.000	155	103.04	3.921	215	0.	0.
36	96.73	1.823	96	102.46	0.000	156	103.04	0.737	216	0.	0.
37	96.73	0.000	97	102.46	0.000	157	103.04	0.243	217	0.	0.
38	96.73	0.000	98	102.48	3.605	158	103.04	0.737	218	0.	0.
39	96.73	0.000	99	102.50	0.000	159	103.04	0.243	219	0.	0.
40	96.73	0.000	100	102.50	0.000	160	103.04	0.000	220	0.	0.
41	96.73	0.000	101	102.52	1.141	161	103.04	0.000	221	0.	0.
42	96.73	0.000	102	102.52	0.036	162	103.05	0.000	222	0.	0.
43	96.73	0.000	103	102.52	0.036	163	103.05	0.000	223	0.	0.
44	96.75	0.000	104	102.52	1.141	164	103.06	2.916	224	0.	0.
45	96.75	0.000	105	102.53	4.697	165	103.06	0.000	225	0.	0.
46	96.75	0.000	106	102.55	0.000	166	103.06	0.000	226	0.	0.
47	96.75	0.000	107	102.55	0.000	167	103.06	0.000	227	0.	0.
48	96.75	0.000	108	102.56	3.462	168	103.06	0.000	228	0.	0.
49	96.75	0.000	109	102.59	0.000	169	103.06	0.000	229	0.	0.
50	96.75	1.844	110	102.59	0.000	170	103.06	0.000	230	0.	0.
51	96.75	0.000	111	102.97	0.000	171	103.46	0.000	231	0.	0.
52	96.75	0.000	112	102.98	0.000	172	103.46	0.000	232	0.	0.
53	96.75	1.844	113	102.98	0.000	173	103.48	2.582	233	0.	0.
54	96.76	0.000	114	102.98	0.000	174	103.50	0.000	234	0.	0.
55	96.76	0.000	115	102.98	0.000	175	103.50	0.000	235	0.	0.
56	97.16	0.000	116	102.99	0.000	176	103.51	3.382	236	0.	0.
57	97.16	0.000	117	103.00	0.000	177	103.52	0.213	237	0.	0.
58	97.16	0.000	118	103.00	1.000	178	103.52	0.631	238	0.	0.
59	97.17	0.000	119	103.00	0.998	179	103.52	0.631	239	0.	0.
60	97.17	0.000	120	103.00	0.998	180	103.52	0.213	240	0.	0.

−11 −10 −9 −8 −7 −6 −5 −4 −3 −2 −1 0 +1 +2 +3 +4 +5 +6 +7 +8 +9 +10 +11

7-3

J=1.0

Maximum summed intensity is 17.817

LINE	FREQ	INTEN	LINE	FREQ	INTEN	LINE	FREQ	INTEN	LINE	FREQ	INTEN
1	88.58	0.000	61	97.16	0.000	121	103.00	0.980	181	104.12	0.000
2	88.80	0.000	62	97.23	0.000	122	103.00	0.985	182	104.12	0.000
3	88.80	0.000	63	97.23	0.000	123	103.00	1.008	183	104.26	1.960
4	90.35	0.000	64	97.24	0.000	124	103.00	0.000	184	104.30	0.000
5	90.58	0.000	65	97.24	0.000	125	103.00	1.228	185	104.30	0.000
6	90.58	0.000	66	97.24	0.000	126	103.00	0.996	186	107.82	0.000
7	90.61	0.000	67	97.26	2.088	127	103.00	1.016	187	107.82	0.000
8	90.61	0.000	68	97.39	0.000	128	103.00	1.000	188	107.82	0.000
9	90.83	0.000	69	97.39	0.000	129	103.00	0.992	189	107.91	0.000
10	90.83	0.000	70	97.41	0.000	130	103.00	1.236	190	107.91	0.000
11	90.83	0.000	71	97.41	0.000	131	103.00	1.000	191	107.97	0.003
12	90.83	0.000	72	97.41	0.000	132	103.00	0.012	192	108.59	0.000
13	92.42	0.001	73	97.41	0.000	133	103.00	0.764	193	108.59	0.000
14	92.68	0.000	74	97.41	0.000	134	103.02	0.000	194	108.81	0.000
15	92.68	0.000	75	97.41	0.000	135	103.07	0.000	195	108.81	0.000
16	95.28	1.168	76	97.42	0.037	136	103.07	0.000	196	108.85	0.000
17	95.30	0.000	77	97.42	2.252	137	103.07	2.880	197	109.07	0.001
18	95.50	0.000	78	97.42	2.252	138	103.08	0.000	198	109.58	0.000
19	95.52	1.287	79	97.42	0.037	139	103.08	0.000	199	109.58	0.000
20	96.13	1.436	80	97.49	1.685	140	103.08	0.000	200	109.80	0.000
21	96.19	0.000	81	97.49	0.683	141	103.08	0.000	201	109.84	0.000
22	96.19	0.000	82	97.49	0.683	142	103.08	0.000	202	109.84	0.000
23	96.20	0.000	83	97.49	1.685	143	103.08	0.000	203	110.06	0.001
24	96.20	0.000	84	97.50	0.000	144	103.09	0.000	204	110.68	0.000
25	96.20	0.000	85	97.50	0.000	145	103.09	0.000	205	110.70	0.000
26	96.28	0.000	86	97.50	0.000	146	103.09	0.000	206	110.70	0.000
27	96.28	0.000	87	97.50	0.000	147	103.09	0.000	207	110.70	0.000
28	96.28	0.000	88	97.50	0.000	148	103.09	0.000	208	110.77	0.000
29	96.29	0.000	89	97.50	0.000	149	103.09	0.000	209	110.77	0.000
30	96.29	0.000	90	97.52	0.000	150	103.13	3.730	210	115.52	0.000
31	96.35	1.584	91	97.52	0.000	151	103.13	0.000	211	0.	0.
32	96.35	0.000	92	98.18	0.000	152	103.13	0.000	212	0.	0.
33	96.35	0.000	93	98.24	3.040	153	103.15	0.000	213	0.	0.
34	96.41	0.526	94	98.44	3.447	154	103.15	0.000	214	0.	0.
35	96.41	1.106	95	98.50	0.000	155	103.15	0.000	215	0.	0.
36	96.41	1.106	96	101.87	0.000	156	103.17	0.651	216	0.	0.
37	96.41	0.526	97	101.87	0.000	157	103.17	0.270	217	0.	0.
38	96.42	0.000	98	101.97	4.446	158	103.17	0.270	218	0.	0.
39	96.42	0.000	99	102.00	0.000	159	103.17	0.651	219	0.	0.
40	96.42	0.000	100	102.00	0.000	160	103.18	0.000	220	0.	0.
41	96.42	0.000	101	102.09	0.356	161	103.18	0.000	221	0.	0.
42	96.42	0.000	102	102.09	1.012	162	103.22	0.000	222	0.	0.
43	96.42	0.000	103	102.09	1.012	163	103.22	0.000	223	0.	0.
44	96.50	0.000	104	102.09	0.356	164	103.22	0.000	224	0.	0.
45	96.50	0.000	105	102.13	5.395	165	103.23	0.000	225	0.	0.
46	96.50	0.000	106	102.22	3.832	166	103.23	0.000	226	0.	0.
47	96.50	0.000	107	102.23	0.000	167	103.26	0.000	227	0.	0.
48	96.50	0.000	108	102.23	0.000	168	103.26	0.000	228	0.	0.
49	96.50	0.000	109	102.35	0.000	169	103.26	0.000	229	0.	0.
50	96.51	0.001	110	102.35	0.000	170	103.28	2.592	230	0.	0.
51	96.51	1.710	111	102.85	0.000	171	103.82	0.000	231	0.	0.
52	96.51	1.710	112	102.91	0.000	172	103.82	0.000	232	0.	0.
53	96.51	0.001	113	102.91	0.000	173	103.90	2.287	233	0.	0.
54	96.57	0.000	114	102.92	0.000	174	104.00	0.000	234	0.	0.
55	96.57	0.000	115	102.92	0.000	175	104.00	0.000	235	0.	0.
56	97.13	1.950	116	102.98	0.000	176	104.04	2.871	236	0.	0.
57	97.15	0.000	117	102.98	0.000	177	104.08	0.403	237	0.	0.
58	97.15	0.000	118	102.98	0.000	178	104.08	0.308	238	0.	0.
59	97.15	0.000	119	103.00	0.772	179	104.08	0.308	239	0.	0.
60	97.16	0.000	120	103.00	0.012	180	104.08	0.403	240	0.	0.

−11 −10 −9 −8 −7 −6 −5 −4 −3 −2 −1 0 +1 +2 +3 +4 +5 +6 +7 +8 +9 +10 +11

7 - 4

J= 1.5

Maximum summed intensity = 15.217

LINE	FREQ	INTEN	LINE	FREQ	INTEN	LINE	FREQ	INTEN	LINE	FREQ	INTEN
1	87.13	0.000	61	97.01	0.000	121	103.00	0.966	181	104.74	0.000
2	87.59	0.000	62	97.14	0.000	122	103.00	0.759	182	104.74	0.000
3	87.59	0.000	63	97.14	0.000	123	103.00	1.886	183	105.08	1.505
4	89.59	0.001	64	97.17	0.000	124	103.00	0.670	184	105.14	0.000
5	90.06	0.000	65	97.17	0.000	125	103.00	1.009	185	105.14	0.000
6	90.06	0.000	66	97.17	0.000	126	103.00	0.998	186	107.56	0.000
7	90.16	0.000	67	97.35	2.039	127	103.00	1.036	187	107.56	0.000
8	90.16	0.000	68	97.37	0.000	128	103.00	0.000	188	107.56	0.000
9	90.63	0.001	69	97.37	0.000	129	103.00	0.262	189	107.77	0.000
10	90.63	0.000	70	97.54	0.000	130	103.00	0.975	190	107.77	0.000
11	90.63	0.000	71	97.54	0.000	131	103.00	1.907	191	107.93	0.014
12	90.63	0.001	72	97.54	0.000	132	103.00	1.034	192	108.46	0.000
13	92.61	0.008	73	97.54	0.000	133	103.00	0.084	193	108.46	0.000
14	93.19	0.000	74	97.54	0.000	134	103.03	0.000	194	108.92	0.000
15	93.19	0.000	75	97.54	0.000	135	103.03	0.000	195	108.92	0.000
16	94.28	0.890	76	97.59	1.801	136	103.10	2.815	196	109.03	0.000
17	94.34	0.000	77	97.59	0.600	137	103.16	0.000	197	109.49	0.003
18	94.75	0.000	78	97.59	1.801	138	103.16	0.000	198	109.91	0.000
19	94.81	1.072	79	97.59	0.600	139	103.16	0.000	199	109.91	0.000
20	95.41	1.101	80	97.71	0.575	140	103.16	0.000	200	110.39	0.000
21	95.58	0.000	81	97.71	1.991	141	103.16	0.000	201	110.49	0.000
22	95.58	0.000	82	97.71	1.991	142	103.16	0.000	202	110.49	0.000
23	95.61	0.000	83	97.71	0.575	143	103.18	0.000	203	110.96	0.002
24	95.61	0.000	84	97.75	0.000	144	103.20	3.514	204	111.48	0.001
25	95.61	0.000	85	97.75	0.000	145	103.21	0.000	205	111.66	0.000
26	95.78	0.000	86	97.75	0.000	146	103.21	0.000	206	111.66	0.000
27	95.78	0.000	87	97.75	0.000	147	103.21	0.000	207	111.66	0.000
28	95.78	0.000	88	97.75	0.000	148	103.21	0.000	208	111.82	0.000
29	95.82	0.000	89	97.75	0.000	149	103.21	0.000	209	111.82	0.000
30	95.82	0.000	90	97.93	0.000	150	103.21	0.000	210	116.22	0.000
31	95.88	0.000	91	97.93	0.000	151	103.26	0.000	211	0.	0.
32	95.88	0.000	92	98.44	0.000	152	103.26	0.000	212	0.	0.
33	95.99	1.387	93	98.67	3.495	153	103.37	0.198	213	0.	0.
34	96.04	0.371	94	99.02	4.461	154	103.37	0.637	214	0.	0.
35	96.04	1.063	95	99.25	0.000	155	103.37	0.637	215	0.	0.
36	96.04	1.063	96	101.24	0.000	156	103.37	0.198	216	0.	0.
37	96.04	0.371	97	101.24	0.000	157	103.37	0.000	217	0.	0.
38	96.09	0.000	98	101.50	0.000	158	103.37	0.000	218	0.	0.
39	96.09	0.000	99	101.50	0.000	159	103.37	0.000	219	0.	0.
40	96.09	0.000	100	101.53	5.454	160	103.42	0.000	220	0.	0.
41	96.09	0.000	101	101.71	0.426	161	103.42	0.000	221	0.	0.
42	96.09	0.000	102	101.71	1.140	162	103.47	0.000	222	0.	0.
43	96.09	0.000	103	101.71	1.140	163	103.47	0.000	223	0.	0.
44	96.25	0.000	104	101.71	0.426	164	103.47	0.000	224	0.	0.
45	96.25	0.000	105	101.81	6.009	165	103.53	0.000	225	0.	0.
46	96.25	0.000	106	101.97	4.110	166	103.53	0.000	226	0.	0.
47	96.25	0.000	107	102.10	0.000	167	103.58	0.000	227	0.	0.
48	96.25	0.000	108	102.10	0.000	168	103.58	0.000	228	0.	0.
49	96.25	0.000	109	102.28	0.000	169	103.58	0.000	229	0.	0.
50	96.29	0.000	110	102.28	0.000	170	103.75	2.032	230	0.	0.
51	96.29	1.598	111	102.63	0.000	171	104.08	0.000	231	0.	0.
52	96.29	0.000	112	102.79	0.000	172	104.08	0.000	232	0.	0.
53	96.29	1.598	113	102.79	0.000	173	104.27	2.071	233	0.	0.
54	96.46	0.000	114	102.82	0.000	174	104.50	0.000	234	0.	0.
55	96.46	0.000	115	102.82	0.000	175	104.50	0.000	235	0.	0.
56	96.80	1.556	116	102.82	0.000	176	104.56	2.458	236	0.	0.
57	96.97	0.000	117	102.84	0.000	177	104.66	0.163	237	0.	0.
58	96.97	0.000	118	102.84	0.000	178	104.66	0.436	238	0.	0.
59	96.97	0.000	119	103.00	0.302	179	104.66	0.436	239	0.	0.
60	97.01	0.000	120	103.00	0.112	180	104.66	0.163	240	0.	0.

7 - 5

J=2.0

Maximum summed intensity = 15.233

LINE	FREQ	INTEN	LINE	FREQ	INTEN	LINE	FREQ	INTEN	LINE	FREQ	INTEN
1	85.57	0.000	61	96.73	0.000	121	103.00	1.023	181	105.38	0.000
2	86.34	0.000	62	96.93	0.000	122	103.00	1.063	182	105.38	0.000
3	86.34	0.000	63	96.93	0.000	123	103.00	0.994	183	106.00	1.143
4	88.59	0.002	64	97.00	0.000	124	103.00	0.269	184	106.06	0.000
5	89.38	0.000	65	97.00	0.000	125	103.00	0.017	185	106.06	0.000
6	89.38	0.000	66	97.00	0.000	126	103.00	1.235	186	107.55	0.000
7	89.56	0.000	67	97.14	0.000	127	103.00	1.562	187	107.55	0.000
8	89.56	0.000	68	97.14	0.000	128	103.00	0.942	188	107.55	0.000
9	90.35	0.002	69	97.49	2.001	129	103.00	0.209	189	107.93	0.000
10	90.35	0.002	70	97.63	0.000	130	103.00	0.650	190	107.93	0.000
11	90.35	0.000	71	97.63	0.000	131	103.00	0.684	191	108.24	0.035
12	90.35	0.000	72	97.63	0.000	132	103.00	0.162	192	108.37	0.000
13	92.45	0.020	73	97.63	0.000	133	103.00	0.144	193	108.37	0.000
14	93.23	0.686	74	97.63	0.000	134	103.00	1.768	194	109.14	0.000
15	93.34	0.000	75	97.63	0.000	135	103.00	1.276	195	109.14	0.000
16	93.45	0.000	76	97.73	1.106	136	103.09	2.772	196	109.34	0.000
17	93.45	0.000	77	97.73	1.387	137	103.20	3.340	197	110.12	0.006
18	94.00	0.000	78	97.73	1.387	138	103.27	0.000	198	110.27	0.000
19	94.11	0.908	79	97.73	1.106	139	103.27	0.000	199	110.27	0.000
20	94.54	0.820	80	97.90	2.570	140	103.27	0.000	200	111.06	0.000
21	94.86	0.000	81	97.90	0.189	141	103.27	0.000	201	111.27	0.000
22	94.86	0.000	82	97.90	0.189	142	103.27	0.000	202	111.27	0.000
23	94.94	0.000	83	97.90	2.570	143	103.27	0.000	203	112.06	0.003
24	94.94	0.000	84	98.00	0.000	144	103.37	0.000	204	112.17	0.002
25	94.94	0.000	85	98.00	0.000	145	103.37	0.000	205	112.66	0.000
26	95.23	0.000	86	98.00	0.000	146	103.37	0.000	206	112.66	0.000
27	95.23	0.000	87	98.00	0.000	147	103.37	0.000	207	112.66	0.000
28	95.23	0.000	88	98.00	0.000	148	103.37	0.000	208	112.93	0.000
29	95.31	0.000	89	98.00	0.000	149	103.37	0.000	209	112.93	0.000
30	95.31	0.000	90	98.45	0.000	150	103.40	0.000	210	117.21	0.000
31	95.31	0.000	91	98.49	0.000	151	103.40	0.000	211	0.	0.
32	95.31	0.000	92	98.49	0.000	152	103.49	0.000	212	0.	0.
33	95.62	1.216	93	99.00	3.857	153	103.65	0.308	213	0.	0.
34	95.63	0.020	94	99.45	5.429	154	103.65	0.426	214	0.	0.
35	95.63	1.219	95	100.00	0.000	155	103.65	0.426	215	0.	0.
36	95.63	1.219	96	100.60	0.000	156	103.65	0.308	216	0.	0.
37	95.63	0.020	97	100.60	0.000	157	103.69	0.000	217	0.	0.
38	95.73	0.000	98	101.00	0.000	158	103.69	0.000	218	0.	0.
39	95.73	0.000	99	101.00	0.000	159	103.69	0.000	219	0.	0.
40	95.73	0.000	100	101.21	6.414	160	103.73	0.000	220	0.	0.
41	95.73	0.000	101	101.37	1.254	161	103.73	0.000	221	0.	0.
42	95.73	0.000	102	101.37	0.507	162	103.77	0.000	222	0.	0.
43	95.73	0.000	103	101.37	0.507	163	103.77	0.000	223	0.	0.
44	96.00	0.000	104	101.37	1.254	164	103.77	0.000	224	0.	0.
45	96.00	0.000	105	101.57	6.494	165	103.96	0.000	225	0.	0.
46	96.00	0.000	106	101.77	4.314	166	103.96	0.000	226	0.	0.
47	96.00	0.000	107	102.18	0.000	167	104.00	0.000	227	0.	0.
48	96.00	0.000	108	102.18	0.000	168	104.00	0.000	228	0.	0.
49	96.00	0.000	109	102.31	0.000	169	104.00	0.000	229	0.	0.
50	96.10	0.582	110	102.34	0.000	170	104.27	0.000	230	0.	0.
51	96.10	0.922	111	102.34	0.000	171	104.27	0.000	231	0.	0.
52	96.10	0.582	112	102.51	0.000	172	104.49	1.425	232	0.	0.
53	96.10	0.922	113	102.51	0.000	173	104.59	1.906	233	0.	0.
54	96.17	1.084	114	102.51	0.000	174	105.00	0.000	234	0.	0.
55	96.41	0.000	115	102.63	0.000	175	105.00	0.000	235	0.	0.
56	96.41	0.000	116	102.63	0.000	176	105.06	2.122	236	0.	0.
57	96.66	0.000	117	102.73	0.000	177	105.27	0.131	237	0.	0.
58	96.66	0.000	118	102.73	0.000	178	105.27	0.375	238	0.	0.
59	96.66	0.000	119	102.88	0.000	179	105.27	0.375	239	0.	0.
60	96.73	0.000	120	102.88	0.000	180	105.27	0.131	240	0.	0.

−11 −10 −9 −8 −7 −6 −5 −4 −3 −2 −1 0 +1 +2 +3 +4 +5 +6 +7 +8 +9 +10 +11

7 -6

J= 2.5

Maximum summed intensity = 16.604

LINE	FREQ	INTEN	LINE	FREQ	INTEN	LINE	FREQ	INTEN	LINE	FREQ	INTEN
1	83.93	0.001	61	96.41	0.000	121	103.00	0.381	181	106.04	0.000
2	85.05	0.000	62	96.64	0.000	122	103.00	0.364	182	106.04	0.000
3	85.05	0.000	63	96.64	0.000	123	103.00	0.635	183	107.00	0.871
4	87.42	0.003	64	96.72	0.000	124	103.00	0.014	184	107.07	0.000
5	88.58	0.000	65	96.72	0.000	125	103.00	1.174	185	107.07	0.000
6	88.58	0.000	66	96.75	0.000	126	103.00	0.627	186	107.77	0.000
7	88.85	0.000	67	96.75	0.000	127	103.00	1.972	187	107.77	0.000
8	88.85	0.000	68	96.75	0.000	128	103.00	1.007	188	107.77	0.000
9	90.01	0.001	69	97.66	0.000	129	103.00	0.833	189	108.34	0.000
10	90.01	0.003	70	97.66	0.000	130	103.00	0.000	190	108.34	0.000
11	90.01	0.003	71	97.66	0.000	131	103.00	1.095	191	108.35	0.000
12	90.01	0.001	72	97.66	0.000	132	103.00	0.986	192	108.35	0.000
13	91.98	0.030	73	97.66	0.000	133	103.00	1.988	193	108.83	0.054
14	92.13	0.537	74	97.66	0.000	134	103.00	0.005	194	109.46	0.000
15	92.30	0.000	75	97.70	1.998	135	103.00	0.919	195	109.46	0.000
16	93.25	0.000	76	97.84	1.956	136	103.05	2.750	196	109.77	0.000
17	93.42	0.779	77	97.84	0.613	137	103.12	3.237	197	110.66	0.000
18	93.48	0.000	78	97.84	0.613	138	103.41	0.000	198	110.66	0.000
19	93.48	0.000	79	97.84	1.956	139	103.41	0.000	199	110.89	0.008
20	93.56	0.608	80	98.07	0.001	140	103.41	0.000	200	111.82	0.000
21	94.04	0.000	81	98.07	2.939	141	103.41	0.000	201	112.16	0.000
22	94.04	0.000	82	98.07	0.001	142	103.41	0.000	202	112.16	0.000
23	94.18	0.000	83	98.07	2.939	143	103.41	0.000	203	112.75	0.003
24	94.18	0.000	84	98.23	0.000	144	103.53	0.000	204	113.32	0.004
25	94.18	0.000	85	98.25	0.000	145	103.53	0.000	205	113.70	0.000
26	94.63	0.000	86	98.25	0.000	146	103.59	0.000	206	113.70	0.000
27	94.63	0.000	87	98.25	0.000	147	103.59	0.000	207	113.70	0.000
28	94.63	0.000	88	98.25	0.000	148	103.59	0.000	208	114.11	0.000
29	94.68	0.000	89	98.25	0.000	149	103.59	0.000	209	114.11	0.000
30	94.68	0.000	90	98.25	0.000	150	103.59	0.000	210	118.46	0.000
31	94.77	0.000	91	99.20	0.000	151	103.59	0.000	211	0.	0.
32	94.77	0.000	92	99.20	0.000	152	103.95	0.000	212	0.	0.
33	95.16	0.915	93	99.25	4.129	153	103.99	0.388	213	0.	0.
34	95.16	0.141	94	99.73	6.176	154	103.99	0.242	214	0.	0.
35	95.16	0.141	95	99.97	0.000	155	103.99	0.242	215	0.	0.
36	95.16	0.915	96	99.97	0.000	156	103.99	0.388	216	0.	0.
37	95.25	1.068	97	100.50	0.000	157	104.07	0.000	217	0.	0.
38	95.29	0.707	98	100.50	0.000	158	104.07	0.000	218	0.	0.
39	95.34	0.000	99	100.75	0.000	159	104.07	0.000	219	0.	0.
40	95.34	0.000	100	101.00	7.152	160	104.09	0.000	220	0.	0.
41	95.34	0.000	101	101.09	0.518	161	104.09	0.000	221	0.	0.
42	95.34	0.000	102	101.09	1.425	162	104.12	0.000	222	0.	0.
43	95.34	0.000	103	101.09	1.425	163	104.12	0.000	223	0.	0.
44	95.34	0.000	104	101.09	0.518	164	104.12	0.000	224	0.	0.
45	95.75	0.000	105	101.40	6.854	165	104.41	0.000	225	0.	0.
46	95.75	0.000	106	101.62	4.463	166	104.41	0.000	226	0.	0.
47	95.75	0.600	107	101.93	0.000	167	104.48	0.000	227	0.	0.
48	95.75	0.000	108	102.05	0.000	168	104.48	0.000	228	0.	0.
49	95.75	0.000	109	102.05	0.000	169	104.50	0.000	229	0.	0.
50	95.75	0.000	110	102.05	0.000	170	104.50	0.000	230	0.	0.
51	95.93	1.375	111	102.41	0.000	171	104.50	0.000	231	0.	0.
52	95.93	0.052	112	102.41	0.000	172	104.88	1.776	232	0.	0.
53	95.93	0.052	113	102.43	0.000	173	105.45	0.949	233	0.	0.
54	95.93	1.375	114	102.43	0.000	174	105.50	0.000	234	0.	0.
55	96.23	0.000	115	102.52	0.000	175	105.50	0.000	235	0.	0.
56	96.23	0.000	116	102.52	0.000	176	105.57	1.843	236	0.	0.
57	96.23	0.000	117	102.59	0.000	177	105.91	0.131	237	0.	0.
58	96.34	0.000	118	102.59	0.000	178	105.91	0.300	238	0.	0.
59	96.34	0.000	119	102.64	0.000	179	105.91	0.300	239	0.	0.
60	96.41	0.000	120	102.64	0.000	180	105.91	0.131	240	0.	0.

-11 -10 -9 -8 -7 -6 -5 -4 -3 -2 -1 0 +1 +2 +3 +4 +5 +6 +7 +8 +9 +10 +11

7 - 7

J=3.0

Maximum summed intensity is 17.943

LINE	FREQ	INTEN	LINE	FREQ	INTEN	LINE	FREQ	INTEN	LINE	FREQ	INTEN
1	82.23	0.001	61	96.16	0.000	121	103.00	3.200	181	106.71	0.000
2	83.73	0.000	62	96.29	0.000	122	103.00	0.058	182	106.71	0.000
3	83.73	0.000	63	96.29	0.000	123	103.00	0.895	183	108.06	0.672
4	86.10	0.003	64	96.44	0.000	124	103.00	0.189	184	108.14	0.000
5	87.68	0.000	65	96.44	0.000	125	103.00	1.868	185	108.14	0.000
6	87.68	0.000	66	96.44	0.000	126	103.00	0.315	186	108.14	0.000
7	88.02	0.000	67	96.44	0.000	127	103.00	0.827	187	108.14	0.000
8	88.02	0.000	68	96.44	0.000	128	103.00	0.000	188	108.14	0.000
9	89.60	0.000	69	97.66	0.000	129	103.00	1.023	189	108.34	0.000
10	89.60	0.005	70	97.66	0.000	130	103.00	0.652	190	108.34	0.000
11	89.60	0.005	71	97.66	0.000	131	103.00	1.835	191	108.98	0.000
12	89.60	0.000	72	97.66	0.000	132	103.00	1.196	192	108.98	0.000
13	91.00	0.429	73	97.66	0.000	133	103.00	0.142	193	109.64	0.063
14	91.23	0.000	74	97.66	0.000	134	103.00	1.036	194	109.84	0.000
15	91.30	0.035	75	97.86	0.000	135	103.00	1.037	195	109.84	0.000
16	92.50	0.457	76	97.94	0.596	136	103.00	0.926	196	110.27	0.000
17	92.50	0.000	77	97.94	2.036	137	103.00	2.743	197	111.06	0.000
18	92.73	0.676	78	97.94	2.030	138	103.56	0.000	198	111.06	0.000
19	93.16	0.000	79	97.94	2.036	139	103.56	0.000	199	111.77	0.010
20	93.16	0.000	80	97.94	0.596	140	103.56	0.000	200	112.64	0.000
21	93.36	0.000	81	98.22	3.013	141	103.56	0.000	201	113.12	0.000
22	93.36	0.000	82	98.22	0.088	142	103.56	0.000	202	113.12	0.000
23	93.36	0.000	83	98.22	0.088	143	103.56	0.000	203	113.27	0.005
24	93.36	0.000	84	98.22	3.013	144	103.66	0.000	204	114.70	0.004
25	93.36	0.000	85	98.50	0.000	145	103.66	0.000	205	114.77	0.000
26	94.00	0.000	86	98.50	0.000	146	103.84	0.000	206	114.77	0.000
27	94.00	0.000	87	98.50	0.000	147	103.84	0.000	207	114.77	0.000
28	94.00	0.000	88	98.50	0.000	148	103.84	0.000	208	115.32	0.000
29	94.00	0.000	89	98.50	0.000	149	103.84	0.000	209	115.32	0.000
30	94.00	0.000	90	98.50	0.000	150	103.84	0.000	210	119.90	0.000
31	94.21	0.000	91	99.34	0.000	151	103.84	0.000	211	0.	0.
32	94.21	0.000	92	99.34	0.000	152	104.40	0.339	212	0.	0.
33	94.23	0.462	93	99.44	4.328	153	104.40	0.192	213	0.	0.
34	94.66	0.882	94	99.92	6.687	154	104.40	0.192	214	0.	0.
35	94.66	0.012	95	100.00	0.000	155	104.40	0.339	215	0.	0.
36	94.66	0.012	96	100.00	0.000	156	104.50	0.000	216	0.	0.
37	94.66	0.882	97	100.00	0.000	157	104.50	0.000	217	0.	0.
38	94.86	0.937	98	100.00	0.000	158	104.50	0.000	218	0.	0.
39	94.94	0.000	99	100.84	1.236	159	104.50	0.000	219	0.	0.
40	94.94	0.000	100	100.84	0.871	160	104.50	0.000	220	0.	0.
41	94.94	0.000	101	100.84	0.871	161	104.50	0.000	221	0.	0.
42	94.94	0.000	102	100.84	1.236	162	104.50	0.000	222	0.	0.
43	94.94	0.000	103	100.87	7.658	163	104.50	0.000	223	0.	0.
44	94.94	0.000	104	101.27	7.114	164	104.50	0.000	224	0.	0.
45	95.50	0.000	105	101.50	0.000	165	104.50	0.000	225	0.	0.
46	95.50	0.000	106	101.50	0.000	166	104.50	0.000	226	0.	0.
47	95.50	0.000	107	101.50	0.000	167	105.06	0.000	227	0.	0.
48	95.50	0.000	108	101.50	0.000	168	105.06	0.000	228	0.	0.
49	95.50	0.000	109	101.50	0.000	169	105.06	0.000	229	0.	0.
50	95.50	0.000	110	101.50	4.571	170	105.06	0.000	230	0.	0.
51	95.73	0.000	111	102.16	0.000	171	105.06	0.000	231	0.	0.
52	95.73	0.000	112	102.16	0.000	172	105.13	1.672	232	0.	0.
53	95.73	0.000	113	102.34	0.000	173	106.00	0.000	233	0.	0.
54	95.78	1.092	114	102.34	0.000	174	106.00	0.000	234	0.	0.
55	95.78	0.271	115	102.44	0.000	175	106.08	1.607	235	0.	0.
56	95.78	0.271	116	102.44	0.000	176	106.56	0.637	236	0.	0.
57	95.78	1.092	117	102.77	0.000	177	106.56	0.121	237	0.	0.
58	95.88	0.000	118	102.77	0.000	178	106.56	0.247	238	0.	0.
59	95.88	0.000	119	102.79	0.000	179	106.56	0.247	239	0.	0.
60	96.16	0.000	120	102.79	0.000	180	106.56	0.121	240	0.	0.

-11 -10 -9 -8 -7 -6 -5 -4 -3 -2 -1 0 +1 +2 +3 +4 +5 +6 +7 +8 +9 +10 +11

7 - 8

J=4.0

Maximum summed intensity = 14.004

LINE	FREQ	INTEN	LINE	FREQ	INTEN	LINE	FREQ	INTEN	LINE	FREQ	INTEN
1	78.71	0.000	61	95.57	1.235	121	103.00	1.311	181	108.07	0.000
2	81.03	0.000	62	95.57	1.235	122	103.00	0.773	182	108.46	0.000
3	81.03	0.000	63	95.57	0.030	123	103.00	0.000	183	108.46	0.000
4	83.15	0.002	64	95.71	0.000	124	103.00	1.060	184	109.02	0.322
5	85.68	0.000	65	95.71	0.000	125	103.00	0.013	185	109.16	0.000
6	85.68	0.000	66	95.71	0.000	126	103.00	0.966	186	109.16	0.000
7	86.11	0.000	67	96.55	0.000	127	103.00	0.943	187	109.16	0.000
8	86.11	0.000	68	96.55	0.000	128	103.00	0.014	188	110.29	0.421
9	88.64	0.007	69	96.84	0.000	129	103.00	0.920	189	110.43	0.000
10	88.64	0.003	70	97.54	0.000	130	103.00	0.877	190	110.43	0.000
11	88.64	0.003	71	97.54	0.000	131	103.00	1.039	191	110.62	0.000
12	88.64	0.007	72	97.54	0.000	132	103.00	1.084	192	110.62	0.000
13	88.68	0.286	73	97.54	0.000	133	103.00	0.000	193	110.79	0.000
14	89.03	0.000	74	97.54	0.000	134	103.42	0.000	194	110.79	0.000
15	89.55	0.033	75	97.54	0.000	135	103.42	0.000	195	111.42	0.000
16	90.23	0.274	76	98.10	2.706	136	103.69	0.000	196	111.61	0.061
17	91.00	0.000	77	98.10	0.019	137	103.69	0.000	197	111.90	0.000
18	91.21	0.000	78	98.10	0.019	138	103.86	0.000	198	111.90	0.000
19	91.21	0.000	79	98.10	2.706	139	103.86	0.000	199	113.74	0.010
20	91.36	0.522	80	98.14	0.000	140	103.90	0.000	200	114.24	0.008
21	91.57	0.000	81	98.14	0.000	141	103.90	0.000	201	114.43	0.000
22	91.57	0.000	82	98.43	1.414	142	103.90	0.000	202	115.19	0.000
23	91.57	0.000	83	98.43	1.942	143	103.90	0.000	203	115.19	0.000
24	91.85	0.221	84	98.43	1.942	144	103.90	0.000	204	116.97	0.000
25	92.55	0.000	85	98.43	1.414	145	103.90	0.000	205	116.97	0.000
26	92.55	0.000	86	98.44	2.157	146	104.46	0.000	206	116.97	0.000
27	92.68	0.000	87	99.00	0.000	147	104.46	0.000	207	117.72	0.003
28	92.68	0.000	88	99.00	0.000	148	104.46	0.000	208	117.87	0.000
29	92.68	0.000	89	99.00	0.000	149	104.46	0.000	209	117.87	0.000
30	92.84	0.000	90	99.00	0.000	150	104.46	0.000	210	123.13	0.000
31	92.84	0.000	91	99.00	0.000	151	104.46	0.000	211	0.	0.
32	93.03	0.000	92	99.00	0.000	152	104.61	0.000	212	0.	0.
33	93.03	0.000	93	99.00	0.000	153	104.61	0.000	213	0.	0.
34	93.54	0.053	94	99.00	0.000	154	105.32	0.000	214	0.	0.
35	93.54	0.581	95	99.71	4.579	155	105.32	0.000	215	0.	0.
36	93.54	0.581	96	100.13	7.254	156	105.32	0.000	216	0.	0.
37	93.54	0.053	97	100.27	0.000	157	105.36	0.346	217	0.	0.
38	94.02	0.718	98	100.27	0.000	158	105.36	0.023	218	0.	0.
39	94.10	0.000	99	100.27	0.000	159	105.36	0.023	219	0.	0.
40	94.10	0.000	100	100.46	1.273	160	105.36	0.346	220	0.	0.
41	94.10	0.000	101	100.46	1.093	161	105.39	0.000	221	0.	0.
42	94.10	0.000	102	100.46	1.093	162	105.39	0.000	222	0.	0.
43	94.10	0.000	103	100.46	1.273	163	105.45	0.000	223	0.	0.
44	94.10	0.000	104	100.55	0.000	164	105.45	0.000	224	0.	0.
45	94.58	0.000	105	100.74	8.226	165	105.45	0.000	225	0.	0.
46	94.58	0.000	106	101.09	7.439	166	105.54	1.514	226	0.	0.
47	94.58	0.000	107	101.32	4.714	167	105.73	0.000	227	0.	0.
48	94.81	0.000	108	101.54	0.000	168	106.29	0.000	228	0.	0.
49	94.81	0.000	109	101.54	0.000	169	106.29	0.000	229	0.	0.
50	94.81	0.000	110	101.73	0.000	170	106.29	0.000	230	0.	0.
51	94.81	0.000	111	101.73	0.000	171	106.35	0.000	231	0.	0.
52	95.00	0.000	112	101.74	0.000	172	106.35	0.000	232	0.	0.
53	95.00	0.000	113	101.74	0.000	173	107.00	0.000	233	0.	0.
54	95.00	0.000	114	102.10	0.000	174	107.00	0.000	234	0.	0.
55	95.00	0.000	115	102.10	0.000	175	107.14	1.231	235	0.	0.
56	95.00	0.000	116	102.72	3.249	176	107.90	0.009	236	0.	0.
57	95.00	0.000	117	102.88	2.754	177	107.90	0.266	237	0.	0.
58	95.48	0.000	118	103.00	1.386	178	107.90	0.266	238	0.	0.
59	95.48	0.000	119	103.00	0.728	179	107.90	0.009	239	0.	0.
60	95.57	0.030	120	103.00	0.886	180	108.07	0.000	240	0.	0.

-11 -10 -9 -8 -7 -6 -5 -4 -3 -2 -1 0 +1 +2 +3 +4 +5 +6 +7 +8 +9 +10 +11

7 - 9

J=6.0

Maximum summed intensity = 12.044

LINE	FREQ	INTEN	LINE	FREQ	INTEN	LINE	FREQ	INTEN	LINE	FREQ	INTEN
1	71.33	0.000	61	94.00	0.000	121	103.00	0.889	181	110.68	0.050
2	75.45	0.000	62	94.00	0.000	122	103.00	1.171	182	110.87	0.000
3	75.45	0.000	63	94.31	0.000	123	103.00	0.991	183	110.87	0.000
4	76.50	0.001	64	95.32	0.473	124	103.00	0.019	184	111.69	0.000
5	81.28	0.000	65	95.32	0.679	125	103.00	0.686	185	111.69	0.000
6	81.28	0.000	66	95.32	0.679	126	103.00	0.003	186	111.69	0.000
7	81.53	0.000	67	95.32	0.473	127	103.00	0.787	187	113.12	0.000
8	81.53	0.000	68	95.88	0.000	128	103.00	0.781	188	113.12	0.000
9	83.88	0.150	69	95.88	0.000	129	103.00	1.340	189	113.68	0.000
10	84.45	0.000	70	96.80	0.000	130	103.00	0.879	190	113.68	0.000
11	85.31	0.020	71	96.80	0.000	131	104.12	0.000	191	114.03	0.000
12	85.40	0.123	72	97.00	0.000	132	104.12	0.000	192	114.22	0.125
13	86.32	0.005	73	97.00	0.000	133	104.68	0.000	193	114.69	0.000
14	86.32	0.009	74	97.00	0.000	134	104.68	0.000	194	114.69	0.000
15	86.32	0.009	75	97.00	0.000	135	104.68	0.000	195	115.00	0.200
16	86.32	0.005	76	97.00	0.000	136	104.68	0.000	196	115.47	0.000
17	86.74	0.080	77	97.00	0.000	137	104.68	0.000	197	115.47	0.000
18	86.88	0.000	78	97.00	0.000	138	104.68	0.000	198	116.17	0.039
19	86.88	0.000	79	97.00	0.000	139	104.68	0.000	199	116.33	0.015
20	87.53	0.000	80	97.78	0.000	140	104.68	0.000	200	118.15	0.008
21	87.53	0.000	81	97.78	0.000	141	105.03	0.000	201	118.47	0.000
22	87.53	0.000	82	97.78	0.000	142	105.03	0.000	202	119.68	0.000
23	88.00	0.	83	98.32	0.101	143	105.22	0.000	203	119.68	0.000
24	88.57	0.335	84	98.32	2.733	144	105.22	0.000	204	121.55	0.000
25	89.52	0.000	85	98.32	2.733	145	105.69	0.000	205	121.55	0.000
26	89.52	0.000	86	98.32	0.101	146	105.69	0.000	206	121.55	0.000
27	89.88	0.000	87	98.52	0.000	147	106.00	0.000	207	123.24	0.000
28	89.88	0.000	88	98.68	3.595	148	106.00	0.000	208	123.24	0.000
29	89.88	0.000	89	98.68	0.058	149	106.00	0.000	209	124.47	0.002
30	90.53	0.000	90	98.68	0.058	150	106.00	0.000	210	130.24	0.000
31	90.53	0.000	91	98.68	3.595	151	106.00	0.000	211	0.	0.
32	91.00	0.018	92	99.22	2.441	152	106.00	0.000	212	0.	0.
33	91.00	0.315	93	100.00	0.000	153	106.00	0.	213	0.	0.
34	91.00	0.315	94	100.00	0.000	154	106.08	1.320	214	0.	0.
35	91.00	0.018	95	100.00	2.667	155	107.12	0.000	215	0.	0.
36	91.31	0.000	96	100.00	0.000	156	107.12	0.000	216	0.	0.
37	91.31	0.000	97	100.00	0.000	157	107.12	0.000	217	0.	0.
38	91.78	0.000	98	100.00	0.000	158	107.32	0.000	218	0.	0.
39	91.78	0.000	99	100.00	0.000	159	107.32	0.000	219	0.	0.
40	91.97	0.000	100	100.00	0.000	160	107.48	0.000	220	0.	0.
41	91.97	0.000	101	100.00	2.667	161	107.48	0.000	221	0.	0.
42	91.97	0.000	102	100.00	0.000	162	107.48	0.000	222	0.	0.
43	92.02	0.420	103	100.00	0.000	163	107.68	0.002	223	0.	0.
44	92.32	0.000	104	100.00	0.000	164	107.68	0.180	224	0.	0.
45	92.32	0.000	105	100.00	4.800	165	107.68	0.180	225	0.	0.
46	92.32	0.000	106	100.31	7.673	166	107.68	0.002	226	0.	0.
47	92.32	0.000	107	100.65	8.654	167	108.22	0.000	227	0.	0.
48	92.32	0.000	108	100.78	0.000	168	109.00	0.000	228	0.	0.
49	92.32	0.000	109	100.78	0.000	169	109.00	0.000	229	0.	0.
50	92.32	0.000	110	100.92	7.726	170	109.00	0.000	230	0.	0.
51	92.32	0.000	111	101.12	4.850	171	109.00	0.000	231	0.	0.
52	93.65	0.000	112	101.32	0.000	172	109.00	0.000	232	0.	0.
53	93.65	0.000	113	101.32	0.000	173	109.00	0.	233	0.	0.
54	94.00	0.000	114	102.26	3.472	174	109.00	0.000	234	0.	0.
55	94.00	0.000	115	102.63	2.807	175	109.17	0.000	235	0.	0.
56	94.00	0.000	116	103.00	0.491	176	109.17	0.000	236	0.	0.
57	94.00	0.000	117	103.00	1.062	177	109.47	0.739	237	0.	0.
58	94.00	0.000	118	103.00	1.446	178	110.68	0.050	238	0.	0.
59	94.00	0.000	119	103.00	0.022	179	110.68	0.116	239	0.	0.
60	94.00	0.000	120	103.00	1.433	180	110.68	0.116	240	0.	0.

−11 −10 −9 −8 −7 −6 −5 −4 −3 −2 −1 0 +1 +2 +3 +4 +5 +6 +7 +8 +9 +10 +11

7 - 10

J=8.0

Maximum summed intensity = 12.770

LINE	FREQ	INTEN	LINE	FREQ	INTEN	LINE	FREQ	INTEN	LINE	FREQ	INTEN
1	63.73	0.000	61	93.00	0.000	121	103.00	1.900	181	113.55	0.076
2	69.29	0.000	62	93.00	0.000	122	103.00	1.101	182	113.72	0.000
3	69.73	0.000	63	93.00	0.000	123	103.00	0.908	183	113.72	0.000
4	69.73	0.000	64	93.74	0.000	124	103.00	0.031	184	114.46	0.000
5	76.38	0.000	65	93.74	0.000	125	103.00	0.605	185	114.46	0.000
6	76.38	0.000	66	95.00	0.000	126	103.00	0.673	186	114.46	0.000
7	76.62	0.000	67	95.00	0.000	127	103.00	0.805	187	115.55	0.000
8	76.62	0.000	68	95.19	0.054	128	103.00	1.221	188	115.55	0.000
9	79.00	0.091	69	95.19	1.041	129	103.00	0.082	189	115.74	0.000
10	79.73	0.000	70	95.19	1.041	130	103.00	1.287	190	115.74	0.000
11	80.44	0.069	71	95.19	0.054	131	104.26	0.000	191	116.83	0.000
12	80.69	0.012	72	95.42	0.000	132	104.26	0.000	192	118.69	0.018
13	81.58	0.041	73	95.42	0.000	133	104.70	0.000	193	119.21	0.000
14	82.26	0.000	74	95.42	0.000	134	104.70	0.000	194	119.21	0.000
15	82.26	0.000	75	96.26	0.000	135	105.55	0.000	195	119.43	0.067
16	83.12	0.000	76	96.26	0.000	136	105.55	0.000	196	119.85	0.114
17	83.12	0.000	77	96.26	0.000	137	105.55	0.000	197	120.88	0.000
18	83.12	0.000	78	96.26	0.000	138	105.55	0.000	198	120.88	0.000
19	83.71	0.010	79	96.26	0.000	139	105.55	0.000	199	121.02	0.025
20	83.71	0.004	80	96.26	0.000	140	105.55	0.000	200	122.83	0.006
21	83.71	0.004	81	96.44	0.000	141	106.40	1.212	201	122.88	0.000
22	83.71	0.010	82	97.01	0.000	142	106.83	0.000	202	124.40	0.000
23	85.00	0.000	83	97.01	0.000	143	106.83	0.000	203	124.40	0.000
24	85.73	0.230	84	98.26	0.000	144	107.72	0.000	204	126.27	0.000
25	86.44	0.000	85	98.26	0.000	145	107.72	0.000	205	126.27	0.000
26	86.44	0.000	86	98.45	1.679	146	107.74	0.000	206	126.27	0.000
27	87.00	0.000	87	98.45	1.212	147	107.74	0.000	207	128.82	0.000
28	87.00	0.000	88	98.45	1.212	148	107.74	0.000	208	128.82	0.000
29	87.00	0.000	89	98.45	1.679	149	107.74	0.000	209	131.73	0.001
30	87.87	0.000	90	98.81	2.104	150	107.74	0.000	210	137.73	0.000
31	87.87	0.000	91	98.81	1.688	151	107.74	0.000	211	0.	0.
32	88.26	0.033	92	98.81	1.688	152	108.58	0.000	212	0.	0.
33	88.26	0.161	93	98.81	2.104	153	108.58	0.000	213	0.	0.
34	88.26	0.161	94	99.74	2.638	154	109.00	0.000	214	0.	0.
35	88.26	0.033	95	99.74	2.781	155	109.00	0.000	215	0.	0.
36	88.67	0.000	96	99.74	0.025	156	109.00	0.000	216	0.	0.
37	88.67	0.000	97	99.74	0.025	157	109.00	0.000	217	0.	0.
38	89.17	0.000	98	99.74	2.781	158	109.30	0.000	218	0.	0.
39	89.17	0.000	99	100.15	4.886	159	109.30	0.000	219	0.	0.
40	89.17	0.000	100	100.16	0.000	160	109.56	0.000	220	0.	0.
41	89.54	0.000	101	100.16	0.000	161	109.56	0.000	221	0.	0.
42	89.54	0.000	102	100.39	7.818	162	109.56	0.000	222	0.	0.
43	89.60	0.000	103	100.45	0.000	163	109.74	0.000	223	0.	0.
44	89.60	0.000	104	100.45	0.000	164	109.74	0.000	224	0.	0.
45	89.68	0.253	105	100.63	8.805	165	110.29	0.076	225	0.	0.
46	90.45	0.000	106	100.83	7.840	166	110.29	0.024	226	0.	0.
47	90.45	0.000	107	101.00	0.000	167	110.29	0.024	227	0.	0.
48	90.45	0.000	108	101.00	0.000	168	110.29	0.076	228	0.	0.
49	90.45	0.000	109	101.00	0.000	169	110.58	0.000	229	0.	0.
50	90.45	0.000	110	101.00	0.000	170	111.00	0.000	230	0.	0.
51	90.45	0.000	111	101.00	0.000	171	111.00	0.000	231	0.	0.
52	91.54	0.000	112	101.00	0.000	172	111.85	0.000	232	0.	0.
53	91.72	0.000	113	101.00	4.909	173	111.85	0.000	233	0.	0.
54	91.72	0.000	114	101.98	3.645	174	111.85	0.000	234	0.	0.
55	92.15	0.000	115	102.44	2.855	175	112.03	0.464	235	0.	0.
56	92.15	0.000	116	103.00	1.655	176	112.11	0.000	236	0.	0.
57	92.15	0.000	117	103.00	0.640	177	112.11	0.000	237	0.	0.
58	93.00	0.000	118	103.00	0.000	178	113.55	0.076	238	0.	0.
59	93.00	0.000	119	103.00	0.705	179	113.55	0.033	239	0.	0.
60	93.00	0.000	120	103.00	0.388	180	113.55	0.033	240	0.	0.

−11 −10 −9 −8 −7 −6 −5 −4 −3 −2 −1 0 +1 +2 +3 +4 +5 +6 +7 +8 +9 +10 +11

7 - 11

J=10.0

Maximum summed intensity = 15.456

LINE	FREQ	INTEN	LINE	FREQ	INTEN	LINE	FREQ	INTEN	LINE	FREQ	INTEN
1	56.00	0.000	61	92.00	0.000	121	103.00	0.704	181	116.46	0.071
2	61.79	0.000	62	92.00	0.000	122	103.00	0.010	182	116.62	0.000
3	63.92	0.000	63	92.00	0.000	123	103.00	1.295	183	116.62	0.000
4	63.92	0.000	64	92.00	0.000	124	103.00	1.401	184	117.33	0.000
5	70.91	0.000	65	92.00	0.000	125	103.00	1.842	185	117.33	0.000
6	70.91	0.000	66	93.00	0.000	126	103.00	0.667	186	117.33	0.000
7	71.83	0.000	67	93.00	0.000	127	103.00	0.491	187	117.46	0.000
8	71.83	0.000	68	93.17	0.000	128	103.00	1.116	188	117.46	0.000
9	74.07	0.061	69	93.17	0.000	129	103.00	0.913	189	118.51	0.000
10	74.92	0.000	70	93.17	0.000	130	103.00	0.971	190	118.51	0.000
11	75.44	0.043	71	94.37	0.000	131	104.34	0.000	191	119.71	0.000
12	75.92	0.008	72	95.13	1.064	132	104.34	0.000	192	121.25	0.019
13	76.46	0.025	73	95.13	0.000	133	104.70	0.000	193	123.92	0.000
14	77.49	0.000	74	95.13	0.000	134	104.70	0.000	194	123.92	0.000
15	77.49	0.000	75	95.13	1.064	135	106.46	0.000	195	124.59	0.042
16	78.50	0.000	76	95.41	0.000	136	106.46	0.000	196	124.76	0.073
17	78.50	0.000	77	95.41	0.000	137	106.46	0.000	197	125.96	0.017
18	78.50	0.000	78	95.41	0.000	138	106.46	0.000	198	126.50	0.000
19	80.95	0.007	79	95.41	0.000	139	106.46	0.000	199	126.50	0.000
20	80.95	0.005	80	95.41	0.000	140	106.46	0.000	200	127.50	0.000
21	80.95	0.005	81	95.41	0.000	141	106.58	1.148	201	127.63	0.005
22	80.95	0.007	82	96.41	0.000	142	108.71	0.000	202	129.22	0.000
23	82.00	0.000	83	96.41	0.000	143	108.71	0.000	203	129.22	0.000
24	82.85	0.167	84	97.17	0.000	144	109.59	0.000	204	131.08	0.000
25	83.37	0.000	85	97.17	0.000	145	109.59	0.000	205	131.08	0.000
26	83.37	0.000	86	98.54	2.693	146	109.59	0.000	206	131.08	0.000
27	84.07	0.000	87	98.54	0.230	147	109.59	0.000	207	134.53	0.000
28	84.07	0.000	88	98.54	0.230	148	109.59	0.000	208	134.53	0.000
29	84.07	0.000	89	98.54	2.693	149	109.59	0.000	209	139.25	0.000
30	85.09	0.000	90	98.87	0.361	150	109.74	0.000	210	145.40	0.000
31	85.09	0.000	91	98.87	3.502	151	109.74	0.000	211	0.	0.
32	85.41	0.014	92	98.87	3.502	152	110.59	0.000	212	0.	0.
33	85.41	0.110	93	98.87	0.361	153	110.59	0.000	213	0.	0.
34	85.41	0.110	94	99.54	0.000	154	110.93	0.000	214	0.	0.
35	85.41	0.014	95	99.54	0.000	155	110.93	0.000	215	0.	0.
36	85.58	0.000	96	99.59	0.723	156	110.93	0.000	216	0.	0.
37	85.58	0.000	97	99.59	2.153	157	111.30	0.000	217	0.	0.
38	86.29	0.000	98	99.59	2.153	158	111.30	0.000	218	0.	0.
39	86.29	0.000	99	99.59	0.723	159	111.63	0.000	219	0.	0.
40	86.29	0.000	100	99.76	0.000	160	111.63	0.000	220	0.	0.
41	86.78	0.000	101	99.76	0.000	161	111.63	0.000	221	0.	0.
42	86.78	0.000	102	100.07	2.756	162	111.83	0.000	222	0.	0.
43	87.14	0.161	103	100.24	4.927	163	111.83	0.000	223	0.	0.
44	87.67	0.000	104	100.43	7.885	164	112.00	0.000	224	0.	0.
45	87.67	0.000	105	100.62	8.875	165	112.83	0.000	225	0.	0.
46	88.54	0.000	106	100.78	7.896	166	113.00	0.000	226	0.	0.
47	88.54	0.000	107	100.93	4.939	167	113.00	0.000	227	0.	0.
48	88.54	0.000	108	101.80	3.755	168	113.05	0.017	228	0.	0.
49	88.54	0.000	109	102.00	0.000	169	113.05	0.043	229	0.	0.
50	88.54	0.000	110	102.00	0.000	170	113.05	0.043	230	0.	0.
51	88.54	0.000	111	102.00	0.000	171	113.05	0.017	231	0.	0.
52	88.67	0.000	112	102.00	0.000	172	114.74	0.309	232	0.	0.
53	89.75	0.000	113	102.00	0.000	173	114.76	0.000	233	0.	0.
54	89.75	0.000	114	102.00	0.000	174	114.76	0.000	234	0.	0.
55	90.24	0.000	115	102.29	2.889	175	114.76	0.000	235	0.	0.
56	90.24	0.000	116	103.00	1.138	176	115.09	0.000	236	0.	0.
57	90.24	0.000	117	103.00	0.146	177	115.09	0.000	237	0.	0.
58	91.66	0.000	118	103.00	0.687	178	116.46	0.071	238	0.	0.
59	91.66	0.000	119	103.00	0.519	179	116.46	0.006	239	0.	0.
60	92.00	0.000	120	103.00	0.100	180	116.46	0.006	240	0.	0.

-11 -10 -9 -8 -7 -6 -5 -4 -3 -2 -1 0 +1 +2 +3 +4 +5 +6 +7 +8 +9 +10 +11

7 - 12

J=12.0

Maximum summed intensity = 18.085

LINE	FREQ	INTEN	LINE	FREQ	INTEN	LINE	FREQ	INTEN	LINE	FREQ	INTEN
1	48.19	0.000	61	91.00	0.000	121	103.00	0.716	181	119.39	0.009
2	54.14	0.000	62	91.00	0.000	122	103.00	0.248	182	119.39	0.017
3	58.07	0.000	63	91.00	0.000	123	103.00	0.000	183	119.39	0.039
4	58.07	0.000	64	91.00	0.000	124	103.00	0.648	184	119.54	0.000
5	65.28	0.000	65	91.00	0.000	125	103.00	1.215	185	119.54	0.000
6	65.28	0.000	66	91.00	0.000	126	103.00	0.248	186	120.24	0.000
7	66.98	0.000	67	91.00	0.000	127	103.00	0.007	187	120.24	0.000
8	66.98	0.000	68	91.00	0.000	128	103.00	0.648	188	120.24	0.000
9	69.13	0.043	69	91.00	0.000	129	103.00	0.000	189	121.36	0.000
10	70.07	0.000	70	91.00	0.000	130	103.00	0.000	190	121.36	0.000
11	70.43	0.030	71	92.31	0.000	131	104.39	0.000	191	122.63	0.000
12	71.07	0.005	72	94.51	0.000	132	104.39	0.000	192	123.93	0.018
13	71.37	0.017	73	94.51	0.000	133	104.70	0.000	193	128.72	0.000
14	72.64	0.000	74	94.51	0.000	134	104.70	0.000	194	128.72	0.000
15	72.64	0.000	75	94.51	0.000	135	106.69	1.108	195	129.70	0.029
16	73.76	0.000	76	94.51	0.000	136	107.39	0.000	196	129.70	0.051
17	73.76	0.000	77	94.51	0.000	137	107.39	0.000	197	130.93	0.012
18	73.76	0.000	78	94.51	0.000	138	107.39	0.000	198	132.24	0.000
19	78.12	0.008	79	94.51	0.000	139	107.39	0.000	199	132.24	0.000
20	78.12	0.003	80	95.09	0.978	140	107.39	0.000	200	132.24	0.000
21	78.12	0.003	81	95.09	0.068	141	107.39	0.000	201	132.50	0.003
22	78.12	0.008	82	95.09	0.068	142	110.63	0.000	202	134.09	0.000
23	79.00	0.000	83	95.09	0.978	143	110.63	0.000	203	134.09	0.000
24	79.94	0.126	84	97.30	0.000	144	111.49	0.000	204	135.93	0.000
25	80.31	0.000	85	97.30	0.000	145	111.49	0.000	205	135.93	0.000
26	80.31	0.000	86	98.61	1.465	146	111.49	0.000	206	135.93	0.000
27	81.13	0.000	87	98.61	1.465	147	111.49	0.000	207	140.32	0.000
28	81.13	0.000	88	98.61	0.007	148	111.49	0.000	208	140.32	0.000
29	81.13	0.000	89	98.61	0.014	149	111.49	0.000	209	146.93	0.000
30	82.25	0.000	90	98.61	0.007	150	111.49	0.000	210	153.17	0.000
31	82.25	0.000	91	98.61	2.930	151	111.49	0.000	211	0.	0.
32	82.51	0.000	92	98.91	3.903	152	111.75	0.000	212	0.	0.
33	82.51	0.000	93	98.91	0.000	153	111.75	0.000	213	0.	0.
34	82.51	0.013	94	98.91	0.000	154	112.87	0.000	214	0.	0.
35	82.51	0.072	95	98.91	3.903	155	112.87	0.000	215	0.	0.
36	82.51	0.072	96	99.49	0.000	156	112.87	0.000	216	0.	0.
37	82.51	0.013	97	99.49	0.000	157	113.30	0.000	217	0.	0.
38	83.37	0.000	98	99.49	0.070	158	113.30	0.000	218	0.	0.
39	83.37	0.000	99	99.49	2.845	159	113.69	0.000	219	0.	0.
40	83.37	0.000	100	99.49	2.845	160	113.69	0.000	220	0.	0.
41	83.91	0.000	101	99.49	0.070	161	113.69	0.000	221	0.	0.
42	83.91	0.000	102	100.30	2.828	162	115.00	0.000	222	0.	0.
43	84.46	0.108	103	100.30	4.949	163	115.00	0.000	223	0.	0.
44	85.76	0.000	104	100.46	7.920	164	115.00	0.000	224	0.	0.
45	85.76	0.000	105	100.61	8.914	165	115.00	0.000	225	0.	0.
46	85.76	0.000	106	100.75	7.927	166	115.00	0.000	226	0.	0.
47	86.61	0.000	107	100.87	4.957	167	115.00	0.	227	0.	0.
48	86.61	0.000	108	101.69	3.823	168	115.88	0.037	228	0.	0.
49	86.61	0.000	109	102.18	2.914	169	115.88	0.003	229	0.	0.
50	86.61	0.000	110	103.00	0.626	170	115.88	0.003	230	0.	0.
51	86.61	0.000	111	103.00	0.001	171	115.88	0.037	231	0.	0.
52	86.61	0.000	112	103.00	1.608	172	117.54	0.217	232	0.	0.
53	87.77	0.000	113	103.00	0.779	173	117.70	0.000	233	0.	0.
54	87.77	0.000	114	103.00	0.604	174	117.70	0.000	234	0.	0.
55	88.30	0.000	115	103.00	1.392	175	117.70	0.000	235	0.	0.
56	88.30	0.000	116	103.00	0.902	176	118.09	0.000	236	0.	0.
57	88.30	0.000	117	103.00	0.766	177	118.09	0.000	237	0.	0.
58	89.61	0.000	118	103.00	0.001	178	119.39	0.020	238	0.	0.
59	89.61	0.000	119	103.00	0.986	179	119.39	0.009	239	0.	0.
60	91.00	0.000	120	103.00	0.604	180	119.39	0.020	240	0.	0.

-11 -10 -9 -8 -7 -6 -5 -4 -3 -2 -1 0 +1 +2 +3 +4 +5 +6 +7 +8 +9 +10 +11

7 - 13

J=15.0

Maximum summed intensity = 23.926

LINE	FREQ	INTEN	LINE	FREQ	INTEN	LINE	FREQ	INTEN	LINE	FREQ	INTEN
1	36.40	0.000	61	87.83	0.000	121	103.00	0.775	181	123.82	0.032
2	42.48	0.000	62	87.83	0.000	122	103.00	1.114	182	123.82	0.032
3	49.23	0.000	63	88.00	0.000	123	103.00	1.602	183	123.82	0.006
4	49.23	0.000	64	88.00	0.000	124	103.00	0.735	184	123.95	0.000
5	56.64	0.000	65	89.23	0.000	125	104.44	0.000	185	123.95	0.000
6	56.64	0.000	66	89.50	0.000	126	104.44	0.000	186	124.65	0.000
7	59.64	0.000	67	89.50	0.000	127	104.50	0.000	187	124.65	0.000
8	59.64	0.000	68	89.50	0.000	128	104.50	0.000	188	124.65	0.000
9	61.68	0.028	69	89.50	0.000	129	104.50	0.000	189	125.71	0.000
10	62.73	0.000	70	89.50	0.000	130	104.50	0.000	190	125.71	0.000
11	62.91	0.019	71	89.50	0.000	131	104.50	0.000	191	127.04	0.000
12	63.71	0.003	72	91.62	0.000	132	104.50	0.000	192	128.10	0.015
13	63.79	0.010	73	91.62	0.000	133	104.69	0.000	193	136.03	0.000
14	65.29	0.000	74	93.12	0.000	134	104.69	0.000	194	136.03	0.000
15	65.29	0.000	75	93.12	0.000	135	106.80	1.073	195	137.14	0.032
16	66.52	0.000	76	93.12	0.000	136	108.82	0.000	196	137.31	0.018
17	66.52	0.000	77	93.12	0.000	137	108.82	0.000	197	138.42	0.008
18	66.52	0.000	78	93.12	0.000	138	108.82	0.000	198	139.48	0.000
19	73.79	0.008	79	93.12	0.000	139	108.82	0.000	199	139.86	0.002
20	73.79	0.001	80	95.06	1.017	140	108.82	0.000	200	140.98	0.000
21	73.79	0.001	81	95.06	0.014	141	108.82	0.000	201	140.98	0.000
22	73.79	0.008	82	95.06	0.014	142	112.88	0.000	202	141.46	0.000
23	74.50	0.000	83	95.06	1.017	143	112.88	0.000	203	141.46	0.000
24	75.55	0.088	84	97.18	0.000	144	113.54	0.000	204	143.27	0.000
25	75.73	0.000	85	97.18	0.000	145	113.54	0.000	205	143.27	0.000
26	75.73	0.000	86	97.45	0.000	146	114.38	0.000	206	143.27	0.000
27	76.68	0.000	87	97.45	0.000	147	114.38	0.000	207	149.10	0.000
28	76.68	0.000	88	98.68	0.109	148	114.38	0.000	208	149.10	0.000
29	76.68	0.000	89	98.68	2.853	149	114.38	0.000	209	158.61	0.000
30	77.91	0.000	90	98.68	2.853	150	114.38	0.000	210	164.92	0.000
31	77.91	0.000	91	98.68	0.109	151	114.38	0.000	211	0.	0.
32	77.95	0.000	92	98.94	3.455	152	114.77	0.000	212	0.	0.
33	77.95	0.000	93	98.94	0.483	153	114.77	0.000	213	0.	0.
34	78.12	0.008	94	98.94	0.483	154	115.82	0.000	214	0.	0.
35	78.12	0.046	95	98.94	3.455	155	115.82	0.000	215	0.	0.
36	78.12	0.046	96	99.21	0.000	156	115.82	0.000	216	0.	0.
37	78.12	0.008	97	99.21	0.000	157	116.31	0.000	217	0.	0.
38	78.96	0.000	98	99.38	0.183	158	116.31	0.000	218	0.	0.
39	78.96	0.000	99	99.38	2.763	159	116.77	0.000	219	0.	0.
40	78.96	0.000	100	99.38	2.763	160	116.77	0.000	220	0.	0.
41	79.54	0.000	101	99.38	0.183	161	116.77	0.000	221	0.	0.
42	79.54	0.000	102	100.36	4.968	162	118.00	0.000	222	0.	0.
43	80.29	0.066	103	100.49	7.949	163	118.00	0.000	223	0.	0.
44	81.35	0.000	104	100.54	2.890	164	118.17	0.000	224	0.	0.
45	82.85	0.000	105	100.61	8.945	165	119.50	0.000	225	0.	0.
46	82.85	0.000	106	100.72	7.953	166	119.67	0.000	226	0.	0.
47	83.68	0.000	107	100.82	4.972	167	119.67	0.000	227	0.	0.
48	83.68	0.000	108	101.60	3.883	168	120.21	0.019	228	0.	0.
49	83.68	0.000	109	102.05	2.938	169	120.21	0.005	229	0.	0.
50	83.68	0.000	110	103.00	0.024	170	120.21	0.005	230	0.	0.
51	83.68	0.000	111	103.00	1.249	171	120.21	0.019	231	0.	0.
52	83.68	0.000	112	103.00	0.849	172	121.84	0.138	232	0.	0.
53	84.78	0.000	113	103.00	1.329	173	122.14	0.000	233	0.	0.
54	84.78	0.000	114	103.00	0.549	174	122.14	0.000	234	0.	0.
55	85.36	0.000	115	103.00	1.103	175	122.14	0.000	235	0.	0.
56	85.36	0.000	116	103.00	0.872	176	122.32	0.000	236	0.	0.
57	85.36	0.000	117	103.00	0.040	177	122.32	0.000	237	0.	0.
58	86.56	0.000	118	103.00	0.637	178	122.59	0.000	238	0.	0.
59	86.56	0.000	119	103.00	1.121	179	122.59	0.000	239	0.	0.
60	87.83	0.000	120	103.00	0.000	180	123.82	0.006	240	0.	0.

7 - 14

J=18.0

Maximum summed intensity = 26.428

LINE	FREQ	INTEN	LINE	FREQ	INTEN	LINE	FREQ	INTEN	LINE	FREQ	INTEN
1	24.55	0.000	61	84.72	0.000	121	103.00	1.260	181	128.27	0.003
2	30.71	0.000	62	84.72	0.000	122	103.00	2.964	182	128.27	0.003
3	40.34	0.000	63	85.00	0.000	123	103.00	0.031	183	128.27	0.025
4	40.34	0.000	64	85.00	0.000	124	103.00	0.004	184	128.39	0.000
5	47.88	0.000	65	86.17	0.000	125	104.47	0.000	185	128.39	0.000
6	47.88	0.000	66	88.00	0.000	126	104.47	0.000	186	129.09	0.000
7	52.24	0.000	67	88.00	0.000	127	104.68	0.000	187	129.09	0.000
8	52.24	0.000	68	88.00	0.000	128	104.68	0.000	188	129.09	0.000
9	54.21	0.020	69	88.00	0.000	129	106.00	0.000	189	130.10	0.000
10	55.34	0.000	70	88.00	0.000	130	106.00	0.000	190	130.10	0.000
11	55.39	0.013	71	88.00	0.000	131	106.00	0.000	191	131.49	0.000
12	56.23	0.007	72	88.68	0.000	132	106.00	0.000	192	132.38	0.013
13	56.31	0.002	73	88.68	0.000	133	106.00	0.000	193	143.41	0.000
14	57.90	0.000	74	91.68	0.000	134	106.00	0.000	194	143.41	0.000
15	57.90	0.000	75	91.68	0.000	135	106.85	1.052	195	144.60	0.022
16	59.19	0.000	76	91.68	0.000	136	110.27	0.000	196	144.88	0.013
17	59.19	0.000	77	91.68	0.000	137	110.27	0.000	197	145.92	0.006
18	59.19	0.000	78	91.68	0.000	138	110.27	0.000	198	146.81	0.000
19	69.41	0.000	79	91.68	0.000	139	110.27	0.000	199	147.27	0.002
20	69.41	0.006	80	95.04	0.003	140	110.27	0.000	200	148.87	0.000
21	69.41	0.006	81	95.04	1.018	141	110.27	0.000	201	148.87	0.000
22	69.41	0.000	82	95.04	1.018	142	114.32	0.000	202	149.81	0.000
23	70.00	0.	83	95.04	0.003	143	114.32	0.000	203	149.81	0.000
24	71.13	0.064	84	95.73	0.000	144	116.49	0.000	204	150.66	0.000
25	71.17	0.000	85	95.73	0.000	145	116.49	0.000	205	150.66	0.000
26	71.17	0.000	86	97.55	0.000	146	117.32	0.000	206	150.66	0.000
27	72.21	0.000	87	97.55	0.000	147	117.32	0.000	207	157.93	0.000
28	72.21	0.000	88	98.73	1.635	148	117.32	0.000	208	157.93	0.000
29	72.21	0.000	89	98.73	1.337	149	117.32	0.000	209	170.40	0.000
30	73.40	0.000	90	98.73	1.337	150	117.32	0.000	210	176.75	0.000
31	73.40	0.000	91	98.73	1.635	151	117.32	0.000	211	0.	0.
32	73.51	0.000	92	98.96	3.650	152	117.77	0.000	212	0.	0.
33	73.51	0.000	93	98.96	0.306	153	117.77	0.000	213	0.	0.
34	73.68	0.005	94	98.96	0.306	154	118.79	0.000	214	0.	0.
35	73.68	0.032	95	98.96	3.650	155	118.79	0.000	215	0.	0.
36	73.68	0.032	96	99.03	0.000	156	118.79	0.000	216	0.	0.
37	73.68	0.005	97	99.03	0.000	157	119.32	0.000	217	0.	0.
38	74.51	0.000	98	99.32	0.803	158	119.32	0.000	218	0.	0.
39	74.51	0.000	99	99.32	2.160	159	119.83	0.000	219	0.	0.
40	74.51	0.000	100	99.32	2.160	160	119.83	0.000	220	0.	0.
41	75.13	0.000	101	99.32	0.803	161	119.83	0.000	221	0.	0.
42	75.13	0.000	102	100.40	4.978	162	121.00	0.000	222	0.	0.
43	76.02	0.043	103	100.51	7.965	163	121.00	0.	223	0.	0.
44	76.91	0.000	104	100.61	8.962	164	121.28	0.000	224	0.	0.
45	79.91	0.000	105	100.69	2.925	165	124.00	0.000	225	0.	0.
46	79.91	0.000	106	100.70	7.967	166	124.28	0.000	226	0.	0.
47	80.73	0.000	107	100.79	4.980	167	124.28	0.000	227	0.	0.
48	80.73	0.000	108	101.54	3.918	168	124.59	0.013	228	0.	0.
49	80.73	0.000	109	101.96	2.954	169	124.59	0.003	229	0.	0.
50	80.73	0.000	110	103.00	1.459	170	124.59	0.003	230	0.	0.
51	80.73	0.000	111	103.00	0.230	171	124.59	0.013	231	0.	0.
52	80.73	0.000	112	103.00	0.161	172	125.27	0.000	232	0.	0.
53	81.79	0.000	113	103.00	0.613	173	125.27	0.000	233	0.	0.
54	81.79	0.000	114	103.00	1.180	174	126.21	0.095	234	0.	0.
55	82.40	0.000	115	103.00	0.571	175	126.60	0.000	235	0.	0.
56	82.40	0.000	116	103.00	0.011	176	126.60	0.000	236	0.	0.
57	82.40	0.000	117	103.00	1.326	177	126.60	0.000	237	0.	0.
58	83.53	0.000	118	103.00	0.449	178	127.10	0.000	238	0.	0.
59	83.53	0.000	119	103.00	0.950	179	127.10	0.000	239	0.	0.
60	84.72	0.000	120	103.00	0.790	180	128.27	0.025	240	0.	0.

```
                                                                                                                     X
                                                                                                                     X
                                                                                                                     XX
                                                                                                                     XX
                                                                                                                     XX
                                                                                                                    XXX
                                                                                                                    XXX
                                                                                                                    XXX
                                                                                                                    XXX
                                                                                                                    XXX
                                                                                                                    XXXX
                                                                                                                    XXXX
                                                                                                                   XXXXX
                                                                                                                   XXXXX
                                                                                                                   XXXXX                        X
                                                                                                                   XXXXX                        X
                                                                                                     X             XXXXX                        X
                                                                                                   XXX             XXXXX                       XXX
                                                                                                   XXX             XXXXXX                      XXX
                                                                                                   XXXX  X         XXXXXXX                     XXX
                                                                                                   XXXXXXX         XXXXXXX                     XXX
                                                                                                 XXXXXXXXX         XXXXXXX                     XXX
                                                                                                 XXXXXXXXX         XXXXXXX    XX   XX         XXXXX
                                                             XX                                  XXXXXXXXXXX      XXXXXXXXX  XXXXXXXX         XXXXX                                       XXX
                                                            XXXX                                XXXXXXXXXXXX      XXXXXXXXX XXXXXXXXX        XXXXXXX
-11      -10       -9       -8       -7       -6       -5       -4       -3       -2       -1        0       +1       +2       +3       +4       +5       +6       +7       +8       +9      +10      +11
```